THE INVERTEBRATES:

Platyhelminthes and Rhynchocoela

McGraw-Hill Publications in the Zoological Sciences

E. J. Boell, CONSULTING EDITOR

Baitsell · HUMAN BIOLOGY

Breland · MANUAL OF COMPARATIVE ANATOMY

Chapman · ANIMAL ECOLOGY

Haupt · FUNDAMENTALS OF BIOLOGY

Hyman · THE INVERTEBRATES: PROTOZOA THROUGH CTENOPHORA (Vol. I)

THE INVERTEBRATES: PLATYHELMINTHES AND RHYNCHOCOELA (Vol. II)

THE INVERTEBRATES: ACANTHOCEPHALA, ASCHELMINTHES, AND ENTOPROCTA (Vol. III)

THE INVERTEBRATES: ECHINODERMATA (Vol. IV)

Leach · FUNCTIONAL ANATOMY OF THE MAMMAL

Mayr, Linsley, and Usinger · METHODS AND PRINCIPLES OF SYSTEMATIC ZOOLOGY

Metcalf and Flint · FUNDAMENTALS OF INSECT LIFE

Mitchell · A TEXTBOOK OF GENERAL PHYSIOLOGY

Mitchell and Taylor · LABORATORY MANUAL OF GENERAL PHYSIOLOGY

Pearse · ANIMAL ECOLOGY

Quiring · FUNCTIONAL ANATOMY OF THE VERTEBRATES

Rogers · TEXTBOOK OF COMPARATIVE PHYSIOLOGY

Shull · EVOLUTION

Shull · HEREDITY

Shull, LaRue, and Ruthven · PRINCIPLES OF ANIMAL BIOLOGY

Shull, LaRue, and Ruthven · LABORATORY DIRECTIONS IN PRINCIPLES OF ANIMAL BIOLOGY

Snodgrass · PRINCIPLES OF INSECT MORPHOLOGY

Storer · GENERAL ZOOLOGY

Storer · LABORATORY MANUAL FOR GENERAL ZOOLOGY

Storer and Usinger · ELEMENTS OF ZOOLOGY

Weichert · ANATOMY OF THE CHORDATES

Weichert · ELEMENTS OF CHORDATE ANATOMY

Weichert · REPRESENTATIVE CHORDATES

Welch · LIMNOLOGY

Wieman · AN INTRODUCTION TO VERTEBRATE EMBRYOLOGY

Wolcott · ANIMAL BIOLOGY

Wolcott and Powell · LABORATORY GUIDE IN ANIMAL BIOLOGY

There are also the related series of McGraw-Hill Publications in the Botanical Sciences, of which Edmund W. Sinnott is Consulting Editor, and in the Agricultural Sciences, of which R. A. Brink is Consulting Editor.

THE INVERTEBRATES:

Platyhelminthes and Rhynchocoela
The acoelomate Bilateria

VOLUME II

BY

LIBBIE HENRIETTA HYMAN

American Museum of Natural History
New York

NEW YORK   TORONTO   LONDON

McGRAW-HILL BOOK COMPANY, INC.

1951

THE INVERTEBRATES: PLATYHELMINTHES AND RHYNCHOCOELA

VII

31661

PREFACE

Following the publication in 1940 of *The Invertebrates: Protozoa through Ctenophora*, the second volume of my invertebrate treatise, planned to include the acoelomate and pseudocoelomate Bilateria, was projected. It was interrupted by work on my volume on *Comparative Vertebrate Anatomy*, published in 1942. I then resumed work on the treatise; the task proved long and laborious, for in these groups are included all the parasitic worms on which there exists a vast literature that had to be read, digested, and organized into an adequate account. In addition, the preparation of the numerous figures required great expenditure of time. The task was finally completed by the end of 1949, but, upon examination of the material, the publishers ruled for its division into two volumes. Although I should much have preferred retention of the original plan of presenting the material in a single volume, practical considerations naturally took precedence, and therefore the present volume is limited to the acoelomate groups, to be followed shortly by the third volume dealing with the pseudocoelomate phyla.

Although the present volume contains a good deal of original material, like the preceding volume it is essentially a compilation from the literature. As such it should not be referred to, as some zoologists have done, as if it were a piece of original research for the statements in which I am personally responsible. In general, the contents of these volumes reflect a majority opinion or the opinion of outstanding specialists in a given group and are not to be ascribed to me as an individual. My own opinions are always accompanied by the phrase "in the author's opinion."

I have made all the illustrations of the present volume, except those that have been reproduced by photography. I realize that the quality of the figures is inferior to the work of a professional illustrator, but I think the figures adequately show the points intended. Probably the greatest difficulty in the way of writing zoological books resides in the matter of preparing the illustrations, and doing the latter myself has seemed the most practical method of disposing of this difficulty.

I wish to thank all those who took the time and trouble to write me encouraging letters with regard to the first volume. The letters and comments received by me and my publishers from zoologists the world over prove clearly enough the desperate need for a treatise of this kind in the English language. I trust these well-wishers will not be disappointed in the present volumes for which they have waited so long and so patiently.

LIBBIE HENRIETTA HYMAN

NEW YORK, N. Y.
December, 1949

CONTENTS

CHAPTER IX

INTRODUCTION TO THE BILATERIA

I. THE BILATERAL PHYLA

The remaining phyla of the animal kingdom are characterized by bilateral symmetry which appears early in development or even in the uncleaved egg and persists throughout life, except in the phylum Echinodermata in which the bilateral larva undergoes a remarkable metamorphosis into a secondary radial condition. Less extensive modifications of bilateral symmetry are common, as the spiral twisting of many Mollusca. The general occurrence of bilateral symmetry, typical or modified, throughout these phyla justifies their designation as the Bilateria (or Bilateralia), in contrast to the Radiata. The essential feature of bilateral symmetry is that a section along one plane, and one plane only, the *median sagittal plane*, divides the body into right and left halves which are mirror images of each other. The body parts either lie in the median plane and are cut in half by it, in which case they are termed *unpaired* structures; or they lie on a transverse plane to either side of and equidistant from the median plane, being then termed *paired* structures. Bilateral animals also have differentiated dorsal and ventral surfaces and anterior and posterior ends. The median sagittal plane runs from the middle of the dorsal to the middle of the ventral surface. The main body axis runs in the median sagittal plane from anterior to posterior end and is termed the *anteroposterior axis*. (See further P–C, pages 19, 20.)[1]

The assumption of bilateral symmetry appears to have been an important forward step, since radial animals tend to lead a sessile or sedentary life, which is not conducive to evolutionary advance; or, if free-swimming, they do not direct any particular part of the body forward and hence fail to profit from the stimulating action of the environment. Concomitant with the appearance of bilateral symmetry, the anterior end comes to be consistently directed forward and differentiates into a head with concentrated nervous tissue and highly efficient sense organs. With the development of such a nervous center, body activities become more coordinated, response to external conditions is quicker and more precise, and all the systems differentiate rapidly to a more efficient morphological condition. It is to be noted that there is a tendency to bilateral symmetry among the higher Radiata (P–C, pages 372, 640).

---

[1] The first volume of this treatise, entitled *The Invertebrates: Protozoa through Ctenophora*, will be referred to as P–C.

With the differentiation of dorsal and ventral surfaces, the ventral surface becomes locomotory and is generally held against the substratum. At first cilia continue to serve as the locomotory mechanism, especially while the animal remains of small size; but with increasing size and complexity, movement becomes muscular and the muscular system differentiates correspondingly.

We have seen that the Porifera and the Radiata remain at the tissue grade of construction and have progressed very little in the direction of organ formation. The Bilateria, on the other hand, are anatomically of the *organ grade* of construction. Even the lowest Bilateria show a considerable development of organs, and the differentiation of organs and of organ-systems makes rapid strides as one proceeds toward the higher bilateral groups. The formation of organs is closely related to the presence of *mesoderm*, a characteristic feature of the Bilateria. While, as previously emphasized (P–C, pages 263–268), a form of mesoderm, the mesenchymal ectomesoderm, is present in sponges and most Radiata, the mesoderm there never reaches the extensive development which it attains in the bilateral phyla. The Bilateria are further characterized by the possession of "true" mesoderm, that is to say, *entomesoderm*, mesoderm of entodermal origin. Among a number of bilateral groups (the Protostomia, see below), there is also an early formation of ectomesoderm, also called the *larval mesoblast*, which contributes to larval structures and may persist in adult structures. This larval mesoblast is strictly comparable to and apparently reminiscent of the ectomesoderm of the radial phyla, and in some groups, as the rotifers, comprises the entire mesoderm. But in most Bilateria, after the ectomesoderm has been given off, there is a formation of mesoderm from the entoderm, and it is this mesoderm which is the chief source of the muscles, connective tissues, reproductive system, and other parts of the adult. Nevertheless, the distinction between ectomesoderm and entomesoderm, like most morphological distinctions, must not be taken too literally. The mesoderm provides material and space for the development of many organs and relieves the ectoderm and entoderm from the necessity of forming such parts as muscles and gonads, freeing them for further differentiation along their own special lines, protective-nervous, and digestive, respectively. The mesoderm also makes the body firmer and more solid and permits increase in size and complexity.

Dependent on the presence of mesoderm is the occurrence of two other features limited to the Bilateria but by no means present in all bilateral groups, namely, the *coelom* and *segmentation*. The origin and nature of mesoderm, coelom, and segmentation are difficult questions considered further below.

Common to all the bilateral phyla except the Platyhelminthes is the presence of a rear opening of the digestive tract, the *anus*. Connections of the digestive tract with the surface are not uncommon in the radiate phyla (medusae, P–C, pages 396, 421, 507; ctenophores, page 667); they also occur among several polyclad and trematode flatworms (pages 107, 228). Although there is no objection to considering such connections as anal openings, they are usually of haphazard occurrence, not terminal, and mostly two or more in number. The *definitive anus* is of general occurrence throughout whole phyla, is a single opening terminating the digestive tract, is situated in the median sagittal plane (at least in primitive members of a group), and is typically formed with the aid of an ectodermal invagination, the proctodaeum.[1] The advantages of an anus are obvious. In animals in which the digestive system opens only by the mouth, newly ingested food is continually mixed with partly digested or indigestible material, the entire gastrodermis must be capable both of digestion and absorption, and a high degree of efficiency is impossible. When an anus is present, the food is passed posteriorly, and different sections of the digestive tract can become specialized for various roles, such as mastication, digestion, and absorption.

With increase in size and complexity and the interpolation of many organs between epidermis and digestive tract, the primitive method of respiratory exchange, food distribution, and elimination of nitrogenous wastes by simple diffusion no longer suffices. Among the larger bilateral animals we see the gradual appearance of excretory, respiratory, and circulatory systems, all of which are completely absent in the Radiata. The reproduction system also differentiates, often achieving great complexity. Contrasting with the simple emission of sex cells through the mouth and external fertilization seen among the Radiata, the Bilateria usually have special ducts for conveying the sex cells to the exterior, glands or sacs for conserving and storing the sex cells, and some mechanism for introducing the sperm directly into the body of the partner.[2]

The number of bilateral groups is considerable, and attempts have naturally been made to unite them into larger assemblages. The scheme which seems likely to receive the most acceptance is that of Grobben (1908), who divides the Bilateria into the Protostomia and the Deuterostomia, a division previously suggested with other names by Goette (1902; see further P–C, pages 30–31). In the Protostomia, the blastopore becomes the mouth or the mouth forms about where the blastopore closed, there is a well-developed stomodaeum, embryonic development is of the determinate type with spiral cleavage and often a *trochophore* type of larva, the mesoderm originates by solid ingrowth of cells proliferated

---

[1] However, a proctodaeum seems to be sometimes absent in the lowest bilateral group to have a definite anus, namely, the nemertine worms.

[2] Recall, however, the beginning of sex ducts in ctenophores (P–C, pp. 684, 686).

from the entoderm, and the coelom, if present, is not an enterocoel. Among the Deuterostomia, the blastopore becomes the anus or the anus forms where the blastopore closed, the mouth is a new formation, cleavage is of the indeterminate type with a *dipleurula* larva, and the mesoderm and coelom originate by outfolding of the gut wall (*enterocoelous* method). The Deuterostomia include the phyla Chaetognatha, Echinodermata, Hemichordata, and Chordata. All the other bilateral groups belong to the Protostomia (although the Brachiopoda have an enterocoelous formation of the coelom). The protostomous phyla can be grouped further according to the type and mode of formation of the body cavity, presence or absence of segmentation, etc.

The foregoing scheme necessarily leads to the conception of a splitting of the bilateral phyla immediately after the origin of a bilateral ancestor from the Radiata into two main lines of ascent, one (Deuterostomia) leading to the vertebrates, and the other (Protostomia) leading to the arthropods and mollusks. This theory is termed the *diphyletic* theory of the relations of the Bilateria to each other and to the Radiata. The main alternative theories are the *polyphyletic* theory, which suggests that many of the invertebrate groups have evolved independently in a radiating manner from a remote bilateral ancestor; and the *annelid* theory, according to which annelids, arthropods, and chordates are closely related and lower bilateral groups may have arisen from annelids by degeneration. The diphyletic theory is at present widely accepted. It involves several important corollaries. It divorces the vertebrates from the annelids and arthropods to which they were for many years considered to be related, and it necessitates the assumption that mesodermic segmentation has arisen twice independently in the evolution of animals. A more important objection, which has not been met, is that *Amphioxus* has nephridia of a type found elsewhere only in some polychaete annelids. Serological tests performed by Wilhelmi (1942) indicated closer relationship between echinoderms, hemichordates, and tunicates than between these groups and annelids and arthropods, but the author has been informed by professional immunologists that the methods employed in such tests cannot be relied upon to yield convincing results.

A serological test is usually performed as follows. The animal to be tested is freed of foreign material and dried, and the dried material, either with or without removal of fats, is dissolved in an inert medium, usually saline. This solution, termed the *antigen*, is then injected into rabbits several times at short intervals; and then, after an appropriate lapse of time, blood is drawn from the injected rabbit, allowed to clot, and the serum removed. This serum contains substances called *antibodies* formed in the rabbit as a result of the injection of the antigen, and these will react with the antigen to produce a visible precipitate. This reaction is termed the *precipitin reaction* or *test*. It is very highly specific in that a precipitate appears even with very high dilutions of the antigen; a precipitate may also appear in less dilution with substances related to the antigen but fails to appear with nonrelated substances. Hence the degree of dilution at which a precipitate appears has been commonly used as a measure of the degree of relatedness of the substances being tested. In carrying out the precipitin test, the undiluted rabbit serum carrying the antibodies is put into a test tube, and the solution to be tested diluted to varying amounts is carefully added so as to form a layer over the serum. At the boundary of the two fluids a ring or layer of white precipitate occurs if the test is positive. When the specific antigen used to obtain that particular serum (*homologous* test) is employed, a precipitate will usually be obtained in dilutions of a million or more. Related substances (*heterologous* test) give the reaction only in much stronger concentrations. In Wilhelmi's experiments, rabbit serum from sea-urchin antigen gave an homologous test with sea-urchin antigen at a dilution of 2,048,000; reacted with other echinoderm antigens at dilutions of 21,000 to 32,000; reacted with tunicate antigen at 4000 dilution, with hemichordate antigen at 2000 dilution, and with annelid and arthropod (*Limulus*) antigens at 100 to 200 dilution. Annelid and *Limulus* antigens gave homologous reactions at 250,000 to 2,000,000 dilution and heterologous tests with each other at 2000 to 4000 dilution.

Serological tests offer a new and promising method of attack on problems of invertebrate relationships which are almost insoluble by morphological means, but great improvement in the technique of such tests is needed before dependable results can be obtained. According to information received by the author from immunologists, the dilution method is not a reliable index of relation of antigens, but rather the amounts of precipitate obtained at the dilution of antigen at which the homologous test yields the most precipitate must be compared. Further no decisive result can be expected when whole animals are employed in making the antigen. Instead related chemical substances must be isolated from the animals to be compared and these used as antigens. In any case, zoologists must persevere with embryological and morphological studies of invertebrates, as these will always be important for the evaluation of relationships.

Although the diphyletic theory is here adopted as a working hypothesis, the author is of the opinion that only the Protostomia constitute an assemblage of groups evidently related to each other. The Deuterostomia at present writing appear a heterogeneous assemblage of groups whose relationship to each other remains dubious. There seems to be very little concrete evidence for the widely assumed derivation of the chordates from the echinoderms.

As previously indicated (P–C, page 35), the Bilateria exist in three grades of structure: the acoelomate, the pseudocoelomate, and the eucoelomate. The present volume deals with the acoelomate phyla.

II. ORIGIN OF THE BILATERIA

Since the first Metazoa were almost certainly radial animals, the Bilateria must have sprung from a radial ancestor, and there must have been an alteration from radial to bilateral symmetry. This change constitutes a most difficult gap for phylogeneticists to bridge, and various highly speculative conjectures have been made. It is generally believed that bilateral symmetry originated in consequence of the assumption by a radial ancestor of a creeping mode of life. We have already traced this ancestor to a planuloid form (P–C, pages 248–253; see further Hyman, 1942), resembling the planula larva of the Cnidaria (Fig. 2*A*). This planuloid ancestor was an elongated, radially symmetrical organism, without mouth or archenteron, and consisted of a ciliated or flagellated epidermis, probably composed of epitheliomuscular cells, and a solid interior mass of digestive cells. There was probably a nerve net under the epidermis with an accumulation of neurosensory cells at the anterior pole, and indifferent mesenchyme cells, capable of differentiating into sex cells and other types of cells, were scattered through the interior mass. Food catching and digestion remained wholly of the protozoan type so that the organism had no need of a mouth or archenteron. The creature was polarized with definite anterior or aboral and posterior or oral ends but lacked dorsoventral differentiation.

This planuloid organism may be supposed to have given rise to the coelenterate line by formation of a mouth at the site of the closed blastopore, hollowing out of the interior to form a primitive gut, and sprouting of tentacles, thus becoming a simple medusa similar to an actinula. It is here assumed also to have given rise to the Bilateria by adopting a creeping mode of life, then flattening out and developing bilateral symmetry and dorsoventral differentiation.

There are three chief theories of the steps from the radiate to the bilateral condition: the *ctenophore-polyclad*, the *ctenophore-trochophore*, and the *planuloid-acoeloid* theories. The ctenophore-polyclad theory was first suggested by Kowalevsky in 1880 as a result of his finding of the peculiar ctenophore *Coeloplana* (see P–C, page 685) but has been supported and elaborated chiefly by Arnold Lang, the eminent student of the polyclad flatworms, who based his conclusions on his studies of the anatomy and embryology of various turbellarians (1881–1884), and on the peculiar features of the aberrant ctenophores *Ctenoplana* and *Coeloplana*. These ctenophores resemble polyclads in their oval flattened shape with dorsoventral differentiation; in the presence of two dorsal tentacles; in creeping upon the entire ventral surface; in the centrally located ventral mouth and branched, blindly ending digestive canals; and in the radiating, anastomosing nervous system. There is a certain amount of resemblance in the embryology, as both ctenophores and polyclads have determinate cleavage with the formation of micromeres and macromeres, and in both there is a large stomodaeal invagination which in both contributes to the ventral surface. Many polyclads have a swimming larval stage with eight ciliated lobes which seem comparable to the eight comb rows of ctenophores. However, as Lang fully realized, *Coeloplana* and *Ctenoplana* have no trace of real bilateral symmetry, being in fact biradially symmetrical, and their nervous center is in the middle of the dorsal surface, whereas it is characteristic of the Bilateria that the nervous center is anteriorly located. To bridge these differences, Lang postulated a series of stages (Fig. 1) from the platyctene ctenophores to the polyclads by a forward shift of the nerve center and tentacles and extensive branching of the digestive canals.

Lang's theory of the ctenophores as intermediate forms between the radiates and the polyclad flatworms had a wide and extended acceptance but is to be rejected on the following grounds. First, it is agreed by all students of ctenophores that the Platyctenea are simply highly aberrant ctenophores without phylogenetic significance. Second, the embryology of the two groups is in fact very different and the cleavage patterns follow

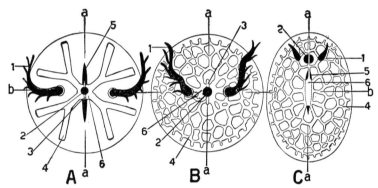

Fig. 1.—Diagram to show change from a ctenophore to a polyclad (*after Lang*, 1884). *A*. Ctenophore. *B*. Hypothetical intermediate stage. *C*. Polyclad. 1, tentacle; 2, nervous center; 3, polar field; 4, gastrovascular branches; 5, pharynx; 6, main canal of gastrovascular system. *aa*, sagittal axis; *bb*, transverse axis.

very diverse plans, that of the ctenophores being biradial, and that of the polyclads spiral. Third, in the theory of Lang, the polyclads are necessarily regarded as the most primitive existing Bilateria; this is a mistaken idea, since it is now clear that the order Acoela occupies that position and the polyclads stem from acoel ancestors.

The ctenophore-trochophore theory is a variant of the trochophore theory, discussed below, and is based on alleged resemblances between ctenophores and the trochophore larva. These resemblances are best stated after the anatomy of the trochophore larva has been described. Here it may be pointed out that this theory proceeds from the ctenophores to the annelids and other higher Bilateria and fails to account for the origin of the lower Bilateria. Supporters of the theory have realized this difficulty and take one or the other of the two possible explanations. Some regard the larvae of the acoelomate Bilateria (i.e., the flatworms and the nemertines) as earlier stages of the trochophore larva. But then, such stages would necessarily fall between the ctenophore and the trochophore and should more nearly resemble the ctenophore than does the

trochophore larva.   This, however, is not the case for in fact the ctenophore similarities are manifested only in the fully developed typical
trochophore larva.   The second explanation is to the effect that the
acoelomate Bilateria are degenerated from the higher Bilateria.   This
cannot possibly be admitted.   It may be regarded as firmly established
that the free-living flatworms, especially the order Acoela, are of exceedingly primitive structure, positively not degenerated from or modified
from a higher anatomical type.   The ctenophore-trochophore theory
therefore appears to the author unacceptable, although it has been widely
supported.

   The planuloid-acoeloid theory is based upon the remarkable features
of the flatworm order Acoela, whose primitive structure was first recognized in 1882 by Ludwig von Graff, the distinguished pioneer in the study
of the free-living flatworms.   The Acoela were nevertheless long regarded
as degenerate forms and hence of no phylogenetic importance until recent
years when their primitive nature has again been recognized by all
students of the Turbellaria.   The Acoela are a group of very small flatworms with the following primitive characteristics.   The ciliated epidermis is often syncytial, as in many coelenterates, and in several members has basal muscle fibers, as also in coelenterates.   There is no distinct
basement membrane beneath the epidermis.   The interior is a solid mass
of cells as in the planula larva without a digestive cavity, and comparison
of the embryonic development with that of other flatworms indicates
that this interior mass represents entoderm and ecto- and entomesoderm.
There is a mouth in the center of the ventral surface, and this leads into
the interior mass either directly or by way of a simple tubular pharynx.
These worms feed by ingesting small animals through the mouth into the
interior mass where intracellular digestion occurs; thus it is directly
proved that an archenteron is not a necessity for the early bilateral
holozoic animal, as supposed by the Haeckelian gastrula theory.   The
nervous system is of primitive construction, consisting of a plexus beneath
the epidermis with several more or less distinct longitudinal strands
radiating from an anterior brain mass; but in some acoels (see page 83)
the nerve plexus is situated in the basal part of the epidermis and the
brain is a mere thickening also epidermally located.   Most of the Acoela
have a statocyst near or embedded in the brain; this structurally is more
like the statocyst of a medusa than of a ctenophore.   There are no distinct gonads, but the sex cells differentiate out of the cells of the interior
mass.   Female ducts are wanting, and the eggs discharge either through
the mouth or by rupture of the body surface.   There are usually indis-
tinct male ducts which lead to a copulatory organ.   Although the animals
are hermaphroditic, cross-fertilization is the rule and is internal.   The
Acoela lack an excretory system.

It is evident that there is no difficulty in passing from a planuloid type of ancestor to an acoeloid form (Fig. 2). Epidermis, muscular system, interior mass, nervous system, and sex cells are, even in present Acoela, distinctly at a coelenterate stage or but slightly advanced from this stage. Consequently we accept the theory of the origin of the Bilateria from a planuloid ancestor by way of an acoeloid form. The main changes necessary are the alteration from radial to bilateral symmetry and the forward shifting of the nervous center. As no intermediate forms are

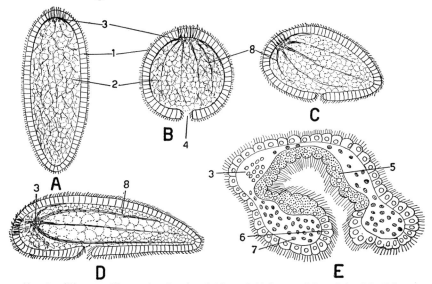

FIG. 2.—Diagrams illustrating the planuloid-acoeloid theory of the origin of the Bilateria. *A.* Planula larva, mouthless with apical nerve center. *B.* Mouth formed, oral-aboral axis shortening. *C.* Body elongating in a sagittal (originally transverse) plane, nervous center shifting forward. *D.* Acoeloid stage, a bilateral creeping worm with anterior nerve center. *E.* Later stage, archenteron formed; actual embryonic stage of a polyclad (*after Surface*, 1907). 1, ectoderm; 2, entodermal mass; 3, nervous center; 4, mouth; 5, archenteron; 6, stomodaeum; 7, mesoderm; 8, nerve cords.

known, the steps by which these changes occurred may be inferred from the embryology of the lower Turbellaria. As the mouth of the Acoela occupies the site of the blastopore, it may be taken as a fixed point. It is then evident that, as postulated by Lang, the planuloid form must have flattened down in the oral-aboral axis and at the same time there must have occurred a forward migration of the sensory center, as actually happens in the development of polyclads, through processes of differential growth (Fig. 2). The result is a simple flatworm with bilateral symmetry, ventral mouth, and anteriorly located brain and sense organs. A later stage, represented by the higher Turbellaria, is attained by the hollowing out of the central part of the interior mass to form an archenteron (Fig. 2E) and the greater differentiation of the anterior region as a head.

It is thus seen that the oral surface of the Radiata becomes the ventral surface of the Bilateria while their sagittal plane is retained as the sagittal plane of the latter. But the dorsoventral flattening is not a mere shortening of the oral-aboral axis, for this axis has been curved forward by the anterior shifting of the nervous center. Thus, whereas in the Radiata the oral-aboral axis of the larva is retained as the oral-aboral axis of the adult, in the Bilateria the gastrular axis has no direct relation to any of the adult axes.

III. SPIRAL CLEAVAGE AND DETERMINATE DEVELOPMENT

Determinate or *mosaic* development, characteristic of most of the Protostomia, is usually associated with the spiral type of cleavage, found in polyclad flatworms, nemertines, annelids, and mollusks. Among these groups the cleavage pattern and the fate of the various blastomeres are so nearly identical that a common descent is scarcely to be doubted. In spiral cleavage, the spindle axes are oriented obliquely with respect to the polar axis of the egg. As a result successive tiers of blastomeres alternate, the cells of one tier resting in the angles between the cells below them (P–C, page 257, Fig. 73F, G). This displacement may be either clockwise (dextrotropic) or counterclockwise (levotropic). Spiral cleavage is commonly holoblastic but unequal, and this inequality is often evidenced even at the first cleavage. In spiral cleavage, the fate of each blastomere can be determined, a type of study known as *cell lineage* and pursued with brilliant results by American embryologists. For clarity in describing the course of events, each blastomere is named. The four blastomeres formed by the first two meridional cleavages are labeled A, B, C, D. The third division is transverse and latitudinal and results in eight cells, four small animal ones called the *first quartet of micromeres* and four large cells below, called *macromeres* (Fig. 3A). The micromeres are named 1a, 1b, 1c, 1d, and the macromeres 1A, 1B, 1C, 1D. At the next cleavage, the macromeres give off above a *second quartet* of micromeres, called 2a, 2b, 2c, 2d, and are themselves then designated as 2A, 2B, 2C, 2D (Fig. 3B); and at the next cleavage the latter again divide, giving off a *third quartet*, 3a, etc., themselves becoming 3A, etc. (Fig. 3C). Meantime the first and second quartets have cleaved, and their offspring are also numbered by a definite system. Thus the two daughter cells of 1a become 1a^1 and 1a^2; the exponent 1 is applied to the cell nearer the animal pole. When these divide again, exponents are added; thus the daughter cells of 1a^1 are numbered 1a^{11} and 1a^{12}, and of 1a^2, 1a^{21} and 1a^{22}, respectively. This system obviously is capable of indefinite expansion and serves to designate exactly the origin of any particular cell. All the cleavages are oblique and are alternately dextrotropic and levotropic. All the blastomeres bearing one letter, as a, are offspring of one of the

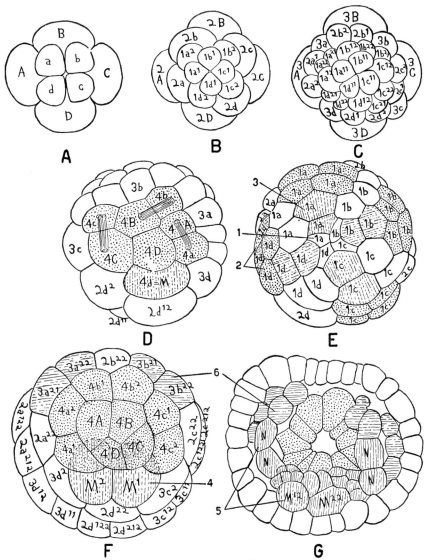

Fig. 3.—Spiral cleavage. A. Third cleavage, division into micromeres and macromeres. B. Formation of the second quartet of micromeres; first quartet has divided. C. Formation of the third quartet of micromeres; second quartet has divided again. (A, B, C, based on development of polyclads.) D. View from vegetative pole, showing the macromeres giving off the fourth quartet of micromeres; entoderm cells stippled, entomesodermal cell, 4d = M, vertically hatched. E. View from the animal pole, showing the rosette and the annelid cross (cells of cross hatched); primary trochoblasts stippled; only the series to which each cell belongs is indicated. (D, E, polychaete Arenicola, after Child, 1900.) F. View from vegetal pole of embryo of the snail Physa, showing entoderm (stippled), the two teloblasts (vertically hatched), and the cells that give rise to the ectomesoderm (crosshatched). G. Later stage of Physa, looking into interior from animal pole, showing the teloblasts giving off the mesoderm bands (vertically hatched), of which the cells marked N become the metanephridia; entoderm stippled, ectomesoderm crosshatched. (F, G, after Wierzejski, 1905; the cleavage of Physa spirals in the reverse direction from that of the other forms figured.) 1, rosette; 2, primary trochoblasts; 3, cross; 4, teloblasts; 5, mesoderm bands; 6, ectomesoderm.

original four blastomeres, in this case A, and hence more or less occupy one quadrant of the embryo.

When the third quartet of micromeres has been given off, the germ layers are already fixed (usually 32-cell stage, as the first and second quartets have cleaved). The three quartets and their offspring form the whole of the ectoderm (and also the larval mesoderm, i.e., the ectomesoderm) and hence are often called *ectomeres*. The four macromeres, $3A$, $3B$, $3C$, $3D$, form the whole of the entoderm and the true or entomesoderm. At their next division, they give off at the vegetal pole a fourth quartet of micromeres, $4a$–$4d$, three of which are also purely entodermal (Fig. 3D). The fourth cell, $4d$, is larger than the corresponding macromere, $4D$, is called the *mesentoblast* cell, or M, and is the entire source of the entomesoderm. It was originally supposed that all its offspring are mesodermal, but later researches have shown that a few of these remain entodermal and contribute to the gut wall. The main offspring of $4d$, however, in annelids and mollusks, are two cells known as the *teloblasts*, *pole cells*, or *primordial mesoderm cells*. These take up a bilateral position just in front of the future anus and each proliferates a band of cells, the *mesoderm band*, the sole source of the entomesoderm (Fig. 3F, G).

The embryo becomes an inequal coeloblastula or, in the case of very yolky eggs, a stereoblastula. The ectomeres spread and grow down over the macromeres, which also invaginate. A typical invaginate gastrula thus arises partly by epiboly and partly by emboly. The mouth forms at the site of the blastopore by way of a stomodaeal invagination. In forms with an anus, the blastopore elongates and closes together medially so as to leave its anterior end as mouth and its posterior end as anus. The anal end usually closes temporarily but later reopens as the permanent anus. A stomodaeum is universal throughout the Protostomia. The mouth is usually shifted forward by growth processes elsewhere in the embryo. The embryo develops an apical tuft of cilia and an equatorial girdle of cilia and swims about as a free-living larva.

The fate of the various cells of the cleavage pattern may be stated briefly. The micromeres of the first quartet form the ectoderm of the aboral part of the larva. The $1a^{111}$–$1d^{111}$ series occupy the animal pole where they make a four-rayed pattern termed the rosette which becomes the aboral sensory plate with its tuft of cilia (Fig. 3E). Their sister cells, the $1a^{112}$–$1d^{112}$ series, in annelids alternate with them as a cross-shaped figure called the *annelid cross* (Fig. 3E). A similar *molluscan cross* occurs in molluscan development but there is formed of the cells which lie between the arms of the annelid cross, namely, the $1a^{12}$–$1d^{12}$ cells, with some assistance from second quartet cells. Thus the arms of the cross are interradial in annelids, radial in mollusks. The cross, very evident in early stages, eventually becomes obliterated and plays no special role in development as such. It is often regarded as a ctenophore reminiscence, and the ctenophore resemblance is enhanced in some cases by the bifurcation of the tips of the arms to form an eight-rayed figure. The $1a^2$–$1d^2$ descendants of the first quartet are termed the *primary trochoblasts;* they form four groups of four cells each, one group in each quadrant of the embryo near the equator (Fig. 3*E*). Each cell develops a transverse tuft of cilia reminiscent of a ctenophore comb. These four groups of ciliary tufts constitute the primitive ciliated girdle, or *prototroch*, of the larva. Later the prototroch is completed by the formation of cilia on the cells between the primary trochoblasts, termed *secondary trochoblasts*, which come from the first or second quartet or both.

The cells of the second and third quartets contribute to the surface ectoderm, and certain ones, termed *stomatoblasts*, invaginate as the stomodaeum. In annelids, the cell 2*d*, known as the first *somatoblast*, gives rise to practically the entire ectoderm of the adult trunk. Cells are also given off from the second and third quartets into the blastocoel as mesenchyme which differentiates into larval muscles (Fig. 3*F, G*). This mesenchyme constitutes the larval mesoderm or ectomesoderm and is undoubtedly a reminiscence of the original ectomesoderm of the ancestral stem form of the Bilateria. Descendants of $3c^2$ and $3d^2$ give rise in annelids to the larval excretory organs, the *archinephridia*. In the most primitive case, that of the annelid *Polygordius*, the archinephridium comes from two cells, one forming the tubule, and the other the solenocyte.

The entoderm originates almost wholly from seven cells, namely, 4*a*, 4*b*, 4*c*, 4*A*, 4*B*, 4*C*, and 4*D* (Fig. 3*D*), which invaginate and produce the entodermal wall of the stomach and intestine of the larva. As already noted, a few cells descended from 4*d* become incorporated into the intestinal wall. The intestine (in the higher Protostomia) connects to the exterior by an anus formed at the site of the rear end of the blastopore. In producing the anus, the ectoderm invaginates slightly, and this ectodermal termination of the gut is called the *proctodaeum*.

The two teloblasts, offspring of 4*d*, lie in the blastocoel just in front of the anus (Fig. 3*F*). By repeated divisions each gives rise to a band of cells which extends forward into the blastocoel. These bilateral *mesoderm bands* (Fig. 3*G*) are the whole of the entomesoderm and give rise to muscle, connective tissues, gonads, excretory system at least in part, blood vessels, etc. The formation of typical mesoderm bands from teloblasts is confined to the phyla Annelida and Mollusca, but the bands are well evidenced in the Arthropoda.

In the annelids and mollusks, spiral cleavage often results in a characteristic larva, known as the *trochophore*,[1] and somewhat similar larvae

---

[1] Discovered in 1840 by the Swedish naturalist Loven and known for many years as Loven's larva. It was then called *trochosphaera* or *trochosphaere* by Ray-Lankester

occur in other protostomous phyla.   As great phylogenetic significance
has been attributed to the trochophore larva, it becomes necessary to
describe its characters before proceeding further.

IV. THE TROCHOPHORE LARVA, THE TROCHOPHORE THEORY, AND THE GENERAL PHYLOGENETIC SIGNIFICANCE OF LARVAL TYPES

The trochophore larva (Fig. 4) is a somewhat biconical creature with a
protruding equator.   Its external surface consists of a one-layered epithelium (ectoderm) thickened at the apical pole into a sensory plate which
bears a tuft of cilia.   Around the equator there is a girdle of cilia termed
the *prototroch* which passes above the mouth; and there may be present a
second equatorial girdle, the *metatroch*, passing below the mouth, and
sometimes also a ciliated circlet around the anus, the *paratroch*.   A complete digestive tube is present extending in an L-shape from the mouth at
the equator to the anus at the lower pole; it consists of a ciliated stomodaeum leading into an expanded rounded stomach from which the short
narrowed intestine proceeds to the anus.   Between the digestive tube
and the ectoderm there is a spacious cavity which is the blastular cavity
or blastocoel.   This is more or less occupied by mesenchyme cells and
well-developed muscle cells, all derived from the ectomesoderm.   The
muscular system is often quite complicated consisting not only of bands
acting on the digestive tube and ciliary girdles but also of bands under
the ectoderm accompanying the nerves (Fig. 5).   The nervous system
according to the best description (E. Meyer, 1901) may attain an astonish-
ing degree of complexity (Fig. 5), consisting of a ganglionic mass under
the apical plate, a variable number of longitudinal nerves radiating from
this mass, and one to several nerve rings connecting the radial nerves.
The main nerve ring underlies the prototroch.   Various sense organs,
including eyes and statocysts, may be present.   To either side of the
intestine lies a mesoderm band derived from a teloblast, and near this
there is on each side a nephridium consisting of a tubule whose inner end
is closed by one or more solenocytes.   A solenocyte (Fig. 12D) is a long
tubular cell having a flagellum playing in the tube.   Solenocytes occur
in several invertebrate groups and also in *Amphioxus*, and nephridia with
solenocytes are undoubtedly only a variant of nephridia with flame bulbs
(see below); the latter are general throughout the acoelomate and pseudocoelomate Bilateria.

The *trochophore theory*, elaborately developed by Hatschek (1878),
is to the effect that the trochophore is the larva of an ancestral form, the
trochozoon, which was the common ancestor of most, if not all, the bilateral
phyla, and which, of living forms, most nearly resembled a rotifer.   It

---

(1877), but this name was abandoned because it had earlier been used for a genus of
rotifers.   The name trochophore originated with Hatschek (1878).

is to be noted that the trochophore is regarded as recapitulating the *larva* of the ancestor, not as being itself a replica of the ancestor. The rotifer resemblances usually cited are the general pseudocoelomate grade of structure, the ciliary girdles, the structure and location of the brain and the nature of its attached sense organs, the muscle bands, the nephridia, the form of the digestive tract, and the presence of an anus. The rotifer-like nature of the hypothetical trochozoon was considered

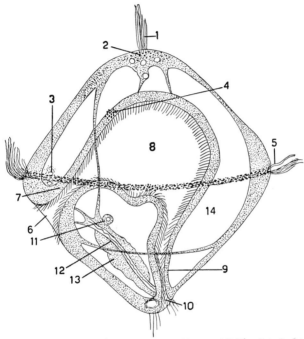

Fig. 4.—Trochophore larva of an annelid (*after Shearer*, 1911). 1, apical tuft of cilia; 2, apical sensory plate; 3, ectomesoderm; 4, eye; 5, prototroch; 6, mouth; 7, stomodaeum; 8, stomach; 9, proctodaeum; 10, anus; 11, statocyst; 12, archinephridium, consisting of one solenocyte; 13, mesoderm bands; 14, blastocoel.

strongly supported by the discovery by Semper in 1859 in the rice fields of the Philippines of a rotifer which he named *Trochosphaera* and which through its inflated spherical form and equatorial ciliary girdle bears considerable superficial resemblance to a trochophore larva. Time has detracted from the rotifer part of the trochophore theory, for those rotifers whose ciliary arrangements most suggest the girdles of the trocho-phore are now regarded as specialized types and the primitive ciliary apparatus of the rotifers has not much likeness to the trochophore girdles. Further the rotifer *Trochosphaera*, which has been refound and restudied in various localities, is now known to be merely an aberrant type of no especial evolutionary significance. Nevertheless, while discarding the

rotifer part of the trochophore theory, one must admit the general sound-
ness of Hatschek's view that the trochophore is about at the structural
level of a rotifer, i.e., is of the pseudocoelomate grade of structure.   The
fact further that nearly identical trochophores occur in two phyla in
which the adults are anatomically very different, i.e., the annelids and
the mollusks, suggests that the trochophore is indeed a reminiscence of
the common ancestor of the eucoelomate Protostomia and perhaps also

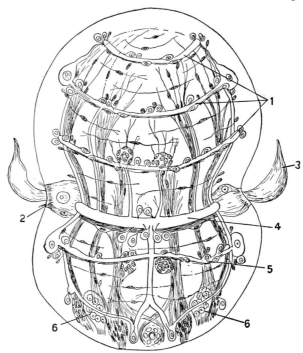

FIG. 5.—Trochophore of the annelid *Lopadorhynchus* (*after E. Meyer*, 1901), showing
nervous system (blank) and muscular system (striated).   The orientation of the larva is
such that the apical sensory center does not show.   1, upper three nerve rings; 2, ciliary
cell of the prototroch; 3, prototroch; 4, main nerve ring underlying the prototroch; 5, lower
nerve ring; 6, mesoderm bands.

of the pseudocoelomate groups.   However, the origin of the acoelomate
Bilateria remains unaccounted for on this theory.

The ctenophore-trochophore theory, mentioned above, is a more
recent and widely accepted version of the trochophore theory.   It proposes to pass directly from a ctenophore-like ancestor to the trochozoon
and so to bridge the gap between the radiate and bilateral animals.
The chief ctenophore resemblances of the trochophore are: the apical
nerve center with its attached sense organs, the radiating subectodermal
nerves, often (but not always) eight in number, the occurrence of the
"cross" in the cleavage pattern, and the origin of the prototroch from

four groups of ciliated cells. The apical nerve plate and sense organs are, however, also a feature of the planuloid ancestor, and the other resemblances are a necessary consequence of the quadripartite pattern characteristic of spiral cleavage. This quadripartite pattern is the result of the two meridional cleavages producing four blastomeres, each of which roughly forms one-fourth of the embryo. The argument therefore boils down to the question whether cleavage into four blastomeres is in fact reminiscent of a ctenophore ancestry. And this does not appear to be the case since the ctenophore egg goes through three meridional cleavages producing a wreath of eight blastomeres, and the details of its cleavage are not similar to the course of spiral cleavage. Further the nervous system of the developed trochophore with its longitudinal nerves connected by circular nerves is more like that of the acoel flatworms (which often also have eight longitudinal nerve trunks) than it is like that of a ctenophore. The ctenophore-trochophore theory is therefore rejected on these grounds and those previously mentioned.

A main difficulty in the path of the trochophore theory and its variants has been to allocate the acoelomate groups, for these can no longer be disregarded as degraded from higher bilateral phyla. This difficulty is here met by the interpolation in the phylogeny of an acoeloid grade of ancestor from which the flatworms are readily derived. The phylogenetic series here proposed is then: planuloid ancestor–acoeloid ancestor–trochozoon (pseudocoelomate grade). The gap from the acoeloid ancestor to the trochozoon is probably too large and may need to be filled by a type with a digestive tract but no anus, resembling stages seen in the development of polyclads (Fig. 2*E*).

An attitude of conservatism should always be maintained in regard to the evaluation of larval types. A larva is a developmental stage that leads a free existence. Larvae are practically limited to marine animals. The main reasons given for this (Needham, 1930) are: that larvae are too delicate to withstand the much wider range of environmental factors in fresh water than in the sea; that they would be swept away by currents; and that fresh water is poor in the salts needed by many larvae. It results that animals, to reproduce successfully in fresh water, must produce larger and fewer eggs, better provided with food and salts than their marine relatives; the eggs must be protected with shells, jelly, etc.; must be fastened to objects or develop inside the mother; and the young animal must hatch in a fully developed condition. Consequently, the development of fresh-water animals is generally highly modified and furnishes poor material for phylogenetic speculations. It is therefore difficult to work out the relationships of groups of animals which are predominantly fresh-water. Even among related marine groups, some may have free larvae and others not, without apparent reason. In such cases the question arises which type of development is the more primitive. Again as larvae must fend for themselves and find food, they are very apt to display adaptive modifications which are without phylogenetic significance. Pelagic larvae tend to present common characters adapted to pelagic life, as transparency and lightness of body, swimming apparatus mostly in the form of ciliated bands, lobes and projections for buoyancy, and a food-catching mechanism, mostly of the mucous-ciliary type. Evidently great caution must be exercised in the interpretation of larvae, and most weight should be placed on characters not common to pelagic animals. In the case of the trochophore larva, the most salient features are the form of the nervous system, the presence of an anus, and the occurrence of primitive nephridia. These suggest an ancestral form higher than a flatworm and lower than an annelid.

The foregoing analysis carries the line of evolution from the radiates to and through the protostomous Bilateria. The relation of the Deuterostomia to this line of ascent remains very dubious, and this situation casts much doubt on the generally accepted ideas of the original modes of origin of mesoderm and coelom.

V. MODES OF ORIGIN OF THE MESODERM

The term mesoderm is rather loosely applied to all cells, cell layers, or cell masses which occur in the embryo between the ectoderm and the entoderm. The mesoderm is also spoken of as the third germ layer. As already noted, there are two kinds of mesoderm which seem to be phylogenetically distinct, the ectomesoderm and the entomesoderm. The ectomesoderm exists in both the Radiata and the Protostomia and is undoubtedly the oldest form of mesoderm. It is always mesenchymal and typically consists of inwandered ectodermal cells, in spiral cleavage of cells descended from the second and third quartets of micromeres. Ectomesoderm appears to be absent in the Deuterostomia. The Protostomia presumably inherited the ectomesoderm from a radiate ancestor, and their entomesoderm is a later development originating in the evolution of the Protostomia from a radiate ancestor.

The entomesoderm, the "true" or definite mesoderm, includes all mesoderm which arises from or with the entoderm. It may form as mesenchyme or as bands, plates, or sacs, more or less epithelial in character. The attempt of the Hertwigs (1882) to draw a sharp distinction between entomesoderm of mesenchymal origin and that of epithelial origin (mesothelium) was mistaken. The entomesoderm may arise by either method, and mesoderm which begins as epithelium may later become mesenchymal or vice versa. The time of origin of the entomesoderm is also variable. The following modes of formation of the entomesoderm occur among the Bilateria.

1. Teloblastic Method.—As already noted, this method is associated with spiral cleavage. The cell 4*d* gives off the two teloblasts or primordial mesoderm cells which pass into the blastocoel and there proliferate on each side a mesoderm band (Fig. 3*F, G*). The fact that some of the offspring of 4*d* are entoderm and participate in the gut wall is taken to establish the entodermal nature of the mesoderm so formed. This is also indicated by the purely entodermal character of the sister cells of 4*d*.

2. Derived Mesoderm-band Method.—In arthropods the entomeso-derm also comes from paired bands, but the latter do not originate from teloblasts. They come from a mass of cells arising around the blastopore. Since the later development of these bands is very similar to that in annelids, from which arthropods are believed to have evolved, the entomesoderm of arthropods is regarded as originating by a modified teloblastic method.

3. Enterocoelous Method.—The mesoderm is formed in whole or in part by the outpouching of the archenteron wall as one or more pouches (Fig. 6*A*). This is an epithelial mode of entomesoderm formation. It is characteristic of the Deuterostomia, i.e., the Chaetognatha, Echinodermata, and lower Chordata, but also occurs in the Brachiopoda.

4. Lamellar Method.—The mesoderm grows out as a flattened stratum of cells from around the blastopore and is more or less mesenchymal in character. This manner of mesoderm formation is correlated with meroblastic development and is best seen in vertebrates where it is commonly regarded as a modified enterocoelous process.

5. Mesenchymal Method.—The formation of entomesoderm by inwandering of entoderm cells (Fig. 6*B*) en masse or more or less singly is common and may be combined with other modes of mesoderm production. Since in fact all methods of mesoderm origin except the enterocoelous are more or less mesenchymal, no very sharp line can be drawn between them.

With regard to the theoretical interpretation of the modes of entomesoderm formation, the same question arises as with regard to entoderm formation, i.e., was the epithelial (enterocoelous) or the mesenchymal method the primitive one? The enterocoelous origin by evagination from the archenteron has been widely accepted as primitive and all others as derived. This view, however, rests not upon direct evidence but on a phylogenetic speculation to the effect that the archenteral evaginations of the Deuterostomia are identical with the gastric pockets of a coelenterate. Adherents of the enterocoelous theory regard the teloblasts as precocious archenteral pockets reduced to single cells.

There are serious objections to the idea of the primary nature of the enterocoelous method of entomesoderm formation. This method is characteristic of the Deuterostomia whose relation to the Radiata cannot be traced. The line of ascent obviously leads from the Radiata to the Protostomia, and hence it is more logical to seek the original mode of entomesoderm formation among the latter. The derivation of the teloblastic method from the enterocoelous is not very convincing. Further,

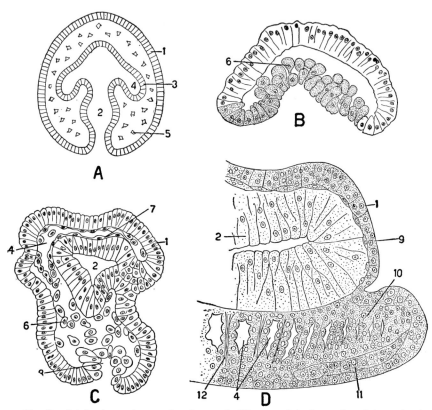

Fig. 6.—Origin of mesoderm and coelom. *A.* Diagram of the formation of the coelomic sacs by the enterocoelous method in an echinoderm. *B.* Formation of the mesoderm by ingression from the invaginating entoderm in *Phoronis;* entoderm and mesoderm stippled. *C.* Formation of the coelom in *Phoronis* by arrangement of mesoderm cells; note formation of protonephridium by an ectodermal invagination. (*B, C, after Ikeda,* 1901.) *D.* Embryo of an earthworm, parasagittal section through the rear end, showing the mesoderm band breaking up into segments in each of which a coelomic split is appearing (*after Wilson,* 1889). 1, ectoderm; 2, archenteron; 3, mesoderm sac; 4, coelom; 5, mesenchyme cells; 6, mesoderm cells; 7, peritoneum; 8, ectoderm invagination to form protonephridia; 9, future proctodaeum; 10, mesoderm band; 11, nephridial cord to form metanephridia separating from mesoderm band; 12, septum.

while the Protostomia show no reminiscence of a preceding enterocoelous method, the chief enterocoelous phylum, the Echinodermata, exhibits a considerable formation of mesoderm by a mesenchymal method prior to the evagination of the archenteron sacs. On the other hand, the teloblastic method can hardly be regarded as primitive, and in fact the determinate mode of development seems specialized and shortened from the indeterminate type; and teloblast formation is more plausibly derived from an ancestral general inwandering than it is from the enterocoelous method. It seems most logical to seek for the original mode of ento-mesoderm formation among the most primitive Protostomia, namely, the turbellarian order Acoela. In this group, the available embryo-logical evidence indicates that the entoderm and the entomesoderm are not distinctly separated but together form an interior mass which origi-nates by inwandering at the blastopore. The evidence thus seems to favor some sort of mesenchymal inwandering as the original method. The entomesodermal inwandering differs from the ectomesodermal one in that it is limited to the region around the blastopore or where the blastopore will form. This association of the entomesoderm with the blastopore is general throughout the protostomous Bilateria, and in fact it may well be that entomesoderm formation is a phenomenon of the blastopore rather than of the entoderm. The relation of entomesoderm to the blastopore is difficult to explain morphologically but physiologically may be related to the known high metabolic activity of the blastopore rim. If, as here suggested, mesenchymal inwandering from around the blastopore was the original mode of entomesoderm formation, the whole process of mesoderm production becomes more logical and understand-able; for then the giving off of ectomesoderm and entomesoderm would constitute two stages of the same process. That this view may be the correct one is further evidenced by the fact that not infrequently the definitive mesoderm is a combination of tissues of ecto- and entomeso-dermal origin (e.g., body-wall musculature of some annelids, E. Meyer, 1901); and in the snail *Paludina*, entomesoderm formation is secondarily suppressed and the whole of the adult mesoderm is of ectomesodermal origin (Dautert, 1929).

VI. BODY CAVITIES OF THE BILATERIA

The body cavities of animals are of several sorts, and it is necessary to distinguish clearly between them. The first cavity to appear is that of the blastula, the *blastocoel* or *primary body cavity*. With the formation of the archenteron, the blastocoel may be completely obliterated by the contact of entoderm with ectoderm or by the accumulation of mesogloea or mesenchyme between them. This happens in the radiate phyla where the digestive cavity is the only body space of the adult.

In the bilateral phyla several things may happen. The space between ectoderm and entoderm may become filled up with mesoderm in the form of muscle fibers and mesenchyme. This is the case in the phyla Platy-helminthes and Rhynchocoela in which again the digestive cavity remains the sole internal space. Such animals may be termed *acoelomate*, i.e., without a body cavity (Fig. 7*A*). In other groups, the original blastocoel remains as a considerable space between digestive tract and body wall. Such a condition obtains in the acanthocephalan worms, nematodes, rotifers, entoprocts, and related forms where a large cavity, known by its embryonic history to be a persistent blastocoel, exists between gut and body wall. Such a cavity will be designated a *pseudocoel*[1] or false coelom, and animals so constructed will be spoken of throughout this treatise as *pseudocoelomate* (Fig. 7*B*).

The true *coelom* or *secondary body cavity* is a cavity in the entomesoderm, and its occurrence is therefore absolutely dependent on the formation of entomesoderm. It has essentially the same different ways of origin as the entomesoderm, three ways.

1. Schizocoel.—In the teloblastic, derived teloblastic, and lamellar modes of mesoderm formation, the coelom arises as a split inside the mesodermic bands, plates, or masses (Fig. 6*D*). The split expands until the mesoderm comes in contact with the body wall on one side and the gut wall on the other.

2. Enterocoel.—In the enterocoelous method of mesoderm formation, the mesodermal sacs evaginated from the archenteron become cut off and lie in the blastocoel. Their cavity is the coelom, their walls the mesoderm. These sacs expand until they touch the body and gut wall, and the end result is therefore the same as by the schizocoelous method.

3. Mesenchymal Coelom.—The mesenchyme may rearrange itself so as to enclose a space which is then a true coelom since it is bounded on all sides by mesoderm. This method is said to occur only in the worm *Phoronis* (Fig. 6*C*).

Certain terms are applicable to all coelomate animals. That portion of the mesoderm which adheres to the inner surface of the body wall is called the *somatic* or *parietal* mesoderm. From it differentiate the muscle fibers and connective tissue of the body wall. That portion which adheres to the outer surface of the gut and other viscera is termed the *splanchnic* mesoderm and is the source of the muscle fibers and connective tissue of the viscera. The mesoderm cells next the coelomic cavity arrange to an epithelium called the coelomic lining or *peritoneum*, and this is termed *parietal* where it lines the inside of the body wall and *visceral* where it clothes the digestive system or other organs. Because of the way in which the coelom arises, every organ that is not embedded in the body wall or gut wall becomes necessarily covered by peritoneum. If an organ does not project into the coelom, the peritoneum clothes that sur-

---

[1] This is not the original usage of the word pseudocoel. This term was employed by the Hertwigs in 1882 in their classical article Die Cölomtheorie as a name for mesenchymal spaces; they confused under one name pseudocoel, haemocoel, and schizocoel.

face of the organ which faces the coelom. Such organs are said to be *retroperitoneal*. If an organ projects into the coelom, it is necessarily sheathed by a layer of peritoneum and is connected to other parts by a sheet composed chiefly of a double layer of peritoneum and called a *mesentery*. As the coelom expands, the splanchnic walls of the mesoderm meet above and below the digestive tract to form the *dorsal* and *ventral* mesenteries of that tract (Fig. 7*C*). The adult relations of coelom and mesenteries and the parts formed by the mesoderm are identical in schizocoelous and enterocoelous forms. Naturally the expansion of the mesoderm completely obliterates the blastocoel.

A true coelom is thus defined as a space between digestive tract and body wall which is bounded on all sides by tissue of entomesodermal origin and lined by peritoneum. Throughout this treatise the word coelom will be used to designate only a true coelom.

It is obvious from the foregoing that the nature of a body space can be determined only by the study of its embryonic history. The embryology of invertebrates is inadequately known, but according to available information, the Bilateria can be arranged as follows with regard to body spaces. These groupings do not, however, entirely correspond to taxonomic relationships.

1. Acoelomate phyla, without body space other than the digestive cavity; mesenchyme and muscle fibers fill region between digestive tube and epidermis (Fig. 7*A*). Phyla Platyhelminthes and Rhynchocoela.

2. Pseudocoelomate phyla, with a persistent pseudocoel (= blastocoel) between digestive tube and body wall (Fig. 7*B*). Phyla Acanthocephala, Aschelminthes (Rotifera, Gastrotricha, Kinorhyncha, Priapulida, Nematoda, Nematomorpha), and Entoprocta.

3. Coelomate phyla, which have a true coelom (Fig. 7*C*).

a. Coelom an enterocoel. Includes the Deuterostomia (Chaetognatha, Echinodermata, Hemichordata, and Chordata). The Brachiopoda also form their coelom by the enterocoelous method.

b. Coelom a schizocoel. Here belong the remaining phyla of the Protostomia, including the Phoronida, which latter form their coelom by a variant of the typical schizocoelous method (Fig. 6*C*).

Some phylogeneticists maintain that all Bilateria should be classified as coelomate animals since, so they say, they are derived from coelomate ancestors. The acoelomate phyla are said by these zoologists to have lost the coelom through invasion by mesenchyme and the pseudocoelomate groups to have retained an embryonic condition. The former statement is certainly untrue, and the latter lacks supporting evidence.

The value of the coelom in the animal economy is to be sought along two lines. First, the coelom frees the digestive tract and other organs from their previous encirclement by mesenchyme and gives them space and freedom for further differentiation and greater activity. The digestive tract no longer need strive for increased surface by lateral branchings but instead elongates and can secure more absorptive surface by coiling. It has also now become provided with a muscular wall which facilitates grinding and passage of food. The second and possibly chief function of the coelom is urogenital. The coelom furnishes a space in which

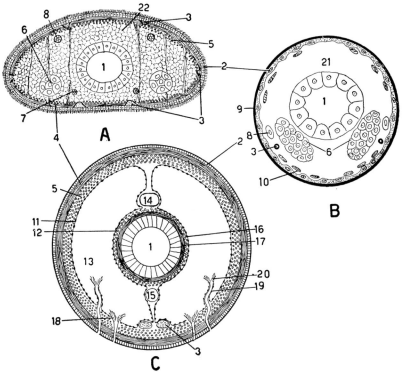

Fig. 7.—Diagrammatic cross sections of grades of structure. *A*. Acoelomate grade. *B*. Pseudocoelomate grade. *C*. Eucoelomate grade. 1, intestine; 2, epidermis; 3, nerve cords; 4, circular muscle layer; 5, longitudinal muscle layer; 6, gonad; 7, gonoduct; 8, protonephridium; 9, cuticle; 10, muscle bands; 11, parietal peritoneum; 12, visceral peritoneum; 13; coelom; 14, dorsal blood vessel; 15, ventral blood vessel; 16, longitudinal muscle layer of gut; 17, circular muscle layer of gut; 18, gonostome; 19, metanephridium; 20, nephrostome; 21, pseudocoel; 22, parenchyma.

nitrogenous wastes and excess water can accumulate and from which they can be discharged by way of excretory ducts; in fact, connection with the exterior by means of excretory ducts is a characteristic feature of the coelom. Usually also gonoducts for the discharge of the sex cells connect the coelom with the exterior. In coelomate animals, the gonads project into the coelom, and this is probably an important relationship since thereby ample space is provided for the enlargement of eggs and hence the production of large-yolked eggs.

Speculation as to the primitive mode of coelom formation necessarily follows the same trends as with regard to entomesoderm formation. The enterocoelous method is commonly accepted as the original one. Arguments against this view were already given. Here it may be repeated that the schizocoelous phyla are much more directly related to the Radiata than are the enterocoelous ones, that the relations of the latter to the other Bilateria are obscure, and that it appears more logical to seek for the original method of coelom formation among the Protostomia. The indications are that the schizocoelous method was the original one.

The question just discussed is intimately related to the further question of the phylogenetic significance of the coelom. On this matter there are three principal theories.

1. Enterocoel Theory.—This theory accepts the enterocoelous origin of the coelom as the primitive method and regards the mesodermal outpouchings as identical phylogenetically with the gastric pockets of the Scyphozoa and Anthozoa (Sedgwick, 1884). The bilateral ancestor is assumed to have had gastric pockets which became constricted off as coelomic sacs. As further evidence it is cited that in the Radiata the gonads often occur in the walls of the gastric pockets and in coelomate animals they are correspondingly located in the coelomic wall. The enterocoel theory has met with much favor, but cogent arguments can be raised against it. First, gastric pockets occur in the more highly organized coelenterates which do not seem suitable as ancestral types. Second, the gastric pockets of coelenterates do *not* arise as evaginations of the entoderm but very differently by ingrowth of septa from the body wall. Third, although the gonads are in fact located in the walls of the pockets, the sex cells themselves are usually of interstitial, not entodermal, origin, and indeed it seems that the sex cells originally were mesenchyme cells. Finally, conditions in the most primitive Bilateria do not support the enterocoel theory of either mesoderm or coelom formation.

2. Gonocoel Theory.—This, the most popular theory of the coelom, regards the coelom as the cavity of an expanded gonad. This idea was first expressed by Hatschek (1878) but was given its first exposition by Bergh (1885), who compared the segmented coelom of annelids with the linear series of gonads of flatworms and nemertines. The theory was further expounded by Lang (1881, 1904) and especially by E. Meyer (1890, 1901); both authors were led to acceptance of the theory by their studies of turbellarian and annelidan anatomy. The theory received much impetus from the finding by Lang of a marine planarian [*Procerodes lobata*, called by Lang (1881) *Gunda segmentina*], in which, as not uncommonly in marine planarians, the testes alternate with the intestinal branches and form a neat longitudinal row on each side. If now the intestinal branches were to be withdrawn and the gonads expand so as to touch each other, the row of gonads on each side would resemble the row of coelomic sacs of an annelid (Fig. 8). This theory, like the previous one, also accounts for the origin or apparent origin of the sex cells from the coelomic wall since this would necessarily be the case if the coelomic sac is nothing but an expanded gonad. The opening of the gonoducts into

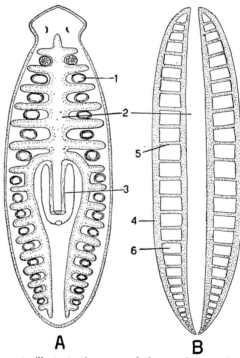

A   B

Fig. 8.—Diagrams to illustrate the gonocoel theory of the coelom. *A*. Triclad flatworm with gonads alternating with intestinal branches. *B*. Annelid with gonads expanded to form cubical coelomic sacs that fuse to body and intestinal walls. 1, gonads; 2, intestine; 3, pharynx; 4, body wall; 5, septum; 6, coelom.

the coelom is also explained. An extensive discussion of the gonocoel theory is given by Lang (1904).

The chief defect of the gonocoel theory, in the author's opinion, is that it links coelom formation with segmentation. The theory is based primarily on the occurrence of gonads in an anteroposterior row in nemertines and flatworms and hence can account only for a segmented coelom such as that of annelids (Fig. 8). It necessitates the assumption that all coelomate animals have passed through a segmented stage. But the majority of the coelomate phyla are not segmented, and there is no evidence that they came from segmented ancestors. Another difficulty of the theory is that it entails an independent origin of entomesoderm and coelom, and this is contrary to all the facts of embryology. This difficulty can be met only by supposing that all the mesoderm cells were originally sex cells. This conclusion has indeed been accepted by the more ardent proponents of the gonocoel theory, but it too is contrary to the facts which indicate that the sex cells of the lower Metazoa are derived from a generalized connective tissue which has many other functions as well. As a further criticism of the gonocoel theory, it is by no means clear that the sex cells actually originate from the coelomic lining in coelomate animals, for in many forms there has been demonstrated a "germ track" or a tracing back of the sex cells to certain cells of embryonic stages. In such forms, the sex cells later wander into the gonads, and indeed it seems probable that the general association of the gonads with the coelom is of secondary nature. Finally it may be questioned that the linear arrangement of the gonads on which the gonocoel theory was based is of real significance. In these lower worms the gonads develop after the intestinal branches have formed, and there is no other room for them except the regions between the intestinal branches. If the gonads are small, a number of them will occur between successive branches; but if they are large, as is the case in Lang's famous marine planarian, then there is room for only one between successive intestinal diverticula. There then results the linear arrangement which so excited earlier zoologists but to which no importance is now assigned by students of planarians.

3. Nephrocoel Theory.—On the basis that the chief function of the coelom is excretory, Ziegler (1898) proposed that the coelom represents the expanded inner end of a nephridium. This theory accounts for the constant association of excretory ducts with the coelom but in general lacks supporting facts. Some coelomate groups, as the echinoderms, do not have excretory organs.

4. Schizocoel Theory.—This fourth possibility has occasionally been mentioned in the literature. If a mesenchymal origin for the mesoderm is accepted as primitive, then it necessarily follows that the coelom was originally formed by the schizocoelous method. On this view the coelom is a new formation, not related in any way to the gonads of the lower Bilateria or the entodermal pouches of the Radiata, and neither entomesoderm nor coelom had any antecedents in lower forms. It seems probable that the appearance of spaces or splits in the mesoderm leading to coelom formation resulted from the accumulation of fluid, possibly of excretory nature.[1] As concerns the relation of the sex cells to the coelom,

[1] The schizocoel theory therefore leans somewhat toward Faussek's version (1899) of the nephrocoel theory. The coelom is not regarded as an expanded nephridial organ but as originally an excretory space for the accumulation of excretory fluid. With such space the already present nephridial tubules become associated.

it may be said that the sex cells seem from the start to be independent of any of the germ layers. The archaeocytes of sponges and the interstitial cells of coelenterates classify as primitive mesenchyme cells. Also among the lower Bilateria the sex cells are of mesenchymal origin. The sex cells tend to become associated with available cavities for discharge to the exterior, in the radiates, with the digestive cavity, in coelomate animals, with the coelom.

VII. SEGMENTATION

Metamerism or *segmentation* is the division of the body along the anteroposterior axis into a serial succession of sections, each of which contains identical or similar representatives of all the organ-systems of the body. The sections are termed *segments* or *metameres* and are delimited externally by constrictions of the body wall. Each segment primitively bears externally a pair of appendages, when such are present, and contains a pair of nerve ganglia, a pair of nephridia, a pair of gonads, paired blood vessels and nerves, and a portion of the digestive and muscular systems. In short all parts which do not run the length of the animal are serially repeated at regular intervals along the axis, and it is this repetition which constitutes the essence of metamerism. In an ideally segmented animal, all the segments are identical; such a condition is termed *homonomous*. No such animal exists since one or more head segments and the anal segment necessarily differ from the others, but the polychaete annelids approach the ideal. In most segmented animals, however, the segmentation is *heteronomous*, i.e., has undergone local alterations through loss or fusion of segments, emphasis of certain organs in some segments, loss of organs from others, migrations of organs to other than the original segments, etc. Such alterations commonly begin anteriorly and proceed posteriorly so that the posterior region of the animal usually retains the more primitive condition. Commonly the head of segmented animals represents several fused segments with emphasis on nervous structures and loss of representatives of other systems. Primitively the number of segments is large and indefinite and becomes limited to a definite, relatively small number in forms with a high degree of heteronomous segmentation.

The foregoing remarks apply to *true* or *mesodermal* segmentation. There appears to be another kind of segmentation among invertebrates, which will be termed *superficial* segmentation. This begins in the cuticle and may proceed inward to a limited extent; it involves the cuticle, often the body-wall musculature, and sometimes the nervous system but not more internally located systems. It is manifested in the Acanthocephala and many of the Aschelminthes. On the other hand mesodermal segmentation appears to be fundamentally a phenomenon of the mesoderm and proceeds from the interior outward, so that the external constrictions of the body wall follow the internal segmentation and presumably represent lines of muscle attachments. Mesodermal segmentation appears to have arisen independently three times in the animal kingdom, in the annelid-arthropod line, in the chordate line, and in the tapeworms, which the author, contrary to usual views, considers to be segmented. Hereafter, whenever the word segmentation is used without qualification, it is to be understood that true or mesodermal segmentation is meant.

In most cases of mesodermal segmentation, the segments form in an anteroposterior sequence so that the first segment is the oldest, the last the youngest; and new segments arise in a growing zone in front of the terminal piece bearing the anus. In tapeworms, however, the opposite condition obtains, for the last segment is the oldest, the first the youngest, and new segments develop in a growing zone in the "neck" region. Some zoologists have attempted to explain this difference by postulating that the "head" (scolex) of tapeworms is really the rear end; but modern studies on tapeworm development prove that the scolex is in fact the anterior end. Hence it is evident that tapeworm segmentation has arisen independently of that of annelids and arthropods, and this would indeed be a necessary conclusion from other lines of evidence. Zoologists usually claim that tapeworms do not have "true" segmentation (without defining what they mean by true segmentation); but the author sees no way of defining segmentation that would exclude tapeworms, unless the region of segment formation enters into the definition. As the region of segment formation appears to the author a minor point, the tapeworms are here regarded as truly segmented animals. Although the mode of formation of segments is identical in annelids, arthropods, and chordates, the last group is not now regarded as directly related to the other two, and hence segmentation must be supposed to have originated independently in the chordates.

There have been several theories of the phylogenetic origin of mesodermal segmentation. They revolve mostly around the question whether the repetition of organs is primary and the segmentation of the mesoderm secondary or whether the organs are serially repeated because the mesoderm from which they develop became segmented. In this connection it may be stated that a tendency for organs to spread throughout the available space is a primitive character and the sharp localization of an organ a more specialized condition. On this general principle it seems a priori probable that the repetition of organs preceded segmentation. The following are the chief theories of segmentation (see also Hatschek, 1888; Lang, 1904).

1. Corm or Fission Theory.—This idea, the most widely accepted of the various explanations of segmentation, states that a segmented animal is really a chain of zooids resulting from incomplete fissions, and seeks the cause of segmentation in asexual reproduction. The number of animals that form such chains of zooids is few, and in none of them (except the scyphistoma of jellyfish) does the process resemble the segmentation of a segmented animal. In zooid formation, a fission plane appears near the middle of the animal, dividing it into anterior and posterior zooids; in each zooid a new fission plane develops, dividing this again into anterior and posterior zooids; and so on (Fig. 9). In the resulting chain of zooids, the successive zooids are not at all serially arranged with respect to age and the youngest zooid may be anywhere in the chain. In fact, the strobilization of a scyphozoan scyphistoma (P–C, page 522) presents the only analogy between asexual reproduction and segment formation; the ephyrae arise in oral-aboral succession in the same way that segments form in an annelid. Strobilation, however, seems to be an adaptation to a sessile mode of life, and it is impossible to conceive of a free-swimming animal reproducing in this manner, since it would lose its head at each fission. Another of the great difficulties of the corm theory, never satisfactorily answered, is to homologize the head and anal segments with the other segments. Hence the corm theory, although at first sight the most plausible, meets insuperable difficulties.

2. Pseudometamerism.—As mentioned above, primitive animals exhibit a tendency toward repetition of parts and the spreading of systems throughout the body, as shown by the branching intestine, numerous gonads, etc., of lower forms. In an elongated worm-shaped body, this tendency would lead to anteroposterior repetition of parts such as is a prominent feature of flatworms. If such a body broke up between head and posterior end into segments, a segmented animal would result. Some theorists assume that such a breaking up was caused by the swelling of the gonads at sexual maturity. The enlarged gonads would impede locomotion, and body bendings would tend to become localized at the regions between the gonads where constrictions leading to a segmented condition might form.

3. Locomotory Metamerism.—This idea is similar to the foregoing, ascribing metamerism to the breaking up of the body as a result of serpentine swimming movements. It differs from pseudometamerism in that it postulates the breaking up of gonads and other organs as a secondary result of muscular segmentation.

4. Theory of Cyclomerism.—This theory may be expressed by the aphorism (Lang, 1904) that the metamerism of the Bilateria is directly derived from the cyclomerism (radial arrangement of parts) of the Radiata. It will be perceived that this hypothesis is a corollary of the enterocoelous theory of mesoderm and coelom formation. The mesodermal segments are considered to be gastric pouches that show a linear instead of a circular arrangement. Now there is but one coelenterate group in which the mode of formation of the septa can be homologized with segment formation, the Ceriantharia. It is generally agreed that the oral surface of coelenterates is the ventral surface of the Bilateria, that the sagittal planes correspond, and that the "dorsal" end of the sagittal plane of coelenterates is the anterior end of this plane in Bilateria. If one then orients a *Cerianthus* in this manner, it is seen that new septa are formed in couples at the "posterior" end as in segmented animals (see P–C, page 628, Fig. 206*B*) and that (omitting the three most dorsal couples) the first metasepta are the oldest and the others decrease in age "posteriorly." Acceptance of the cyclomerism theory entails the following large assumptions: that a cerianthid-like anthozoan was the ancestor of all the Bilateria, that the mesoderm and coelom are primitively enterocoelous and represent the gastrovascular compartments of anthozoans, and that the original Bilateria were segmented and coelomate and these characters have been lost from many groups. What are believed to be cogent arguments have already been advanced against such ideas, and the theory seems to the author wholly unacceptable.

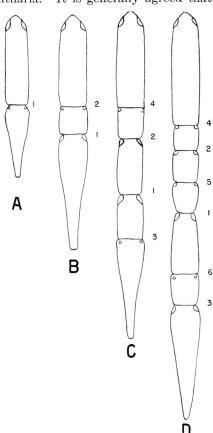

Fig. 9.—Process of fission to form a chain of zooids in the rhabdocoel flatworm *Stenostomum* (after Child, 1941, *Patterns and problems of development, courtesy University of Chicago Press*). *A.* First fission plane dividing worm into two zooids. *B.* Second fission plane has formed in anterior zooid. *C.* Third fission plane has formed in posterior zooid, anterior zooid has another plane. *D.* Both zooids have additional planes. 1–6, order of formation of fission planes.

Of the various theories of segmentation, a combination of pseudometamerism and locomotory metamerism appears most plausible, namely, that the organs were already scattered before segmentation occurred and that the impetus to the segmentary subdivision of the body came from the body musculature.

VIII. THE ORGAN-SYSTEMS OF THE BILATERIA

The fact that the various organ-systems present many differences in morphological detail among the bilateral groups has resulted in a confused terminology. With each phylum one is apt to encounter a new set of names for the various parts of the same organ-system. While this difficulty cannot be altogether eliminated because of the bewildering diversity of form which any one system can manifest, an effort will be made toward a more uniform terminology than is now encountered in zoological works.

An organ is a tissue complex that has definite form and serves some specific function. An organ-system is the sum of the organs that serve one function.

1. Integument.—The integument or body covering consists in invertebrates of a single-layered epithelium plus secreted materials to the outer side of this epithelium. The covering epithelium will be uniformly termed *epidermis* throughout this treatise. It is a continuance of the embryonic ectoderm and in invertebrates consists of a flattened to columnar simple epithelium, cellular or syncytial, and never stratified, although sometimes small cells are intercalated between the bases of the other cells. Gland cells and sensory structures are often interspersed among the regular epithelial cells, and often the epidermis is ciliated. A delicate ciliated epidermis is a primitive character and is suitable only for an aquatic habitat. For better protection and for adaptation to land habitats, invertebrates must develop a more resistant epidermis. Mucus secretion is often adopted as a protective device, but a more efficient method is the secretion by the epidermis of resistant layers which in invertebrates are always noncellular. The most usual of such secretions is a thin or thick membrane secreted on the exposed surface of the epidermis and known as a *cuticle*. The cuticle is commonly protein in nature or a combination of protein and chitin and is often of complicated structural and chemical composition. The cuticle may be sufficiently thick and firm to constitute an encasement or *lorica* for the animal. Sufficiently thickened and hardened epidermal secretions come under the general name of *exoskeleton*. In invertebrates the exoskeleton takes the form of calcareous shells as in mollusks and brachiopods, or chitin impregnated with calcium carbonate as in crustaceans, or other chitin mixtures.

Among invertebrates the tissues beneath the epidermis do not participate in the integument as they do in vertebrates, and therefore invertebrates do not possess a "skin" separable from the muscular layers of the body wall.

2. Endoskeleton.—Hard supporting parts formed in and by the mesoderm are termed endoskeleton. The spicules of sponges and of alcyonarians classify as endoskeleton. Among the Bilateria, endoskeleton is extensively developed only in the Echinodermata, where it takes the form of calcareous spicules, rods, and plates. The cephalopod mollusks also possess endoskeleton in the form of a cartilage-like encasement for the main nervous ganglia.

3. Muscular System.—Of the three types of locomotion occurring in animals (P–C, page 3), only the muscular is feasible for animals of any size and for the production of rapid energetic movements. The term muscular system is usually understood to refer only to the musculature of the body wall by which locomotion is effected and does not include the muscles of the intestinal wall or other viscera. Primitively, the muscular system consists of a sheath of circular and longitudinal layers, lying beneath the epidermis. This condition more or less obtains in the lower Bilateria, with such minor changes as thickening of the layers, especially the longitudinal one; addition of more layers, sometimes diagonal in direction; interspersion of the muscle layers with connective tissue; and division, particularly of the longitudinal layer, into bands. Muscle layers close to the epidermis are called the *subepidermal* musculature; fibers which course through body tissues form the *mesenchymal* musculature; and in coelomate animals where the body wall is definitely separated from the intestinal wall, the musculature becomes the *body-wall* musculature. No great advance in efficiency of the muscular system is possible until the development of hard parts, i.e., either an exo- or an endoskeleton, to which the muscles can attach. When this happens, the muscle layers break up into individual *muscles*, i.e., bundles of muscle fibers molded into a definite shape and attached to hard parts by connective tissue which may form a cord or band termed a *tendon*. Such muscles enable an animal to execute far more rapid, precise, and varied movements than does the simple sheath system.

4. Nervous System.—The nervous system is specialized for rapid conduction and thus constitutes the chief mechanism in the body for communication between parts and for the coordination and correlation of activities. It is made up of nerve cells, also called *ganglion* cells, with a small amount of supporting tissue. A nerve cell has an enlarged portion, the *cell body*, containing the nucleus, and one or more elongated branches, the *neurites*, extending out from the cell body. There are two general types of nervous system, the *diffuse* and the *concentrated*. The diffuse system is the original and more primitive type; it consists of nerve cells and neurites distributed throughout the body, usually within or just beneath the epidermis, as a sort of network. It was formerly believed that the neurites in the diffuse type were actually fused to make continuous pathways, but it now seems established that the diffuse system, like the concentrated, is *synaptic* (P–C, page 397), i.e., the ends of the neurites are in contact but not fused.   In the diffuse system there are no nerves in the proper sense of this term as all the nervous strands contain nerve cell bodies as well as neurites.   The diffuse system is also characterized by a lack of polarization since the neurites are not differentiated into axones and dendrites and functional impulses proceed along them in either direction.   A diffuse nervous system is found in cnidarians, ctenophores, echinoderms, and flatworms.

The diffuse nervous system is more or less correlated with radial symmetry, and the manner in which such a radial system becomes bilateral has already been indicated.   The nerve plexus concentrates into a limited number of meridional strands running from an aboral center. With the assumption of bilaterality, the aboral center shifts forward becoming the brain, and the meridional strands become longitudinal nerve cords (Fig. 2).   Such a condition is seen in the lower orders of flatworms, the Acoela and Polycladida.   Soon, however, the two ventral strands thicken and take precedence over the others, and later the others are eliminated so that the main nervous system behind the head consists of the two *ventral nerve cords*, as in many flatworms, annelids, arthropods, and some mollusks.   The connections between the longitudinal strands, originally net-like, become more or less transverse; and when the longitudinal cords are reduced to two the transverse connections between them are reminiscent of the rungs of a ladder, whence this form of nervous system is called the *ladder type*.   It is evident that the ladder type of nervous system is not an original or fundamental type but simply one of various possible derivatives from the primitive radial type which might be called "barrel" type, as the numerous longitudinal strands are like the staves of a barrel.   As a further evolution of the ladder type, the two ventral cords may approximate so closely as to appear to be a single cord.

Concomitantly the nervous system tends to recede further into the interior, to the inner side of the muscle layers, and the nerve cell bodies tend to concentrate into masses known as *ganglia*.   There thus arises the *concentrated* or *ganglionic* nervous system in which (in its final form) all the nerve cell bodies are located in ganglia while the nervous strands outside the ganglia are true *nerves* composed only of neurites.   However, a complete absence of nerve cell bodies from the nerves is to be seen among invertebrates only in arthropods and higher mollusks.   The ganglia and the direct connections between them known as *connectives* or *commissures* constitute the *central* nervous system while the nerves distributed throughout the body are the *peripheral* nervous system.   There is also in annelids, mollusks, and arthropods a special part of the nervous system supplying the digestive tract, particularly its anterior portion.   This is variously known as the *stomodaeal, stomatogastric,* or *sympathetic* nervous system. It seems best to designate this simply as the *enteric* nervous system. The concentrated type of nervous system is *polarized*, i.e., conduction is functionally effective only in one direction along the neurites. The neurites become differentiated into an *axone* in which effective impulses pass away from the cell body and one to several *dendrites* in which they run to the cell body.

With the concentration of the nerve cell bodies into ganglia, the main nerve center comes to form a *brain*, composed of ganglionic masses, usually two in number, termed the *cerebral ganglia*, also *suprapharyngeal* or *supraesophageal ganglia*, from their position above the anterior part of the digestive tract. As these terms are cumbersome and as the part of the digestive tract concerned varies in different groups, it seems best to adhere to the one name, cerebral ganglia. From the dorsal position of the nerve center and the manner of evolution of the nervous system from a radial pattern it follows that the longitudinal trunks supplying the ventral region of the body must necessarily pass to either side of the anterior part of the digestive tract to reach that region. This embracing of the anterior part of the digestive tract by nerve cords is a characteristic feature of the nervous system of most of the bilateral invertebrates. These embracing cords will be termed the *circumenteric connectives* to avoid such awkward expressions as the usual names, *circumesophageal* or *circumpharyngeal connectives*, which are often in addition misnomers as some other part of the digestive tract may be concerned. In some groups, as nematodes, the nerve center consists of a ganglionated ring around the digestive tract, and this will be called the *circumenteric nerve ring*. The main longitudinal trunks of the nervous system are designated by their position as *dorsal, lateral, ventral cords*, etc. As already noted, the ventral cords are often the most prominent or the only longitudinal cords. In segmented groups each ventral cord has primitively a ganglionic enlargement in the middle of each segment, but often the number is less through fusion of ganglia. Usually the first pair of ganglia of the ventral cords is enlarged or of composite nature and is then designated by a special name, commonly *subesophageal* or *subpharyngeal* ganglia. Here again the simpler term *subenteric* ganglion is suggested.

The central nervous system of invertebrates differs from that of vertebrates in that it is always solid, not hollow as in the latter. The invertebrate nervous system like that of vertebrates is of ectodermal origin.

5. Sensory System.—Sensory cells and sensory organs are specializations which are peculiarly sensitive to environmental conditions and notify the organism of alterations in these conditions. They are designated by the general name of *receptors* which term may be prefixed by a root indicative of the environmental condition concerned. Receptors are most abundant and most differentiated at the body surface where they respond to external factors, but they also exist in internal organs where they register various visceral conditions.   As previously explained (P–C, page 279), sensory cells are of two sorts: *sensory nerve cells* or *neurosensory cells* which are really nerve cells with a neurite running into the interior, and nonnervous sensory cells which are modified epithelial cells and must be supplied by fibers from the nervous system.   The sensory cells of invertebrates are *all* of the neurosensory type, and sensory organs consist of aggregations of such neurosensory cells plus associated cells of other types.   Neurosensory cells despite innumerable variations in detail present a general morphological similarity.   The rounded cell body containing the nucleus is situated in or just below the epidermis, sends to the surface a slender process which terminates in one to several projecting points, bristles, or flagella-like hairs, and sends into the interior a branching nerve fiber which connects with the nervous system or may end directly on an effector (Fig. 10*F*).   If such a neurosensory cell withdraws sufficiently into the interior, it becomes a sensory ganglion cell of the nervous system with free nerve endings at the surface; this is supposed to be the phylogenetic origin of the sensory cells of ganglia.   Free sensory nerve endings have been described for various invertebrates, although relatively uncommon.

A sensory organ or *sensilla* (plural, sensillae) is in invertebrates a cluster of neurosensory cells plus one or more kinds of other cells, which may be pigment cells, gland cells, or supporting and protective cells.

The external factors which stimulate sensory cells may be classified as mechanical, chemical, thermal, and photic.   Mechanical stimuli may be subdivided into contact, gravity, sound waves, and water currents.   Receptors for contact stimuli, such as touch and pressure, are termed in general *tangoreceptors* and usually consist of single neurosensory cells of the type described above.   They are of wide distribution in invertebrates although certain parts, such as palps, tentacles, and antennae, are generally more thickly supplied with tangoreceptors than are other parts. *Static* organs for the perception of the direction of gravity by means of which the animal maintains a certain position and returns to that position when disturbed consist fundamentally of a mineral mass (*statolith*) or bunch of granules (*statoconia*) which rest upon the hairs of neurosensory cells.   Any change in the position of the animal moves the statolith or statoconia so that different hairs are stimulated and the animal is made aware of the change of orientation.   The more advanced types of static apparatus are enclosed in a vesicle, and the whole structure is then termed a *statocyst* (Fig. 10*A*).   In the Bilateria, statocysts are found in the acoel and a few other flatworms, a few nemertine and polychaete worms, some holothurians, most mollusks, and many crustaceans.   Many invertebrates detect the direction of water currents (*rheotactic* response), and special *rheoreceptors* have been described in some forms. While tango-receptors in general probably also serve to detect vibratory stimuli in terrestrial invertebrates, specific organs sensitive to vibration, known as *scolopophorous* organs, occur in insects and a few other arthropods. The essential feature of these organs is a special type of elongated neurosensory cell whose thickened distal tip, termed the *scolops,* is embraced by accessory cells. The whole unit, called a scolopophore, is under tension, being fastened at both ends (Fig. 10*E*). The more complicated types of scolopophorous organs consist of a number of scolopophores plus various accessory parts, particularly one or two thin tensed integumental membranes, known as *tympanic membranes.* Such *tympanal* organs, also called *chordotonal* organs, occur on the legs, thorax, and abdomen of various insects and are *phonoreceptors* or organs of hearing, in the vertebrate sense, although generally responding to sound waves of higher frequency than does the vertebrate ear.

Chemoreceptors for the detection of food and other substances in the medium are of wide occurrence in invertebrates and are strewn all over the body or more or less limited to the anterior end. They are morphologically similar to tangoreceptors. Often patches of chemoreceptors are sunk into pits or grooves to which cilia direct water currents, or they may be mounted on papillae or other projections.

Light perception is often evinced by the entire invertebrate body, although it has not been possible in most cases to identify the sensory cells or endings concerned. Besides this general responsiveness to light, most invertebrates are provided with specific *photoreceptors*, which may consist of single neurosensory cells but are usually compounded structures termed *ocelli* or *eyes,* consisting of neurosensory cells, pigment cells, supporting or other kinds of cells, and often light-refracting structures. The photosensitive neurosensory cell, called a *retinal* cell, may not differ from the general run of receptor cells but often shows characteristic differentiations, especially a striated border or other fibrillar structures. Pigment is a constant feature of photoreceptors; it may be situated in the retinal cells themselves but more often occurs in special pigment cells. The purpose of the pigment is to shut off light except that parallel to the long axis of the retinal cells. The light-refractive bodies found in eyes are of various sorts and origins. Often the cuticle is thickened to a biconvex shape or invaginated as a spherical body; these cuticular accessories are known as *lenses.* Instead or also there may be a gelatinous mass termed the *vitreous body* secreted by cells of the eye, or refractive bodies formed by the fusion of transparent cells.

Eyes are of three general grades of structure: *pigment-spot ocelli, pigment-cup ocelli,* and *vesicular ocelli.* The first consists of a spot flush with the surface composed of intermingled retinal and pigment or sup-

porting cells.   Next this spot invaginates to form a cup or pit, the cavity
of which may contain a refractive body.   By the closure of the cup, the
vesicular eye results; this is usually of complicated structure with one or
more refractive bodies (Fig. 10 *B–D*).

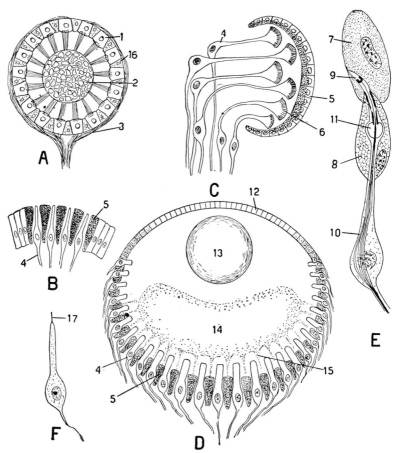

Fig. 10.—Sensory organs.   *A.* Diagram of a statocyst.   *B.* Diagram of a pigment-spot
ocellus.   *C.* Diagram of pigment-cup ocellus of the inverse type (*based on Hesse*, 1897).   *D.*
Diagram of a vesicular ocellus, converse type.   *E.* A scolopophore (*after Schwabe*, 1906).
F. Generalized neurosensory cell.   1, neurosensory cells with sensory bristles; 2, statoconia;
3, nerve fibers; 4, retinal cells; 5, pigment cell; 6, rod border; 7, cap cell; 8, cover cell; 9, peg;
10, neurosensory cell containing bundle of neurofibrils; 11, vacuole; 12, cornea; 13, lens; 14,
vitreous body; 15, secretion strands; 16, supporting cell; 17, sensory bristle.

Eyes in which the retinal cells are oriented in the normal position, i.e.,
with their distal ends facing the exterior, are termed *converse* eyes.   Those
in which the free ends of the retinal cells face the interior of the cup or
vesicle are spoken of as *inverse* eyes.   Both types of eyes occur throughout

the Bilateria often within the same phylum, and inverse retinal cells may occur in eyes of relatively simple construction.

6. Digestive System.—The digestive system or digestive tract consists in its most primitive form, exemplified in the Hydrozoa, of an entoderm tube, the archenteron of embryonic stages, opening only by the mouth. A tendency to increase the digestive and absorptive surface by branching is early exhibited. There also soon becomes added to the original tube an ectodermal invagination at the mouth end, the *stomodaeum*. As the first part of the digestive tract usually serves, not for digestion, but for swallowing prey, often still alive and capable of inflicting injury, the formation of this region from hardened protective epidermis is readily understood. The stomodaeum early becomes invested with muscular coats as an aid to swallowing, thus constituting in whole or part the *pharynx* of adult anatomy. Anthozoans, ctenophores, and flatworms remain at this stage in which the digestive tract consists of a more or less muscular pharynx and a branched intestinal tube. In the next stage, the digestive tube develops a posterior opening, the *anus*, defined above (page 3), usually by way of another ectodermal invagination, the *proctodaeum*. Thus in the higher Bilateria only the middle region of the digestive tract, or *midgut*, has an entodermal lining. The relative contributions of stomodaeum, midgut, and proctodaeum to the adult digestive system vary greatly in different phyla, and the parts formed from them also exhibit so much variation that a uniform terminology is difficult if not impossible.

In most Bilateria, the digestive tract becomes freed from the body wall (except of course at the two ends) by the formation of either a pseudocoel or a coelom, and thereafter tends to achieve increased surface by coiling rather than by lateral branching. In pseudocoelomate animals, the digestive tract still consists chiefly of a single epithelial layer; but in coelomate animals, the splanchnic mesoderm attaches to the epithelium and develops muscular and connective tissue layers. The wall of the digestive tract thus becomes firm, muscular, and many-layered, and capable of carrying on peristaltic movements. Those portions of the digestive tract in which grasping, mastication, grinding, or mixing of the food with digestive juices occur have the strongest musculature.

The following are the chief parts of the digestive system. The *mouth* is primitively situated at about the middle of the ventral surface but shifts anteriorly in most Bilateria. In the Protostomia it is a direct continuation of the blastopore or the anterior part of the elongated blastopore or forms where the blastopore closed; in the Deuterostomia it appears to be a new formation. The mouth may be provided with protrusions termed *lips*. The mouth generally leads into a nonmuscular *buccal tube* or *capsule* (also called *oral cavity, buccal cavity, vestibule,* and other names), and this is usually succeeded by a muscular *pharynx* employed chiefly in grasping and swallowing food.   The cavities of these parts are termed *buccal* and *pharyngeal cavity*, respectively.   Both usually receive secretions from unicellular glands in or attached to their walls or from definite compound *buccal* or *pharyngeal glands* opening into their cavities by ducts.   The pharynx is often provided with teeth, jaws, or other hard structures for gripping prey.   It may be projectable to the exterior either by direct muscular elongation, *protrusible* pharynx, or by turning inside out, *eversible* pharynx[1] (Fig. 11).

When the digestive tube following the pharynx is of similar form throughout its length, it is called simply *intestine*.   Often, however, the

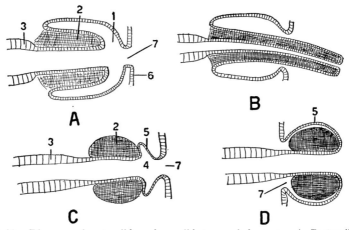

Fig. 11.—Diagrams of protrusible and eversible types of pharynx.   *A.* Protrusible type at rest.   *B.* Same, protruded by simple elongation.   *C.* Eversible type at rest.   *D.* Same everted by turning inside out of buccal capsule.   1, pharyngeal cavity; 2, pharynx; 3, intestine; 4, buccal cavity; 5, buccal capsule; 6, epidermis; 7, mouth.

pharynx is succeeded by a narrowed, scarcely muscular tube, the *esophagus*, and this leads to an enlarged region, the *stomach*.   An expansion of the esophagus called *crop*, serving as a food reservoir, may precede the stomach.   When the stomach is especially adapted for grinding food it is often called *gizzard*, but this term may be indiscriminately applied to any part of the digestive tract specialized for food grinding.   Behind the stomach, the digestive tract continues to the anus as a narrowed tube, the *intestine*, which in invertebrates is not divisible into small and large intestine.   The terminal portion of the intestine when different from the rest may be called *rectum*, and if it receives the urogenital ducts the term *cloaca* is applied.   Large glands, here called simply *digestive glands*, open into the stomach in some invertebrates, particularly mollusks and crus-

[1] The protruded or eversed pharynx is often called *proboscis*, but this name is also used in so many other connections that it will be avoided here.

taceans. Any hollow diverticulum from the digestive tract is usually termed a *caecum* (plural, *caeca*).

7. Respiratory System.—Small animals with a soft epidermis can obtain sufficient respiratory exchange by diffusion through the surface. With increase in size or hardening of the surface, devices for securing a more rapid and greater exchange of respiratory gases are necessary. Such devices may be physiological, consisting of respiratory movements, such as body undulations, for wafting fresh water over the animal; but they are commonly morphological and then constitute a more or less developed respiratory system. The essential features of a respiratory organ are thin walls through which diffusion can take place readily and a large amount of surface exposed to the surrounding medium. Hence such an organ is a thin-walled structure, much folded, branched, or lobed to increase surface, and either evaginated to the outside or invaginated to the interior. The respiratory system consists of one to many such organs, often serially arranged. The evaginations are known as *gills* and in invertebrates are filamentous, lamellar, branched, or feathery structures composed of delicate thin integument enclosing a small amount of other tissue. Gills are adaptations for breathing oxygen dissolved in water and are therefore either freely exposed on the exterior of the animal or, if protected, are situated in the path of water currents. Animals with gills usually exhibit rhythmic respiratory movements or else have a mechanism for pumping water over the gills. Gills may occur in animals which lack a circulatory system and then serve simply to increase the amount of surface exposed to the water, but usually they are richly supplied with blood which conveys the respiratory gases to and from the gills. The chief invertebrates with gills are annelids, mollusks, and the lower arthropods. Invaginations into the interior are usually known as *lungs* and are adaptations for breathing air directly. Lungs are limited to air-breathing vertebrates; among invertebrates a structure analogous to the vertebrate lung occurs only in the pulmonate snails where it consists of a very vascular sac of invaginated integument. Unique among respiratory systems is the *tracheal* system of insects and some other arthropods composed of integument invaginated as a branching set of air tubes permeating the entire body. In this system air is brought directly to the body cells by the tracheal tubes, whereas in other respiratory systems the respiratory gases are conveyed to and from gills or lungs by way of a circulatory system. The tracheal system is an adaptation to aerial life, and air is pumped in and out of the tracheal tubes by respiratory movements; but the system can be utilized for aquatic life by means of tracheal gills, which are gills containing tracheal tubes instead of blood vessels. The tracheal system can also imitate lungs in the way of invaginated integumental sacs whose walls are liberally supplied with tracheae.

8. Circulatory System.—In the smaller and simpler invertebrates some degree of circulation of body fluids is undoubtedly brought about by general body movements and by ciliary currents. But as animals increase in size and complexity a definite circulatory system is needed to distribute the products of digestion throughout the body, to transport the respiratory gases to and from the respiratory system, and to convey the nongaseous metabolic wastes to the excretory organs. The *circulatory* or *blood-vascular* system consists of a set of branching tubes, the *blood vessels*, filled with a fluid, the *blood*, which carries food and oxygen to the body cells and takes away carbon dioxide and other metabolic end products. The blood must necessarily circulate, and this is accomplished by the specialization of part of the circulatory system as a contractile mechanism along which a wave of contraction runs at regular intervals forcing the blood in the direction of the wave. The blood thus makes a continuous circuit through the body returning to the starting point; as it passes through the gills or lungs it receives oxygen and gives up carbon dioxide; as it flows in the walls of the digestive tract it takes up the products of digestion; in the excretory system it gives up metabolic end products; and it brings food and oxygen to all the body cells, receiving from them metabolic wastes. The exchange of materials so far as known takes place by simple diffusion through the thin walls of the finer blood vessels (*capillaries*) or blood spaces (*sinuses*), or else the tissues are directly exposed to the blood.

In lower Bilateria, some of the blood vessels, particularly the mid-dorsal vessel, serve as the contractile mechanism; but in the higher forms, a very muscular organ, the *heart*, is developed to propel the blood. In invertebrates the heart is situated in the middorsal line and represents a specialization of the middorsal blood vessel. As the heart must undergo vigorous contractions, it is always situated in a space which is commonly a portion of the coelom termed *pericardial cavity*. The heart may consist of one or two *auricles* which receive the returning blood and a muscular *ventricle* which pumps it out; but among invertebrates such division does not necessarily occur. *Accessory* hearts may be present. As in verte-brates, the vessels which carry the blood away from the heart are termed *arteries*, and those which return blood to the heart are called *veins*. Blood-containing spaces without definite walls are named *sinuses* when large or *lacunae* when small.

Among the invertebrates there are two types of circulatory system, the *closed* and the *open* or *lacunar* system. In the closed system the blood is always confined in definite blood vessels, tubes with definite walls. These vessels subdivide into finer and finer braches and ultimately into the microscopic *capillaries* which connect the arteries and veins and through which exchange of materials between the blood and the body cells occurs. In the open system there are no small blood vessels or capillaries, but the arteries soon lose their walls and open out into lacunae and sinuses from which the blood slowly works its way into the open ends of veins. An open system is found in mollusks and arthropods in which groups the blood spaces have so expanded as to crowd the coelom almost out of existence. The organs of these animals thus lie directly in a blood-filled space, the *haemocoel*, while the true coelom is restricted to a few small cavities. This process of encroachment of the haemocoel on the coelom was first elucidated by Lankester (1888) who termed it *phlebedesis* (1900).

The fluid which is carried inside the blood vessels is termed the blood; it consists of a nutrient fluid, the *plasma* or *lymph*, and various kinds of free cells floating in the plasma. In invertebrate blood there are relatively few cells as compared with vertebrate blood, and these are mostly similar in appearance to vertebrate white blood corpuscles. Red cells similar to vertebrate red blood corpuscles occur in the blood of nemertines and in the coelomic fluid of sipunculids and some polychaetes, but in invertebrates the red coloring matter of the blood (when present) is usually free in the plasma, not contained in cells.

The blood usually contains a special oxygen-carrying substance which unites readily with oxygen when the oxygen pressure is high, as in the respiratory organ, and gives up oxygen readily when the oxygen pressure is low, as in the body cells. This substance is a chromoprotein (colored protein) containing a metal, usually iron or copper; the iron-containing protein is called *haemoglobin*, the copper-containing one, *haemocyanin*. These differ in chemical construction in different species, so that actually there are a vast number of haemoglobins and haemocyanins. Haemoglobins constitute the red coloring matter of vertebrate blood and in vertebrates are contained inside cells which are therefore called red blood corpuscles. The blood of a number of invertebrates contains a haemoglobin and is therefore red, but as stated above the haemoglobin is seldom contained in cells. Haemocyanins are bluish when loaded with oxygen; they are found in the blood of mollusks and crustaceans.

The fluid which fills body and tissue spaces outside of the circulatory system is called in invertebrates by various names, as *lymph, haemolymph,* and *coelomic fluid*. It will here be termed uniformly the lymph. In invertebrates this does not run in definite channels as in vertebrates; in short, there is no lymphatic system, but the lymph is undoubtedly moved about by body motions and ciliary action. The lymph contains various types of cells identical with those which occur in the blood of the same animal.

A high degree of correlation exists between the circulatory and respiratory systems. Where the respiratory organs are sharply localized, the circulatory system is commonly well developed; and where the respiratory system is diffused throughout the body, as is the case with the tracheal system of insects, the circulatory system shows a marked retrogression.

9. Excretory System.—There are scarcely any more vexed questions in comparative anatomy than the homology of the excretory system in the various phyla and the relations of the excretory and genital ducts. No final decision can be reached on these matters at present.

The function of the excretory system is the regulation of water content and the elimination of unusable metabolic products, especially nitrogenous ones. The essential features of an excretory organ are therefore: a mechanism for filtering water, secretory cells for concentrating nitrogenous substances, and a means of producing a flow of the excretory fluid to the exterior. The last is usually ciliary. In general, excretory organs do not manufacture the substances in the excretory fluid; they obtain them from the lymph or blood. After decades of argument as to whether they separate these substances from the lymph or blood by physical means (such as diffusion) or by active secretory processes on the part of the cells of the excretory organ, it now appears that both processes are involved. There may be a resorption of water and other substances from the excretory fluid before it is discharged.

The morphological unit of the excretory system is a tubule, termed in invertebrates a *nephridial tubule* or more briefly a *nephridium*. This tubule consists of a single-layered epithelium, the cells of which possess special secretory powers. In invertebrates the nephridial tubules are discrete; in short, they are not massed together to form a kidney as they are in vertebrates. An invertebrate may have one to many pairs of nephridia; in coelomate segmented invertebrates there is theoretically one pair to each segment, but actually nephridia are nearly always lacking from some segments, especially the most anterior ones and the genital segments.

Leaving out of account the peculiar excretory tubules of insects (and some other arthropods) which are outgrowths of the digestive tract, there are in invertebrates two main kinds of nephridia, *protonephridia* with closed inner ends and *metanephridia* with open inner ends. There are further two kinds of protonephridia, those with *flame bulbs* and those with *solenocytes*. The phylogenetic relationship between the main kinds of nephridia constitutes one of the difficult questions already mentioned.

Protonephridia with flame bulbs (Fig. 12*A*) are branched tubules whose finer twigs are closed terminally by an apparatus here called a flame bulb. A flame bulb (Fig. 12*B*) is a cup-shaped mass of protoplasm bearing a tuft of cilia which projects into the cavity of the cup. The undulations of the ciliary tuft are suggestive of a flickering flame and create a water current moving distally in the tubule. Flame bulbs are

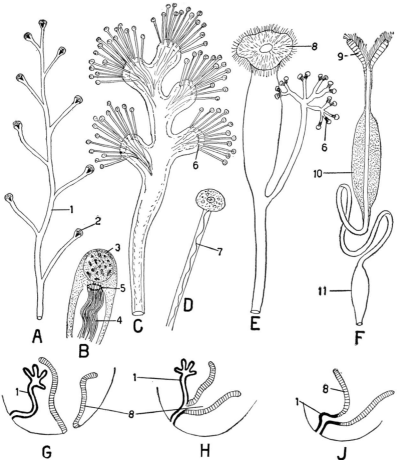

FIG. 12.—Nephridia. *A.* Diagram of a protonephrium with flame bulbs. *B.* Flame bulb of a planarian (*after Willey and Kirschner,* 1938). *C.* Scheme of a protonephridium with solenocytes. *D.* A solenocyte. *E.* A nephromixium, consisting of a gonostome attached to a protonephridium (*based on Goodrich,* 1900). *F.* Diagram of a metanephridium. *G–J,* Diagrams of the formation of a nephromixium simulating a metanephridium (*after Goodrich,* 1900). *G.* Primitive condition, coelomic cavity has a protonephridium and a gonostome. *H.* Gonostome has fused to the protonephridium. *J.* Part of the protonephridium has degenerated, leaving gonostome attached to protonephridial tube, and the whole simulates a metanephridium. 1, protonephridial tubule; 2, flame bulb; 3, flame cell; 4, ciliary tuft; 5, basal bodies of cilia; 6, cluster of solenocytes; 7, flagellum; 8, gonostome; 9, nephrostome; 10, glandular region; 11, bladder.

usually single cells and hence are usually called *flame cells;* but as cases are known in which one cell is subdivided into many flame bulbs and others in which the flame bulb is multinucleate, it seems best to abandon the term flame cell. Protonephridia with flame bulbs are general throughout the acoelomate and pseudocoelomate Bilateria, although not every group in these phyla possesses them, and their occurrence may be taken to indicate some relationship, however remote, between these assemblages.

Protonephridia with solenocytes (Fig. 12C) are closed nephridial tubules which bear one or more cells termed solenocytes; these are long tubular cells with a long flagellum springing from the protoplasmic mass at the end of the tube and playing in the tube (Fig. 12D). Solenocytic protonephridia occur in the trochophore and related larvae and in the adults of kinorhynchs, priapulids, some polychaetes, and *Amphioxus*.

Metanephridia are nephridial tubules whose inner end opens into the coelom by way of a ciliated funnel, the *nephridiostome* or, more briefly, *nephrostome* (Fig. 12F). Metanephridia are necessarily limited to coelomate animals and are found throughout the coelomate Protostomia except insects and some other arthropods. The invertebrate Deuterostomia in general lack excretory organs.

Both protonephridia and metanephridia open to the exterior by one or more pores, the *nephridiopores*. The terminal portion of a nephridial tubule either with or without junction with its partner may enlarge to a contractile sac or *bladder*. It is not uncommon for the nephridial tubules to open into the digestive tract or the genital system, and in such cases separate nephridiopores are, of course, lacking.

The first question for consideration is the relationship of the two kinds of protonephridia. The development of protonephridia with flame bulbs is poorly known; the scanty available evidence indicates an ectodermal origin from cells of one of the first three quartets of micromeres. The development of protonephridia with solenocytes is not known in those invertebrates which possess them in the adult stage but has been followed by several authors in the trochophore larva. The archinephridia of the trochophore are in fact protonephridia with solenocytes (Fig. 4). These develop from ectoderm cells of the third quartet of micromeres (Shearer, 1911). As far as the evidence goes, therefore, the two kinds of protonephridia appear to be variants of the same organ. There is, in fact, little morphological distinction between them and types transitional between solenocytes and flame bulbs occur, as in gastrotrichs.

The second question is the relation of the protonephridia to the metanephridia. According to the classical and widely accepted view of Goodrich (1900), all types of invertebrate nephridia (except nephromixia, see below) are homologous and the nephrostome is merely the opened proximal end of a protonephridium. Thus the relation of the nephrostome to the coelom is secondary. An important part of the Goodrich theory, however, is that there are *genuine primary* coelomic funnels which alone merit the name *coelomostome* and that these connect to the exterior by genuine coelomic ducts or *coelomoducts*. Coelomostome plus coelomoduct constitute the *genital duct* of a coelomate invertebrate. It will be perceived that this idea is a corollary of the gonocoel theory of the origin of the coelom. The Goodrich theory, strongly supported by Lankester, thus admits of but two kinds of ducts from a coelomic cavity, the nephridium and the gonoduct. The nephridium is of ectodermal origin, growing in from the exterior and secondarily connecting with the coelom; hence it is not of the nature of a coelomoduct. The gonoduct is of mesodermal origin, growing from the interior toward the exterior; and it is the true coelomoduct with a true coelomostome (gonostome). Since a coelomic cavity is an expanded gonad it can have but one coelomic duct, and this is the original gonoduct. So runs the Goodrich theory.

It was discovered by Goodrich (1897) and verified by A. Meyer (1926) that in some of the lower polychaetes provided with solenocytes, the coelomostome (= gonostome or genital funnel) may fuse with the protonephridial tubule, forming a *nephromixium* (Fig. 12E), which then has both excretory and genital functions. It was further found that the solenocytic part of this nephromixium may degenerate, so that a tubule provided with a coelomic funnel and hence indistinguishable from a metanephridium results (Fig. 12G–J). Consequently there seem to be among these few polychaetes two kinds of metanephridia, true ones with their own funnel, and compounded ones formed of the fusion of a coelomostome (genital funnel) with a protonephridial tubule. The existence of such nephromixia appears beyond question. The following argument will concern only true metanephridia.

The development of the metanephridia of the annelids has been investigated by a number of workers, but there is some conflict in their accounts. Recent findings are in accord with the old results of Bergh (1899) to the effect that the entire metanephridium including the nephrostome originates from a single cell, the nephridioblast. According to some workers (Penners, 1923; A. Meyer, 1929; Vanderbroeck, 1934), the nephridioblast is of entomesodermal origin, being a cell of the mesoderm band. The nephridioblast proliferates a cord of cells that hollows out to become the metanephridium and forms a connection with the exterior distally, a ciliated funnel proximally. These findings directly contradict the Goodrich theory and indicate that metanephridia are not homologous with protonephridia but a new development in coelomate Protostomia; further that metanephridia are just as truly coelomoducts as are the genital ducts.

In 1945, shortly before his death, Goodrich published an extensive review on the literature of the nephridia and genital ducts that had appeared since his 1896 article. In this review, he reiterated his original position, accepting the gonocoel theory wholeheartedly, and avowing the identity and ectodermal or ectomesodermal origin of both proto- and metanephridia. He agreed with the above findings on the embryology of the metanephridia but refused to accept the nephridioblast as a cell of the mesoderm band.   In support of his position on this point, he quoted mainly the work of Bahl (1922) on the development of the nephridia of the earthworm *Pheretima*.   Bahl plainly showed that the nephridia of *Pheretima* arise from two enlarged ectodermal cells on each side that are still in an ectodermal position after the mesoderm bands have begun to form coelomic cavities.   Later these nephridioblasts pass into the interior between the ectoderm and the mesoderm bands and proliferate the nephric bands.

It appears impossible at present to decide whether or not proto-nephridia and metanephridia are variants of the same organ and therefore whether or not metanephridia classify as coelomoducts.   The gonocoel theory and its corollaries are, however, definitely rejected.

10. Reproductive System.—This system consists of the sex glands or gonads, their ducts, the *gonoducts*, and various accessory parts.   The gonads are usually numerous and distributed throughout the body in primitive forms, reduced to a single, sharply localized pair, or even to a single gonad, through loss of the partner, in more specialized members of a group.   The scattered condition of the gonads is often spoken of as *follicular*, but this term is not very fortunate as the word follicle is also employed to mean a developing egg encircled by nutritive cells.   When both testes and ovaries occur in the same individual, separately or com-bined into one gonad, the condition is spoken of as *hermaphroditism;* when in different individuals, it is called *gonochorism* or *dioeciousness*.   A hermaphroditic animal may appear dioecious from the circumstance that ovaries and testes develop at different times in the annual cycle.   When the testes develop first, the animal is said to be *protandrous;* when the ovaries precede, the term *protogynous* is applied.   Hermaphroditism appears to be more primitive than gonochorism and to be associated with a sessile, sedentary, or parasitic life.   The maturing of the gonads in a larval or juvenile animal is spoken of as *neoteny*.   The gonads of the Bilateria are of mesodermal origin; the sex cells come from mesenchyme cells or cells of the coelomic lining (but see also page 27).

The male gonad is termed *testis* (plural, *testes*) and consists in general of single or clustered vesicles or tubules in which the spermatozoa develop. The main male duct will be called uniformly the *sperm duct* (usual name, *vas deferens*), and the minute ducts that in forms with numerous scattered testes connect these with the main sperm duct will be called *sperm ductules* (usual name, *vasa efferentia*).   An animal usually has one pair of sperm ducts, regardless of the number of testes; or one duct in case of a single testis.   When the sperm ducts unite prior to exit, the resulting duct will be called *common sperm duct*.   That part of the common sperm duct that traverses the copulatory apparatus may be called *ejaculatory duct*.   A part of the male system serving as a reservoir for ripe sperm is termed *seminal vesicle*. When this is merely an expansion of the sperm duct, it will here be called *spermiducal vesicle*, and the expression seminal vesicle will be reserved for a muscular tubular or sacciform chamber appended to the male ducts or interpolated in their course. The separate ducts or common sperm duct may open directly to the exterior by a male gonopore, as is usually the case in animals that shed their sperm into the water; but in many Protostomia the terminal part of the common sperm duct traverses a more or less complicated *copulatory apparatus* serving to transfer the sperm directly into the body of the female. The essential part of the male copulatory apparatus is a *penis* or *cirrus*. The term penis is here restricted to a conical or cylindrical muscular projection that in use is simply lengthened by muscular action so that it can be protruded through the gonopore. The term cirrus will here be applied to a temporary projection that is formed by the turning inside out of the ejaculatory duct. Both penis and cirrus may be armed with spines, thorns, etc.; or the penis may consist essentially of a hard spine, then termed *penis stylet*. Various glands, sacs, or tubules may be appended to the penis or cirrus, and the whole then constitutes the copulatory apparatus. These accessory structures usually secrete substances essential to the life and health of the sperm.

In the act of *copulation* (sexual union), the sperm are typically injected into the female system by the insertion of the penis or cirrus into the female gonopore or the common gonopore. In hermaphroditic animals, this process is generally mutual, i.e., each copulant injects sperm into the partner. Many invertebrates, however, lack a copulatory organ but nevertheless are able to transfer sperm into the female by various devices, some of them incredibly bizarre. Thus the male spider exudes his sperm into a groove on the modified terminal joint of his second pair of appendages and inserts this into the female orifice. Some invertebrates employ *hypodermic impregnation* in which sperm are injected through the epidermis anywhere. The sperm may be done up in packets termed *spermatophores* that are deposited in or on the female.

The female gonad is called *ovary* and its duct *oviduct*. There is but one pair of oviducts or one duct in case of a single ovary; the two oviducts may unite to a *common oviduct* before reaching the female gonopore. When the ovaries are numerous small *oviductules* connect them with the main oviducts. An enlarged more or less modified portion of the oviduct in which the eggs accumulate and in which they may undergo more or less development is called *uterus*. The uterus may also be a tube or sac attached to the female system. Sacs in which the sperm received from the male are stored are termed *seminal receptacles* or *spermathecae;* they may be diverticula of the female system or have no direct connection with it. When the seminal receptacle harbors the sperm for only a short time, soon passing them elsewhere, it is called *copulatory bursa* (*bursa copulatrix*). Various glands or glandular diverticula may be present along the oviducts, common oviduct, or antrum, serving to secrete protective layers and coats for the eggs or adhesive materials for fastening them to objects.

Male and female gonopores in hermaphroditic species may be separate, one behind the other in the mid-ventral line, or there may be a common gonopore. The gonoducts may also open into the digestive tract, either near the mouth or near the anus, and in such case there are no distinct gonopores. The final part of either male or female system may consist of a chamber, the *antrum* (or *atrium*), that in turn leads to the gonopore. Parts of the reproductive system may have special external pores, distinct from the regular gonopores.

The comparative anatomy of the gonoducts and their relation to the nephridia have already been touched upon. In the acoelomate and pseudocoelomate Bilateria, the gonoducts are in continuity with the gonads and appear to have no phylogenetic relationship to the gonoducts of the coelomate forms. The gonoducts of coelomate animals appear to be coelomoducts and in general are not directly connected to the gonads but open into the coelom by ciliated funnels (gonostomes). The genital coelomoducts seem to be phylogenetically distinct from metanephridia. Coelomate animals may, however, lack gonoducts and use the nephridia for the discharge of sex cells. Or, as already noted, the gonostome may fuse to the nephridial structure to form a nephromixium which serves both excretory and genital purposes.

Bibliography

Note.—In general, references cited in P–C are not repeated.

Bahl, K. N. 1922. On the development of the enteronephric type of nephridial system in Pheretima. Quart. Jour. Micro. Sci. 66. **Bergh, R. S.** 1885. Die Exkretionsorgane der Würmer. Kosmos 17. 1899. Nochmals über die Entwicklung des Segmentalorgane. Ztschr. Wiss. Zool. 66. **Boyden, A.** 1942. Systematic serology. Physiol. Zool. 15. **Child, C. M.** 1900. The early development of Arenicola and Sternaspis. Arch. Entw'mech. 9. 1942. *Problems and patterns of development.* Univ. Chicago Press. **Dautert, E.** 1929. Die Bildung der Keimblätter von Paludina. Zool. Jahrb. Abt. Anat. 50. **Erhardt, A.** 1932. Die Verwandtschaftsbestimmungen mittels der Immunitätsreaktion in der Zoologie. Ergeb. Fortschr. Zool. 7. **Faussek, V.** 1899. Über die physiologische Bedeutung des Cöloms. Trav. Soc. Natural. Pétersbourg, Liv. 1, 30. **Goodrich, E. S.** 1895. On the coelom, genital ducts, and nephridia. Quart. Jour. Micro. Sci. 37. 1897, 1898, 1900. On the nephridia of the Polychaeta. Quart. Jour. Micro. Sci. 40, 41, 43. 1945. The study of the nephridia and genital ducts since 1895. Quart. Jour. Micro. Sci. 86. **Graff, Ludwig von.** 1882. Monographie der Turbellarien. I. Rhabdocoeliden. Leipzig. **Hatschek, B.** 1878. Studien über Entwicklungsgeschichte der Anneliden. Ein Beitrag zur Morphologie der Bilaterien. Arb. Zool. Inst. Wien 1.

1886. Entwicklung der Trochophora von Eupomotus. Arb. Zool. Inst. Wien 6. **Hertwig, O.,** and **R. Hertwig.** 1882. Die Cölomtheorie. Jena. Zeitschr. Naturw. 15. **Hesse, R.** 1897. Untersuchungen über die Organe der Lichtempfindung bei niederen Tieren. II. Die Augen der Plathelminthen inbesonderheit der tricladen Turbellarien. Zeitschr. Wiss. Zool. 62. **Hyman, L. H.** 1942. The transition from the unicellular to the multicellular individual. Biol. Symposia VIII. **Ikeda, I.** 1901. Observations on the development, structure, and metamorphosis of Actinotrocha. Jour. Coll. Sci. Imper. Univ. Tokyo 13. **Iwanoff, P. P.** 1928. Die Entwicklung der Larvalsegmente bei den Anneliden. Ztschr. Morphol. Ökol. Tiere 10. **Lang, A.** 1881. Untersuchungen zur vergleichenden Anatomie und Histologie des Nervensystems der Plathelminthen. Mitt. Zool. Stat. Neapel 3. 1881. Der Bau von Gunda segmentina und die Verwandschaft der Plathelminthen mit Coelenteraten und Hirudineen. Mitt. Zool. Stat. Neapel 3. 1884. Die Polycladen des Golfes von Neapel. Fauna Flora Golfes Neapel, Monogr. 11. 1904. Beiträge zu einer Trophocöltheorie. Jena. Ztschr. Naturwiss. 38. **Lankester, E. R.** 1877. Notes on the embryology and classification of the animal kingdom. Quart. Jour. Micro. Sci. 17. 1888. The coelom and the vascular system of Mollusca and Arthropoda. Nature (London) 37. 1900. The Enterocoela and the Coelomocoela. Introd. to *A treatise on zoology*, Pt. 2. 1904. The structure and classification of the Arthropoda Quart. Jour. Micro. Sci. 47. **Mehra, H. R.** 1924. The genital organs of Stylaria with an account of their development. Quart. Jour. Micro. Sci. 68. **Meyer, A.** 1926. Die Segmentalorgane von Tomopterus. Ein Beitrag zur Theorie der Segmentalorgane. Ztschr. Wiss. Zool. 127. 1929. Die Entwicklung der Nephridien und Gonoblasten bei Tubifex. Ztschr. Wiss. Zool. 133. 1930. Vergleichende Untersuchung der Segmentalorgane von Tomopteriden. Ztschr. Wiss. Zool. 136. **Meyer, E.** 1890. Die Abstammung der Anneliden, der Ursprung der Metamerie, und die Bildung des Mesoderms. Biol. Centralbl. 10. (Eng. transl. Amer. Natural. 24). 1901. Studien über den Körperbau der Anneliden. V. Das Mesoderm der Ringelwürmer. Mitt. Zool. Stat. Neapel 14. **Needham, J.** 1930. On the penetration of marine organisms into fresh water. Biol. Centralbl. 50. **Penners, A.** 1923. Die Entwicklung des Keimstreifs und die Organbildung bei Tubifex. Zool. Jahrb. Abt. Anat. 45. **Schwabe, J.** 1906. Beiträge zur Morphologie und Histologie der tympanalen Sinnesapparate der Orthopteren. Zoologica, Stuttgart, Heft 50. **Sedgwick. A.** 1884. On the nature of metameric segmentation and some other morphological questions. Quart. Jour. Micro. Sci. 24. **Semper, C.** 1872. Zoologische Aphorismen (Trochosphaera). Ztschr. Wiss. Zool. 22. **Shearer, C.** 1911. On the development and structure of the trochophore of Hydroides. Quart. Jour. Micro. Sci. 56. **Snodgrass, R. E.** 1938. Evolution of the Annelida, Onychophora, and Arthropoda. Smithson. Miscell. Collect. 97. **Surface, F. M.** 1907. The early development of a polyclad. Proc. Acad. Natur. Sci. Philadelphia 59. **Thiele, J.** 1890. Die Stammesverwandtschaft der Mollusken. Jena. Ztschr. Naturwiss. 25. **Vanderbroeck, G.** 1934. Organogénèse du système nephridien chez les oligochètes. Recueil Inst. Zool. Torley-Rousseau 5. **Wierzejski, A.** 1905. Embryologie von Physa. Ztschr. Wiss. Zool. 83. **Wilhelmi, R. W.** 1942. The application of the precipitin technique to theories concerning the origin of vertebrates. Biol Bull. 82. **Willey, C. H.,** and **P. A. Kirschner.** 1938. Studies on the flame cells of Euplanaria. Trans. Amer. Micro. Soc. 57. **Wilson, E. B.** 1889. The embryology of the earthworm. Jour. Morphol. 3. **Woltereck, R.** 1904. Wurmkopf, Wurmrumpf, und Trochophora. Zool. Anz. 28. **Zeigler, H.** 1898. Über den derzeitigen Stand der Cölomfrage. Verhandl. Deutsch. Zool. Gesell. 8.

CHAPTER X

THE ACOELOMATE BILATERIA—PHYLUM PLATYHELMINTHES

I. HISTORICAL

The phylum Platyhelminthes has had a long and devious history, chiefly because of persistent and recurrent attempts, evident even at the present time, to unite all vermiform animals under a phylum Vermes. Since there are many kinds of worms of very different morphology, naturally no two authors could agree upon the groups to be included in the Vermes and their relational arrangement, and throughout the nineteenth century the number of arrangements published was about equal to the number of interested zoologists. An exhaustive history of these attempts is given by Pagenstecher and Braun, 1879–1893. In the author's opinion, a phylum Vermes is an impossible conception. The mere fact that an animal is vermiform, i.e., many times longer than wide, can obviously be of no phylogenetic or systematic significance. Vermiform shapes as adaptive types are to be found in almost every invertebrate phylum.

The parasitic flatworms naturally attracted attention from ancient times. There is mention of parasitic worms, some probably tapeworms, in an Egyptian papyrus, dating from 1550 B.C., and tapeworms and bladder worms are recorded by various ancient writers. Linnaeus in the first edition (1735) of his *Systema Naturae* founded the ill-starred phylum Vermes, into which he threw all invertebrates except insects. In the 10th edition (1758), which forms the basis of scientific nomenclature, he recognized five orders of Vermes: Intestina, Mollusca, Testacea, Lithophyta, and Zoophyta; flukes and planarians fell under Intestina, tapeworms under Zoophyta. Pallas in 1766 first recognized the cestode nature of bladder worms and O. F. Müller (1773) added a new order Infusoria, which was a mixture of protozoans, rotifers, cercariae, and microscopic nematodes. These improvements were incorporated by Linnaeus in the 13th edition (1788) of the *Systema Naturae*, in which Lithophyta and Zoophyta were combined under the latter name, tapeworms were placed under Intestina, and Infusoria was made the lowest order of Vermes with much the same content as given by Müller. Goeze (1787) added much to the knowledge of tapeworms and Zeder's 1800 edition of Goeze's work gave the first natural grouping of parasitic worms under the common names of roundworms, hooked worms, flukes, tapeworms, and bladder worms. For these same groups scientific names were created by Rudolphi (1808–1810), namely, Nematoidea, Acanthocephala, Trematoda, Cestoidea, and Cystica. Lamarck had a better understanding of animal relationships than most of his predecessors and contemporaries and began the separation of the annelids and noninsectan arthropods from the lower worms, creating the name Annelida (1809). Later (1816) he placed the various groups of flatworms together under the name Vers molasses or soft worms. Cuvier, following Lamarck's leads, eliminated the phylum Vermes, placing protozoans, coelenterates, echinoderms, and the parasitic worms under the Radiata or Zoophyta. Under Radiata, the group Intestinaux or Entozoa included roundworms, flatworms, acanthocephalans, and nemertines. As a result of Cuvier's prestige, the phylum Vermes was submerged for some years and the parasitic worms plus the free-living flatworms were generally termed Helminthes or Entozoa. In

1831, Ehrenberg created the name Turbellaria but had a poor conception of the group, including in it annelids, nematodes, nemertines, and various free-living flatworms. In 1835 he limited the name Turbellaria to be practically equivalent to the present group Rhabdocoela. Leuckart in 1848 combined the flatworms with nemertines and leeches under the name Apodes, which he later (1854) altered to Platodes. The greatest advance at this time was made by C. Vogt (1851), who correctly recognized the leeches as annelids, placed the nematodes, gordiaceans, acanthocephalans, and gregarines under the class Nematelmia, and the true flatworms plus the nemertines under the class Platyelmia. Gegenbaur (1859), following Vogt's lead, presented a similar arrangement but altered Vogt's names to the etymologically better forms, Platyelminthes and Nemathelminthes. Gegenbaur's Platyelminthes comprised three groups: Turbellaria (including nemertines), Trematoda, and Cestoda. Gegenbaur also revived the phylum Vermes, under which he included, in addition to the Platyelminthes, Annulata, Oestelminthes (Sagitta), and Nemathelminthes (nematodes, gordiaceans). Ehlers (1864) also recognized the phylum Vermes, which he considered to comprise the classes Annelida, Gephyrea, Nematoda, Nemertina, Turbellaria, Trematoda, Acanthocephala, and Cestoda. Here for the first time the nemertines were separated from the Turbellaria. This separation was recognized by most later authors so that the phylum Platyelminthes was considered to consist of four classes, Turbellaria, Trematoda, Cestoda, and Nemertina, an arrangement still widely employed. It remained for Minot (1876) to appreciate the many differences between the nemertines and the flatworms and to eliminate the former from the phylum, which he spelled Plathelminthes. Minot's conception of the phylum therefore corresponds with that adopted here, and hence the phylum is attributed to him. The etymologically correct form of the phylum name is Platyhelminthes, from the Greek *platys*, flat, and *helminthes*, worms; the spellings Platyelminthes, Plathelminthes, Platyelmia, and the recently proposed Platyhelmintha are not acceptable. Some other names sometimes used are Leuckart's Platodes and Haeckel's (1896) Platodaria, which latter has the advantage of being euphonious with Cnidaria; but as these authors had very poor conceptions of the scope and limitations of the phylum, their names should not be honored.

The phylum Platyhelminthes has had the attention of a long succession of distinguished zoologists. Pioneer work on the Turbellaria was done by such men as O. F. Müller, von Baer, Ehrenberg, and Oersted; but modern knowledge of this class (except Polycladida) is due almost entirely to the herculean labors of Ludwig von Graff, of the University of Graz, Austria. He has recorded his work in numerous papers and several large volumes, notably the two volumes on the Turbellaria in Bronn's *Klassen und Ordnungen des Tier-Reichs* (1904–1908, 1912–1917). Von Graff has been followed by a long succession of worthy students of the Turbellaria, many of them disciples of his; among them may be mentioned Arndt, Beauchamp, Beklemichev, Böhmig, Bresslau, Hofsten, Iijima, Kenk, Komarek, Luther, Meixner, Nasonov, Reisinger, Steinböck, Steinmann, Westblad, and J. Wilhelmi. Arnold Lang, in his famous monograph of the polyclads (1884), brought together and greatly enlarged our knowledge of this order: since then notable advances in this group have been made by Bock, Kaburaki, Kato, Palombi, and Stummer-Traunfels. The study of the parasitic flatworms owes its first clarification, as noted above, to Zeder and Rudolphi; through the nineteenth century there were numerous contributors in this field, of whom some of the more prominent were Braun, Cobbold, Diesing, Filippi, Kölliker, Leidy, Leuckart, Linstow, Looss, Lühe, Moniez, Monticelli, Pagenstecher, Pintner, von Siebold, Steenstrup, Stossich, Van Beneden, and Zschokke. Modern students of trematodes and cestodes are legion, and the study of these forms and their life cycles has constituted one of the most active fields of zoological research in the United States under the leadership of such men as Chandler, Cort, Faust, Guberlet, Krull, La Rue, Linton, Stiles, Stunkard, and Ward. The outstanding modern account of the flatworms is that of Bresslau for the Turbellaria, and Fuhrmann for the Trematoda and Cestoda in the second volume of the *Handbuch der Zoologie,* and the present text owes much to this work. *The Trematoda* by Ben Dawes (1946) is very useful for the flukes.

II. CHARACTERS OF THE PHYLUM

1. Definition.—The Platyhelminthes or flatworms are dorsoventrally flattened Bilateria without coelom, definitive anus, circulatory, respiratory, or skeletal systems, with flame-bulb protonephridia, and with a connective tissue filling all spaces between organ-systems. More briefly, the Platyhelminthes are *acoelomate Bilateria without a definitive anus.*

2. General Characters.—This phylum stands at the bottom of the bilateral animals. It is characterized by a strongly marked bilateral symmetry accompanied by a greater or less degree of dorsoventral flattening and the differentiation of the anterior end as a head. The members of the phylum have a general worm-like appearance but vary from the typical moderately elongated flattened shape to the excessively long flat ribbons of the tapeworms as one extreme, and the broad leaf-like forms of some polyclads as the other extreme. The body is generally of simple contour, but bizarre shapes occur among the trematodes, and in the majority of tapeworms, the tape-like body is segmented, being divided up into squarish or rectangular segments, termed *proglottids,* which increase in size in the anteroposterior direction. In size the members of the phylum range from microscopic worms no larger than protozoans to the extreme elongation seen in tapeworms, amounting to as much as 10 to 15 m; but most flatworms are of small to moderate dimensions. The majority of flatworms are white or colorless or owe their color to ingested food; the free-living forms when not white are often brown, gray, or black; but bright colors and patterns are seen among the polyclads and the land planarians (Figs. 14*A*, 61*F*).

The anterior end may be set off as an easily recognizable head by a neck-like constriction but in the frequent absence of such a constriction is nevertheless organized as a definite head as shown by the presence therein of the main nervous center; by the numerous sensory organs which it bears, especially in the free-living members; and by its being directed forward in locomotion. In parasitic flatworms the head also usually bears organs of adhesion in the form of hooks and suckers, although these may also occur elsewhere on the body.

A ventral surface on which locomotion occurs and which also bears the mouth and genital pores is well differentiated among the turbellarians but is less marked in trematodes and in cestodes is established only by arbitrary definitions.

Characteristic of the phylum is the presence of a great variety of adhesive secretions and of organs of adhesion and attachment. These begin in the free-living members as sticky secretions and adhesive papillae, patches, and cushions and reach their culmination in the muscular suckers and formidable hooks of flukes and tapeworms. Fully developed suckers are not, however, limited to parasitic forms but also occur among the fresh-water planarians.

In the class Turbellaria, the body is clothed with a cellular or syncytial one-layered epidermis, ciliated in whole or in part; but in the two parasitic classes, an epidermis is lacking and the body surface is formed of a secreted cuticle. Beneath the surface layer there is generally present a subepidermal musculature, of circular, longitudinal, and often also diagonal fibers. Muscle fibers also course through the mesenchyme and form an important constituent of the pharynx, the copulatory apparatus, and the adhesive structures. The muscle fibers are of the smooth type, although indications of cross striations occur.

The phylum lacks exo- and endoskeleton and therefore is characterized in general by a soft consistency. Hardened parts include the cuticle mentioned above and its differentiations such as surface spines and attachment hooks, further the hooks, spines, thorns, and teeth often borne by the male copulatory organ and also sometimes by other parts of the copulatory apparatus. These hardened parts were formerly considered to be of chitinous nature but are now known to consist of scleroproteins and will be spoken of as *cuticularized;* chitin is conspicuously absent from the phylum, being recorded in only two instances (see pages 144, 413).

All space between the various organ-systems is filled with a mesenchyme, usually called *parenchyma.* This solid construction, this lack of any internal cavity except the lumen of the digestive tract, is one of the most diagnostic characters of the phylum and constitutes what is here termed the *acoelomate* type of structure. It is true that small clefts or spaces may occur in the mesenchyme, especially in the Rhabdocoela, but these never fuse to form large cavities; they would appear to classify as pseudocoel, i.e., as remnants of the blastocoel, but there is considerable confusion of terminology in regard to them. The histological structure of the mesenchyme is a difficult question considered later.

The nervous system of the more primitive flatworms is directly derivable from that of cnidarians, consisting of an epidermal nerve net and a slight massing of nervous tissue representing a brain. In most flatworms, however, the nervous system has sunk to subepidermal and submuscular positions and the main (submuscular) nerve net shows concentration into several longitudinal ganglionated cords of which the two ventral ones are often the most conspicuous or the only ones present. Thus a system primarily radial becomes bilateral by the elimination of some of the radiating cords. The main nervous center, or brain, located in the head, consists of a pair of conjoined swellings, the *cerebral ganglia*, or *brain*. Numerous transverse connections occur between the longitudinal cords; and when the latter are reduced to two, these two and their transverse connectives represent the first appearance among the Bilateria of the so-called *ladder* type of nervous system. However, in many cases flatworms which are stated to have but two longitudinal cords often actually possess others, which are so inconspicuous as to escape casual notice.

The Turbellaria are richly supplied with sensory organs, but these are greatly reduced in the parasitic classes. Chemo- and tangoreceptors are of wide distribution in the phylum. Statocysts occur in the orders Acoela and Alloeocoela and a few other forms. Ciliated pits and grooves which appear to be chemoreceptive at least in part are of common occurrence among the Turbellaria. Ocelli are found throughout the latter, also in larval and adult monogenetic trematodes, and in larval digenetic trematodes. They are mostly of the pigment-cup type with inverse retinal cells, and vary in number from two to hundreds.

A digestive system is totally absent in the turbellarian order Acoela and in the tapeworms; in other flatworms it resembles that of anthozoans and ctenophores, consisting of mouth, pharynx, and blind intestine. The mouth is primitively situated at about the center of the ventral surface but in various flatworms may occupy any position along the mid-ventral line. The pharynx, which presumably is of stomodaeal nature, shows great variation in the phylum; typically it is a strongly muscular tube, protrusible or not. The intestine also displays a wide variety of form, from a simple sac to complicated branchings; it rarely has one or more anal openings. It consists of a single-layered epithelium which has strong phagocytic and digestive powers.

Respiratory and circulatory systems are absent in the phylum, although some trematodes have a system of tubes of uncertain function which has been called a lymphatic system. An excretory system is of wide occurrence throughout the phylum, consisting of single or paired protonephridial tubules provided with flame bulbs and often entering a terminal contractile bladder. Protonephridia are absent in the Acoela and tend in general to be reduced in marine Turbellaria. Special cells known as *athrocytes* or *paranephrocytes* often accompany the protonephridia.

The Platyhelminthes are with very few exceptions hermaphroditic, and the reproductive system is usually of great complexity, contrasting strongly with the relative simplicity of the other organ-systems. This complexity has, however, evolved within the phylum, as the system is in a primitive state in the Acoela, which lack definite gonads and oviducts. The gonads come from mesenchyme cells and are primitively numerous and scattered, eventually reduced to one or two. Not infrequently there are numerous testes but only one or two ovaries. Peculiar to the phylum is the separation of the female gonad into two structures, the ovaries proper and the yolk or vitelline glands. Whereas in other animals the ovary provides yolk for the eggs and this yolk is incorporated into the structure of the egg, in the majority of the Platyhelminthes (except Acoela, Polycladida, and a few other Turbellaria) the eggs are devoid of yolk, which instead is supplied by special yolk cells. These yolk cells are abortive eggs given off by the yolk or vitelline glands. They accompany the eggs, become incorporated with them inside the eggshell or capsule, and furnish food to the embryo during development. There is commonly present one pair of oviducts and one pair of sperm ducts, and these generally fuse distally to form common ducts. Despite their hermaphroditism, the flatworms generally practice cross-fertilization, and for this purpose a complicated copulatory apparatus is usually present. This consists in the male of a protrusible penis or eversible cirrus, either of which may be armed with spines, thorns, etc., and of various accompanying glands, as well as a single or paired vesicle for storing sperm. The female apparatus includes a sac, the seminal bursa or copulatory bursa or seminal receptacle, for storing sperm, and various glands associated with the formation of eggshells or the production of adhesive secretions for fastening the eggs after laying. In parasites, a long tubular or branched uterus in which large numbers of ripe eggs accumulate is often a conspicuous part of the female system. There may be a common gonopore or separate male and female pores, or the gonoducts may join the digestive tract and the sex products then exit through the mouth. Other types of genitointestinal connections are not uncommon (see below). In some flatworms there is present an extra female pore, the bursal or vaginal pore, which seems to serve for copulation only. The gonopores usually open on the ventral surface but are occasionally dorsal, mostly lateral in tapeworms. Multiplication of copulatory apparatus and also of gonopores is not uncommon in the phylum.

Internal fertilization obtains among the flatworms, and the fertilized shelled eggs, often already containing embryos, are shed to the exterior or fastened to objects by adhesive secretions. The embryonic development is generally greatly modified because, as mentioned above, the food supplies for the embryo are contained in separate cells, the yolk cells. Only in those groups which lack yolk glands, namely, the Acoela and the Polycladida, is the development of unmodified character. In these groups cleavage is of the spiral determinate type, resembling that of annelids and mollusks, with an entomesoderm derived from the 4*d* cell, and the production of definite germ layers whose fate can be followed. In part of the polyclads, a free-swimming larva is produced which is supposed to foreshadow the trochophore and hence has been termed a *protrochula*. The development of other groups of flatworms is highly modified and proceeds without the formation of definite germ layers. The various organ-systems arise simply from masses of cells and consequently cannot be assigned to any particular germ layer, except on theoretical grounds. Peculiar to the classes Trematoda and Cestoda is the loss of the surface epithelium during development and to the Acoela and the Cestoda the failure of the entoderm to differentiate from the entomesodermal mass. Very complicated life histories with a succession of larval stages in one to three intermediate hosts characterize the Trematoda and Cestoda.

Asexual multiplication occurs in many fresh-water and land triclads by fragmentation or transverse fission without the formation of fission planes; and in two rhabdocoel families (Catenulidae and Microstomidae) and two fresh-water planarians by transverse fission preceded by the formation of fission planes dividing the animal into a chain of zooids. The larval stages of digenetic trematodes multiply by a process regarded by some as parthenogenesis, by others as polyembryony, and the larval stages of some tapeworms propagate by endogenous or exogenous budding.

The flatworms are either free-living or are ecto- or entocommensals or parasites. The free-living flatworms, comprising the class Turbellaria, live in fresh water, in springs, streams, ponds, and lakes; or in the ocean, chiefly along shores; or in moist terrestrial habitats, mostly in tropical or subtropical regions. Some few are commensal or parasitic. The classes Trematoda and Cestoda are wholly parasitic, chiefly entoparasitic; the adult stage parasitizes vertebrates with rare exceptions; the larval stages often occur in invertebrates. The hosts may be fresh-water, marine, or terrestrial animals.

The phylum as here understood is divided into the three classes Turbellaria, Trematoda, and Cestoda. These differ so much in anatomy and life history that a general presentation is not feasible, and hence the account of the phylum will proceed directly to a consideration of the three classes.

III. CLASSIFICATION OF THE PHYLUM

The usual disagreements exist among students of the Platyhelminthes as to the details of the classification, and in particular the classification of the Trematoda is in a very unsettled state.

Class I. Turbellaria, the free-living flatworms. Platyhelminthes clothed with a cellular or syncytial epidermis, usually ciliated at least in part, usually provided with rhabdoids; body undivided; intestine present except in the Acoela; life cycles simple; mostly free-living, some ecto- or entocommensal or parasitic.

Order 1. Acoela. Small Turbellaria with mouth, pharynx simplex or none, no intestine; without protonephridia, oviducts, yolk glands or definitely delimited gonads; exclusively marine.

Order 2. Rhabdocoela.[1] Small Turbellaria with complete digestive tract; intestine sac-like, without evident diverticula; mostly with protonephridia and oviducts; gonads few, mostly compact; usually with cuticularized structures in place of soft penis papilla; nervous system mostly with two main longitudinal trunks.

Suborder 1. Notandropora or Catenulida. Rhabdocoela with simple pharynx, single median protonephridium, anterior dorsal male pore, single testis mass, unarmed penis; no yolk glands; asexual fission with formation of chains of zooids; exclusively fresh-water.

Suborder 2. Opisthandropora or Macrostomida. Rhabdocoels with simple pharynx, paired protonephridia, ventral male pore behind female pore, compact testes, penis armed with a stylet; no yolk glands; one of the two families forms chains of zooids; fresh-water or marine.

Suborder 3. Lecithophora or Neorhabdocoela. Rhabdocoels with bulbose pharynx, paired protonephridia, ventral gonopores, germovitellaria, or separate ovaries and yolk glands; reproduction exclusively sexual; fresh-water, marine, or terrestrial, mostly free-living, some commensal or parasitic.

Section 1. Dalyellioida. Lecithophora without a proboscis, pharynx of the doliiform type, mouth at anterior tip or nearly so; gonopore single; without rhammite tracts.

Section 2. Typhloplanoida. Lecithophora without a proboscis, pharynx usually of the rosulate type, mouth ventral back from anterior tip; with one or two gonopores; often with rhammite tracts.

Section 3. Kalyptorhynchia. Lecithophora with a protrusible or eversible proboscis in a sheath at the anterior end; pharynx of the rosulate type; without rhammite tracts.

Suborder 4. Temnocephalida. Ectocommensal fresh-water rhabdocoels, devoid of cilia or but slightly ciliated, anterior end extended into 2 to 12 tentacles, posterior end with one or two adhesive disks, pharynx doliiform, gonopore single.

Order 3. Alloeocoela. Small Turbellaria with simple, bulbose, or plicate pharynx; intestine may have short diverticula; protonephridia paired, often with more than one main branch and nephridiopore; testes generally numerous; penis papilla usually present; nervous system with

---

[1] Formerly the Rhabdocoela and Alloeocoela were often united under the name Rhabdocoelida, but this is no longer customary.

three or four pairs of longitudinal trunks; mostly marine, a few in fresh water.

Suborder 1. Archoophora. Alloeocoels with plicate pharynx and very primitive female system, as in Acoela; one species, marine.

Suborder 2. Lecithoepitheliata. Alloeocoels without typical yolk glands; may have nutritive cells embracing the ova; simple or bulbose pharynx; male apparatus generally with a cuticular stylet; marine, fresh-water, or terrestrial.

Suborder 3. Cumulata or Holocoela. Alloeocoels with germovitellaria or with separate ovaries and yolk glands; bulbose or plicate pharynx; intestine mostly without diverticula; male apparatus mostly unarmed; marine or fresh-water.

Suborder 4. Seriata. Alloeocoels with plicate pharynx and separate ovaries and yolk glands; intestine usually has lateral diverticula; mostly with statocysts; mostly marine, some in fresh water.

Order 4. Tricladida. Larger Turbellaria of elongated form, often very elongated; with plicate pharynx, usually directed backward; intestine with three highly diverticulated branches, one forward, two backward; with one pair of ovaries, two to numerous testes; with yolk glands; female apparatus usually with a bursa (sometimes two), male apparatus with a penis papilla; single gonopore; marine, fresh-water, or terrestrial.

Suborder 1. Maricola or Retrobursalia. With two eyes; bursa when present behind the penis or else with separate pore, may be paired; sexual reproduction only; exclusively marine or brackish.

Suborder 2. Paludicola or Probursalia. With two to many eyes, or eyeless; bursa nearly always present, anterior to the penis, connected with common antrum by a long bursal canal; often with asexual reproduction; fresh-water, sometimes brackish.

Suborder 3. Terricola. With two to many eyes, body mostly elongated; bursa mostly absent, when present behind the penis and may have bursal pore to exterior; usually marked separation of male and female antra; may have asexual reproduction; terrestrial in humid habitats, mostly tropical or subtropical.

Order 5. Polycladida. Larger Turbellaria, mostly of broad flattened form, but some elongated; plicate pharynx opens into a main intestine from which numerous branches radiate to the periphery; nervous system with numerous radiating nerve cords; eyes numerous, more than two (a few eyeless species); ovaries and testes numerous and scattered; without yolk glands; with one or two gonopores; male pore, when separate, anterior to the female pore; almost exclusively marine.

Suborder 1. Acotylea. Polyclads without a sucker behind the female pore; tentacles when present of the nuchal type; eyes not in paired clusters on the anterior margin.

Section 1. Craspedommata. Eyes in a band along the whole or part of the body margin.

Section 2. Schematommata. Without marginal eyes; eyes mostly in four groups well back from anterior margin.

Section 3. Emprosthommata. Anterior end strewn with eyes.

Suborder 2. Cotylea. Polyclads with a sucker behind the female pore; with a pair of marginal tentacles or if not with a cluster of eyes in place of each tentacle, or eyes in a band across the anterior margin.

An alternative classification of the Turbellaria was proposed by Meixner in 1938 (*Tierwelt der Nord- und Ostsee*, Teil IVb), as follows:

Order 1. Acoela.
Order 2. Catenulida (= Notandropora).
Order 3. Macrostomida (= Opisthandropora).
Order 4. Polycladida.
Order 5. Alloeocoela.
  Suborder 1. Archoophora.
  Suborder 2. Lecithoepitheliata.
  Suborder 3. Cumulata (= Holocoela).
  Suborder 4. Seriata.
    Section 1. Proseriata.
    Section 2. Tricladida.
      Tribe 1. Maricola.
      Tribe 2. Paludicola.
      Tribe 3. Terricola.
Order 6. Neorhabdocoela (= Lecithophora).
  Suborder 1. Dalyellioida.
  Suborder 2. Typhloplanoida.
  Suborder 3. Kalyptorhynchia.
Order 7. Temnocephalida.

The main features of this classification are that the rhabdocoels are split into three orders and that the triclads are made a suborder of alloeocoels. Although there are good grounds for Meixner's arrangement, the more conservative system is here followed.

Class II. Trematoda, the flukes. Ecto- or entoparasitic Platyhelminthes without an epidermis, rhabdoids, or external cilia; body undivided, covered with a cuticle, and provided with one or more suckers, usually not limited to the anterior end; with a complete digestive tract consisting of mouth, pharynx, and mostly two-forked, but sometimes simple or many-branched intestine; one ovary; life cycles simple or complicated.

Order 1. Heterocotylea or Monogenea. Oral sucker absent or weak; anterior end usually with a pair of adhesive structures; posterior end with an adhesive disk usually provided with hooks; excretory pores paired, anterior, dorsal; uterus short to moderate containing few eggs; ecto- or entoparasites with a simple life cycle and no alternation of hosts.

Suborder 1. Monopisthocotylea. Ectoparasitic monogenetic trematodes in which the posterior adhesive organ is single, although it may be subdivided by septa.

Suborder 2. Polyopisthocotylea. Ecto- or entoparasitic monogenetic trematodes with a large posterior adhesive organ bearing several to many suckers and usually also hooks.

Order 2. Aspidobothria or Aspidocotylea. Oral sucker absent; anterior end without paired adhesive structures; with an enormous ventral sucker subdivided into compartments or with a ventral row of suckers; no hooks; single nephridiopore, posterior; entoparasites with simple life cycle and no alternation of hosts.

Order 3. Malacocotylea or Digenea. Mostly with two suckers, an anterior sucker that generally encircles the mouth and a ventral sucker, but either or both may be reduced or wanting; no hooks; single excretory pore; uterus usually a relatively long tube containing many capsules; entoparasites with a complicated life cycle and several larval stages occupying one or more intermediate hosts.

The classification of the Digenea is at the present time in a state of great confusion. An arrangement based on the suckers has been strongly supported by Faust (1932) and has been widely promulgated in textbooks but, as repeatedly pointed out in the following text, the number and location of the suckers are not reliable taxonomic characters. The arrangement of the flame bulbs has also been repeatedly urged by Faust and others as a basis for classification but appears less reliable than formerly supposed. It has therefore been thought best in the present state of knowledge to omit any grouping of the Digenea into suborders or sections and to consider them only by family names. Probably the classification proposed by Poche (1926) is the best at present available. There appears to be a general agreement that those families in which the miracidia have two pairs of flame bulbs are related and the group so formed is usually called Strigeata. Other attempted family groupings have failed to meet with general approval from students of the Digenea.

Class III. Cestoda, the tapeworms. Entoparasitic Platyhelminthes without an epidermis, rhabdoids, or external cilia; body clothed with a cuticle and usually divided into a few to many segments, although sometimes undivided; adhesive structures limited to the anterior end except in Cestodaria; mouth and digestive tract wholly wanting; each segment with one or two complete hermaphroditic reproductive systems; embryo hooked; life cycle complicated, usually involving two or more hosts; majority inhabiting the intestine of vertebrates.

SUBCLASS 1. CESTODARIA. Tapeworms with undivided body, no scolex, one set of reproductive organs, and 10-hooked larva.

Order 1. Amphilinidea. With a protrusible proboscis and frontal glands at the anterior end; uterus traverses body length three times, opening near anterior end; male and vaginal pores posterior.

Order 2. Gyrocotylidea. Anterior end with eversible proboscis; posterior end with adhesive ruffle; uterus runs directly to pore; uterine, male, and vaginal pores together in anterior half.

SUBCLASS 2. EUCESTODA. Body usually very elongated and ribbon-like, divided into a few to many segments, but sometimes undivided; anterior end generally expanded into a scolex bearing adhesive organs; generally with more than one set of reproductive organs; larva six-hooked.

Order 1. Tetraphyllidea or Phyllobothrioidea. Segmented tapeworms with a scolex bearing four bothridia, often armed with hooks or subdivided by septa; intestine of elasmobranch fishes.

Order 2. Lecanicephaloidea. Segmented tapeworms with scolex bearing four acetabula; yolk glands numerous; reproductive system as in Tetraphyllidea; in intestine of elasmobranchs.

Order 3. Proteocephaloidea. Segmented tapeworms with scolex provided with four acetabula and an apical sucker or glandular organ; otherwise as in Tetraphyllidea; in the intestine of fish, amphibians, and reptiles.

Order 4. Diphyllidea. Segmented tapeworms of not more than 20 segments with scolex provided with two bothria and a spiny head stalk; in intestine of elasmobranchs; contains only the genus *Echinobothrium*.

Order 5. Trypanorhyncha or Tetrarhynchoidea. Segmented tapeworms with a scolex provided with four bothria and four protrusible spiny proboscides; parasitic in fishes.

Order 6. Pseudophyllidea or Bothriocephaloidea. Segmented or unsegmented tapeworms with a scolex provided with two to six shallow bothria, or sometimes without adhesive organs; yolk glands numerous; in intestine of all classes of vertebrates.

Order 7. Nippotaeniidea. Segmented tapeworms with a scolex having an apical sucker but no other adhesive structures; yolk gland single; excretory system of numerous longitudinal vessels; in intestine of fishes.

Order 8. Taenioidea or Cyclophyllidea. Segmented tapeworms with a scolex bearing four acetabula, also often provided with an apical rostellum armed with hooks; yolk gland single, compact; excretory system of four longitudinal canals; mostly in the intestine of birds and mammals.

Order 9. Aporidea. Unsegmented tapeworms with a scolex provided with four acetabula and an armed rostellum; excretory system as in Taenioidea; devoid of sex ducts, sex pores, and distinct yolk glands; follicles of germovitellaria become uterine capsules; contains only the genera *Nematoparataenia* and *Gastrotaenia*, in swans.

IV. CLASS TURBELLARIA

1. Definition.—The Turbellaria are mostly free-living, sometimes commensal or parasitic, unsegmented flatworms with simple life cycles, clothed with a cellular or syncytial epidermis, which is usually ciliated, at least in part, and is usually provided with rhabdoids.

2. External Features.—The Turbellaria are on the whole rather small animals, and the majority are less than 5 mm. in length, many being of microscopic dimensions. Larger forms are limited to the orders Tricladida and Polycladida; the land planarians may reach 50 cm. or more in length, and the polyclads are usually of considerable size. The body shape is typically vermiform, i.e., several times longer than wide, and this shape obtains among the smaller forms. The larger types vary on the one hand to the long slender shape common among land planarians (Fig. 14*D*) and on the other to the leaf-like oval to almost circular forms seen among polyclads. The body is mostly dorsoventrally flattened, usually strongly so in triclads and polyclads, but many forms are cylindroid. The ventral surface is generally flat, the dorsal convex, often greatly so. The body contour is generally simple, mostly wider in the middle and tapering to one or both ends, or broadest at one end and tapering toward the other. In some species of the acoel genus *Convoluta*, the sides of the body are held curved ventrally (Fig. 13*B*). There are usually no projections, but the acoel genera *Amphiscolops* (Fig. 13*D*) and *Polychoerus* (Fig. 13*E*) have two caudal lobes, the latter and some sand-dwelling rhabdocoels have a little tail filament, and tentacles are not uncommon. Thus a pair of tentacles occurs at the anterior end of the alloeocoel *Vorticeros* (Fig. 14*C*), and many polyclads bear a pair of tentacles, either as *nuchal* tentacles on the dorsal surface near the brain (Fig. 63*B*) or as *marginal* tentacles formed by a pair of folds of the anterior margin (Fig. 14*B*). The presence of 2 to 12 pointed tentacles at the anterior end or in one genus also along the body sides is characteristic of the suborder Temnocephalida (Figs. 57, 58). In some polyclads the dorsal surface is covered with tubercles or papillae (Fig. 15*A*), and in the genus *Thysanozoon* there is an intestinal branch inside each papilla. *Adhesive organs* (see below) are of common occurrence among the Turbellaria and may constitute conspicuous external features. In some fresh-water planarians the head bears delicate lateral projections, known as *auricles*, which carry numerous sensory cells (Fig. 15*B*).

The anterior end may be set off as an obvious head by a neck-like constriction, notably in fresh-water planarians of the genus *Dugesia*

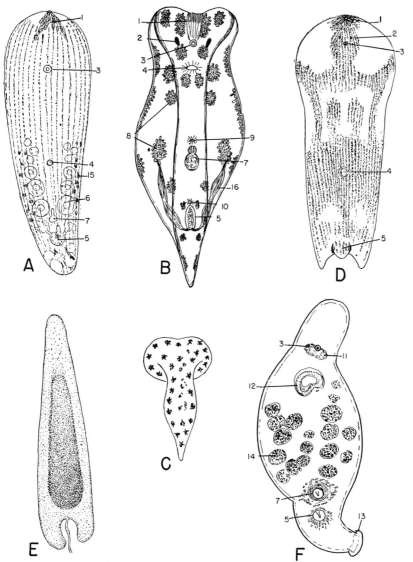

FIG. 13.—Some representatives of the Acoela. *A.* Typical acoel, from life, California. *B–F*, less usual shapes. *B. Convoluta*, with curved sides and pigment cells (*after Graff*, 1904). *C.* Same, crawling (*after Graff*, 1904). *D. Amphiscolops bermudensis*, from life, Bermuda, showing caudal lobes and pattern of concrement granules. *E. Polychoerus carmelensis*, from life, California, with caudal lobes and tail filament. *F. Ectocotyla paguri*, ectocommensal on hermit crabs, Maine, with plicate pharynx and caudal adhesive disk (*from sketches and specimens courtesy of Dr. E. G. Reinhard*). 1, frontal glands; 2, eyes; 3, statocyst; 4, mouth; 5, penis; 6, strands of eggs; 7, seminal bursa; 8, pigment cells; 9, female pore; 10, male pore; 11, brain; 12, pharynx; 13, caudal adhesive disk; 14, embryos; 15, strands of sperm; 16, sperm ducts.

(= *Euplanaria*) and in land planarians of the genus *Bipalium* (Figs. 14D, 15B). Usually, however, there is no such constriction, and often in fact the head end may be the narrowest part of the body. The head is always recognizable by being directed forward, by the presence of eyes and other sense organs, and by the accumulation of nervous tissue within. Among the sensory organs borne by the head are tentacles, auricles, eyes, ciliated pits and grooves, and sensory hairs, spines, and bristles.

The Turbellaria, especially the smaller forms, when not translucent or white, are generally of sober coloration, mostly brown, gray, or black. However, brilliant colors and striped, barred, and flecked patterns occur among the larger members, especially the land planarians and the polyclads (Fig. 14A). In the former, white, yellow, or orange stripes on a dark ground or vice versa are common (Fig. 61F). Frequently forms really white or transparent appear to be colored from the ingestion of colored food. The intrinsic coloration is generally caused by pigment granules or rods located in or beneath the epidermis, or by dissolved pigment in these locations.

3. Epidermis.—The Turbellaria are clothed with a one-layered epidermis (Figs. 16, 17C) which varies from a flat to a columnar form, being generally cuboidal, and also varies in thickness in different body regions; usually the dorsal epidermis is taller than the ventral; and often also the body margins, including the two ends, have an especially tall epidermis. The epidermis is generally ciliated, completely so in most members, especially the smaller forms, but not infrequently the dorsal surface lacks cilia, as in the case in the marine and fresh-water planarians; the ciliation also tends to degenerate in commensal and sand-dwelling forms. The Temnocephalida, a group that leads an ectocommensal existence, are mostly devoid of cilia. Cilia are also absent from glandular and adhesive areas but may be especially developed on sensory areas, acting to bring water currents to the sensory endings. The cilia may vary in length in different body regions, and the ventral cilia are often longer than the dorsal ones, being of greater importance in locomotion. In many land planarians, especially those of cylindroid shape, the ventral surface bears a special median strip, ridge, or group of ridges, termed the *creeping sole*, on which the animal glides and which is provided with especially powerful and closely placed cilia (Figs. 14D, 16E). The cilia are provided with basal bodies, have roots extending into the epidermis, and appear to be interconnected by a fibrillar system similar to that of ciliate Protozoa (P–C, page 167).

The epidermis is devoid of any secreted protective layer or structures, such as a cuticle, as this would be incompatible with ciliation. However, the nonciliated Temnocephalida have a clear structureless border resem-

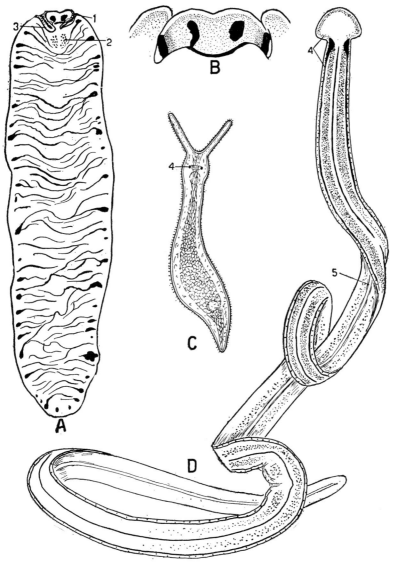

Fig. 14.—Various Turbellaria. *A*. Cotylean polyclad, *Pseudoceros crozieri*, from life, Bermuda, with marginal tentacles and pattern of black bars on a greenish ground. *B*. Anterior end of same, to show marginal type of tentacle. *C*. Plagiostomid alloeocoel, *Vorticeros*, only alloeocoel with tentacles, European Coast (*after Schmidt*, 1852); has red central net-like pigment. *D. Bipalium kewense*, cosmopolitan land planarian, found in greenhouses and outdoors in Florida, Louisiana, and California, 20 to 35 cm, long, has expanded head, three narrow and two broad purple to black stripes on a yellow, olive, or gray ground; dark pigment areas at the "neck" are distinctive; note creeping sole and numerous eyes on head margin and in row along body margin. 1, tentacular eyes; 2, cerebral eyes; 3, marginal tentacles; 4, eyes; 5, creeping sole.

bling a cuticle, and the polyclad genus *Enantia* has spines along the body margin (Fig. 17A). Each spine begins as a secretion over an epidermal papilla and is later broadened by columns secreted by adjacent cells (Fig. 17B). The chemical nature of these spines is unknown, but they are presumably scleroprotein.

The epidermis may be cellular and usually is so in the larger forms, the triclads and polyclads; it then consists of polygonal or prismatic cells, cuboidal to columnar (Figs. 16, 17C), often narrowed basally. Not infrequently, however, the epidermis is syncytial or partly so, especially among the Acoela, Rhabdocoela, and Alloeocoela (Fig. 16C). Further it may exhibit a peculiar condition termed *insunk* ("eingesenkt" by German writers), in which the nuclei accompanied by some cytoplasm have descended into the mesenchyme internal to the subepidermal musculature (Fig. 16E). In such cases the epidermis appears as a flat almost structureless layer devoid of nuclei. An insunk epidermis is seen in many Acoela and Alloeocoela, in the Bdellouridae, a family of marine triclads, and in the creeping sole of land planarians of the family Bipaliidae (Fig. 16E). The epidermis may contain fluid-filled spaces that divide the syncytial cytoplasm into vertical strands or columns; this condition is often seen in the Acoela (Fig. 16C). Often, too, the epidermis contains large oval gland cells secreting a mucous substance and opening at the surface between the bases of the cilia (Fig. 16D). Other types of gland cells may also occur sparingly in the epidermis, but in general the gland cells of Turbellaria are situated in the mesenchyme and only their necks traverse the epidermis. Various types of sensory cells (discussed later) also occur in the epidermis; the participation of the epidermis in adhesive structures is also considered later.

Very characteristic of the epidermis of the Turbellaria are bodies known as *rhabdoids*. The most common of these are the *rhabdites*, straight or slightly curved rods shorter than the height of the epidermis (Fig. 17D). They occur singly or grouped into bundles, oriented with their long axis at right angles to the surface, and are often so numerous as to obscure the structure of the epidermis (Fig. 16A). Rhabdites are secreted by gland cells (Fig. 16A) located either in the epidermis or in the mesenchyme; if the former, they are termed *epidermal* rhabdites, if the latter, *adenal* rhabdites. Rhabdites are frequently more numerous dorsally and along the body margins or body ends than ventrally (Figs. 16A, B) and are also usually longer in such locations. A second, less common type of rhabdoid is the *rhammite* (Fig. 17F), long, slender, and often sinuous, longer than the height of the epidermis. Rhammites are always adenal, and in some rhabdocoels there are two anterior groups of rhammite-forming glands, so that the rhammites traveling to the anterior margin along the necks of these gland cells form two conspicuous "rod

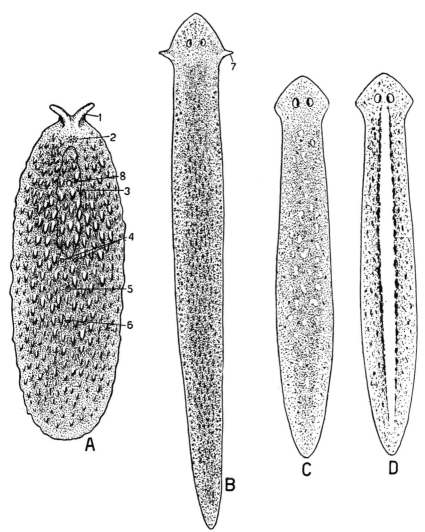

FIG. 15.—Types of Turbellaria. *A.* Cotylean polyclad, *Thysanozoon nigrum*, from life, Bermuda, black, with marginal tentacles, dorsal papillae, and double male apparatus. *B–D*, fresh-water planarians of the genus *Dugesia* with triangular head and definite auricles, from life. *B. Dugesia dorotocephala*, common United States planarian, dark brown to black, to 30 mm. long, may have light middorsal stripe, found in springs. *C, D.* Color variants of *Dugesia tigrina* (= *Planaria maculata*), most common United States planarian, brown, 10 to 20 mm. long, found in ponds, lakes, and streams. 1, marginal tentacles; 2, cerebral eyes; 3, outline of ruffled pharynx; 4, double male pores; 5, female pore; 6, adhesive disk ("sucker"); 7, auricles; 8, mouth.

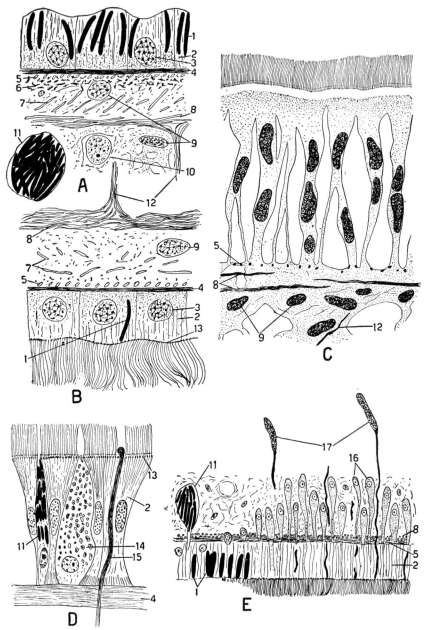

Fig. 16.—Structure of the epidermis. *A*. Longitudinal section through the dorsal epidermis of a fresh-water planarian, showing also the subepidermal musculature. *B*. Same through the ventral epidermis; note ciliation, paucity of rhabdites. *C*. Longitudinal section through the epidermis of an acoel (*after An der Laan*, 1935–1936). *D*. Section through the epidermis of a polyclad (*after Bock*, 1913). *E*. Cross section through the creeping sole of the land planarian *Bipalium*, showing insunk type of epidermis; at left

tracks." A third kind of rhabdoid, limited to land planarians, is the chondrocyst (Fig. 17G), merely an especially large rhabdite of somewhat granular texture. Rhabdoids in general consist of a hull enclosing material of more fluid consistency. Rhabdoid-secreting cells belong to the general category of eosinophilous glands (see below). Rhabdoids are absent in many Acoela, some of the more primitive Rhabdocoela and Alloeocoela, sand-dwelling Rhabdocoela, and in parasitic and commensal Turbellaria generally; also on glandular and sensory areas and on the creeping sole of land planarians. Polyclads mostly lack adenal rhab‐ doids. Two other kinds of epidermal inclusions that appear related to rhabdoids are *pseudorhabdites*, indefinite masses of slimy secretion inside epidermal cells, found commonly in polyclads and alloeocoels, occasion‐ ally in rhabdocoels; and *sagittocysts*, pointed vesicles containing a central protrusible rod or needle (Fig. 17E), limited to certain Acoela.

Little is definitely known of the nature or function of rhabdoids. According to Prenant (1919), rhabdoids are formed by nuclear break‐ down, consist of a calcium nucleoproteinate, and are useless excreta en route to elimination through the surface. This last view appears incom‐ patible with the general occurrence throughout the Turbellaria of special rhabdoid-forming gland cells. The usual belief is that rhabdoids on dis‐ charge to the exterior disintegrate to form a slimy or adhesive hull about the animal that protects it from enemies or adverse conditions, partici‐ pates in cyst formation, and may have some toxic action on prey. How‐ ever, definite proof of these statements is lacking. It is a fact that extensive discharge of rhabdites occurs when turbellarians are put into harmful solutions; but such discharge might be the incidental result of the convulsive contractions induced under those circumstances.

Nematocysts are found in the epidermis of a few Turbellaria, espe‐ cially the rhabdocoel *Microstomum* (Fig. 50B); also in a few other rhab‐ docoels, and two or three polyclads and alloeocoels. It is now known that these originate from ingested hydroids (Martin 1908, 1914). The nematocysts freed by the digestion of the soft parts of the hydroids are ingested by the gastrodermis, passed into the mesenchyme, and engulfed by mesenchyme cells which carry them to the epidermis. According to Kepner and his students, who have made a study of the ingestion of hydra by *Microstomum*, the nematocysts are actually employed against prey, being discharged when sufficiently bumped by the prey. These workers also state that *Microstomum* eats hydra only when in need of a

junction with normal epidermis. 1, rhabdites; 2, epidermis; 3, nucleus of epidermis; 4, basement membrane; 5, circular muscle layer; 6; pigment; 7, diagonal muscle layer; 8, longitudinal muscle layer; 9, fixed nuclei of mesenchyme; 10, free cell of mesenchyme; 11, rhabdite-forming gland cell; 12, parenchymal muscles; 13, basal bodies of cilia; 14, mucous gland cell; 15, neck of mesenchymal gland cell; 16, insunk nuclei with cytoplasm; 17, cyanophilous gland cells of the creeping sole.

new supply of nematocysts, that it normally prefers other food, that it will reject hydra if already loaded with nematocysts, and regurgitate other food to make room for hydra if in need of nematocysts (Kepner *et al.*, 1924, 1929, 1938). These workers therefore conclude that *Microstomum* seeks out hydras "for the purpose of" obtaining their nematocysts "in order" to use these nematocysts against prey. The question whether *Microstomum* is able to capture prey without the use of nematocysts is not considered by these authors; the lack of this control weakens the whole argument. The discharge of the nematocysts would seem to depend upon the prey's accidentally striking the nematocysts in just the right fashion, not upon any behavior of the *Microstomum*.

The epidermis is generally separated from the underlying mesenchyme by a definite basement membrane (Fig. 16D), sometimes very thick, usually homogeneous, but sometimes showing a lamellate structure. A basement membrane is lacking in many Acoela (Fig. 16C) and other primitive Turbellaria, and in such case there is a close relation of the epidermis with the mesenchyme and subepidermal musculature.

4. The Subepidermal Glands.—The Turbellaria are richly provided with glands, which nearly always are unicellular glands. Although, as seen above, gland cells may occur in the epidermis, the vast majority are located in the mesenchyme and send their long "necks" or canals through or between the epidermal cells, to open at the surface. They apparently are insunk epidermal cells. The gland cells have a rounded, pyriform, or elongated body and a long neck which also serves as a canal for the discharge of the secretion. The cell is commonly packed with fine to coarse granules representing the secretion. Little is known directly of the chemistry or function of these secretions. From histological studies of the staining properties of the gland cells it has been found that the latter fall into two categories: the *cyanophilous* glands which take haematoxylin and stain blue with connective tissue stains; and the *eosinophilous* or *erythrophilous* glands which stain pink with eosin, erythrosin, fuchsin, and similar dyes. From these staining reactions and scattered observations on the secretions in life, it is inferred with reasonable probability that the cyanophilous secretion is of slimy or mucus-like nature and acts to lubricate the ventral surface and to form a slime trail on which the cilia get a purchase; and the eosinophilous secretion is of a sticky or adhesive nature, used for adhesion, capture of prey, cementing eggs to a substratum, etc. There are a number of different kinds of glands in each category, and each of these presumably plays a specific role in the activities of the animal.

a. The Cyanophilous Glands.—The common type of cyanophilous gland cell occurs anywhere in the body but is particularly abundant in the ventral mesenchyme, especially in the anterior body half (Fig. 19A, H). These ventral cyanophilous glands undoubtedly secrete the slime trail, important in locomotion, also acting to entangle prey. The mucous secretion also probably serves to protect the animal from harmful substances or conditions, to make a cyst under some circumstances, and, according to Wilhelmi, to prevent the eosinophilous secretion from reaching the ventral surface (Wilhelmi, 1909). In land planarians having a creeping sole, the cyanophilous glands open on the sole (Fig. 16E).

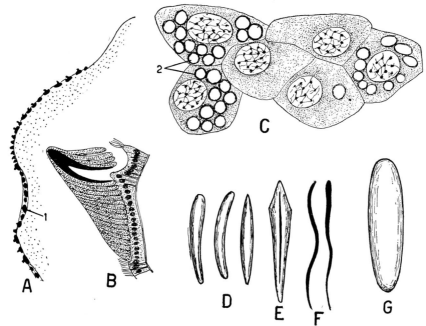

Fig. 17.—Epidermal structure (continued).   A. Margin of the polyclad *Enantia spinifera*, showing spines.   B. Section through one of the spines.   (*A, B after Graff*, 1889.)   C. Section through the epidermis of a fresh-water planarian, showing polygonal shape of epidermal cells and cross sections of rhabdites.   D. Various shapes of rhabdites.   E. Sagittocyst of *Convoluta* (*after Graff*, 1891).   F. Rhammites.   G. Chondrocyst of *Bipalium*. 1, spine; 2, section through rhabdites.

A characteristic structure of the Turbellaria is the frontal gland. This consists of a cluster of cyanophilous gland cells located near the brain with long necks that form a bundle and open by a pore or group of pores on the anterior tip, into an area devoid of rhabdoids and cilia, but often abundantly supplied with sensory cells (Fig. 18). The frontal gland is common among the Acoela and Alloeocoela, infrequent in the Rhabdocoela, and lacking in the other orders, although the adhesive organ found in the center of the anterior margin in many fresh-water triclads and the kalyptorhynchid rhabdocoels (Figs. 22, 56) is probably phylogenetically related to the frontal gland. The frontal gland seems to play a role in the capture of food.

b. *The Eosinophilous Glands.*—The ordinary type of eosinophilous gland occurs singly and sparingly anywhere in the body (Fig. 19*A*, *B*) and is characterized by its coarse granules staining red with eosin.   Its exact function is not known.   The rhabdoid-forming cells mentioned above, often very numerous, especially in the dorsal mesenchyme, are eosinophilous cells whose secretion takes the form of rods rather than the usual granules (Figs. 16*A*, 19*A*).

The most striking of the eosinophilous glands are the *marginal adhesive glands* of the fresh-water and marine triclads, whose pores form a zone or ring encircling the ventral surface near the margin (Fig. 19).   This *marginal adhesive zone* is devoid of rhabdoids and cilia and consists of epidermal cells perforated by the fine necks of the eosinophilous gland cells (Fig. 19*C*).   These necks terminate in little knobs that can be protruded beyond the epidermis as *adhesive papillae* acting like little suckers (Wilhelmi, 1909, Fig. 19*C*).   The animal can therefore cling very strongly to objects by means of this adhesive zone supplied by the sticky secretion of the eosinophilous cells.   Among ectocommensal triclads, the adhesive zone may be broadened in some regions to form an adhesive disk (e.g., *Bdelloura*, Fig. 19*D*, *E*).   In land planarians that lack a specialized creeping sole and hence creep on the entire ventral surface, as the Geoplanidae, there is often present at or just ventral to the margin a white strip, the *Drüsenkante* or *glandular margin*.   This bounds the creeping surface and appears to correspond to the marginal adhesive zone of other triclads, being fed by eosinophilous glands, although apparently not identical with that zone in histological details.

A group of eosinophilous glands termed *caudal glands* opening at the posterior tip or along the posterior margin occurs commonly among the Acoela, Rhabdocoela, and Alloeocoela.   These glands appear to have an adhesive function; and in some forms, notably members of the rhabdocoel genus *Macrostomum* and the alloeocoel family Monocelididae, their terminations are protrusible or permanently protruded as clear finger-like *adhesive papillae* (Figs. 29*C*, 51*C*).

c. *Multicellular Glands.*—These are uncommon among the Turbellaria, but what seem to be multicellular glands have been reported for the acoel genus *Convoluta*.   Flask-shaped multinucleate bodies are probably genuine glands, but the so-called poison glands are more probably of the nature of prostatoids (see page 117).

5. The Muscular System.—This consists in general of the subepidermal and the parenchymal musculature; the muscular layers of the pharynx and of the copulatory apparatus are treated with those organs. The *subepidermal musculature* forms a stratum just beneath the epidermis or the basement membrane when the latter is present.   It consists in its simplest form of an outer layer of circular fibers and an inner layer

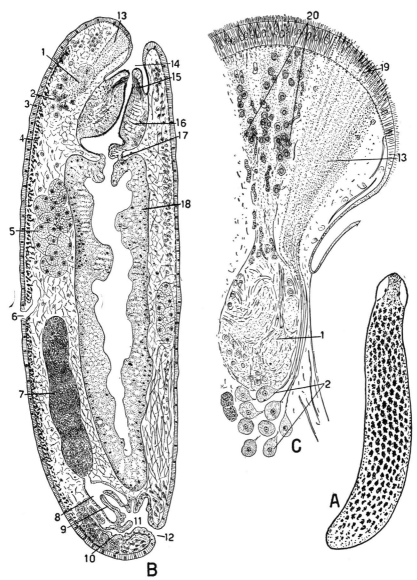

F IG . 18.—The frontal gland. *A. Hydrolimax grisea*, from life, fresh-water plagiostomid alloeocoel of the eastern United States. *B.* Median sagittal section of same showing
general structure and relations of frontal gland. *C.* Enlarged view of frontal gland and
accompanying sensory tracts. (*B, C after Hyman*, 1938). 1, brain; 2, frontal gland; 3,
epidermis; 4, pigment; 5, yolk gland; 6, excretory pore; 7, prostatic vesicle; 8, penis bulb; 9,
introverted penis papilla; 10, common ovovitelline duct; 11, genital antrum; 12, common
gonopore; 13, bundle of ducts of frontal glands; 14, buccal cavity; 15, bundle of gland ducts
of pharynx; 16, pharynx; 17, esophagus; 18, intestine; 19, outlets of frontal glands; 20,
sensory tract just above frontal gland ducts.

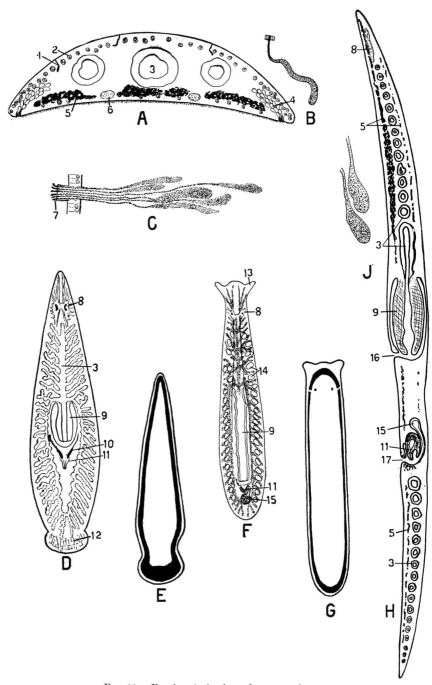

Fig. 19.—For descriptive legend see opposite page.

of longitudinal fibers; usually there is interpolated between these one or more layers of diagonal fibers (Fig. 20C). The subepidermal musculature is often extremely delicate in the small forms such as the Acoela but may be very thick and strong in larger members as planarians (Fig. 20B) and polyclads. It is frequently more powerfully developed ventrally than dorsally and often thins toward the margins and anteriorly. In polyclads the subepidermal musculature of the ventral side usually consists of five or six layers: outer circular, outer longitudinal, outer diagonal, inner circular, inner diagonal, inner longitudinal. The longitudinal fibers are often highly developed in the larger Turbellaria and may occur in bundles rather than as a simple stratum (Fig. 20B).

Very interesting is the fact that in several primitive turbellarians muscle fibers course through the epidermis parallel to the surface and appear to be part of the epidermis as in coelenterates (Fig. 20D). This condition has been found in the acoels *Childia* and *Palmenia* (Luther, 1912), the rhabdocoel *Rhynchoscolex* (Reisinger, 1924a), and the alloeocoels *Prorhynchus* (Steinböck and Reisinger, 1924) and *Hofstenia* (Bock, 1923). This epidermal musculature usually consists of outer longitudinal and inner circular fibers, and the latter may substitute for the usual circular layer of the subepidermal musculature.

The subepidermal musculature is undoubtedly homologous with the muscle cylinder of the coelenterates and is one of the indications of a coelenterate ancestry of the Turbellaria; the existence just mentioned of epithelio-muscular cells in Turbellaria greatly strengthens this supposition.

The parenchymal musculature consists of fibers coursing through the mesenchyme and comprises dorsoventral, transverse, and longitudinal fibers. This musculature may be of bewildering complexity in the larger turbellarians (Fig. 20B). Usually the dorsoventral fibers are the best developed, but often also there are strong longitudinal bundles in the ventral mesenchyme.

In ordinary preparations, the muscle fibers appear as long slender strands, either homogeneous or fibrillar; in some highly muscular organs they may show a primitive cross striation. The beautiful silver prepara-

---

FIG. 19.—Subepidermal glands. *A.* Transverse section through a fresh-water planarian, to show location and arrangement of the main gland cells. *B.* Eosinophilous gland cell enlarged. *C.* Cluster of marginal adhesive glands enlarged showing also adhesive papillae. *D. Bdelloura candida,* from life, marine triclad ectocommensal on Limulus, has caudal adhesive plate. *E.* Adhesive zone (in black) of *Bdelloura candida.* *F. Procerodes littoralis,* from life, marine triclad of New England Coast. *G.* Same, showing adhesive zone. (*C, E, G after Wilhelmi,* 1909.) *H.* Longitudinal section of fresh-water planarian, showing distribution of the cyanophilous glands. *J.* Cyanophilous gland cells enlarged. 1, eosinophilous glands; 2, rhabdite-forming gland cells; 3, intestine; 4, marginal adhesive glands; 5, cyanophilous glands; 6, nerve cords; 7, adhesive papillae; 8, brain; 9, pharynx; 10, sperm ducts; 11, penis; 12, caudal adhesive disk; 13, auricles; 14, testes; 15, copulatory bursa; 16, mouth; 17, common gonopore.

tions of Gelei (1912, 1927) show, however, that the fibers ordinarily seen are only the contractile part of the muscle cell and that in many cases such fibers are enveloped by a protoplasmic sheath containing a nucleus and often sending off processes believed to be of nutritive nature (Fig. 20A). The muscle fibers commonly terminate on the basement membrane of the epidermis by one or more fine filaments that may even extend into the epidermis.

6. The Mesenchyme.—The interior of the flatworm body between organs is filled with a connective tissue or mesenchyme (parenchyma). This appears to be an entomesoderm except in the Acoela where it seems to be compounded of ectomesoderm, entoderm, and entomesoderm. The histological construction of the mesenchyme is exceedingly difficult to ascertain and is not yet thoroughly understood. In some Turbellaria, the mesenchyme consists simply of contiguous rounded cells. In most cases, however, it is composed of a fixed net-like *syncytium* and of *free cells* that wander about through the syncytium (Prenant, 1922, Fig. 20E). The syncytium is nucleated, often has a fibrillar appearance, and contains numerous fluid-filled interstices. In a few rhabdocoels and alloeocoels these interstices may fuse to form spaces of some size. Such spaces are usually considered to be remnants of the blastocoel and hence to classify as pseudocoel. The free cells of the mesenchyme are somewhat rounded cells capable of amoeboid wandering; they are often termed *formative* cells since they play an important role in regenerative and reproductive processes, but to avoid unwarranted implications they will here be called simply amoebocytes or free mesenchymal cells. The mesenchyme is not to be regarded as a mere filling tissue, for it functions importantly in the assimilation and transport of food and in the disposal of excretory substances.

7. Pigment.—The coloration of the Turbellaria is caused by dissolved or particulate pigment situated in either the epidermis or the mesenchyme or both. Epidermal pigment is common in all the orders except Tricladida; in the Acoela it usually consists of rods in epidermal cells; in the Rhabdocoela and Alloeocoela it may be dissolved or in the form of granules or rods; in the Polycladida the yellow to red pigments are mostly epidermal, vested in cells that contain a large vacuole filled with a colored fluid or a colorless fluid containing pigment granules. Epidermal pigment cells are probably modified gland cells.

Mesenchymal pigment occurs throughout the Turbellaria, consisting of pigment granules strewn in the syncytium, or of granules or dissolved pigment in the lymph of the syncytial interstices, or of vesicular cells containing dissolved pigment, or of branched pigment cells. Pigment cells (Fig. 13B) occur chiefly among the smaller orders, being rare in the triclads and polyclads. The mesenchymal pigment is commonly limited

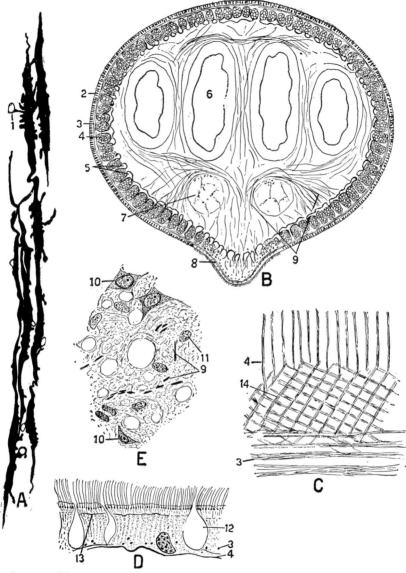

FIG. 20.—Musculature. *A.* Muscle cells of the longitudinal layer of the subepidermal musculature of a planarian (*after Gelei*, 1917). *B.* Cross section of a land planarian of the family Rhynchodemidae, showing musculature and nervous system. *C.* Tangential section through the subepidermal musculature of a planarian, showing the three layers. *D.* Section through the epidermis of the acoel *Palmenia*, showing epidermal muscle fiber (*after Luther*, 1912). *E.* Mesenchyme (parenchyma) of a planarian. 1, bulge containing nucleus; 2, epidermis; 3, circular layer of subepidermal musculature; 4, longitudinal layer of same, arranged in bundles; 5, submuscular nerve net; 6, intestine; 7, so-called ventral nerve cords, enlargements in ventral nerve plate; 8, creeping sole; 9, parenchymal muscle fibers; 10, free cells of the mesenchyme; 11, fixed nucleus of the mesenchymal syncytium; 12, epidermal gland cell; 13, epidermal muscle fiber; 14, diagonal layer of muscle fibers.

to or more abundant in the dorsal side.   The pigmentation of triclads is almost exclusively mesenchymal, consisting of a fine granulation in the syncytium; pigment cells have been reported in a few land planarians. Polyclads also have mesenchymal pigment granules which are usually responsible for the gray, brown, and black colors of these animals, although in some black species the pigment is in the vesicular epidermal cells mentioned above.   Color patterns of polyclads often result from combinations of epidermal and mesenchymal pigment.

The chemical nature of turbellarian pigment appears not to have been investigated, although it is often surmised that the granules in some cases are excretory bodies.   Certain Acoela have large accumulations of crystal-like bodies, called *concrement* by von Graff, chiefly in the epidermis, but also in the mesenchyme.   These are regarded without good evidence as urates by some.   They are brown in transmitted, white in reflected light, and confer a pattern on the animal which varies with individuals (Fig. 13*D*).

Green and brown colors among the Acoela and Rhabdocoela are often caused by symbiotic organisms, zoochlorellae or zooxanthellae living in the mesenchyme.

8. The Adhesive Organs.—The Turbellaria are richly supplied with adhesive organs, and in this regard no distinction can be drawn between them and the parasitic classes of flatworms.   These adhesive organs are generally compounded of epidermis, gland cells, muscle layers, and mesenchyme.   Many types of adhesive organs have been described and named by von Graff, but such complication appears unnecessary; there are in fact three general types.

a. Glandulo-epidermal Adhesive Organs.—These, already noted, consist of altered areas of epidermis, usually devoid of cilia and rhabdites, through which open the necks of subepidermal eosinophilous glands. This type lacks especial musculature.   It is exemplified by the marginal adhesive zone (Fig. 19) already described (Haftzellenring of the Germans) which may expand to an adhesive plate (Haftplatte) or disk.   The adhesive properties of such epidermis appears to result in part from the sticky secretion of the glands (Haftdrüsen) and in part from the ability of the gland exits to protrude as adhesive papillae (Haftpapillen) (Fig. 19*C*).

b. Glandulo-muscular Adhesive Organs.—These are of common occurrence among the fresh-water and land triclads and have been classified as cushions (Drüsenpolster), swellings (Haftwülste), pockets (Drüsentaschen), and pits (Haftgruben, Sauggruben).   As any one of these is highly variable in shape and often can be protruded and withdrawn, there appears no good basis for the variety of names.   In general, these organs consist of crescentic to circular, often irregularly folded protrusions bordering one or more depressions (Fig. 21*C*, *D*). The epidermis of the organ is highly modified into slender attenuated cells without cilia or rhabdites, crowded almost out of recognition by the necks of subepidermal eosinophilous glands that reach the surface between them (Fig.

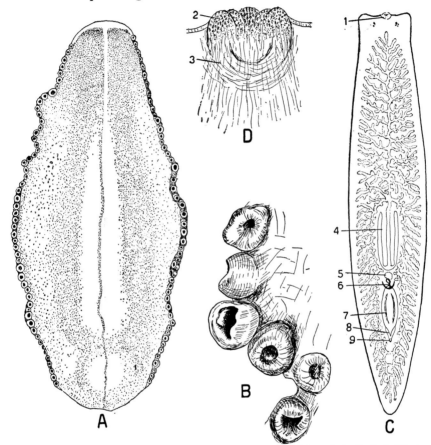

Fig. 21.—Adhesive organs. *A. Polycotylus validus*, triclad from Lake Baikal, Siberia, with marginal rows of suckers (acetabula). *B.* Some of the suckers enlarged. (*A, B after Korotnoff*, 1912.) *C. Procotyla fluviatilis* (family Dendrocoelidae), common white planarian of the northeastern United States, with an adhesive organ in the center of the anterior margin. *D.* Adhesive organ of *Procotyla* seen from below. 1, adhesive organ; 2, outlets of gland cells; 3, muscles of adhesive organ; 4, pharynx; 5, copulatory bursa of sex apparatus; 6, sperm duct; 7, penis bulb; 8, penis papilla; 9, gonopore.

22*A*). The organ is also supplied with an extensive musculature derived from the subepidermal muscle stratum and often attaining great complexity with fibers running in various directions (Fig. 22*A, C*). Conspicuous among the muscles is often a longitudinal bundle acting as a retractor. Many of these adhesive organs can be rapidly protruded and retracted.

The glandulo-muscular adhesive organ reaches its best development in fresh-water planarians, especially the families Dendrocoelidae and Kenkiidae, and the remarkable triclads found in Lake Baikal, Siberia (Korotneff, 1912). There is usually present a single such organ, in the center of the anterior margin or on the ventral side of the head; but there may be two or even four such organs on the ventral side of the head and in *Polycotylus* from Lake Baikal there are about 200 in a row along the lateral body margins (Fig. 21*A*, *B*). Probably the most remarkable of all these organs is that of the triclad *Kenkia rhynchida* from an Oregon cave (Hyman, 1937). The organ here consists of a muscular cylindrical snout (Fig. 22*B*) having a central lumen provided distally with cyanophilous glands, proximally with eosinophilous glands; a strong retractor muscle attached to the eosinophilous portion indicates that this can be everted to the outside (Fig. 22*C*). The function of the glandulo-muscular adhesive organ in the triclads appears to be twofold; the organ is used for adhesion in locomotion in a leech-like manner, and it is used in the capture of prey. Planarians provided with such an organ have been seen to lunge at small crustaceans and grasp them by folding the margins of the organ over them. In general planarians provided with these adhesive organs also have a zone of especially large rhabdites along the body margin; and it would appear that these are used to grip the substratum while the animal is struggling with prey.

Probably the proboscis in the anterior end of rhabdocoels of the section Kalyptorhynchia is to be regarded as a special form of glandulo-muscular adhesive organ. This shows varying degrees of complexity (Figs. 55, 56) but typically is a highly muscular conical or bipartite body provided with eosinophilous glands and sharply marked off from the parenchyma by a septum. The proboscis is protrusible or eversible through a pore at the anterior tip of the animal and is employed in the capture of prey.

Polyclads of the suborder Cotylea are provided on the ventral surface with an adhesive organ usually called sucker but really a glandulo-muscular organ. A similar organ, the genital sucker, is found between the male and female gonopores in the acotylean genus *Leptoplana;* it apparently assists in copulation.

c. True Sucker or Acetabulum.—This is distinguished from the glandulo-muscular type through being separated from the body parenchyma by a distinct muscular septum. The true sucker is generally of circular form with a raised rim and marked central depression and may or may not be stalked. Its adhesive action is attained by the vacuum principle rather than by sticky secretions. Among the Turbellaria a true sucker is found only in some of the Lake Baikal triclads mentioned above (Fig. 21*A*, *B*).

9. Nervous System.—The nervous system of the most primitive Turbellaria is in a condition resembling that of coelenterates, and this condition appears to be the original type of nervous system of the phylum. In such forms as the acoels *Tetraposthia* and *Nemertoderma* (Steinböck, 1931, An der Lan, 1936, Westblad 1937) and the alloeocoel *Hofstenia* (Bock, 1923), the nervous system consists of a layer in the base of the epidermis, outside the subepidermal musculature, the same situation that it possesses in the Cnidaria (Fig. 23). This epidermal nervous layer is best developed anteriorly and there forms a more or less continuous stratum; posteriorly it thins out, becoming a net-like plexus with some indications of longitudinal strands, mostly three pairs. In *Hofstenia* there is in the anterior tip an additional delicate plexus outside the main nervous layer. What is to be considered brain in these forms is a matter of dispute; some regard a pair of lateral thickenings of the main stratum to constitute the brain whereas others designate as brain a nervous layer over the statocyst. The latter view is probably correct if one judges from conditions in other Acoela. Whether the brain of these forms has retrogressed or is in process of evolution cannot be stated.

In all other Turbellaria the main nervous system has sunk into the mesenchyme immediately to the inner side of the subepidermal musculature where it forms what will be here termed the *submuscular plexus*. In this plexus there are usually emphasized a number of longitudinal cords which primitively have a radiating arrangement and of which the ventral pair is usually the most prominent. Transverse connections between the longitudinal strands are also often differentiated in the plexus and may form regularly repeated rings (Fig. 24A). In the anterior part of the body the plexus communicates, chiefly by way of the ventral cords, with the *brain* situated more internally than the plexus. The brain, also called *cerebral ganglia*, commonly is a slightly or deeply bilobed mass but may consist simply of the thickened anterior beginnings of the ventral cords. The shape of the brain is frequently correlated with the shape of the head. From the brain numerous nerves of sensory nature radiate to the margins and sense organs of the head, and there are connections, direct or indirect, with the other longitudinal cords of the submuscular net. In many Turbellaria there is, in addition to the submuscular plexus, a delicate plexus just beneath the basement membrane of the epidermis; this will here be called the *subepidermal plexus*.

In the Acoela (except those named above), the nervous system is composed of a brain and a submuscular plexus in which there are evident three to six, mostly five, pairs of longitudinal strands (Fig. 23B, E), dorsal, dorsolateral, marginal, ventrolateral, and ventral, spaced around the periphery. Lack of the marginal pair reduces the number of nerve

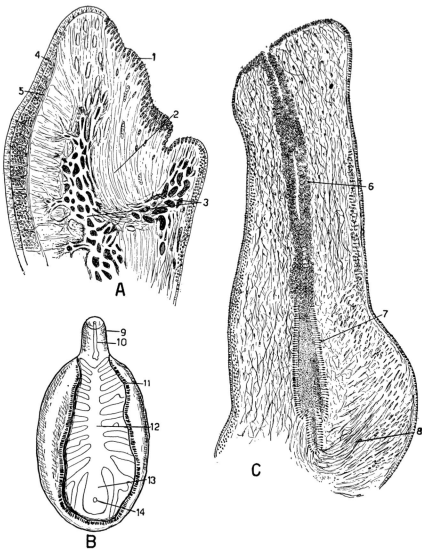

FIG. 22.—Adhesive organs (continued). *A.* Longitudinal section of the adhesive organ of *Procotyla*, showing its glandulo-muscular construction. *B. Kenkia rhynchida*, remarkable planarian from an Oregon cave with snout-like adhesive organ containing a complicated gland; animal lacks postpharyngeal intestine. *C.* Longitudinal section of the snout of *Kenkia rhynchida.* (*B, C after Hyman*, 1937.) 1, eosinophilous gland outlets; 2, muscle fibers; 3, nervous tissue; 4, circular layer of subepidermal musculature; 5, longitudinal layer of subepidermal musculature; 6, cyanophilous portion of snout gland; 7, eosinophilous portion of snout gland; 8, retractor muscle of snout; 9, snout; 10, snout gland; 11, margin of large rhabdites; 12, prepharyngeal intestine; 13, pharynx; 14, mouth.

strands to eight, but this cannot be regarded as a ctenophore reminiscence since ten is the more common number. The plexus consists of large meshes connected by a finer net. The brain is a mass around the statocyst and is usually formed into four lobes by the passage through it of the bundle of necks of the frontal glands. *Polychaerus* has in addition to the main brain mass a ganglion on each side from which the dorsal strands proceed (Löhner, 1910, Fig. 24*D*).

The polyclad nervous system is similar to that of the Acoela, consisting of a large-meshed submuscular plexus much more strongly developed ventrally than dorsally (Fig. 24*B*). In the ventral part of the plexus there are evident many larger strands radiating from the brain. Of these, the pair that runs alongside the pharynx is often the most conspicuous, especially in slender polyclads, and probably corresponds to the ventral cords of other Turbellaria. A fine subepidermal net is general among the polyclads. The brain is a rounded, bilobed body enclosed in a capsule; there is frequently present a group of small deeply staining sensory ganglion cells at the front end of each brain lobe outside the capsule (Fig. 28). These were formerly taken to be some kind of granule, hence were called Körnerhaufen (granule masses).

In the remaining groups of Turbellaria, the nervous system takes on a more bilateral character. There are primitively differentiated in the submuscular plexus four pairs of longitudinal cords, *dorsal, lateral* or *marginal, ventrolateral,* and *ventral,* as seen in such forms as *Prorhynchus, Bothrioplana,* and *Rhynchoscolex* (Fig. 24*A*). These are connected by ring commissures often regularly repeated and also of course by the meshes of the plexus. In the marine triclads, most alloeocoels, and some rhabdocoels, there are three pairs of cords, through loss of the ventrolateral pair. Direct vertical commissures between the dorsal and ventral cords may occur (Fig. 25*C*). Some fresh-water triclads also have the three pairs of cords, but in this group the dorsal cords are often lacking and the lateral cord, also called marginal or ring nerve, is usually merely the marginal bend of the submuscular plexus (Fig. 25*D*). Consequently in most fresh-water planarians, only the ventral cords are present; these are strongly developed with transverse connectives and lateral branches, and often continue anterior to the brain. A subepidermal plexus is general in triclads and alloeocoels. In most rhabdocoels, probably because of their small size, the nervous system is somewhat reduced, and here too usually only the ventral longitudinal cords are present, although short dorsal ones may occur, as in *Mesostoma* (Fig. 24*C*). There is a dearth of lateral branches and transverse connectives; commonly the ventral cords have one or more cross connections behind the pharynx (Fig. 24*C*) or else a nerve ring encircles the pharynx (Fig. 51*A*). A submuscular plexus has been seen in *Mesostoma* (Bresslau and Voss, 1914)

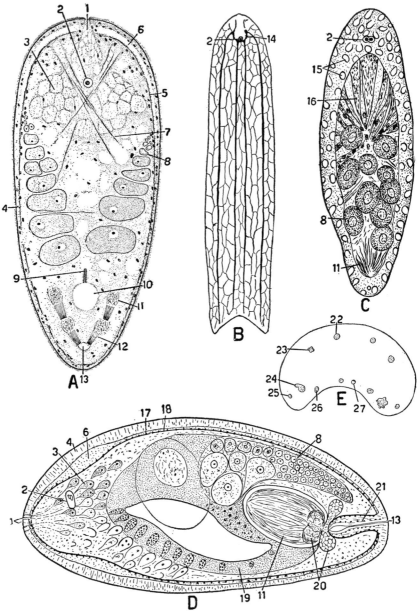

Fig. 23.—Nervous system of Acoela. *A.* Frontal section of *Tetraposthia colymbetes* showing general structure and epidermal nervous system (*after An der Lan*, 1936). *B.* Dorsal half of the submuscular plexus of *Amphiscolops*, from life, Bermuda; there are eight longitudinal strands in the plexus. *C. Nemertoderma bathycola*, general appearance with central epidermis removed to show internal structure (*after Westblad*, 1937). *D.* Sagittal section of *Nemertoderma*, showing general structure and epidermal nervous system (*after Westblad*, 1937). *E.* Section through *Convoluta*, showing the five pairs of longitudinal cords

and is probably general among rhabdocoels. The brain in rhabdocoels, alloeocoels, and fresh-water and marine triclads is either an anterior thickening of each ventral cord or a bilobed mass springing from the dorsal surface of these cords. Forms with triangular heads tend to have the thickened cords as brain (Fig. 26A), whereas those with truncate heads are more apt to have two rounded brain ganglia with radiating nerves (Fig. 26B). The exact arrangement of the nerves of the head has been worked out in several alloeocoels (Fig. 25A) and fresh-water and marine planarians, but the details vary with each species (*Bothrioplana*, Reisinger, 1925; *Prorhynchus*, *Geocentrophora*, Steinböck, 1927; *Procerodes*, *Bdelloura*, Wilhelmi, 1909; fresh-water planarians, Micoletzky, 1906, 1907; Weiss, 1910). In general, the dorsal part of the brain receives a number of sensory nerves from the head margins and the main sense organs of the head and also connects by commissures with the dorsal longitudinal cords or gives rise to these directly (Fig. 26). The ventral part of the brain is continuous with the ventral cords and may give off connectives to the marginal nerve or plexus. Frequently the ventral cords continue beyond the brain to the anterior tip and in this precerebral region are provided with transverse and lateral connectives (Fig. 26).

The most complicated nervous system in the phylum occurs among the land planarians. In this group there is a subepidermal and a strongly developed submuscular plexus. The latter, however, has no differentiated longitudinal cords. Instead there is a thick nervous layer, termed the *ventral nerve plate*, in the mesenchyme below the digestive tract; this is continuous laterally with the submuscular plexus (Fig. 25E). In this nerve plate, which is either solid or a plexus, there may be evident a number of longitudinal thickenings or, especially in land planarians of cylindroid shape, a single pair of thickenings, that simulate the ventral cords of other Turbellaria and are often so called. A definite brain is wanting; the nerve plate simply continues to the anterior end where in the Bipaliidae it expands into a lunate head plate.

The nerve cells resemble those of other animals, being uni-, bi-, or multipolar, with neurites all morphologically alike (no differentiated axone). Although the turbellarian nervous system is plexiform, with nerve cell bodies strewn everywhere along the strands of the plexus, it is a strictly synaptic system with no continuity of neurites. The finer details of the nervous system have been worked out by means of the Golgi

of the submuscular plexus (*slightly altered after Graff*, 1891). 1, frontal pore; 2, statocyst; 3, frontal glands; 4, epidermis; 5, subepidermal musculature; 6, epidermal nervous layer; 7, parenchymal muscle fibers; 8, ovary; 9, nozzle; 10, seminal bursa; 11, seminal vesicle; 12, armed penis; 13, male gonopore; 14, brain; 15, large epidermal glands; 16, digestive gland cells; 17, circular fibers of subepidermal musculature; 18, longitudinal fibers of same; 19, intestine; 20, prostatic glands; 21, male canal (penis); 22, dorsal nerve; 23, dorsolateral nerve; 24, marginal nerve; 25, branch of marginal nerve; 26, ventrolateral nerve; 27, ventral nerve.

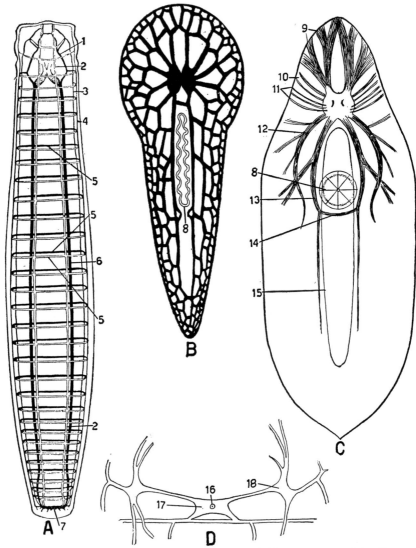

Fig. 24.—Nervous system of various Turbellaria. A. Nervous system of the alloeocoel
Bothrioplana (after Reisinger, 1925); dorsal part in white, ventral part in black.   B. Ventral
part of the submuscular net of the pelagic polyclad *Gnesioceros,* from life, Bermuda.   C.
Nervous system (submuscular) of the rhabdocoel *Mesostoma (after Bresslau and Voss,* 1913).
D. Brain of the acoel *Polychoerus (after Löhner,* 1910).   1, anterior continuation of ventral
cords; 2, dorsal cords; 3, ventrolateral cords; 4, marginal cords; 5, ring commissure; 6,
ventral cords; 7, terminal fusion; 8, pharynx; 9, four anterior sensory nerves; 10, ventral
brain nerves; 11, dorsal brain nerves; 12, dorsal cords; 13, ventral cords; 14, postpharyngeal
commissure: 15. intestine; 16, statocyst; 17, main brain ganglion; 18, lateral ganglia.

silver technique by Hanström (1926) for the marine triclad *Bdelloura candida*. His preparations show that the so-called marginal nerve here consists of sensory nerve cells and their much-branched neurites penetrating the epidermis (Fig. 27). Certain cells whose neurites lie entirely within the ventral cords or transverse commissures are regarded by Hanström as probably associative cells. Richly branched unipolar cells in the ventral cords are motor, since they send one long neurite into parenchymal muscles. The brain of the Turbellaria consists centrally of bundles of fibers, peripherally of the bodies of nerve cells, of several different types and sizes, generally arranged in groups (Fig. 28*B*). The brain appears to reach its highest complication in the polyclads where a detailed study has been made by Hadenfeldt (1929). The fiber bundles of the brain are continuous with the main nerves but subdivide and reconnect to make complicated pathways. What is known of the functions of the brain is discussed later under behavior.

The nervous system of the pharynx is considered with that organ. There is also a rich nerve supply to the copulatory apparatus and to the adhesive organs.

10. Sense Organs.—The Turbellaria are richly supplied with sensory cells, of which the most common is the *tactile* cell or *tangoreceptor*. These are sensory nerve cells that send one or more processes to the surface, each terminating in one or more hairs or bristles (Fig. 29*F*). These bristles are often longer than the cilia and easily seen along the margins in the living animal (Fig. 51*A*, *B*). In the rhabdocoel *Mesostoma*, Gelei (1930) found that every epidermal cell is pierced by three to five such sensory bristles (Fig. 30*B*), and the same probably holds for other Turbellaria. The tangoreceptors are even more thickly strewn on special tactile regions such as tentacles, auricles, and along the body margins where there is, in land planarians, a definite sensory strip (Sinneskante).

Chemoreception is well developed among the Turbellaria, all of which perceive and orient toward food juices at a distance. The chemoreceptors are mostly limited to the head region and comprise ciliated pits and grooves and their variants; these are depressed epidermal areas devoid of rhabdoids and usually also of gland-cell exits, although sometimes well supplied with gland cells. Ciliated pits are rounded or flask-like depressions lined by an altered, usually depressed epidermis; generally the pit sides are heavily ciliated whereas the bottom bears short stiff cilia that are probably really the bristles of sensory cells (Fig. 30*A*). Pits are supplied with a sensory nerve or else are so close to the brain as to be directly connected with it (Fig. 30*A*). A single pit on the ventral side of the head is seen in a number of land planarians. A pair of pits on the sides of the head occurs in a number of rhabdocoels (*Stenostomum*, Fig. 29*A*; *Rhynchoscolex*, *Microstomum*, Fig. 50*B*; some species of *Macro-*

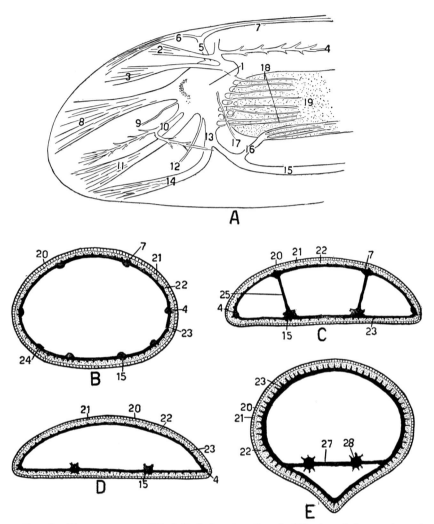

Fig. 25.—Nervous system of Turbellaria (continued).   A. Side view of the anterior end
cf the alloeocoel *Hydrolimax* (*after Hyman*, 1938), showing main brain nerves and manner
of origin of the three main nerve cords.   B–E. Diagrams of cross sections comparing the
nervous systems of B, alloeocoel; C, marine triclad; D, fresh-water triclad; E, land planarian.
1, brain; 2, 3, dorsal sensory branches; 4, lateral nerve cord; 5, main mediodorsal trunk; 6,
anterior sensory branch of 5; 7, dorsal nerve cord; 8–14, anterior and ventral sensory nerves;
13, main ventral trunk; 15, ventral nerve cord; 16, pharyngeal branch of 15; 17, small
nerve; 18, branches from brain into pharynx; 19, pharynx; 20, epidermis; 21, subepidermal
nerve net; 22, subepidermal musculature; 23, submuscular nerve net; 24, ventrolateral
nerve cord; 25, commissure between dorsal and ventral cords; 27, ventral nerve plate; 28,
simulated ventral cords in the ventral nerve plate.

stomum and *Mesostoma*, Fig. 45*B*) and alloeocoels (*Otoplana*, Fig. 60*D;*
Prorhynchus, Fig. 59*A; Geocentrophora*, Fig. 59*B); two pairs of head pits
are found in the alloeocoel genera *Bothrioplana* (Fig. 35*D*) and *Otomesostoma*. Ciliated grooves are also of common occurrence. A pair of such
grooves borders the anterior end of the creeping sole in a number of land
planarians, or sometimes the creeping sole terminates anteriorly in a
groove or cleft of glandulo-sensory nature. A transverse ciliated furrow
partly or wholly encircling the rear of the head occurs in several alloeocoels (*Plagiostomum*, *Allostoma*, *Pseudostomum*, Fig. 60*E*). Among the
marine and fresh-water triclads there is constantly present on each side of
the head a groove, the *auricular groove* or *auricular sense organ* (Fig. 31*H*).
This is readily noticed in dark-colored planarians as a white line along the
head margin or across the base of the auricles when present; it may be
straight or curved or broken up into a line of short grooves (Fig. 31*B–E*).
The passage of a water current along the auricular groove from in front
backward can be demonstrated by adding carbon or carmine particles to
the water (Steinmann, 1929). The various kinds of sensory groove consist of a depressed altered epidermis, devoid of rhabdoids and gland-cell
exits, generously provided with nerves and bearing short cilia that are
probably sensory bristles (Fig. 30*A*). In the rhabdocoels *Mesostoma*
(Gelei, 1930) and the related *Bothromesostoma* (Müller, 1936), the presence of sensory endings in the chemoreceptive grooves of the head has
been demonstrated by special nerve stains (toluidin blue). The cells
concerned are bipolar nerve cells whose neurite to the surface subdivides
into a number of short stiff hairs (Fig. 30*B*). Wherever definite chemoreceptors are absent, probably the general head margin or lateral sensory
margin serves the same function. The sensory margin (Sinneskante) of
land planarians consists of a marginal groove bearing various pits and
swellings, some probably chemoreceptive. The frontal gland (page 73)
also probably participates in chemoreception, since the gland outlets are
usually accompanied by numerous sensory fibers (Fig. 18*C*) so that the
whole forms a *frontal organ* with tactile and chemical sensitivity. The
necessity of associating chemoreceptive elements with a food-catching
organ will be obvious. No definite chemoreceptive organs have been
reported for polyclads, but a sensory groove along the anterior margin is
general throughout this order, and the epidermis may have depressed
cells, probably of chemoreceptive nature.

The chemoreceptive nature of ciliated pits and grooves has been
demonstrated by Müller (1936), who showed that *Stenostomum* after
extirpation of its ciliated pits cannot detect the presence of food juices or
orient toward food, and the same is true of *Bothromesostoma* after removal
of the pair of sensory grooves on the sides of its head corresponding to
the auricular sense organ of planarians (Fig. 29*E*). The chemoreceptive

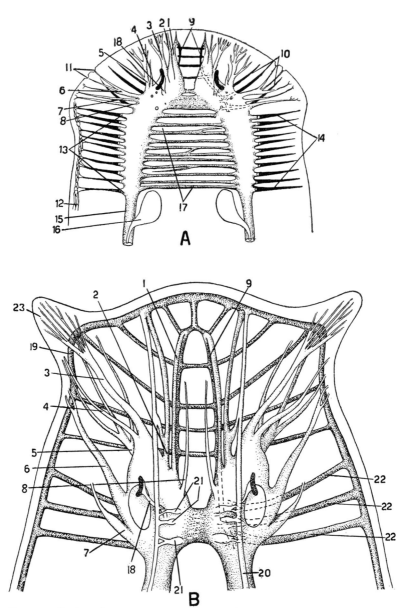

FIG. 26.—Brain and anterior nervous system of fresh-water triclads. *A.* Type with triangular head (*Dugesia polychroa*). *B.* Type with truncate head (*Crenobia alpina*). (*Both after Micoletzky, 1907.*) Dorsally located nerves white, ventral ones black. In *A* the transition of brain to ventral cord is believed to occur after nerve 8. The grouping of the sensory nerves in *A*, and the origin of the dorsal cords from three roots in *B* indicate that the brain ganglia are composed of three fused ganglia. 1–8, main sensory brain nerves; 9, anterior continuation of ventral cords; 10, three lateral nerves from 9; 11, auricular sensory groove; 12, marginal plexus; 13, series of dorsal sensory nerves from ventral cords; 14, ventral commissures between ventral cords and marginal plexus; 15, ventral cords; 16, ovaries; 17, dorsal commissures between ventral cords; 18, optic nerve to eye; 19, marginal nerve; 20, dorsal cords; 21, roots of dorsal cords; 22, commissures between ventral and marginal cords; 23, auricle.

organs are thus also directive or chemotopotactic, enabling their posses-
sors to find food by means of the water currents that pass along the
organs. For this reason cilia are a necessary part of chemoreceptive
organs.

Rheoreceptive cells have been identified in *Mesostoma* and *Bothromesostoma* (Gelei, 1930; Müller, 1936) and are probably of general occurrence. In these animals there are four pairs of such cells distributed
along the body sides (Fig. 29E). Each is a large cell that branches into
a number of sensory bristles that project through the epidermis (Fig.

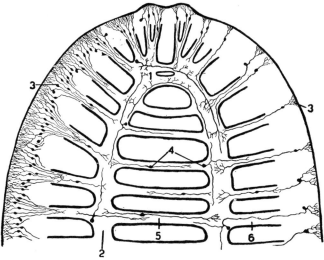

Fig. 27.—Anterior end of *Bdelloura candida* showing details of nerve-cell arrangement
(*after Hanström*, 1926). 1, brain; 2, ventral cords; 3, sensory nerve cells forming marginal
nerve; 4, associative neurons; 5, transverse commissures; 6, lateral nerves.

30B, 31A). The extirpation experiments of Müller (1936) indicate that
these groups of bristles act as current detectors.

A statocyst is general throughout the Acoela, is also common among
the Alloeocoela (*Hofstenia*, Fig. 31F, *Otomesostoma*, all members of the
family Monocelididae, Fig. 29C), and occurs in the rhabdocoel genus
Catenula (Fig. 29D); in short, a statocyst is characteristic of the
more primitive Turbellaria and is probably inherited from coelenterate
ancestors. Structurally the turbellarian statocyst is similar to the
hydrozoan statocyst. It consists of a nucleated vesicle within which
there is a lithocyte (sometimes two) enclosing a statolith (Fig. 31G).
The statocyst is embedded in the brain or is very close to it and therefore
has a strong nervous supply, although sensory endings have not been
traced into the statocyst. The close association of the brain with the
statocyst suggests that the brain may have arisen phylogenetically as a

nervous accumulation around the statocyst.   Conditions in *Hofstenia*, if they could be shown to be primitive, would strongly support this suggestion (page 83).

Light perception is of general occurrence among the Turbellaria and is mediated by definite photoreceptors, the eyes or ocelli.   General body sensitivity to light apart from the ocelli is also present, but the sensory structures involved have not been identified.   The eyes are rarely epidermal pigment spots (acoel *Otocelis*, rhabdocoels *Microstomum*, *Alaurina*, Fig. 32*C*); nearly always they are pigment-cup ocelli sunk into the mesenchyme.   There is usually one pair of eyes, sometimes two or three pairs, near the brain; but many eyes occur in some groups.   Thus in the fresh-water triclads *Sorocelis* (Fig. 32*E*) and *Polycladodes* there are two clusters of eyes in place of the usual two eyes, and the genus *Polycelis* has a band of eyes around the anterior margin (Fig. 32*D*).   The land planarian family Rhynchodemidae has but one pair of eyes; but in the Geoplanidae there are numerous eyes in a band or row along the whole body margin (Fig. 32*A*), and the Bipaliidae also possess numerous eyes on the lunate head and along the body margin (Fig. 14*D*).   Polyclads nearly always have numerous eyes, in paired clusters in the brain region, on tentacles, in a band along whole or part of the body margin, or strewn over the head (Figs. 35*F-J*, 63*A*, 63*B*).   Eye arrangement is employed as an important taxonomic character in land planarians and polyclads. Eyes are altogether lacking in the cave-dwelling planarians of the family Kenkiidae (Figs. 22*B*, 61*B*), in some endoparasitic rhabdocoels (Fig. 53), in many acoels, rhabdocoels, and alloeocoels, especially sand- and muck-dwelling forms, and in other cases without apparent relation to habits of life.

Each eye has the structure of a pigment-cup ocellus (page 37).   It consists of one or more pigment cells forming a bowl or cup and of one to many photosensitive neurosensory cells projecting into the cup through its opening.   The eye is therefore of the inverse type.   The photosensitive cells, or *retinal* cells, are bipolar nerve cells whose rounded, expanded, or club-shaped distal end projects into the cup and whose proximal fiber joins the central nervous system (Fig. 32*F, G*).   The distal tip is marked with longitudinal striations forming the *rod border*, of uncertain function. In the more advanced types, termed *retinal clubs*, the rod border extends along the whole surface of the club-like end of the sensory cell; hypothetical stages in the evolution of the retinal club are shown in Fig. 32*G*. In a very few turbellarians pigment cells are lacking and the retinal cells lie free in the mesenchyme near the brain.   The most advanced eyes occur among the land planarians, but their structure is not thoroughly understood.   Here the retinal clubs pass into the cup between the pigment cells (Fig. 32*F*) so that at least some of the clubs face the mouth of

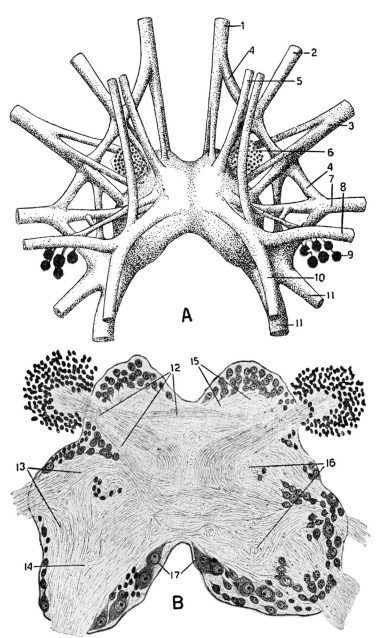

Fig. 28.—Brain of the leptoplanid polyclad *Notoplana atomata* (*after Hadenfeldt*, 1929). *A*. Dorsal view of the brain showing nerves. *B*. Horizontal section through the brain showing different types of nerve cells. 1, 2, 3, anterior nerves; 4, commissure connecting them; 5, anterior dorsal nerve; 6, granule mass (group of sensory cells outside the brain capsule); 7, lateral nerve; 8, lateral dorsal nerve; 9, cluster of tentacular eyes; 10, posterior dorsal nerve; 11, posterior nerves; 12, tracts of the granule mass; 13, tracts of the lateral nerve; 14, tract of the posterior nerve; 15, anterior nerve tract; 16, vertical tracts; 17, two types of large nerve cells.

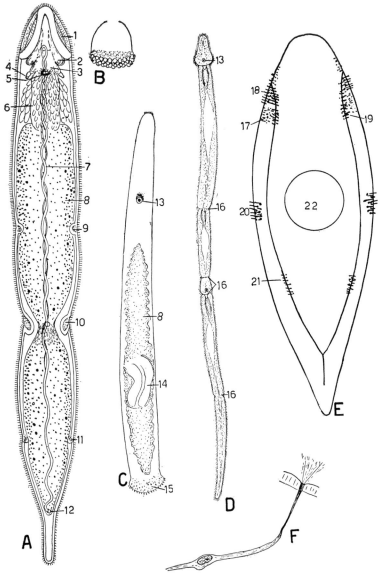

Fig. 29.—Some Turbellaria with conspicuous sense organs.   A. Catenulid rhabdocoel *Stenostomum tenuicauda*, from life, with a pair of ciliated pits and bowl-shaped bodies; note single protonephridium.   B. Bowl-shaped body of A enlarged.   C. Alloeocoel *Monocelis*, from life, with conspicuous statocyst.   D. Catenulid rhabdocoel *Catenula lemnae*, from life, with statocyst but no ciliated pits.   E. Typhloplanid rhabdocoel *Bothromesostoma* (*after Müller*, 1936) with four pairs of rheoreceptors and one pair of chemoreceptive areas. F. A tangoreceptor, from the alloeocoel *Otoplana* (*after Hofsten*, 1918).   Note that A and D consist of a chain of zooids.   1, ciliated pit; 2, pit ganglion; 3, brain; 4, bowl-shaped body; 5, mouth; 6, simple pharynx with gland cells; 7, protonephridium; 8, intestine; 9–11, ciliated pits of zooids; 12, nephridiopore; 13, statocyst; 14, plicate pharynx; 15, caudal adhesive area with adhesive papillae; 16, fission planes of zooids· 17, chemoreceptive areas; 18–21, the four rheoreceptive areas; 22, rosulate pharynx.

the cup, hence are of the converse type. There is further an epithelium over the mouth of the cup, forming a cornea, probably with some refractive power, so that possibly such eyes can form dim images. But in general the turbellarian eye can only distinguish light from dark and cannot form images, since it has no refractive apparatus. When two or few in number the eyes are close to or in contact with the brain so that the retinal nerve fibers enter the brain directly or form a short optic nerve passing to the brain. Otherwise, the retinal fibers enter the general submuscular plexus.

In a few rhabdocoels, especially *Stenostomum*, there are found in place of eyes one to four pairs of bodies attached to the brain and believed to be of light-refractive nature. These bodies consist of one to many refringent granules, plates, or rods or a single biconvex or bowl-shaped mass; they are generally attached to a clear vesicle that in turn connects with the brain (Fig. 29*A*, *B*). Since the mass or collection of bodies usually (but not always) forms a bowl over the vesicle (Fig. 29*B*), the structure is often termed the *bowl-shaped* (schüsselformig) body. There is no good evidence for the assumption of a photosensitive function of the bowl-shaped body.

11. Digestive System.—The digestive system consists of mouth, pharynx, and intestine. A mouth is present in all Turbellaria except the endoparasitic rhabdocoel family Fecampiidae in which it is lost in the adult state with other accompanying degeneration. The mouth is primitively situated at about the middle of the ventral surface but may occur anywhere along the mid-ventral line from anterior to posterior end. It is generally circular but may be a longitudinal or transverse slit and is provided with radial and circular fibers from the subepidermal musculature, by which it can be opened and closed. It is usually very expansible and capable of admitting large objects. The mouth may be regarded as phylogenetically identical with the blastopore of the Radiata.

A pharynx is primitively absent in some Acoela, secondarily lost in the *Fecampiidae;* otherwise the Turbellaria are provided with a pharynx, which is a muscular tube, presumably of stomodaeal nature, serving to grasp food and convey it to the intestine. The pharynx exists in three grades of structure: *simple, bulbous,* and *plicate.* The simple pharynx or *pharynx simplex* occurs in Acoela, *Hofstenia,* and the rhabdocoel suborders Notandropora and Opisthandropora. It is merely a short tube formed of inturned ciliated epidermis accompanied by the usual subepidermal musculature not noticeably thickened or altered (Fig. 33*A*) except in *Hofstenia* which has an extremely long and muscular pharynx simplex (Fig. 31*F*). The simple pharynx is not delimited from the mesenchyme; mesenchymal unicellular glands may open through its epithelium.

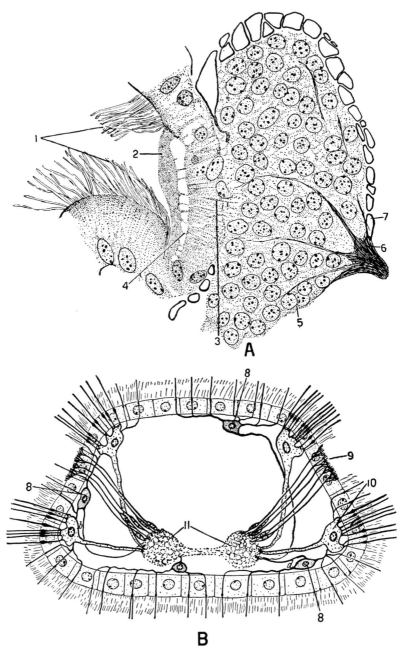

FIG. 30.—Rhabdocoel sense organs. *A.* Section through the ciliated pit of *Stenostomum* (*after Kepner and Cash*, 1915). *B.* Diagrammatic section through the head of *Mesostoma* to show four of the eight rheoreceptors, the two groups of chemoreceptors, and four tangoreceptors (*after Gelei*, 1930). 1, cilia of the sides of the pit; 2, secretion mass in bottom of pit; 3, sensory epithelium of bottom of pit; 4, sensory processes of same; 5, pit ganglion; 6, fibers to brain; 7, muscles; 8, tangoreceptor; 9, group of chemoreceptors; 10, rheoreceptor; 11, brain.

In the bulbous type of pharynx, the proximal part of the pharyngeal tube is much thickened, has greatly increased muscularity, and is sharply delimited from the mesenchyme (Fig. 33*B*). The distal portion remains nonmuscular, forming the *pharyngeal cavity* into which the tip of the bulbous part may project. The pharyngeal cavity is generally short and broad but may be much lengthened, forming a *buccal tube* (Fig. 59). These cavities are lined by an altered epidermis, flattened, unciliated, often syncytial, underlain by the usual subepidermal musculature. The pharynx bulb consists of muscles, mesenchyme, gland cells, and nervous tissue. There are outer and inner muscle strata of circular and longitudinal fibers, of which the inner stratum, next the lumen, is the stronger, particularly as to its circular layer; this may form a sphincter at one or both ends of the pharynx. Numerous radial fibers also course between the two surfaces of the bulb (Fig. 33*B*). The pharynx is provided with gland cells, eosinophilous or cyanophilous, or both, strewn between the muscle fibers and also often entering the pharynx from without. Their necks usually open at the pharynx tip, often after aggregating into bundles (Fig. 18*B*). The bulbous pharynx has an abundant nerve supply (Fig. 25*A*) by way of one or more pairs of nerves entering it from the brain or from the ventral cords; these break up into a plexus in the bulb often concentrated into a nerve ring near the tip. Besides its intrinsic musculature, the bulbous pharynx is also usually attached to the body wall by extrinsic muscle bands that permit its eversion and retraction. Usually the pharynx bulb can be protruded by the turning inside out of the pharyngeal cavity.

The bulbous pharynx occurs in two main types, the *rosulate* and the *doliiform*. The rosulate pharynx, characteristic of the rhabdocoel section Typhloplanoida, is spherical, oriented at right angles to the body axis, and provided with conspicuous radial muscle fibers and numerous gland cells, both intrinsic and extrinsic (Fig. 36*A*). The doliiform pharynx, characteristic of the section Dalyellioida, is cask-shaped, oriented parallel to the body axis, has a sparse gland supply, and its muscle layers, viewed from above, often have a lattice-like appearance (Fig. 34*D*). A variant of the doliiform pharynx called the *variable* pharynx is found among the lower Alloeocoela, differing in a less rigid shape and various alterations of the arrangement of the muscle layers.

The plicate pharynx is a free cylindrical fold projecting into the large pharyngeal cavity (Fig. 11*A*, *B*). It may project from the anterior end of the cavity, hence point backward, or from the rear end, hence point forward, or may depend from the roof of the cavity, hence hang downward. It is usually a simple hollow cylinder but is much ruffled in those polyclads in which it hangs from the roof and also in some land planarians. The plicate pharynx is characteristic of triclads, polyclads, and the higher

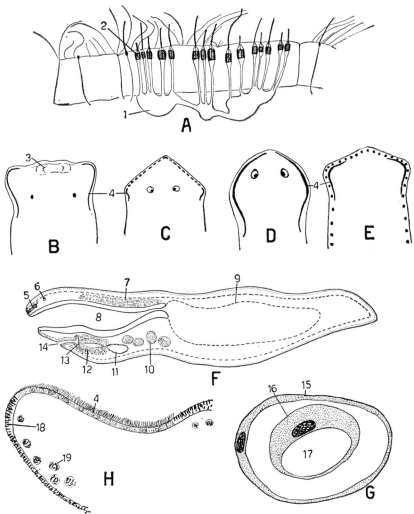

Fig. 31.—Sense organs of Turbellaria (continued). *A.* One of the rheoreceptors of *Mesostoma* (*after Gelei*, 1930). *B–E,* Heads of four species of European fresh-water planarians to show the auricular sense organ (*after Steinmann*, 1930). *B. Dendrocoelum lacteum. C. Dugesia gonocephala. D. Dugesia polychroa. E. Polycelis tenuis. F.* Sagittal section of *Hofstenia atroviridis,* Japan, to show general structure (*after Bock,* 1923). *G.* The statocyst of *Hofstenia* (*after Bock,* 1923). *H.* Transverse section through the auricle of a fresh-water planarian, to show the auricular sense organ. 1, rheoreceptive neurosensory cell; 2, sensory processes of same; 3, adhesive organ; 4, auricular sense organ; 5, frontal gland; 6, statocyst; 7, testes; 8, simple pharynx; 9, intestine; 10, ovary; 11, seminal vesicle; 12, prostatic vesicle; 13, penis; 14, male gonopore; 15, vesicle; 16, lithocyte; 17, statolith (dissolved out); 18, rhabdites; 19, rhabdite-forming glands.

alloeocoels. It belongs to the protrusible type (Fig. 11*A*, *B*), i.e., when used becomes much elongated through muscular action and is protruded through the mouth. Hence in those turbellarians which have a plicate pharynx, food is ingested through the orifice of the pharynx and not through the mouth. Numerous pharynges occur in some fresh-water and land planarians (Fig. 34*C*), and this *polypharyngy* may be accompanied by a similar multiplication of mouth openings.

The plicate pharynx is of complicated histological construction, having muscular, glandular, and nervous layers. The layers usually present are: outer epithelium, outer longitudinal muscle layer, outer circular muscle layer, outer zone of gland cells, nerve plexus, inner zone of gland cells, inner longitudinal muscle layer, inner circular muscle layer, lining epithelium; and all these layers are crossed by numerous radial muscle fibers extending from the inner to the outer epithelium (Fig. 33*D*). The pharyngeal epithelia are mostly of the insunk type, with nuclei sunk beneath the muscle layers, and are provided with peculiar short stiff cilia. The gland cells are of both cyanophilous and eosinophilous types and open mostly at the pharynx tip. They appear to be similar to body gland cells and seem to have no special digestive function; rather their slimy and sticky secretions serve to entangle, possibly also to paralyze, prey and to lubricate the ingestion process. The pharynx is often also supplied with extrinsic gland cells situated in the mesenchyme near its attached end. The nerve plexus of the plicate pharynx springs from the ventral cords and is usually a thick conspicuous layer but may be limited to a nerve ring near the free end. Not uncommonly subsidiary plexi occur among the muscle layers (Fig. 33*D*). In the pharyngeal plexus of the marine triclad *Bdelloura candida* (Fig. 34*A*), there occur sensory nerve cells whose fibers break up into numerous endings at both epithelia, motor cells with endings on the pharynx musculature, and associative cells (Hanström, 1926). Hence the nerve plexus of the triclad pharynx forms a self-sufficient system, and the isolated pharynx can carry out all activities, including the ingestion of food (Wulzen, 1917; Kepner and Rich, 1918).

The plicate pharynx is not delimited from the mesenchyme, as is the bulbous pharynx, and its histological layers are continuous with those of the general body.

The pharynx may lead directly into the intestine, but often a very short narrow *esophagus* intervenes. The intestine, absent in the Acoela, varies from a simple rounded or elongated sac to a highly branched tubular system (Fig. 35). It is composed of a single-layered epithelium, the gastrodermis, sometimes syncytial, especially during digestion, but usually consisting of large clavate cells with narrowed bases and bulging free ends. The gastrodermal cells may be all of one kind but often are of

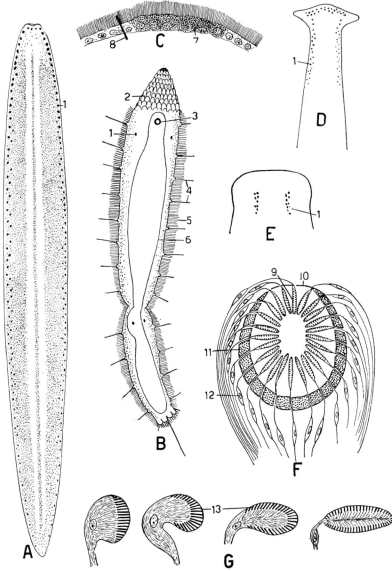

FIG. 32.—Eyes of Turbellaria.   A. Land planarian *Geoplana mexicana* (*after Hyman*, 1939a), introduced into California; has row of eyes along entire margin.   B. Pelagic microstomid rhabdocoel *Alaurina prolifera* (*after Busch*, 1851) with papillate snout, buoyant bristles, and epidermal eyes.   C. Section through the eye of Alaurina (*after Brinkmann*, 1906).   D. Head of fresh-water planarian, *Polycelis coronata*, northwestern United States, to show eye arrangement, from life.   E. Head of fresh-water planarian *Sorocelis americana*, from Oklahoma cave, to show eyes.   F. Diagram of advanced type of eye of a land planarian with retinal clubs (*after Hesse*, 1902).   G. Stages in the evolution of the retinal club (*after Hofsten*, 1918).   1, eyes; 2, papillate snout; 3, mouth; 4, bristles; 5, cilia; 6, intestine; 7, epidermal eye; 8, neck of gland cell; 9, retinal clubs; 10, cornea; 11, pigment cells; 12, nerve cell bodies of retinal clubs; 13, rod border.

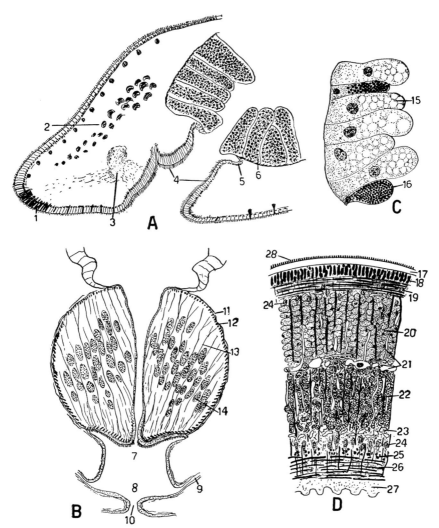

FIG. 33.—Digestive system. *A.* Longitudinal section through the anterior end of *Macrostomum* to show the pharynx simplex. *B.* Cross section through *Mesostoma* to show the bulbous pharynx of the rosulate type; also shows excretory beaker. *C.* Gastrodermis of a planarian, showing the two types of cells. *D.* Cross section through the triclad pharynx showing its histological construction. 1, rhammites, 2, rhammite tracks; 3, brain; 4, simple pharynx; 5, esophagus; 6, intestine; 7, pharyngeal cavity; 8, excretory beaker; 9, termination of protonephridium; 10, mouth; 11, circular muscle fibers; 12, longitudinal muscle fibers; 13, radial muscle fibers; 14, gland cells; 15, phagocytic cells; 16, granular clubs; 17, outer insunk epithelium; 18, outer longitudinal muscle layer; 19, outer circular muscle layer; 20, zone of cyanophilous gland cells; 21, main nerve plexus; 22, zone of eosinophilous gland cells; 23, inner nerve plexus; 24, nuclei of insunk epithelium; 25, inner longitudinal muscle layer; 26, inner circular muscle layer; 27, inner insunk epithelium; 28, cilia.

two sorts: the regular intestinal cells just described, usually called *phago-cytic* cells; and the smaller *granular clubs*, cells filled with spherules, usu-ally of eosinophilous nature (Fig. 33*C*). The granular clubs are generally regarded as gland cells and their spherules as forerunners of digestive enzymes, but they have not been consistently observed to show any changes during digestion and it is probable that they are protein reserve cells (page 204). The phagocytic cells generally contain much stored fat and after feeding are packed with food vacuoles. The gastrodermis is ciliated in the lower rhabdocoels (Catenulida, Macrostomida), a few alloeocoels such as *Bothrioplana*, and throughout the polyclads. The gastrodermis is underlain by a muscular stratum in some rhabdocoels and alloeocoels and especially in the polyclads.

In the Acoela the mouth may open directly into the mesenchyme or a short, rarely long, pharynx simplex, lined by ciliated epidermis, may intervene. The remarkable acoel, *Ectocotyla paguri* (Fig. 13*F*, page 129), differs from all other Acoela in having a protrusible plicate pharynx of simple histological construction. The Acoela lack an intestine (Fig. 37*D*), and the phagocytic cells occur in the mesenchyme, either scattered throughout this in the simpler cases, or limited to a central region where they may fuse to form a digesting syncytium, more or less definitely dis-tinguishable from the peripheral mesenchyme. The food consists of diatoms, algae, and small animals such as protozoans and copepods, swallowed whole and digested entirely by the intracellular method in the phagocytic cells or the central syncytium.

A pharynx simplex (Fig. 33*A*) is characteristic of the rhabdocoel orders Catenulida and Macrostomida; other rhabdocoels have a rosulate or doliiform bulbous pharynx preceded by a pharyngeal cavity. A brief esophagus is usually present leading into the blind intestine of sac-like or tubular form, generally of simple contour but sometimes with slight lateral outpouchings. Prey is generally swallowed whole or sucked in by forms with a rosulate pharynx as this is not distensible.

The Alloeocoela may have any type of pharynx; the intestine is often similar to that of rhabdocoels but in the higher alloeocoels tends to have lateral diverticula and in *Bothrioplana* approaches the triclad condition, parting around the pharynx although single again behind this (Fig. 35*D*).

The digestive system is of very uniform construction throughout the triclads. The mouth situated near the body middle leads into a large cylindrical pharyngeal cavity from whose anterior wall the tubular plicate pharynx projects posteriorly. A very short esophagus leads into the intestine which immediately forks into three branches or rami (whence the name Tricladida), one running anteriorly to the anterior end and two passing backward, one to either side of the pharyngeal cavity (Fig. 35*E*). Each ramus gives off numerous lateral diverticula, often secondarily

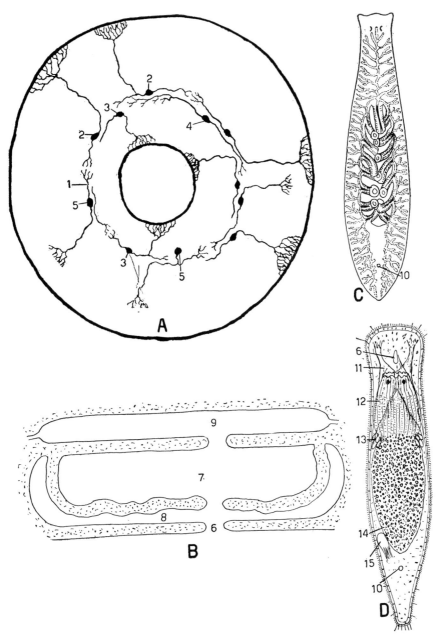

Fig. 34.—Digestive system (continued). *A.* Golgi preparation of a cross section through the triclad pharynx showing neuron arrangement (*after Hanström*, 1926). *B.* Longitudinal median section of a polyclad showing relation of ruffled pharynx to the main intestine. *C. Phagocata gracilis* with multiple pharynges, from life, Pennsylvania. *D. Dalyellia*, with doliiform pharynx, from life, Maine. 1, main nerve plexus; 2, sensory nerve cells with nerve endings at outer surface; 3, sensory nerve cells with nerve endings at inner surface; 4, associative neuron; 5, motor neurons; 6, mouth; 7, pharynx; 8, pharyngeal cavity; 9, main intestine; 10, gonopore; 11, brain; 12, doliiform pharynx; 13, pharyngeal gland cells; 14, intestine; 15, penis stylet.

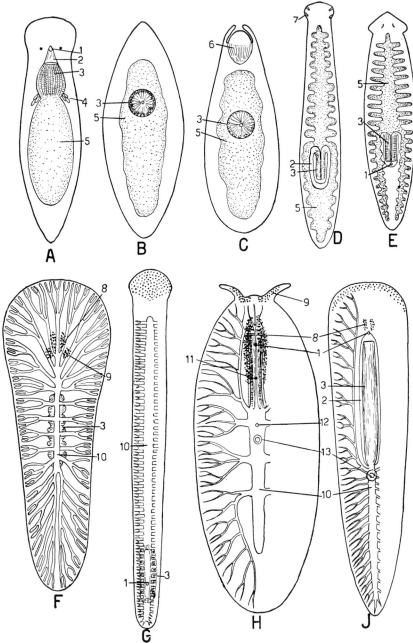

Fig. 35. Digestive system (continued). Diagrams of various turbellarian digestive
tracts. *A.* Dalyellioid rhabdocoel, with doliiform pharynx. *B.* Typhloplanoid rhabdocoel,
with rosulate pharynx. *C.* Kalyptorhynchid rhabdocoel, with rosulate pharynx and
anterior protrusible proboscis. *D.* Alloeocoel *Bothrioplana* with two pairs of ciliated

branched and united by anastomoses. The two posterior rami may be united by cross branches and confluent at the posterior ends. The gastrodermis has many granular clubs and usually lacks a muscular layer. The only exceptions to the above description occur in some land planarians that may have a flaring or ruffled pharynx. The triclads do not swallow their food whole but suck it in by peristaltic action of the protruded pharynx.

The polyclad digestive system (Fig. 35*F–J*) is less uniform. The mouth may open into the anterior, middle, or rear part of the pharyngeal cavity which also may be situated anywhere in the body, although usually central or anterior. The pharynx is always plicate but varies from ruffled to tubular. The ruffled type found in most Acotylea and several cotylean families hangs down from the dorsal wall of the pharyngeal cavity as a much frilled or ruffled oval or circular curtain (Fig. 34*B*) whose attachment is also sinuous and whose folds are accompanied by corresponding pouches of the pharyngeal cavity. Through transitional bell-like or flaring shapes of pharynx whose attachment tends to shift horizontally, the cylindrical horizontal type of pharynx like that of triclads is attained in the higher acotylean and cotylean families; this is, however, attached at its rear end and directed anteriorly (Fig. 35*H, J*). The polyclad intestine consists of the *main* or *central* intestine, a median tube that lies either above the ruffled type of pharynx (Fig. 34*B*) or behind the anteriorly located tubular type; and of the numerous branches (whence the name Polycladida) given off from the main intestine and ramifying throughout the body, often uniting to form a network. The form of the branching depends upon the shape of the animal; several types of intestinal branching in polyclads are shown in Fig. 35*F–J*. Anal pores occur in a few cotylean polyclads, usually as a series of dorsal or lateral pores (*Cycloporus*, Fig. 65*C*, *Yungia*), but in one species (*Leptoteredra maculata*) as a single posterior dorsal pore.

12. Excretory System.—This consists of protonephridia provided with terminal flame bulbs. It is entirely wanting in the Acoela and in general is less developed in marine than in fresh-water Turbellaria. The tubule consists of a one-layered, usually unciliated cuboidal or syncytial epi-

---

pits, plicate pharynx, and intestine forked around the pharynx. *E.* Triclad, with plicate pharynx and three-forked intestine. *F–J.* Various types of polyclad digestive tracts; note also eye arrangement. *F.* Acotylean leptoplanid type, seen from above, with four eye clusters, central ruffled pharynx, main intestine above it, and radiating branches. *G.* Acotylean genus *Cestoplana*, with eyes strewn over the anterior end, posterior ruffled pharynx, long main intestine with lateral branches. *H.* Cotylean euryleptid type with marginal tentacles bearing eyes, also cerebral eye clusters, plicate tubular pharynx directed forward, adhesive disk, and main intestine behind the pharynx, giving off a few main branches. *J.* Cotylean prosthiostomid type with band of eyes across the anterior margin, otherwise similar to *H.* 1, mouth; 2, pharyngeal cavity; 3, pharynx; 4, pharyngeal glands; 5, intestine; 6, proboscis; 7, ciliated pits; 8, cerebral eye cluster; 9, tentacular eye cluster; 10, main intestine; 11, male gonopore, 12, female gonopore; 13, adhesive disk.

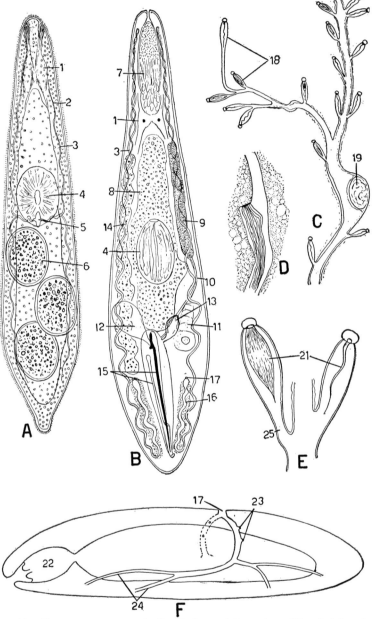

Fig. 36. Excretory system. *A. Typhloplana viridata*, from life, rhabdocoel with rosulate pharynx, symbiotic zoochlorellae, three subitaneous eggs, and protonephridia opening into the pharyngeal cavity by way of an excretory beaker. *B. Gyratrix hermaphroditus*, from life, kalyptorhynchid rhabdocoel with posterior nephridiopores preceded by ampullae. *C.* Part of the nephridium of *Mesostoma*, showing numerous flame bulbs derived from one cell (*after Reisinger*, 1923). *D.* Lateral flame of *Mesostoma* (*after Luther*, 1904). *E.*

thelium. The tubule gives off numerous fine branches termed capillaries, each of which terminates in a flame bulb. The capillary is considered to be part of the cell that forms the bulb or bulbs. Generally the flame bulb and its capillary constitute a single tubular cell, the flame cell, whose bulbous free end bears a tuft of cilia, the "flame," that vibrates within the capillary. However, in some rhabdocoels, especially mesostomine genera, one cell may differentiate into a number of capillaries and flame bulbs (Reisinger, 1923, Fig. 36C), so that the name flame cell should not be used as synonymous with flame bulb. The ciliary flame may be flat and ribbon-like (Fig. 36E) or may have the shape of a hollow cone or cylinder (Fig. 12B). The free end of the flame bulb may send delicate cytoplasmic processes into the mesenchyme. Not uncommonly in rhabdocoels, tufts of cilia, here termed *lateral flames*, may occur along the main tubule (Fig. 36D), and their occurrence may be correlated with a paucity of terminal flame bulbs.

The external opening of the protonephridium is termed the nephridiopore, and the terminal part of the tubule just prior to the pore may be expanded into a contractile region, the ampulla or bladder (Fig. 36B). Ampullae seem to occur only in fresh-water representatives of marine Turbellaria.

In the Catenulida there is a single median protonephridium doubled on itself and with a posterior nephridiopore (Fig. 29A). It has been claimed that the Catenulida have no flame bulbs; but Kepner, Carter, and Hess (1933) and Hess (1937) saw them in *Stenostomum*. Other rhabdocoels have a pair of protonephridia that run the body length and turn back on themselves at one or both ends (Fig. 36A, B). Where the nephridiopores are centrally located, each tubule commonly soon divides into an anterior and a posterior branch, each of which doubles back at the body ends (Fig. 36A). Distally the main tubules may fuse to a common tubule and pore or separately or after fusion may join the pharyngeal cavity (Fig. 36A) or the genital antrum. In the typhloplanine and mesostomine rhabdocoels the two tubules enter a so-called excretion beaker that is interpolated between the pharyngeal cavity and the mouth (Fig. 33B) or may be considered part of the pharyngeal cavity.

In alloeocoels the system is similar to that of rhabdocoels, but there may be two or three main stems on each side, and often additional nephridiopores occur (Fig. 36F).

Flame bulbs of *Mesostoma* in front and side view showing shape of the flame (*after Reisinger*, 1923). F. Excretory system of the plagiostomid alloeocoel *Hydrolimax grisea* (*after Hyman*, 1938). 1, brain; 2, zoochlorellae; 3, protonephridium; 4, rosulate pharynx; 5, excretory beaker; 6, subitaneous eggs; 7, proboscis; 8, intestine; 9, single testis; 10, sperm duct; 11, ovary; 12, seminal bursa; 13, prostatic vesicle; 14, single yolk gland; 15, penis stylet and sheath; 16, ampulla; 17, nephridiopore; 18, flame bulb; 19, nucleus; 20, lateral flame; 21, flame; 22, variable pharynx; 23, accessory nephridiopores; 24, branches of protonephridum; 25, capillary.

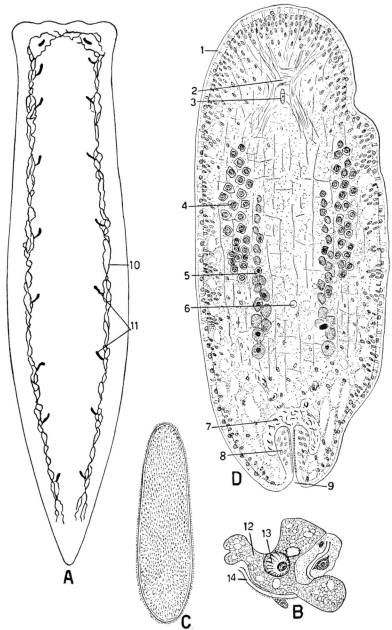

FIG. 37.—Excretory system (continued). Reproductive system. *A.* Triclad *Dendro-coelum lacteum*, showing excretory system (*after Wilhelmi*, 1906). *B.* Athrocyte wrapped around an excretory canal of *Rhynchomesostoma* (*after Luther*, 1904). *C.* Acoel *Afronta aurantiaca*, family Proporidae, from life, Main Coast. *D.* Frontal section of *Afronta* (*after Hyman.* 1944), showing simplest type of reproductive system found among the Turbellaria;

In triclads there are usually one to four tubules on each side, and these are commonly anastomosed into a network or if single broken up into a network, with numerous nephridiopores (up to several hundred). There may be two dorsal and two ventral pairs of tubules or one dorsal and one ventral pair or one or two dorsal pairs without ventral pairs (Fig. 37A). The tubules are located just beneath the epidermis and open on the nearest adjacent surface so that there may be both dorsal and ventral pores.

Little is known of the nephridial system of polyclads beyond the fact that flame bulbs occur.

In a number of Turbellaria there have been noticed associated with the nephridial system large cells with conspicuous nuclei and vacuolated cytoplasm. These cells, termed *athrocytes* or *paranephrocytes*, occur singly or in clusters that may be anastomosed into a syncytium in the vicinity of or wrapped around nephridial tubules (Fig. 37B). They are assumed to be of excretory nature from the fact that they readily take up vital dyes and so may be made conspicuous in small and more or less translucent turbellarians by immersing these in solutions of vital dyes.

13. Reproductive System.—The Turbellaria are hermaphroditic with very few exceptions, that is, each individual contains a complete male and a complete female reproductive system. These may be wholly separate, each with its own gonopore, or their terminal parts may join to form a common antrum and pore. The Cercyrinae, a subfamily of the marine triclad family Procerodidae, tend to dioeciousness, and to date two dioecious species of this group have been discovered [*Sabussowia dioica* (Claparéde) 1863 and *Cercyra teissieri* Steinmann 1930]. Reisinger (1924a) failed to find any male system in *Rhynchoscolex simplex* and believes permanent parthenogenesis obtains in this and some other Turbellaria (*Bothrioplana semperi*, *Graffilla parasitica*).

The sex cells of the Turbellaria come from the free cells of the mesenchyme that migrate to appropriate locations and undergo gametogenesis. In primitive forms as the Acoela there are no definite gonads but the gametogonia lie free in the mesenchyme mostly arranged in longitudinal strands, with the spermatogonia lateral to the ovogonia (Fig. 37D). But in most Turbellaria there are definite gonads more or less distinctly bounded from the mesenchyme. They may be rounded, oval, elongated, lobed, or branched. When numerous small gonads are present, the condition is spoken of as *follicular*. The polyclads have numerous testes and ovaries, the triclads and alloeocoels commonly possess a few to many

lacks all female ducts; male system consists of seminal vesicle and male canal (penis). 1, epidermis; 2, brain; 3, statocyst; 4, spermatogonia; 5, ovogonia; 6, mouth; 7, seminal vesicle; 8, penis; 9, male gonopore; 10, protonephridial network; 11, nephridiopores; 12, athrocyte; 13, its nucleus; 14, protonephridial canal.

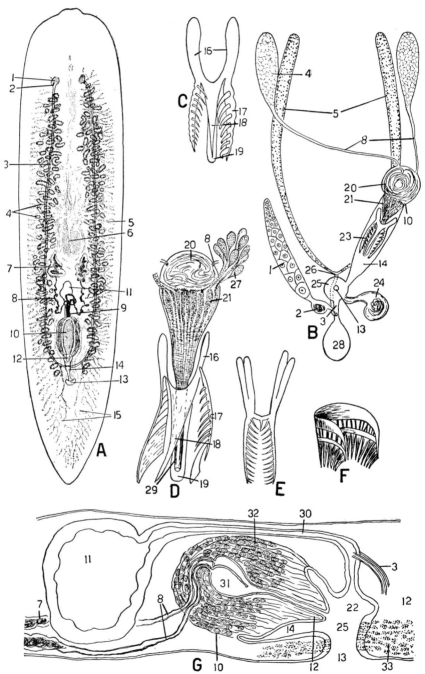

FIG. 38.—For descriptive legend see opposite page.

testes and one pair of ovaries, and in rhabdocoels there are usually present one pair of testes and one or two ovaries. The process of gametogenesis is the same as in other animals (Fig. 41*A*).

The copulatory complex of the Turbellaria can attain a high degree of complexity, but this complexity has evolved within the class and hence cannot be taken as indicative of the degenerative descent of the flatworms from some higher phylum. The copulatory complex is usually located posteriorly behind the pharynx or the intestinal sac but may have any other location.

a. Male Reproductive System.—There is only one pair of sperm ducts regardless of the number of testes but only one duct when the testis is single and several pairs in cases of multiple copulatory complexes (Fig. 40*A*). When numerous testes are present each connects with the sperm duct of that side by a minute *sperm ductule*. The sperm ducts may or may not unite to a *common sperm duct* before entering the copulatory complex. On approaching the latter, each duct or the common duct may present a tubular or sacciform expansion, the *spermiducal vesicle* (old name, *false seminal vesicle*), serving to store ripe sperm. This may have a thick muscular wall but usually is thin-walled. The sperm ducts or common duct open into the male copulatory complex, the lumen of which, termed *ejaculatory duct*, is the final part of the common sperm duct.

The male copulatory complex of the Turbellaria rings innumerable changes on a few fundamental parts. It is impossible here to give a detailed account of these variations. The main parts of the complex are the *seminal vesicle* and the *penis*, but in most Turbellaria there is also present a gland complex, the *prostatic* apparatus.

The seminal vesicle is a rounded, pyriform, or tubular structure usually with a thick muscular wall; it receives the sperm from the sperm ducts, stores them, and helps propel them onward during ejaculation. A worm may have both spermiducal and seminal vesicles (Fig. 51*D*), but generally when one is present the other is lacking. In the absence of a

Fig. 38.—Reproductive system (continued). *A. Procotyla fluviatilis*, to show reproductive system of a fresh-water triclad. *B.* Reproductive system of *Dalyellia* (*after Graff*, 1911); note seminal vesicle and prostatic vesicle end to end in the penis bulb. *C–F.* Penis stylet of various species of *Dalyellia* to show a few of its many variations. *C. Dalyellia rossi*, eastern United States (*after Graff*, 1911). *D. Dalyellia sillimani*, eastern United States (*after Graff*, 1911). *E. Dalyellia viridis*, cosmopolitan (*after Graff*, 1882). *F. Dalyellia ornata*, Europe (*after Hofsten*, 1911). *G.* Copulatory complex of *Dugesia* in sagittal section; the entrance of the ovovitelline ducts into the curve of the bursal canal is diagnostic of the genus *Dugesia* (= *Euplanaria*). 1, ovary, 2; seminal receptacle with mass of sperm; 3, ovovitelline duct; 4, testes; 5, yolk glands; 6, pharynx; 7, spermiducal vesicle; 8, sperm duct; 9, common sperm duct; 10, penis bulb; 11, copulatory bursa; 12, penis papilla; 13, common gonopore; 14, male antrum; 15, accessory yolk ducts; 16, main stems of stylet; 17, distal stems bearing spines; 18, median dorsal piece; 19, median ventral piece; 20, seminal vesicle; 21, prostatic vesicle; 22, female antrum; 23, penis stylet; 24, seminal bursa; 25, common antrum; 26, common yolk duct; 27, bundle of prostatic glands; 28, uterus; 29, ejaculatory duct; 30, bursal canal; 31, bulbar lumen; 32, gland cells of penis bulb; 33, cement glands.

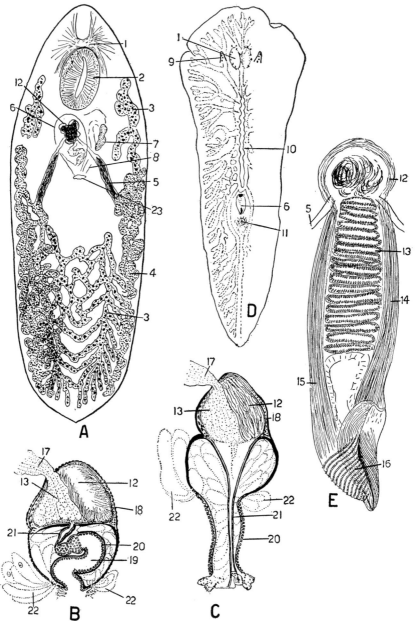

Fig. 39.—Reproductive system (continued). *A. Phaenocora kepneri*, typhloplanid rhabdocoel of the eastern United States (*from slide, courtesy Prof. U. Dahlgren*). *B.* Cirrus of *P. kepneri* in the resting state; note seminal and prostatic vesicles side by side in the penis bulb. *C.* Cirrus everted to form a copulatory organ. (*B, C after Gilbert*, 1935.) *D. Gnesioceros sargassicola*, family Planoceridae, pelagic polyclad common on the floating *Sargassum*, from life, Bermuda. *E.* Male copulatory complex of *G. sargassicola*, showing

seminal vesicle the sperm ducts or duct open directly into the prostatic apparatus or into the penis.

The prostatic apparatus in its simplest form consists of a group of gland cells, the *prostatic* or *granule glands*, that open into the ejaculatory duct or the penis base. Usually, however, they open into a special vesicle, the *prostatic vesicle*, that may be *interpolated* (Fig. 64*B*) between the seminal vesicle and the penis or may be incorporated within a common muscular wall with the seminal vesicle or may connect with the ejaculatory duct by a special *prostatic duct*. In the last case the prostatic vesicle is said to be "free" (Fig. 63*C*). The prostatic vesicle is a rounded, oval, or tubular body with a thick muscular wall. The gland cells may open into the vesicle from without or may be buried in its walls. The prostatic glands produce a granular secretion, or in some forms two kinds of secretion, coarsely and finely granular, of unknown nature and function; but it seems evident that the secretion, which is discharged in the ejaculate, must be of importance to the health and vitality of the sperm. A typical prostatic vesicle and glands are lacking in the triclads but are of general occurrence in other Turbellaria; but probably what is called penis bulb in the triclads is really a prostatic vesicle.

The penis or last part of the male copulatory complex is in its simplest state as seen in some Acoela and Alloeocoela (Fig. 37*D*) merely the terminal part of the male canal with or without a special thickened wall. Usually, however, the wall of the male canal is evaginated to form a muscular conical projection, the *penis papilla*, traversed by the final section of the ejaculatory duct (Fig. 38*G*). The male canal containing the papilla is then usually widened to a chamber termed the *male antrum*. The relations of the penis papilla to the male antrum are the same as those of the plicate pharynx to the pharyngeal cavity, i.e., the penis papilla is protruded by muscular elongation. The penis papilla may be armed with thorns or spines or with a long or short *stylet;* in some cases such a stylet may take the place of the papilla. The stylet is usually a straight or curved hollow tube; but in some rhabdocoels, notably the genus *Dalyellia* (Fig. 38*B–F*), the stylet consists of a complicated array of bars and teeth that differs for each species and constitutes a diagnostic taxonomic character. Quite commonly that part of the male apparatus supporting the penis papilla is formed into a highly muscular rounded body termed the *penis bulb*, considered to be a part of the penis. This bulb may incor-

---

the cirrus of toothed bands; contraction of retractor muscle pulls bands to inside contraction of protractor muscle pulls them to the exterior (*after Hyman*, 1939). 1, brain; 2, rosulate pharynx; 3, yolk glands; 4, testes (incomplete on right side); 5, sperm ducts; 6, male copulatory complex; 7, ovary; 8, female canal; 9, tentacles; 10, pharynx; 11, female gonopore; 12, seminal vesicle; 13, prostatic vesicle; 14, retractor of cirrus; 15, protractor of cirrus: 16, cirrus: 17, ducts of prostatic glands; 18, penis bulb; 19, ejaculatory duct constituting the cirrus; 20, teeth of same; 21, noneversible part of ejaculatory duct; 22, cytoplasmic lobes, unknown function; 23, common gonopore.

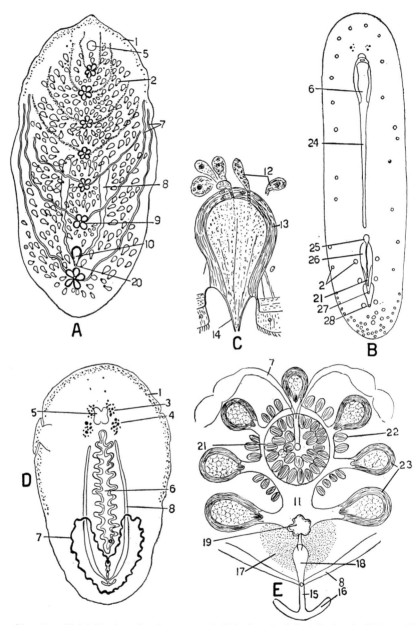

Fig. 40.—Multiplication of male parts. A. Pelagic polyclad of the family Polyposthi-idae, Straits of Karimata (*after Palombi*, 1924), with multiple sperm ducts, male copulatory apparatus, and prostatoids. B. *Apidioplana mira*, polyclad from the Fiji Islands (*after Bock*, 1926) with numerous prostatoids. C. Prostatoid of *Apidioplana*, enlarged (*after Bock*, 1926). D. *Coronadena mutabilis*, family Discocelidae, Atlantic Coast of United States. E. Copulatory complex of *Coronadena*, with large prostatoids in pockets around the male antrum, and smaller ones in the penis papilla and wall of antrum (*after Hyman*,

porate either the seminal vesicle or the prostatic vesicle or both side by side or end to end (Figs. 38*D*, 54). A penis bulb is particularly characteristic of triclads and also occurs in many rhabdocoels.

Some Turbellaria, e.g., the rhabdocoel genus *Phaenocora* (Fig. 39*A–C*) and the polyclad family Planoceridae (Fig. 39*D*, *E*), have a cirrus instead of a penis. The cirrus is the terminal part of the ejaculatory duct generally lined with spines, thorns, etc., that is eversible to the exterior to act as a copulatory organ.

Multiplication of the male copulatory apparatus or parts thereof is very common among the Turbellaria. Thus among the acoels, *Childia* has two and *Tetraposthia* (Fig. 23*A*) four male apparatus composed of seminal vesicle and penis stylet. The alloeocoel *Multipeniata* has a series of male apparatuses in graded stages of development (Nasonov, 1927). Such multiplication is particularly common among polyclads. The male complex is paired in *Thysanozoon* and some species of *Pseudoceros*, and there is a curved row of male apparatus on each side in *Anonymus* (Lang, 1884). Several male apparatus occur around the antrum in *Cryptocelides* and *Polyposthia*, and in some other Polyposthiidae there is a median row of such clusters (Fig. 40*A*, Palombi, 1924). Even more common, also especially among polyclads, is the presence of multiple prostatic apparatus; these have been called by various names such as *pyriform organs*, *apioid organs, musculo-glandular organs*, etc., but *prostatoid* seems a convenient name for them. They consist of a pyriform body with a thick muscular wall, attached glands, and pointed tip, often hardened (Fig. 40*C*). These prostatoids may occur in numbers around the male antrum as in the Discocelidae (Fig. 40*E*) and *Boninia* (Bock, 1923), or they may be scattered throughout the ventral surface as in *Apidioplana* (Fig. 40*B*, *C*, Bock, 1926). Similar bodies, termed *adenodactyls*, occur in the wall of the common antrum in some fresh-water (Fig. 45*C*, *D*) and land triclads, and are also found among the Acoela. The purpose of this multiplication in the male system has not been ascertained, but it is usually supposed that the extra parts act as stimulators in copulation.

The male antrum either joins the female antrum to form a common antrum opening below by the common gonopore, or it opens independently by a male gonopore. However, it is not uncommon for the male apparatus to open into the pharyngeal cavity (Fig. 59*C*).

The sperm of the Turbellaria resemble those of other animals. They

1940). 1, marginal eyes; 2, prostatoids; 3, cerebral eye cluster; 4, tentacular eye cluster; 5, brain; 6, pharynx; 7, sperm ducts; 8, oviducts (uteri); 9, cluster of male copulatory apparatus; 10, female antrum; 11, male antrum; 12, prostatic gland; 13, muscular wall of prostatoid; 14, tip of prostatoid with cuticularized surface; 15, bursal canal; 16, seminal bursa (Lang's vesicle); 17, cement glands; 18, vagina (female canal); 19, common gonopore; 20, female gonopore; 21, penis papilla (seen from above) full of prostatoids; 22, small prostatoids in antral wall; 23, large prostatoids.

are usually long and filamentous and are provided with two flagella or two bristles (Fig. 41*C*, *D*), or tapering at one or both ends to a flagella-like filament. The alloeocoel genus *Plagiostomum* has characteristic broad sperm with wing-like lateral extensions (Fig. 41*C*). In some genera the

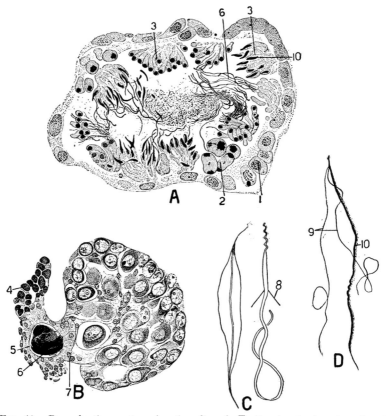

Fig. 41.—Reproductive system (continued). *A.* Testis of a fresh-water planarian, showing spermatogenesis. *B.* Ovary of a fresh-water planarian, showing also seminal receptacle with sperm mass at head of ovovitelline duct. (*A, B after Hyman*, 1925b.) *C.* Sperm of *Plagiostomum* (left) and *Macrostomum* (right). *D.* Sperm of *Dendrocoelum lacteum* (*after Hammerschmidt*, 1908). 1, spermatogonia; 2, spermatocytes in reduction division; 3, spermatids in various stages of transformation to sperm; 4, most anterior yolk glands; 5, seminal receptacle; 6, mass of sperm; 7, closing membrane of ovary; 8, bristles; 9, flagella; 10, nucleus.

sperm are aggregated into packets termed *spermatophores* that are discharged into the fellow copulant.

b. Female Reproductive System.—This system may be even more complicated and variable than the male system. Primitively as in many acoels there are no female ducts at all (Fig. 37*D*), and the eggs discharge either through the mouth or by rupture. The beginning of the female system appears to be the formation of a tube, the female canal or *vagina*, leading inward from the gonopore. The distal part of this canal may enlarge to become the female antrum, and various other differentiations then ensue. The female antrum and gonopore may be distinct from the male ones or fuse with them to a common antrum and pore. In the Acoela the female gonopore is nearly always anterior to the male pore, but in most other Turbellaria the reverse is the case.

The Platyhelminthes are unique among animals in that the yolk supplies of the egg are usually not stored in the egg itself but in special cells, the *yolk* or *vitelline cells*, considered to be altered ovocytes. This state of affairs has arisen within the Turbellaria. Yolk cells are lacking, and the eggs store their own yolk as in other animals in the Acoela, the Polycladida, and the catenulid and macrostomid Rhabdocoela; however, in *Polychoerus* and a few other acoels, the ovocytes lie in a nutritive tissue differing in appearance from the rest of the mesenchyme. The first step toward the evolution of yolk glands is seen in the alloeocoel group Lecithoepitheliata in which some of the ovocytes become eggs and the others differentiate into follicle cells that embrace each growing ovocyte and pass food supplies into it (Fig. 43). Such an ovary therefore consists of a proximal germinal part producing ovocytes and a series of follicles that gradually increase in size toward the oviduct (Figs. 42B, F, 59B). Next the ovary differentiates into yolk-producing and egg-producing regions (Fig. 42C). Such sex glands are termed *germovitellaria* and exist in several types as illustrated in Fig. 42B, C, G, H. Finally as in most Turbellaria there is a complete separation of the yolk-producing part to form the *yolk glands* or *vitellaria* (Fig. 42D, E). These may be elongated, lobed, or branched bodies, or may consist of numerous scattered clusters of yolk cells, a condition termed follicular. The yolk glands may discharge directly into the oviducts as in triclads, in which case the oviducts are more properly termed *ovovitelline* ducts, or there may be special *yolk ducts* leading from the yolk glands to the oviducts.

Among the rhabdocoels and alloeocoels, the ovary-yolk-gland complex seems to have been derived from an originally tetrapartite condition (Fig. 42). No turbellarian is known that has a tetrapartite ovary (theoretical stage in Fig. 42A), but an alloeocoel *Gnosonesima* has been described by Reisinger (1926) from the antarctic that has a tetrapartite germovitellarium with follicles (Fig. 42B). In most present rhabdocoels and alloeocoels the condition shown in Fig. 42D, E obtains, i.e., there is a pair of yolk glands and one or two ovaries.

When the ovary is single there is a single oviduct; otherwise there are two oviducts to which, in the case of numerous ovaries, connection is made by minute *oviductules*. The Acoela and some primitive Alloeocoela lack oviducts altogether, and this condition is undoubtedly primitive. Following the entrance of the yolk cells, the oviduct becomes an ovovitelline duct (old name, *ductus communis*), and proceeds toward the female copulatory complex.   This is very variable in different Turbellaria so that general statements are impractical.   A typical part of the apparatus is a sac for receiving sperm from the fellow copulant.   This sac is termed

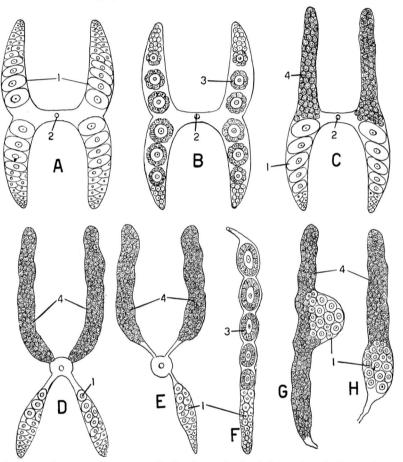

Fig. 42.—Evolution of ovary–yolk gland complex in rhabdocoels and alloeocoels.   *A.* Hypothetical ancestral stage with tetrapartite ovary.   *B.* Condition in *Gnosonesima* with tetrapartite germovitellaria composed of follicles.   *C.* More usual type of germovitellaria with ovarian and vitelline regions.   *D, E.* Usual condition of the female system in rhabdocoels and alloeocoels: two yolk glands and one or two ovaries.   *F.* Condition in the Prorhynchidae, with one germovitallarium composed of follicles.   *G, H.* Other types of germovitellaria.   1, ovary; 2, gonopore; 3, follicle; 4, yolk gland.

copulatory bursa (*bursa copulatrix*) when it retains the sperm for only a brief period, *seminal bursa* (*bursa seminalis*) when it keeps them a longer time, and *seminal receptacle* (*receptaculum seminis*) when it is the permanent abiding place of the sperm.   The last is frequently merely a widened place in the oviduct; the other two are frequently set off from the antrum by a *bursal canal*. A given worm may have both copulatory or seminal bursa and seminal receptacle as *Mesostoma* (Fig. 54) or *Dalyellia* (Fig. 38*B*). The copulatory or seminal bursa may open to the exterior by a *bursal* pore independent of the regular genital pore and sometimes not in the median line (Figs. 61*A*, 62*E*). The canal leading from the bursa to this bursal pore may be termed *copulation canal* (sometimes called *ductus vaginalis*) since it presumably serves for copulation. The bursa may also have special *insemination* canals (old name, *ductus spermaticus*) through which the sperm reach the oviducts, and these may occur in addition to the regular bursal canal (Figs. 53*A*, *B*, 61*A*). In the marine triclads *Bdelloura* and *Uteriporus*, the paired or single seminal bursa opens directly to the exterior (Fig. 61*A*) and is connected with the rest of the

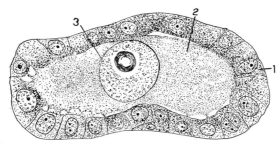

FIG. 43.—A follicle of the germovitellarium of *Prorhynchus*, showing maturing ovum surrounded by a follicle of nurse cells, presumed to be altered ova. 1, follicle; 2, egg; 3, nucleus of egg.

female system only by delicate insemination canals. Most Acoela lack all female parts, but the family Convolutidae is characterized by the presence of one to many seminal bursae. These are glandulo-muscular bodies connected or not with the vagina and provided with one or more nozzles (page 129) through which the sperm received at copulation exit into the mesenchyme. Various relations of vagina and seminal bursa in the Acoela are shown in Fig. 44.

In some Turbellaria, especially polyclads, the oviducts serve as storage places for large accumulations of ripe eggs and are then expanded as uteri. But as most Turbellaria lay their eggs singly or a few at a time a uterus is not necessary. However, in some rhabdocoels there is a single or paired uterus in the form of a blind sac or tube extending from the female or common antrum; the shelled eggs singly or a few at a time are held in this before laying, and it seems to play some role in the formation and particularly in the shaping of the shell. More often the shell is formed in the male or female antrum.

Large numbers of eosinophilous gland cells are usually associated with the female complex, opening into the bursal canal or the terminal parts of the oviducts, or the wall of the antrum, or the body wall around the

gonopore.   They were formerly considered to be shell glands, but it is now
known that the shell is formed from droplets present in the egg or in the
yolk cells, and the glands are mostly of the nature of *cement* glands that
secrete the material uniting the eggs into cakes or ribbons (Acoela,
Polycladida) or fastening them to objects by means of stalks and filaments.

The oviducts or ovovitelline ducts may or may not unite to a common
duct before entering the female copulatory complex.   They may open
into the bursal canal or into the male, female, or common antrum.

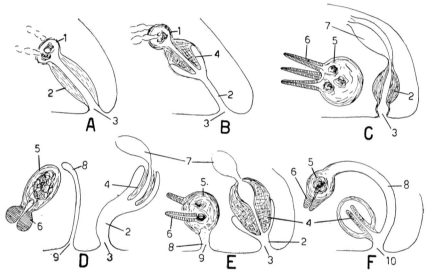

Fig. 44.—Diagrams of the reproductive system of various Acoela, based chiefly on
Luther, 1912.   *A. Afronta*, with male canal, no female parts.   *B. Proporus*, similar, but
with penis papilla in the male canal.   *C. Palmenia*, similar to A, but with seminal bursa not
connected to the gonopore.   *D. Convoluta*, with vagina leading toward but not connected
with seminal bursa.   *E. Amphiscolops*, vagina connected with seminal bursa.   *F. Otocelis*,
similar to *E* but with common gonopore.   1, seminal vesicle; 2, male canal; 3, male gonopore;
4, penis papilla; 5, seminal bursa; 6, nozzles of bursa; 7, spermiducal vesicles; 8, vagina; 9,
female gonopore; 10, common gonopore.   In *F*, the penis papilla is everted into the male
canal.

The parts of the female system are lined with a one-layered epithelium
that varies greatly in height in different regions or in different states of
activity.   It may be ciliated in certain areas or glandular, either through
the presence in its cells of secretory granules or through being penetrated
by the outlets of gland cells situated in the adjacent mesenchyme.   In
some groups all the gland cells associated with egg laying enter one particular region which is then termed *glandular duct* or *cement sac* (Figs.
62D, 65D).   All parts of the female system except the ovaries are underlain by a muscular stratum usually of both circular and longitudinal fibers.
This is often very thick around the terminal parts of the female system
where it may form sphincters.

The eggs of the Acoela and Polycladida enclosed in delicate capsules are laid embedded in gelatinous material. In the other orders they are enclosed singly or severally in a hard shell, here termed *capsule* (also called *cocoon*). In those forms with yolk glands, hundreds of yolk cells are included with the eggs inside the capsule. The capsule is formed in the antrum, most commonly the male antrum, sometimes at least in part in a special uterus. It is usually pale and soft at first, but becomes brown and hard after laying. During its passage through the gonopore, the capsule becomes coated with the adhesive secretion of the cement glands, and this secretion may be drawn out into a stalk fastening the capsule to an object. During the breeding season, each worm usually copulates repeatedly and lays a succession of capsules, one at a time, at intervals of a few days. These hatch in a few weeks to complete tiny worms; free-swimming larvae occur only in some polyclads. In some species the eggs develop to young worms in the parent body, either in the uteri (Fig. 45*A*) or in the mesenchyme (Fig. 36*A*) or even in the lumen of the intestine (*Bresslauilla*). Such young escape by mouth or gonopore or through rupture and death of the parent.

A relatively common feature of the female system among the Turbellaria is a connection with the intestine, the *genito-intestinal canal* (Fig. 59*C*) or aperture; this is sometimes paired. Usually it is the seminal or copulatory bursa or its equivalent that opens into the intestine; in polyclads the connection when present is between the vagina or oviducts and the intestine. Very great phylogenetic importance has been attributed to this genito-intestinal connection by some students of the Turbellaria. They regard its occurrence as proof that the eggs were originally discharged by way of the intestine and mouth with the connection constituting the primitive oviduct (Steinböck, 1924; Reisinger, 1930). They argue that, when the Acoela evolved into turbellarians with a hollow intestine, a definite passage formed for the discharge of eggs into the intestinal lumen. Great weight has been placed by Reisinger on the rhabdocoel *Bresslauilla* (Reisinger, 1930) which lacks all female parts except a pair of yolk glands and one ovary; these connect broadly with the intestine into which the eggs discharge and where they develop into young worms. Equally prominent students of the Turbellaria reject these ideas altogether (Bock, 1927; Meixner, 1938). Bock points out that the connection is rather too variable in its relationship to permit of any generalization and further emphasizes the general tendency already mentioned toward fusion of contiguous structures among the Turbellaria. The author is of the opinion that the original mode of discharge of turbellarian eggs was in fact the mouth but that the sporadic occurrence of a genito-intestinal connection cannot be taken as proof of this or as indicative that the original female canal ran from the ovaries into the intestine.

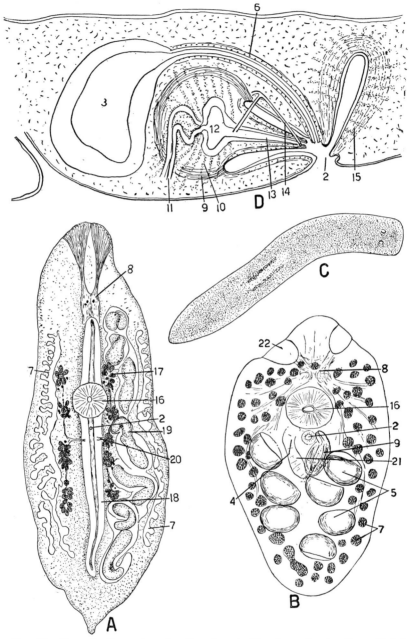

FIG. 45.—Reproductive system (continued). *A. Mesostoma ehrenbergii wardii (after Woodworth,* 1897), showing young worms developed from subitaneous eggs in the right uterus (left uterus not shown). *B. Mesostoma columbiana* with dormant hemispherical capsules *(after Hyman,* 1939). *C. Planaria dactyligera,* Virginia *(after Kenk,* 1935). *D.* Copulatory apparatus of *Planaria dactyligera* in sagittal view showing the adenodactyl

Conditions in the Acoela suggest on the contrary that the original female canal ran inward from the gonopore and had no direct connection with any other structure, serving only to receive the sperm of the partner. The impetus for the evolution of a female system appears to have been the desirability of safeguarding the sperm received in copulation.

A corollary of the genitointestinal theory is the intestinal derivation of the copulatory or seminal bursa, considered to be a sac cut off from the intestine. This idea is in the author's opinion acceptable although violently criticized by Meixner (1938). The bursa is usually lined by a tall bulbous epithelium closely resembling the intestinal epithelium and capable like the latter of intracellular digestion. One of the main functions of the bursa, in fact, is the digestion of excess sperm and prostatic secretion (Cernosvitov, 1931). The seminal bursa of the Acoela, however, appears to be of quite a different nature from that of other Turbellaria and is clearly unrelated to the intestine.

c. Copulation.—Internal fertilization is the rule among the Turbellaria, and for this purpose they are almost without exception provided with a copulatory apparatus. Although the Turbellaria are with few exceptions hermaphroditic and although the fertilization of the eggs by the sperm of the same animal would be anatomically possible, especially in those forms where both male and female ducts open into a common antrum, self-fertilization is of rare occurrence and is definitely absent in fresh-water planarians (probably all triclads) and polyclads. Isolated triclads may lay capsules, but these do not hatch as the contained eggs are unfertilized (Gelei, 1924; Goetsch, 1925). Self-fertilization fails to occur apparently because the sperm masses in the spermiducal or seminal vesicles are motionless and do not become motile until ejaculated along with necessary glandular secretions into another individual.

Two methods of cross insemination occur, hypodermic impregnation and regular copulation. In the former, practised among a few Acoela, Rhabdocoela, and Polycladida, one animal injects sperm through the epidermis of another at any place, mostly by means of an armed penis (Fig. 48*A*). The sperm so injected wander through the mesenchyme to the eggs. An ordinary copulation is, however, the rule and is probably the usual method even among the Acoela. This copulation is mutual, i.e., the protruded penis papilla or everted cirrus is inserted into the female or common gonopore of the partner by each copulant and each injects sperm into the other. The sperm are emitted directly into the copulatory or seminal bursa (Fig. 48*C*) when this structure is present;

characteristic of the genus *Planaria* (*after Kenk*, 1935). 1, mouth; 2, common gonopore; 3, copulatory bursa; 4, ovary; 5, dormant capsules; 6, bursal canal; 7, testes; 8, brain; 9, penis bulb; 10, glands of same; 11, sperm ducts; 12, bulbar lumen; 13, ejaculatory duct; 14, common ovovitelline duct; 15, adenodactyl; 16, rosulate pharynx; 17, yolk glands; 18, intestine; 19, young worms in uterus; 20, yolk duct; 21, oviduct; 22, sensory pits.

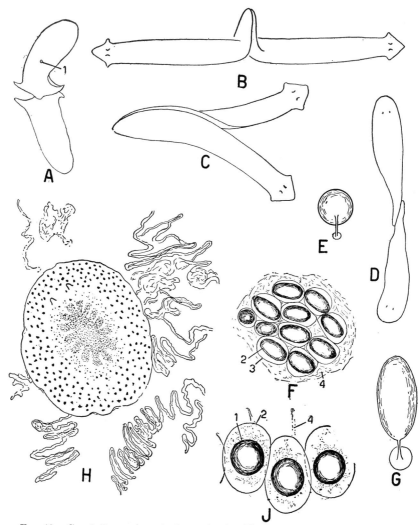

Fig. 46.—Copulation and egg laying.   A. *Amphiscolops langerhansi*, acoel, in copulation, from life, Bermuda.   B and C. Fresh-water planarians of the genus *Dugesia* in copulation, from life.   D. Rhabdocoel *Macrostomum* in copulation, from life.   E. Stalked capsule
of *Dugesia*, from life.   F. Egg mass of *Amphiscolops*, from life.   G. Egg capsule of *Bdelloura*, marine triclad commensal on *Limulus*, from life; the capsules are fastened to the gill
lamellae.   H. Polyclad *Stylochus* in process of laying egg ribbons.   J. Part of the ribbon,
showing each egg enclosed in a capsule.   (*H, J after photographs by Kato*, 1940.)   1, mouth;
2, egg; 3, capsule; 4, jelly.

otherwise they find their way into the oviducts or seminal receptacle.
The copulation of the Acoela is of interest as these are the most primitive
animals in which this process occurs.   The details have been ascertained
for only one species, however, *Amphiscolops langerhansi*, in which it was
possible to section copulating pairs (Hyman, 1937).   Here the penes

grasp each other and the sperm, guided by a body projection, pass into the seminal bursa (Fig. 47).

Copulation is generally preceded by a brief "courtship" consisting of head or body contacts. The copulatory attitude is similar throughout the class. Usually the copulants face more or less away from each other with genital regions pressed together and often elevated, rest of body

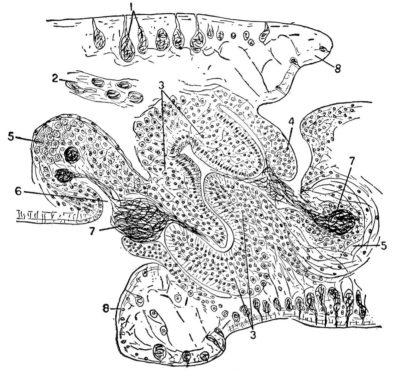

Fig. 47.—Sagittal section through the rear ends of a copulating pair of the acoel *Amphiscolops langerhansi*, showing penes interlocked and stream of sperm pouring into the seminal bursa of each copulant; sperm guide prevents dispersion of sperm into the water (*after Hyman*, 1937). 1, gland cells; 2, sperm duct; 3, penis papilla; 4, sperm guide; 5, seminal bursa; 6, vagina; 7, mass of sperm; 8, tail end of animal.

attached to substratum (Fig. 46A–D). A parallel position, however, is not infrequent in the same species. Copulation is generally of brief duration, a few minutes or less, but in the acoel mentioned above lasted 40 to 60 minutes and in polyclads may last an hour or more (Kato, 1940). During the breeding season any one individual copulates repeatedly. Adhesive secretions probably aid the copulatory process.

14. Order Acoela.—The Acoela are a group of small worms ranging mostly from below one millimeter to several millimeters in length; the largest known species is the 12-mm. *Anaperus sulcatus* from the Caspian

Sea (Beklemischev, 1914). The Acoela are mostly of plump, broad to elongate, oval form, of inconspicuous white or drab coloration, except when colored brown or green by symbionts. The contour is simple except for a pair of caudal lobes in *Amphiscolops* and *Polychoerus* (Fig. 13D, E) plus a tail filament in the latter. The characters of the epidermis are described above (page 68). There are nearly always present a statocyst (sometimes double) and a cluster of frontal glands opening by a pore or infrequently numerous pores at the anterior tip. Eyes are frequently wanting, but some have two or rarely four eyes. The eyes of *Otocelis rubropunctata* are pigment-spot ocelli, but those of other Acoela are of the usual pigment-cup type, of one to a few pigment and retinal cells. The nervous system in the most primitive forms (*Tetraposthia*, *Nemertoderma*) is epidermally located but in most Acoela is a submuscular plexus with three to six pairs of longitudinal strands (page 83, Fig. 23). The mouth, usually located near the middle or in the anterior half of the ventral surface, rarely at the posterior end (*Diopisthoporus*, Westblad, 1940), opens directly into the mesenchyme or into a long or short pharynx simplex, sometimes provided proximally with extra musculature. A digestive cavity is lacking (except *Nemertoderma*, see below), and mouth or pharynx lead directly into a syncytial vacuolated mass that fills the interior. The digestive phagocytic cells or areas of this are either scattered or aggregated into a central digestive zone in which temporary spaces form around the digesting food. The Acoela are totally devoid of an excretory system.

The reproductive system starts from simple conditions and concentrates on the development of male and female copulatory mechanisms. The sex cells originate directly from mesenchymal cells mostly in paired dorsolateral regions, sometimes in a median region; the male cells are lateral to the female ones (Fig. 37D). In some species there is a median common source of both eggs and sperm. As the sex cells ripen, they proceed posteriorly, forming longitudinal tracts of eggs and sperm (Fig. 37D). There may be single or paired seminal or spermiducal vesicles or both in which sperm collect and which lead into the penis. This is primitively simply a canal with or without special muscular wall (Fig. 37D), but in many Acoela a conical muscular penis papilla, sometimes armed with one or more hard stylets, projects into the male canal from its proximal end. Prostatic glands usually open into the penis base, and sometimes there is a vaguely indicated prostatic vesicle. There may be two or four penes (page 117). The male canal leads to the male gonopore usually at or near the posterior end, or it may join the female canal. All Acoela lack oviducts, and the more primitive members also lack all other female parts (*Nemertoderma*, *Diopisthoporus*, family Proporidae). The family Convolutidae has a female canal (vagina) springing from the common antrum or opening by a separate female gonopore anterior to the male pore (Fig. 44). This family also usually has one to many (to 64 in *Anaperus*, Fig. 49*B*) seminal bursae connected or not with the vagina (Fig. 44). The seminal bursa may be merely a mesenchymal space in which received sperm accumulate (Fig. 23*A*) but usually is a glandulo-muscular body with a poor lumen and one to many nozzles by which the sperm exit to fertilize the eggs. These nozzles consist of flat disk-like cells whose centers, perforated by a canal, are cuticularized and of a yellow color (Fig. 49*C*). The Acoela are hermaphroditic; but protandry seems to be of common occurrence, and in *Diopisthoporus*, male, female, and hermaphroditic specimens may occur simultaneously (Westblad, 1940).

Although hypodermic impregnation certainly occurs among the Acoela, copulation is the rule (Fig. 47, page 125). The sperm pass directly from the vagina into the bursa or reach this through the mesenchyme or in the absence of a bursa wander through the mesenchyme to the eggs. After once attaining mature size, the Acoela appear to remain permanently in a sexual state and probably breed throughout the year in warmer waters, seasonally in colder zones. The eggs are laid through the mouth or gonopore or by body rupture. A few to many eggs are enclosed in a thin gelatinous capsule or in a rounded to cake-like gelatinous mass stuck to objects (Fig. 46*F*). This gelatinous material is secreted by gland cells opening into the antrum or onto the general body surface. In *Amphiscolops langerhansi*, observed by the author in tanks at Bermuda, copulation and laying of flat cakes of 3 to 16 eggs (Fig. 46*F*) occurred at frequent intervals in the same individuals; the eggs were laid between midnight and dawn (Hyman, 1937). The eggs of the Acoela develop in a few days directly into young worms that escape from the jelly.

The Acoela are exclusively marine, living under stones, among algae, and most commonly on the bottom mud from the littoral zone to rather deep waters. Several species, mostly of the genus *Haplodiscus* (Fig. 49*A*), of flat, broadly oval shape and translucent texture, are pelagic; but as they are known only from townet collections, their habits have not been observed (Böhmig, 1895; Löhner and Micoletzky, 1911).[1] *Amphiscolops sargassi* lives on the floating *Sargassum* (Hyman, 1939).[1] The curious *Ectocotyla paguri* with a caudal adhesive disk (Fig. 13*F*) is ectocommensal on a hermit crab off the coast of Maine. There are also a number of entocommensal species, inhabiting the intestine of echino-

[1] The *Sargassum* is a seaweed, belonging to the brown algae, that floats loose in the Atlantic Ocean, being most abundant in a stagnant region to the northeast of Bermuda, termed on this account the Sargasso Sea. The *Sargassum* is inhabited by a number of animals that do not occur elsewhere and that are often notable for adaptive resemblance to the seaweed in color and shape.

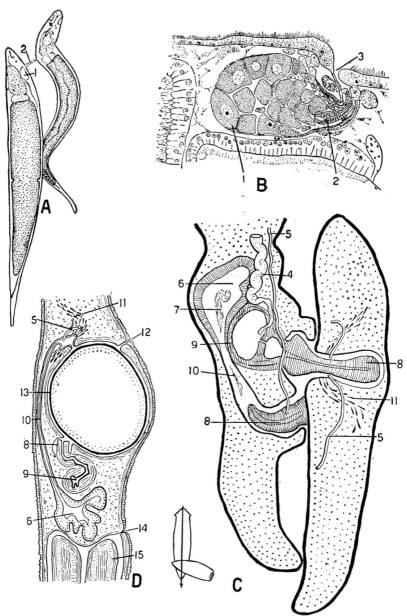

Fig. 48.—Copulation (continued). *A. Stenostomum* in process of hypodermic impregnation. *B.* Sagittal section through the male system of *Stenostomum.* (*A, B after Kepner, Carter, and Hess,* 1933.) *C.* Section through a copulating pair of *Dugesia gonocephala* (*after Burr,* 1912) showing penis papilla inserted into bursal canal; small figure below to left gives plane of section. *D.* Sagittal section of the copulatory complex of *Dugesia polychroa* (*after Burr,* 1912) showing capsule forming in the male antrum. 1, testis; 2, penis papilla (introverted in *B*); 3, male gonopore (dorsal); 4, sperm duct; 5, ovovitelline duct; 6, copulatory bursa; 7, mass of sperm; 8, penis papilla; 9, penis bulb; 10, bursal canal; 11, cement glands; 12, common gonopore; 13, capsule; 14, mouth; 15, pharynx.

derms: *Avagina incola* in a heart urchin (Leiper, 1904) and *Otocelis chirodotae, Aphanostoma pallidum* and *sanguineum*, and *Aechmalotus pyrula* from sea cucumbers on the Murman coast (Beklemischev, 1915). Although the Acoela occur in tropical and subtropical waters (chiefly as pelagic types), they reach their greatest abundance in temperate and arctic zones. Curiously, nearly all the known species come from the

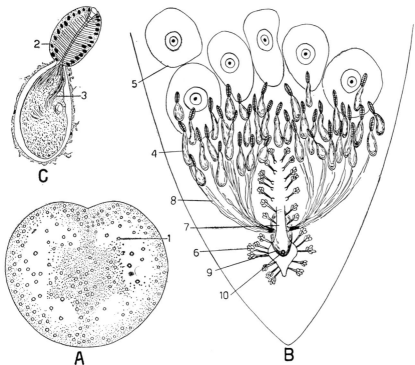

Fig. 49.—Acoela. *A.* Pelagic acoel, *Haplodiscus piger*, Bahamas (*after Böhmig*, 1895). *B.* Rear end of *Anaperus gardineri*, Massachusetts Coast (*after Graff*, 1911) with numerous seminal bursae and adenodactyls. *C.* A bursa enlarged. 1, zooxanthellae; 2, nozzle; 3, mass of sperm; 4, seminal bursa; 5, eggs; 6, adenodactyls; 7, female canal; 8, sperm tracts; 9, penis papilla; 10, common gonopore.

North Atlantic and its adjuncts as the Mediterranean, Caspian Sea, Baltic Sea, Finnish bays, Scandinavian fiords, Murman Coast, etc. Many interesting species were taken on the coasts of Greenland by a collecting expedition in 1926. Several species inhabit the New England coast. Scarcely any acoels are known from Pacific shores (two at Monterey Bay, California, a pelagic species off the Philippines). However, the Acoela have been so insufficiently collected that little weight can be placed on the known distribution.

The taxonomy also suffers from an insufficient knowledge of the group. The known species are arranged in five families, three of which comprise a single species each: *Nemertoderma bathycola, Diopisthoporus longitubus,* and *Ectocotyla paguri.* The first, originally dredged off Greenland at 250 m. (Steinböck, 1931), was later found in numbers in shallow water on the Scandinavian Coast (Westblad, 1937). It combines primitive (epidermal nerve plexus, no female ducts, no penis papilla) and advanced (definite intestinal lumen, well-defined testes) characters (Fig. 23*C, D*). *Diopisthoporus* from the Scandinavian Coast has posterior mouth and male pore, long pharynx, no penis papilla, and no female ducts. *Ectocotyla* (Fig. 13*F*) is unique among acoels in its plicate pharynx and caudal adhesive disk. All other acoels that lack female ducts are grouped into the family Proporidae that includes the genera *Proporus* (Fig. 44*B*), *Rimicola, Haplodiscus* (Fig. 49*A*), *Avagina, Achoerus, Afronta* (Fig. 37*D*), *Childia,* and several of the new Greenland genera. Acoela with one or more seminal bursae, female or common gonopore, and vagina fall into the family Convolutidae with genera *Otocelis* (Fig. 44*F*), *Aphanostoma, Aechmalotus, Convoluta* (Figs. 13*B,* 44*D*), *Amphiscolops* (Figs. 13*D,* 44*E,* 46*A, F,* 47), *Polychoerus* (Figs. 13*E,* 24*D*), *Monochoerus, Palmenia* (Fig. 44*C*), *Tetraposthia* (Fig. 23*A*), *Anaperus* (Fig. 49*B*), and others. The first three are entocommensals of echinoderms. *Convoluta* with many species, some green from algal symbionts, some with the habit of rolling up like a cornucopia (Fig. 13*B, C*), is one of the best known acoels. *Amphiscolops langerhansi,* originally from the Madeira and Canary Islands, has become established in tanks at Bermuda and made the object of several studies (Welsh, 1936; Hyman, 1937). The genus *Polychoerus,* orange-red worms with a tail filament (Fig. 13*E*) and one bursa with many nozzles, is limited to North American coasts, having one species *caudatus* (Mark, 1892) off Cape Cod, and another, *carmelensis* (Costello, 1938b) off California. *Anaperus* and *Monochoerus* are provided with one or more prostatoids along the male canal (Fig. 49*B*).

15. Order Rhabdocoela.—The rhabdocoels are small worms, ranging mostly from 0.3 to 2 or 3 mm. in length, although larger forms, to 15 mm., occur. The body is of elongated slender to plump shape, of simple contour, without tentacles or projections, except that some genera (*Rhynchoscolex, Alaurina,* Figs. 32*B,* 50*A*) have a narrowed snout, and the Temnocephalida (Figs. 57, 58) are provided with 2 to 12 tentacles. Most are colorless or faintly colored and more or less transparent, but some are green from symbiotic algae (Fig. 36*A*) or brown. The body is clothed in a cellular or syncytial epidermis usually completely ciliated; dorsal ciliation is reduced or absent in sand-dwelling and terrestrial rhabdocoels, and ciliation is scanty or wholly lacking in the ectocommensal Temnocephalida. Ciliated pits and grooves are common among the lower rhabdocoels. The epidermis is usually strewn with bundles of rhabdites, and rhammite tracks leading to the anterior tip are often present, notably in the mesotomine and temnocephalid groups. The group as a whole is rather lacking in adhesive organs, although adhesive areas (Fig. 51C) are characteristic of certain genera (*Dalyellia, Macrostomum*) and of ectocommensal (Figs. 57, 58) and sand-dwelling types

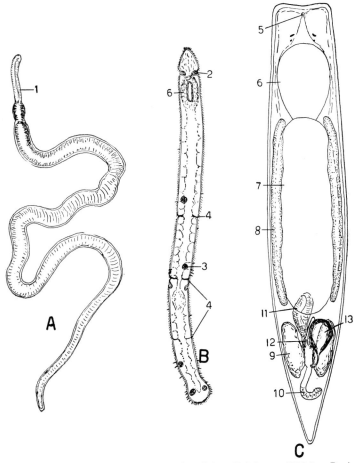

Fig. 50.—Rhabdocoela. *A. Rhynchoscolex* (*after Reisinger*, 1924a). *B.* A marine *Microstomum*, from life, California. *C. Castrella marginata*, family Dalyelliidae, from life, New York. 1, snout; 2, ciliated pits; 3, cluster of nematocysts; 4, fission plane; 5, mouth; 6, pharynx; 7, intestine; 8, yolk glands; 9, testes; 10, ovary; 11, copulatory bursa; 12, penis stylet; 13, stalked egg capsule forming in uterus.

(Fig. 76). Adhesive papillae are probably responsible for the adhesive power of these areas. The rhabdocoels lack the cluster of frontal glands common among the Acoela although a few such gland cells are sometimes present in the anterior end. The surface usually bears sensory spines, hairs, and bristles. A statocyst occurs only in a few of the lower genera (*Catenula*, Fig. 29D). Most of the rhabdocoels have a pair of

eyes, sometimes one eye, sometimes four (*Castrella*, Fig. 50*C*).   The eyes
are of the epidermal pigment-spot type in *Microstomum* and *Alaurina*
(Fig. 32*C*); otherwise they are of the pigment-cup type with one pigment
cell and one to three retinal cells.   There is mostly a paucity of mesenchymal gland cells apart from those connected with adhesive areas or with
the reproductive system.   The brain is either a bilobed mass or a broad
band passing in front of the eyes; into it stream sensory nerves from the
anterior margin and from it a pair of strong ventral cords proceeds caudad.
Primitive members (*Rhynchoscolex*, Reisinger, 1924a) may have four
pairs of longitudinal cords, and a few others may have short dorsal, sometimes also lateral, cords; but in general rhabdocoels have only the ventral
cords and are also poor in transverse connectives (Fig. 24*C*).   Usually
there is a nerve ring around the pharynx (Fig. 51*A*) or a strong connective
behind it (Fig. 24*C*), or a pair of nerves from the ventral cords branches
into the pharynx.   The digestive system consists of a simple or bulbous
pharynx and a blind sacciform to elongate intestine, mostly of simple
contour, although sometimes lobulated.   There is present a pair of
protonephridia except in the Catenulida which have a single median
nephridium (Fig. 29*A*).   The reproductive system comprises usually a
pair of well-delimited testes, sometimes broken up into lobes or separated
follicles, one ovary or a pair of ovaries, a pair of yolk glands (lacking in
the lower orders), and the copulatory complex.   This on the male side
often includes seminal and prostatic vesicles varyingly related to each
other and to the penis, and a penis that may be a muscular papilla or a
cuticularized structure varying from a simple tube to a complicated array
of rods and teeth (Fig. 38*B–F*).   Some genera have a cirrus (Fig. 39*A–C*).
The female apparatus may include a seminal or copulatory bursa, seminal
receptacle, single or paired uterus, and a variety of gland cells (Fig. 38*B*).

Copulation with mutual insemination (Fig. 46*D*) is the rule among the
rhabdocoels.   The eggs are generally laid singly, each enclosed in a
rounded, oval, or hemispherical albuminoid shell, which will be termed
capsule; this is formed from droplets stored in the periphery of the ripe
egg (Fig. 51*E*) or in the yolk cells.   In some species, two or three or even
several eggs may be enclosed in the capsule.   The lower rhabdocoels
lack yolk glands, and hence only the egg or eggs occupy the interior of
the capsule, but in the higher groups a number of yolk cells is included.
The capsule may have a stalk or filament or disk for attaching it to
objects, and there may be a preformed circular seam along which the
capsule springs open at hatching.   When not attached, the capsules
simply lie among bottom debris.   After attaining sexual maturity, the
rhabdocoels probably continue to reproduce throughout the remainder
of their rather brief existences, but some fresh-water forms show definite
cycles related to habitat.   Particularly inhabitants of temporary ponds,

alpine pools, and arctic and subarctic ponds where the brief season necessitates rapid reproduction, as species of *Dalyellia* and *Mesostoma*, hatch in spring from dormant overwintering eggs, quickly attain sexual maturity, produce a number of thick-shelled eggs, and die as the water dries up or freezes. The eggs can survive freezing and drying, although these are probably not prerequisite to hatching, and hatch the following spring as the ice melts or water again fills the ponds.

It is characteristic of many members of the family Typhloplanidae, as *Mesostoma*, *Typhloplana*, *Bothromesostoma*, etc., that they produce two kinds of eggs, thin-shelled or *subitaneous* and thick-shelled or *dormant* eggs. The former are smaller with a thinner capsule and fewer yolk cells than the latter and develop immediately without passing through a dormant period (Fig. 36*A*). The thick-shelled eggs are the same as the regular eggs of other rhabdocoels and in the typhloplanids probably must lie dormant for some time. The subitaneous eggs appear to be an adaptation for quickly increasing the number of individuals during the summer. Any one worm may produce first subitaneous, then dormant eggs, or may lay only the latter from the start. There is a tendency for the greater production of subitaneous eggs early in the season and for increasing numbers of dormant eggs toward autumn, until finally only the latter are formed. According to Bresslau (1903), subitaneous eggs are produced before the animal has attained full sexual maturity, and this accounts for the thin shell and paucity of yolk cells. The subitaneous eggs are fertilized by the individual's own sperm (this appears to be one of the very few authentic cases of self-fertilization among the Turbellaria) and develop inside the mother, either in the uteri (Fig. 45*A*) or in the mesenchyme (Fig 36*A*), into young worms that escape mostly by rupture and death of the parent. The dormant eggs are cross-fertilized.

The rhabdocoels are common throughout the world in standing fresh waters and the littoral zone of ocean shores, chiefly on sandy and muddy bottoms. They also occur sparingly in flowing fresh waters and in damp terrestrial habitats (Reisinger, 1924b). Species of *Alaurina* are pelagic, and one of these (Fig. 32*B*) has long bristles, presumably for buoyancy. Rhabdocoels also inhabit hot springs as *Macrostomum thermale* in hot salt springs (45°C. 3 per cent salt content) in western Java (Reisinger, 1933). Although ordinary rhabdocoels often get into cave waters, there appears to be a genuine cave rhabdocoel, white and eyeless, "*Vortex*" *cavicolens* Packard 1883, in streams in one of the Kentucky caves.[1] Fresh-water and marine species may spread into brackish waters, and some species appear to be equally at home in salt, brackish, and fresh water as *Macrostomum appendiculatum* and *Gyratrix hermaphroditus* (Fig. 36*B*). *Phae-*

---

[1] The generic name *Vortex* is invalid for turbellarians, and it is impossible to determine the genus of this worm without further study.

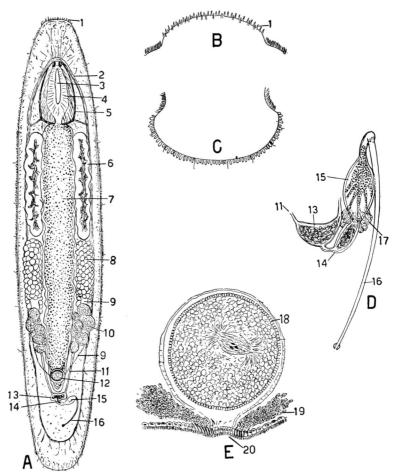

Fig. 51. Rhabdocoela (continued). *A. Macrostomum gigas. B.* Anterior end of same, showing sensory spines. *C.* Posterior end of same, showing protrusible adhesive papillae. *D.* Male copulatory apparatus of same. *E.* Section through the female antrum of the same, showing shell-forming droplets in periphery of the egg. (*All after Hyman,* 1943.) 1, sensory spines; 2, ventral nerve cords (confluent at rear); 3, mouth; 4, pharynx simplex; 5, nerve ring around pharynx; 6, testes; 7, intestine; 8, ovary; 9, oviduct; 10, ripe eggs in oviduct; 11, sperm duct; 12, egg in female antrum; 13, spermiducal vesicle; 14, seminal vesicle; 15, prostatic vesicle; 16, penis stylet; 17, prostatic glands; 18, shell-forming droplets; 19, cement glands; 20, female gonopore.

nocora (?) *salinarum* occurs in salt pits of high salt content near Trieste. A number of rhabdocoels, chiefly dalyellioids, inhabit the digestive tract or body spaces of mollusks, echinoderms, and crustaceans; they are probably commensal rather than parasitic except *Fecampia* (see below). There are a number of rhabdocoels with ectocommensal or epizoic habits, and these are generally provided with one or more adhesive areas for clinging to the host animal. They belong to the suborder Temnocephalida, discussed later, except *Typhlorhynchus nanus*, a typhloplanoid species, with a tactile snout and posterior adhesive region, inhabiting the parapodia of the polychaete *Nephthys* (Laidlaw, 1902).

Although the rhabdocoels are among the most common animals of fresh water and the ocean littoral, they have been poorly studied outside of Europe and Asia, greatly neglected in the western hemisphere, and but little investigated in tropical and subtropical regions. The indications are that both fresh-water and marine species are much more numerous in temperate and cold zones than in warmer regions. In the United States, rhabdocoels have been made the object of particular study only in a few eastern states and their coasts, chiefly under the leadership of Kepner of the University of Virginia, and undoubtedly rich material awaits study in other areas. The genera known to occur in the United States have been arranged in key form by Ruebush (1941), but many additional genera will certainly be discovered in the future. Many fresh-water species are cosmopolitan, and others are undoubtedly poly-typic with many geographical races and varieties. Thus the cosmo-politan *Mesostoma ehrenbergii* exists in the United States as a subspecies *wardii* (Fig. 45A), differing from the European type in size, form and number of chromosomes, and some details of the copulatory apparatus (Husted and Ruebush, 1940). One must beware, however, of facile identification of American rhabdocoels with Eurasian species.

a. Suborder Notandropora or Catenulida.—This group includes only a few fresh-water genera with simple pharynx, single median protonephrid-ium, and four pairs of longitudinal nerve cords. The gastrodermis is ciliated. Reports that the protonephridium lacks flame bulbs are clearly mistaken as Kepner, Carter, and Hess (1933) saw them in *Stenostomum* and Marcus (1945) recorded them throughout the Catenulida. The principal genera are: *Catenula* (Fig. 29D) with a statocyst, *Rhynchoscolex* (Fig. 50A) with a long snout, *Stenostomum* (Fig. 29A) with ciliated pits, and *Suomina* (= *Fuhrmannia*) with a transverse ciliated groove around the base of the head. Excellent work has been done on the Catenulida by Marcus (1945), who divides the order into three families and reports two new genera, *Chordarium* with brain at the anterior tip and *Dasyhormus*, similar to *Catenula*. *Stenostomum* with many species, most of them cosmopolitan, is one of the most common invertebrates, found everywhere in standing waters and protozoan cultures, and is probably the most familiar and investigated rhabdocoel. The Catenulida repro-duce asexually by transverse fission, forming chains of zooids (Figs. 9, 29, 32B) and are seldom seen in the sexual state. Sexual conditions are best known for *Stenostomum* (Sabussow, 1897; Sekera, 1903, 1906; Van Cleave, 1929; Nuttycombe, 1932; Kepner *et al.*, 1933; Marcus, 1945) but have also been described for other genera by Marcus. *Stenostomum* is

markedly protandrous, developing testes in early fall, ovaries later.
From a single testicular mass dorsal to the pharynx a short male canal
having a muscular penial thickening leads to a dorsal gonopore (Fig.
48*B*). The female system consists in its entirety of one to several

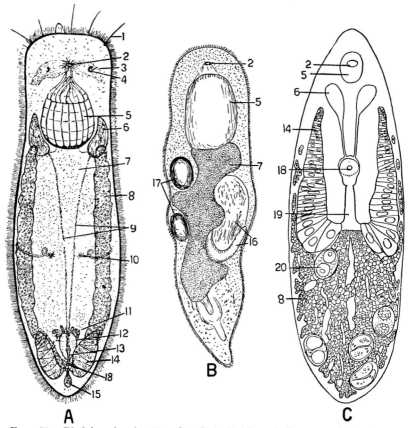

Fig. 52.—Rhabdocoela (continued). Dalyellioida. *A. Provortex (after Ruebush,*
1935a). B. Plagiostomum infested with two specimens of *Oekiocolax plagiostomorum (after*
Reisinger, 1930).   *C. Paravortex gemellipara (after Ball,* 1916) from the clam *Modiolus.*   1,
sensory hairs; 2, mouth; 3, brain; 4, eye; 5, pharynx; 6, testes; 7, intestine; 8, yolk gland;
9, sperm ducts; 10, nephridiopore; 11, prostatic glands; 12, penis bulb; 13, penis stylet;
14, ovary; 15, seminal receptacle; 16, parasite; 17, eggs of parasite; 18, common gonopore;
19, female antrum; 20, capsules containing two embryos.

ovaries, each of which matures one egg per season.   Reisinger (1924a)
failed to find any male system in *Rhynchoscolex* and claims parthenogenesis for this and other Catenulida; Sekera believed that self-fertilization
obtains; but Kepner *er al.* saw hypodermic impregnation (Fig. 48*A*) in
Stenostomum during the male phase, and this is probably the correct state
of affairs, for this genus at least.   The fertilized egg enclosed in a capsule
is released by rupture, and thereafter the female usually dies.   The egg

hatches in the laboratory in 2 to 4 weeks but in nature probably remains dormant until spring. Asexual reproduction continues during the male phase but is inhibited and regenerative power lost during the female condition. Although external factors appear to control the onset of sexuality in *Stenostomum* in nature, no one has succeeded in inducing the sexual phase in laboratory cultures. Such cultures may run for years through hundreds of asexual generations or may continue indefinitely in the male phase.

b. Suborder Opisthandropora or Macrostomida.—This group has a simple pharynx, one pair of longitudinal nerve cords, and complete male and female systems with separate gonopores. The gastrodermis is ciliated as in the Catenulida, but there are the usual two protonephridia. The suborder comprises two families: Macrostomidae, without asexual reproduction, and Microstomidae, with zooid formation. In the former the principal genus is *Macrostomum* (Fig. 51) with many species and sub-species, common in fresh waters, and also extending into brackish and salt waters (Ferguson, 1939–1940). The rear end, often of spatulate shape, is adhesive. There is a pair of ovaries and oviducts connected to the female antrum and a pair of testes and sperm ducts connected to the male apparatus, which consists of spermiducal vesicle (not always present), seminal vesicle, prostatic vesicle, and tubular penis stylet of varying form (Fig. 51*D*). The Microstomidae comprise two genera, *Alaurina* with papillate snout and marine pelagic habits (Fig. 32*B*), and *Microstomum* (Fig. 50*B*) with ciliated pits and intestine extending anterior to the mouth. Both form chains of zooids as in *Stenostomum*. The nematocysts of *Microstomum* were discussed above (page 71). Most microstomids have eyes which may be of the pigment-spot type (Fig. 32*C*). Sexually mature specimens, probably related to environmental conditions, have seldom been seen. Marked protandry obtains; the sexual system differs from that of *Macrostomum* chiefly in that the ovary and oviduct are single (Meixner, 1924a). The fertilized egg remains dormant until spring.

Both the Catenulida and Macrostomida lack yolk glands, and yolk and shell substance are stored by the egg's own activity. As the egg is about to be laid, its shell-forming spherules assemble at the egg periphery and fuse and harden to a capsule (Fig. 51*E*).

c. Suborder Lecithophora: Dalyellioida.—All the Lecithophora lack asexual reproduction and have one or two yolk glands that furnish yolk cells to be incorporated with the egg inside the capsule. The yolk gland is primitively continuous with the ovary forming the *germovitellarium;* but in most Lecithophora the two are distinct. The Lecithophora have a pair of protonephridia, and only the ventral nerve cords are well developed.

The dalyellioid Lecithophora are readily known by the doliiform pharynx leading inward from the anteriorly placed mouth (Fig. 34*D*). There are usually paired testes, an armed penis, single or paired germovitellaria or separate ovaries and yolk glands, often a seminal or copulatory bursa, uterus, and common gonopore (Fig. 38*B*). The Provorticidae, with posterior gonopore and mostly a tubular penis stylet include terrestrial (Reisinger, 1923, 1924c), marine, and fresh-water species, also the parasitic *Oekiocolax plagiostomorum*, Greenland, inhabiting the mesenchyme of the alloeocoel *Plagiostomum* in which it causes ovarian degeneration (Reisinger, 1930, Fig. 52*B*). *Provortex* (Fig. 52*A*) is the only member of this family that has been found in the United States (Ruebush, 1935a). The Graffillidae, with more anterior gonopore and unarmed penis, comprise three genera: *Bresslauilla* (see page 123), free-living, and the entocommensal *Graffilla* and *Paravortex*. *Graffilla*, with long tubular coiled ovaries, has three species inhabiting the viscera of marine snails and one species in the shipworm *Teredo*. *Paravortex*, with branched yolk glands, lives in the viscera or mantle cavity of marine bivalves; the thin capsules, containing usually two eggs and a mass of yolk cells, are given off into the mesenchyme where they develop into young worms that escape by rupture. *Paravortex gemellipara* (Fig. 52*C*) occurs on the New England Coast in the clam *Modiolus* (Linton, 1910; Ball, 1916). The Umagillidae with small rounded pharynx, posterior gonopore, and conspicuous yolk glands, often lobed or branched, all inhabit the coelom or digestive tract of other animals, chiefly echinoderms. In this family the female system has a tubular uterus in which the long-stalked egg capsules are formed (Fig. 53*B*). The genera are: *Anoplodium*, *Anoplodiera* (Fig. 53*A*), *Wahlia*, *Umagilla*, *Xenometra*, and *Cleistogamia* in holothurians; *Desmote*, *Bicladus* in crinoids; *Syndesmis*, *Syndisyrinx* (Fig. 53*B*) in sea urchins; *Collastoma* in sipunculoids (Wahl, 1906, 1909, 1910; Bock, 1925; Westblad, 1926, 1930; Ozaki, 1932; Baer, 1938; Lehman, 1946). Very little is known of the occurrence of these genera on American coasts except that *Syndisyrinx* (Fig. 53*B*) inhabits a Californian sea urchin. *Pterastericola fedotovi*, only member of its family, lives in sea stars of the genus *Pteraster* off north European coasts (Beklemischev, 1916). Whether the umagillids and graffillids are commensals or parasites is not determinable on available evidence, but probably they are harmless commensals. The Fecampiidae, known only from European coasts, are, however, definitely parasitic. The young *Fecampia* (Fig. 53*D*) has eyes, mouth, long buccal tube, pharynx, and intestine; it somehow enters the haemocoel of various marine crustaceans and there grows to sexual maturity, losing all these structures except the intestine (Fig. 53*C*, Caullery and Mesnil, 1903). It then leaves the host and secretes a bottle-shaped capsule in which it deposits clusters, each consisting of two eggs and many yolk

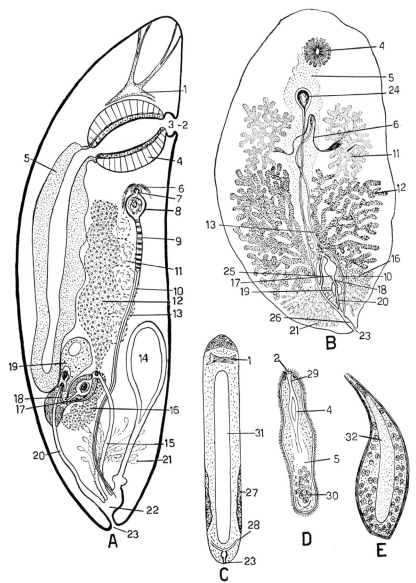

FIG. 53.—Dalyellioida (continued). Umagillidae, Fecampiidae. *A. Anoplodiera voluta (after Westblad, 1930)*, from the gut of sea cucumbers, sagittal section. *B. Syndisyr-inx* from the gut of California sea urchins, from life. *C–E, Fecampia, (after Caullery and Mesnil, 1903).* *C.* Adult without mouth or pharynx. *D.* Juvenile stage with digestive system and eyes. *E. Fecampia* secreting the capsule containing many clusters of eggs and yolk cells. 1, brain; 2, mouth; 3, pharyngeal cavity; 4, pharynx; 5, intestine; 6, sperm ducts; 7, spermiducal vesicle; 8, seminal vesicle; 9, penis bulb; 10, penis stylet; 11, testis (only one shown in *A*); 12, yolk gland (one shown in *A*); 13, ejaculatory duct; 14, uterus; 15, vagina; 16, ovary; 17, seminal receptacle; 18, insemination canal; 19, copulatory bursa; 20, bursal canal; 21, cement glands; 22, common antrum; 23, common gonopore; 24, long-stalked capsule in the uterus; 25, ovovitelline duct; 26, vagina; 27, hermaphroditic gonad; 28, gonoduct; 29, buccal tube; 30, yolk in intestine; 31, space; 32, worm inside capsule.

141

cells (Fig. 53*E*), thereupon dying. The related *Glanduloderma* (Jäger-sten, 1941), also lacking mouth and pharynx, inhabits the mesenchyme of myzostomids.

The Dalyelliidae, a family almost exclusively fresh-water, is distinguished by the cuticularized penis, composed of a complicated array of bars, rods, rings, and teeth (Fig. 38). The principal genus *Dalyellia* (old name, *Vortex*) is common everywhere in fresh waters, presenting numerous species and subspecies, differentiated by the details of the penial apparatus (Fig. 38*B–F*). Species and subspecies of *Dalyellia* in the United States have been discussed by Ruebush (1937) and Ruebush and Hayes (1939). A group of forms, exemplified by *D. viridis* with many geographical races, is green because of algal symbionts (see below).[1] Another dalyelliid genus found in the United States is *Castrella*, with four eyes and penial apparatus in a separate pocket (Fig. 50*C*).

d. Suborder Lecithophora: Typhloplanoida.—The typhloplanid rhabdocoels are distinguished by the rosulate pharynx (although a few species have a doliiform pharynx) and the more posterior mouth; there is a common gonopore or separate male and female pores. Besides the main family, Typhloplanidae, there are several other families of one to a few genera, chiefly of taxonomic interest. The Typhloplanidae are mainly fresh-water forms but also include most of the terrestrial rhabdocoels, which have obviously migrated from forest streams and pools into moist habitats of the forest floor. This is the largest rhabdocoel family, with numerous genera and species, arranged into several subfamilies based on the relative positions of testes and yolk glands and the location of the nephridiopores. The Protoplanellinae with ventral testes and surface nephridiopores include *Protoplanella*, *Amphibolella*, and several terrestrial forms (Reisinger, 1924b). The Typhloplaninae with ventral testes and nephridia opening into the pharyngeal cavity include *Strongylostoma*, *Typhloplana* with green symbionts (Fig. 36*A*), *Castrada*, and several others. *Rhynchomesostoma* with contractile snout and nephridia opening into the genital antrum is the sole genus of the Rhynchomesostominae. The Phaenocorinae are represented chiefly by *Phaenocora* (Fig. 39*A*) with greatly branched yolk glands, dorsal testes, cirrus, and surface nephridiopores. An admirable study of this genus in the United States has been made by Gilbert (1935, 1937, 1938). The Olisthanellinae have dorsal testes and surface nephridiopores but no cirrus; the chief genus *Olisthanella* is represented in the United States (Ruebush, 1935b). The Mesostominae are characterized by the dorsal or lateral testes, often

---

[1] Gieysztor (1938) has proposed that only these green forms retain the name *Dalyellia* and has created a new name, *Microdalyellia*, for nongreen species. The author is unable to grant generic significance to the presence or absence of zoochlorellae.

lobulated or subdivided into several masses, and the opening of the
nephridia into the pharyngeal cavity (Fig. 33*B*). The chief genus
Mesostoma (Fig. 45*A*, *B*) is one of the most common fresh-water rhabdocoels, with numerous species throughout the world, some cosmopolitan.
The reproductive system of *Mesostoma*, with single ovary, seminal
receptacle, copulatory bursa, long paired uteri, and penis bulb usually
combining seminal and prostatic vesicles, is shown in Fig. 54. The
uteri, containing the hemispherical, hard-shelled dormant eggs, are often
conspicuous in the living animal. The known species of *Mesostoma*
have been reviewed by Ferguson and Hayes (1941). *M. ehrenbergii*

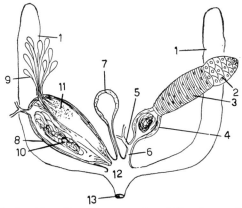

Fig. 54.—Typhloplanoida. Copulatory complex of *Mesostoma*, schematic. 1, uterus;
2, ovary; 3, oviduct; 4, seminal receptacle; 5, common yolk duct; 6, ovovitelline duct; 7,
copulatory bursa; 8, penis bulb; 9, prostatic glands; 10, seminal vesicle in penis bulb; 11,
prostatic vesicle in penis bulb; 12, common antrum; 13, common gonopore.

because of its large size (to 15 mm.) and broad, thin, transparent body
is often selected as a textbook type; a variant of this species termed
wardii (Fig. 45*A*) occurs in the United States and has proved amenable
to laboratory cultivation. *Bothromesostoma* differs from *Mesostoma* in
having a ventral pit and a canal connecting copulatory bursa and ovovitelline duct. Two other subfamilies need not be mentioned.

 e. Suborder Lecithophora: Kalyptorhynchia.—The kalyptorhynchid
rhabdocoels are readily recognized by the presence in the anterior end
of a protrusible glandulo-muscular adhesive organ, usually termed proboscis (Figs. 55, 56), employed in the capture of prey. When the sensory
bristles make contact with prey (chiefly copepods), the proboscis shoots
out with lightning speed, secures the prey by the viscous secretion of its
glands, and then bends around so that the food is brought in contact
with the protruded pharynx (Meixner, 1925). The proboscis exhibits
a great variety of structure and grades of complexity, some of which are
shown in Figs. 55 and 56, and may be armed with hooks. The kalyptor-

hynchids are chiefly marine, inhabiting sandy bottoms of coastal waters, especially in bays, sounds, etc.   Very few were known until recent years when new methods of collecting microscopic forms from such habitats revealed many new genera and species in such regions as the Bay of Kiel, Finnish Gulf, etc. (Meixner, 1923, 1924b, 1925, 1926, 1928, 1929,

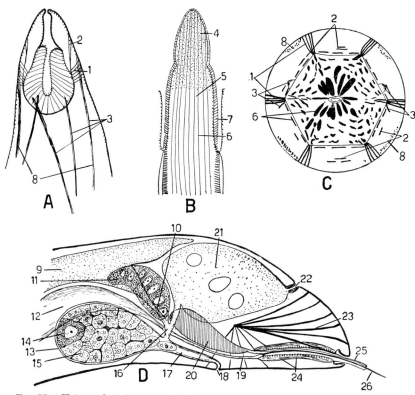

FIG. 55.—Kalyptorhynchia.   *A–D. Gyratrix hermaphroditus (after Meixner, 1915, 1929).* A. Proboscis in resting state.   B. Proboscis protruded.   C. Cross section through the proboscis, showing its musculature.   D. Copulatory complex, sagittal view.   1, fixators; 2, protractors; 3, retractors; 4, end cone; 5, muscle cone; 6, longitudinal musculature; 7, transverse musculature; 8, integumental retractors; 9, yolk gland; 10, yolk duct; 11, ovary; 12, seminal vesicle; 13, uterus; 14, egg; 15, yolk cells; 16, ovovitelline duct; 17, vagina; 18, female gonopore; 19, ejaculatory duct; 20, prostatic vesicle; 21, seminal bursa; 22, bursal pore; 23, protractors of the penis sheath; 24, penis bulb; 25, penis sheath; 26, penis stylet.

1938; Karling, 1931).   The kalyptorhynchids are divided into two groups, the Eukalyptorhynchia with undivided proboscis (Figs. 55, 56) and the Schizorhynchia, in which the proboscis is bifurcated (Fig. 56D).   The best known member of the former group is *Gyratrix hermaphroditus* (Figs. 36B, 55A–D), common throughout the world in fresh, brackish, and salt waters (see page 209).   *Gyratrix* is unique among the flatworms in having chitin; the copulatory bursa has a chitinous lining (Flory and Showalter,

1930). Other well-known eukalyptorhynchids are *Acrorhynchus* (Fig. 56*A*) and *Polycystis* (Fig. 56*B*). The Schizorhynchia for years were known only by the genus *Schizorhynchus* (Fig. 56*D*), but recently many new genera were found and described (Meixner, 1928, 1938; de Beauchamp, 1927).

f. Suborder Temnocephalida.—The Temnocephalida, discovered in Chile in 1846, were first thought to be leeches, then regarded as trematodes, then for a long period made into a separate class Temnocephaloidea between Turbellaria and Trematoda. Their turbellarian nature was realized by Grobben in 1909 and has since been acknowledged by all students of the group. They are often considered to constitute a sixth order of Turbellaria, but their dalyellioid nature is now generally recognized and hence, following Fyfe (1942), they are here placed under Rhabdocoela as a suborder.

The Temnocephalida lead an ectocommensal existence on freshwater animals, chiefly crayfish, prawns, isopods, and other crustaceans, less often turtles and snails, occurring on the external surface or in the branchial chamber. They are limited to tropical and subtropical countries, and are most common in Australia, New Zealand, and South America, but species also occur in India, Balkan Peninsula, Central America, and various South Pacific islands. The Temnocephalida are obviously modified for an epizoic existence. They are small, flattened, mostly colorless and somewhat transparent worms, distinguished from other rhabdocoels by their tentacles and adhesive organs. The tentacles are typically 5, 6, or 12 finger-like anterior projections as in *Temnocephala* (Fig. 57*A*); but in *Scutariella, Monodiscus,* and *Caridinicola* (Fig. 58*C*), there are only 2 short stumpy tentacles, and *Actinodactylella* (Fig. 57*B*) has 12 distributed along the body. Tentacles are absent in *Didymorchis*, formerly placed in the Dalyelliidae. *Craspedella* (Fig. 58*A*) has papillate bands on the dorsal posterior region. All temnocephalids possess an adhesive disk at the rear end; except *Caridinicola* (Fig. 58*C*) in which there is instead a pair of adhesive pits. Some genera also have an anterior adhesive organ. The adhesive organ in no case has the structure of a true sucker such as is characteristic of trematodes. By alternately attaching tentacles and adhesive organ, the temnocephalids are able to move about over their hosts in a leech-like manner.

The syncytial epidermis usually has a clear border apparently cuticular and lacks cilia except in a few species that have a limited ciliation. Paired clusters of gland cells furnish adenal rhabdites to the anterior end and to the tentacles, and gland cells also supply the adhesive organs. The nervous system comprises a subepidermal and a submuscular net; in the latter are differentiated many sensory nerves from the tentacles into the brain and three pairs of longitudinal cords with transverse connec-

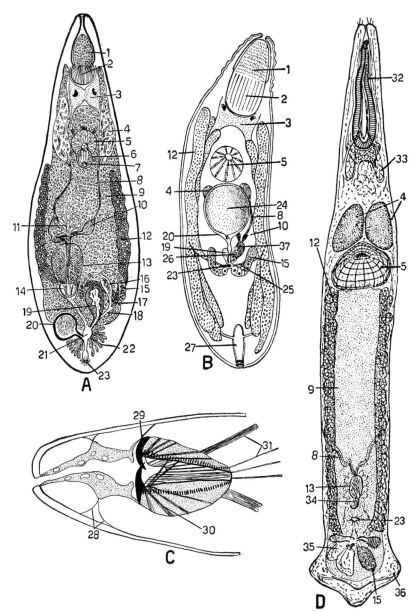

Fig. 56.—Kalyptorhynchia (continued). *A. Acrorhynchus (after Graff*, 1905). *B. Polycystis goettei (after Bresslau*, 1906). *C. Gnathorhynchus*, proboscis armed with hooks *(after Meixner*, 1929). *D. Schizorhynchus arenarius (after Beauchamp*, 1927). 1, end cone of proboscis; 2, muscle cone of proboscis; 3, brain; 4, testes; 5, pharynx; 6, pharyngeal cavity; 7, mouth; 8, sperm ducts; 9, intestine; 10, spermiducal vesicles; 11, prostatic glands; 12, yolk gland; 13, penis bulb; 14, penis papilla; 15, ovaries; 16, seminal receptacle; 17, common yolk duct; 18, ovovitelline duct; 19, seminal bursa; 20, uterus; 21, common antrum; 22, cement glands; 23, common gonopore; 24, capsule forming in uterus; 25, yolk duct; 26, prostatic vesicle; 27, excretory ampulla; 28, dilator muscles; 29, hooks; 30, flexors of hooks; 31, retractor muscles; 32, bifurcated proboscis; 33, proboscis glands; 34, penis stylet; 35, copulatory bursa; 36, caudal adhesive region; 37, seminal vesicle.

146

tions (Fig. 58*B*). The tentacles are undoubtedly tactile, and in addition tactile bristles and papillae may be present. Most species have a pair of eyes, each of which is double with a retinal cell at each end facing the central pigment cell. The digestive system is dalyellioid with doliiform pharynx and sacciform intestine. There is a protonephridium on each side (Fig. 58*C*) provided with terminal bulbs and lateral flames and opening anteriorly, mostly dorsally, by way of an excretory bladder. The nephridia of the two sides are confluent anteriorly and posteriorly, and from the anterior anastomosis branches proceed into the tentacles. Paranephrocytes are also present. The testes occur as one pair, or each is subdivided into two to six parts (Fig. 57). The male system includes a spermiducal vesicle, seminal vesicle, prostatic glands opening into the penis base or into a prostatic vesicle, and a cirrus or a penial cuticular apparatus varying from a simple stylet to a dalyelliid complex. There is a single ovary and a pair of yolk glands often much subdivided or forming an anastomosing net; these connect with the female canal which also usually bears a large seminal bursa and one or more small seminal receptacles. The seminal bursa is unusually active in digesting and absorbing excess sex products. The female antrum, often called uterus, is enlarged and thickened for the secretion of the egg capsule, and sometimes lined with teeth. There is a common antrum and gonopore. The oval capsules are fastened to the exterior of the host or to its gills.

Although the temnocephalids do not voluntarily leave their hosts, some species can live for weeks or months when removed from them; others die in a short time. The group is commensal, not parasitic, since the food consists of small animals and diatoms available in the habitat. The respiratory water currents maintained by the host animals are probably beneficial to the temnocephalids. *Scutariella didactyla* on a prawn in Montenegro apparently feeds on its host's body fluids and hence may be an ectoparasite (Mrazek, 1906).

16. Order Alloeocoela.—The Alloeocoela are a group difficult of precise definition, for the more primitive members grade into the Acoela, from which they differ chiefly in having a digestive cavity, and the higher members grade into the Tricladida.[1] Although some are minute, the alloeocoels are on the whole larger than the acoels and rhabdocoels, many ranging from 1 or 2 to 8 or 10 mm. in length, and some species are 15 to 25 mm. long. The largest member is *Baicalarctia gulo*, from Lake Baikal, 40 mm. in length (Friedmann, 1926). The alloeocoels tend to a cylindroid shape, plump to elongate; the group includes a number of long slender forms such as *Prorhynchus stagnalis* (Fig. 59*A*). Ciliated

[1] Meixner (1938), in recognition of this affinity, makes the triclads a section under the alloeocoel suborder Seriata. He also considers *Hofstenia* to be an acoel, but it would be preferable to transfer *Nemertoderma* to the alloeocoels.

pits and grooves are of common occurrence, and a caudal adhesive region with adhesive papillae is present in most Seriata (Fig. 29*C*).   Reminiscent of the Acoela is the presence of a cluster of frontal glands in several genera (*Hofstenia, Enterostomula, Protomonotresis, Hydrolimax,* Fig. 18, *Bothriomolus, Baicalarctia*), and of a statocyst in some forms (*Hofstenia,* Fig. 31*F, Otomesostoma,* family Monocelididae, Fig. 29*C*). Many alloeocoels lack eyes but some have one or two pairs.   The nervous

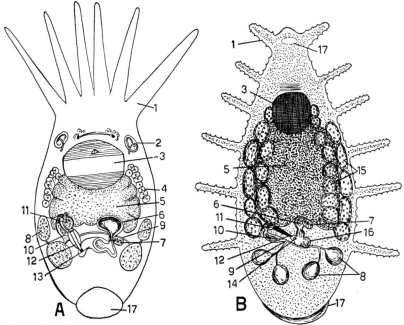

Fig. 57.—Temnocephalida. *A. Temnocephala (after Haswell,* 1893). *B. Actino-dactylella (after Haswell,* 1893). 1, tentacles; 2, excretory ampulla; 3, pharynx; 4, tentacle glands; 5, intestine; 6, bursa; 7, ovary; 8, testis; 9, sperm duct; 10, seminal vesicle; 11, prostatic vesicle; 12, penis stylet; 13, common antrum; 14, common gonopore; 15, yolk glands; 16, uterus; 17, adhesive disk.

system is characterized by three or four pairs of longitudinal cords with transverse connections (Fig. 24*A*).   There is a pair of protonephridia, but these often have two or three main branches on each side and a number of nephridiopores (Fig. 36*F*).   The pharynx is of the simple, doliiform (variable), or plicate type and the intestine varies from a simply contoured sac to a considerably diverticulated organ, finally approaching the triclad condition as in *Bothrioplana* (Fig. 35*D*).   There are usually several to many small testes and a pair of ovaries.   The alloeocoels are predominantly marine, found in the littoral zone, among vegetation and especially on sandy and mucky bottoms; they also extend into brackish waters, and some occur in fresh water, especially *Otomeso-*

stoma, Bothrioplana, and members of the families Prorhynchidae and Plagiostomidae. Species of Prorhynchidae also extend into moist terrestrial habitats. Some alloeocoels have ectoparasitic or ectocommensal habits.

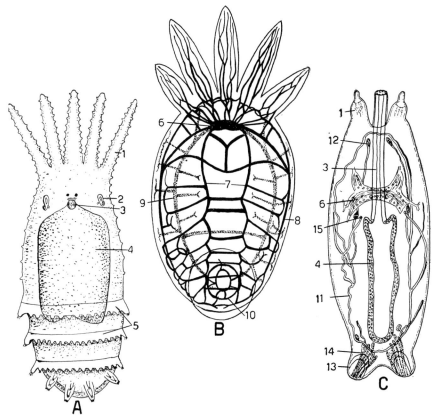

Fig. 58.—Temnocephalida (continued). *A. Craspedella (after Haswell,* 1893). *B.* Nervous system of *Temnocephala (after Merton,* 1913). *C. Caridinicola (after Plate,* 1914). 1, tentacles; 2, excretory ampullae; 3, pharynx; 4, intestine; 5, papillate bands; 6, brain; 7, dorsal cord; 8, lateral cords; 9, ventral cords; 10, nerve ring in adhesive disk; 11, protonephridial tubules; 12, athrocytes; 13, adhesive pit; 14, glands of same; 15, nephridiopore.

a. Suborder Archoophora.—This consists of the single species, *Proporoplana jenseni,* dredged off Greenland (Reisinger, 1935). The animal, 1 mm. long, has a frontal gland, buccal tube, plicate pharynx, no female ducts, and a simple male copulatory apparatus opening posteriorly. Although regarded by Reisinger as a rhabdocoel, the animal fits better into the Alloeocoela.

b. Suborder Lecithoepitheliata.—In this group there are no yolk glands, but the single or paired germovitellaria consist of loose clusters, each composed of an ovocyte encircled by nutritive cells (Figs. 42*F*, 43). There is a simple female duct or none. There is generally a typical male apparatus armed with a penis stylet. This group comprises the already much-mentioned *Hofstenia* (Fig. 31*F*), marine, Japan (Bock, 1923), *Gnosonesima*, Antarctic (Reisinger, 1926, see page 119), and the Prorhynchidae, with one pair of ciliated pits and male apparatus opening into the buccal tube (Fig. 59). The prorhynchids (monographed by Steinböck, 1927), are common throughout the world in fresh and brackish waters, and also extend into moist terrestrial habitats. There are two genera, *Prorhynchus* with straight and *Geocentrophora* with curved penis stylet (Fig. 59*B*, *C*). *Prorhynchus stagnalis* (Fig. 59*A*), a slender white worm to 6 mm. long, is cosmopolitan, one of the commonest fresh-water turbellarians.

   c. Suborder Cumulata or Holocoela.—In this suborder there are yolk glands more or less distinct from the ovaries, although the ovocytes may still be encircled by a nutritive zone. The intestine has a simple or slightly lobulated contour, and the penis is generally unarmed. In the Pseudostomidae (genera *Pseudostomum*, with ciliated groove (Fig. 60*E*) *Protomonotresis*, Reisinger, 1923, with plicate pharynx), the genital antrum joins the anteriorly placed pharyngeal cavity. In the Cylindrostomidae, with plicate pharynx, the common genitopharyngeal cavity is at the posterior end; here belong several marine genera such as *Cylindrostoma*, *Allostoma*, *Enterostomula* (Carolina Coast, Jones, 1941), and *Hypotrichina* (= *Genostoma*). *Cylindrostoma cyprinae* lives commensally on the gills of various marine bivalves on European coasts. Species of *Hypotrichina* (Fig. 60*C*) with anterior adhesive disk and scanty ciliation are ectoparasitic on the crustacean *Nebalia* in the Mediterranean. The Plagiostomidae (Fig. 60*A*, *B*) have an anterior mouth and posterior gonopore. The principal genus, *Plagiostomum*, with bulbous pharynx, comprises numerous marine species on North American and Eurasian coasts and one or two fresh-water species of which *Plagiostomum lemani*, in European lakes, ponds, and streams, is one of the best known alloeocoels (Hofsten, 1907). An interesting plagiostomid, *Hydrolimax grisea* (Fig. 18) inhabits fresh waters in Pennsylvania and adjacent states; it has a frontal gland and an enormous prostatic vesicle (Hyman, 1938). *Vorticeros*, marine, differs in the plicate pharynx and two tentacles (Fig. 14*C*). In the Multipeniatidae with the single genus *Multipeniata* (page 117), and the Baicalarctiidae with one genus *Baicalarctia*, mouth and gonopore are adjacent in the anterior part of the body.

   d. Suborder Seriata.—The members of this group have a plicate pharynx directed backward, slightly or markedly lobulated intestine, and numerous yolk glands opening into a pair of yolk ducts. The principal family, Monocelididae, has a statocyst, caudal or lateral adhesive area with adhesive papillae, and usually a seminal bursa. *Monocelis* (Fig. 29C), a slender white worm with separate bursal pore (hence three genital pores) has many species common along ocean shores. *Archiloa*, of which a species has been found along the Carolina Coast (Stirewalt, Kepner, and Ferguson, 1940) differs in lacking a bursal pore. *Otoplana*, marine, has a pair of ciliated pits and conspicuous anterior tactile bristles (Fig. 60D) whereas *Bothriomolus* lacks these and instead possesses a frontal organ. The Otomesostomidae comprise the single species *Otomesostoma auditivum*, widely distributed in fresh water, with two pairs of ciliated pits and a statocyst but no adhesive papillae. *Bothrioplana* (Reisinger, 1925), common in fresh water, the only genus of the Bothrioplanidae, has two pairs of ciliated pits and caudal adhesive papillae but no statocyst (Figs. 24A, 35D). Whereas in other Seriata, the intestine passes above the pharynx, in *Bothrioplana* it forks around the pharynx (Fig. 35D) as in triclads, although single behind this organ.

17. Order Tricladida.—The triclad Turbellaria, commonly known as planarians, are familiar objects of classroom study and of zoological research. They are readily recognized by the plicate pharynx and three-branched intestine. They are of larger size than the preceding orders, ranging from 2 or 3 mm. to over 50 cm. in length. They are of elongated form, usually with strongly flattened but sometimes cylindroid body, of solid consistency and coated with slime. Adhesive organs of the glandulo-muscular type are of common occurrence, located usually on the ventral side of the anterior end; a marginal adhesive zone also occurs in fresh-water and marine triclads (page 74). The epidermis is usually ciliated only ventrally and is abundantly supplied with rhabdites, probably all of the adenal type. There are two to many pigment-cup ocelli with numerous retinal and pigment cells, attaining their greatest complexity in land planarians (page 94, Fig. 32F). Eyes are lacking in cave planarians of the family Kenkiidae and in some other forms. The triclads lack frontal glands and a statocyst but are well provided with chemo-, tango-, and rheoreceptors such as the auricular grooves (page 91), sense margins and auricles. The mouth, situated near the body middle, leads into the pharyngeal cavity containing the plicate pharynx, usually cylindrical and attached anteriorly, sometimes (some land planarians) ruffled and attached dorsally. From it extends the highly diverticulated intestine with one main anterior branch proceeding forward and two posterior branches passing backward one to either side of the pharyngeal cavity (Fig. 35E). Secondary fusions and anastomoses of the diverticula are of common occurrence. Polypharyngy obtains in a number of species (page 101). The nephridia consist of a network on each side with numerous nephridiopores (page 111). There is a single pair of small ovaries usually near the anterior end, from each of which an

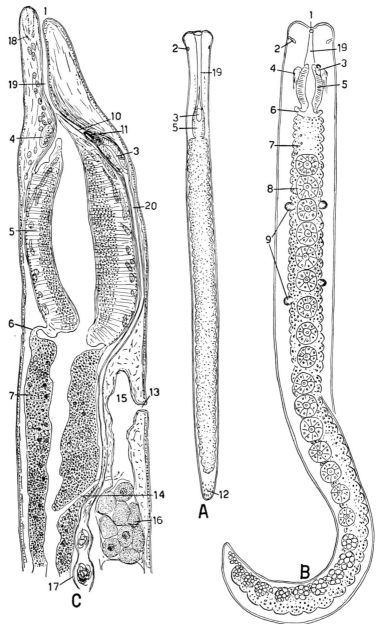

FIG. 59.—Alloeocoela: Prorhynchidae. *A. Prorhynchus stagnalis*, from life, New York State. *B. Geocentrophora tropica*, Canal Zone (*after Hyman*, 1941a). *C.* Sagittal section through the anterior end of *Geocentrophora tropica* (*after Hyman*, 1941a). 1, mouth; 2, ciliated pits; 3, penis; 4, brain; 5, pharynx; 6, esophagus; 7, intestine; 8, follicles of germovitellarium; 9, testes; 10, male canal; 11, penis stylet; 12, adhesive papillae; 13, female gonopore; 14, genitointestinal canal; 15, female antrum; 16, ripe eggs; 17, seminal vesicle; 18, frontal glands; 19, buccogenital canal; 20, ejaculatory duct.

ovovitelline duct proceeds posteriorly collecting from the numerous clusters of yolk glands (Fig. 38*A*). There are several to many testes (rarely, one pair), prepharyngeal in position or strewn along the body length. They connect by sperm ductules with a pair of sperm ducts that as they approach the copulatory complex enlarge to form tubular or rounded spermiducal vesicles packed with masses of sperm. The sperm ducts, singly or after fusion, enter the penis bulb, a spherical or oval muscular and glandular structure, often considered to be a seminal vesicle (Fig. 38*G*). However, it never stores sperm and appears rather to be of the nature of a prostatic vesicle. The triclads lack a typical prostatic apparatus. The penis bulb is continuous with the penis papilla, a conical muscular projection, sometimes lacking, sometimes armed with thorns. This lies in the male antrum continuous with the common antrum receiving the female antrum from behind and opening below by the common gonopore situated posterior to the mouth (Fig. 38*G*). The female system usually includes a copulatory or seminal bursa (sometimes two).[1] The relations of bursa, ovovitelline ducts, and female antrum differ in different groups of triclads and are of taxonomic importance.

Copulation with mutual insemination is the rule among the triclads. In known cases, the sperm are ejaculated directly into the copulatory or seminal bursa (Fig. 48*C*). They soon leave this and travel up the ovovitelline ducts to the ovaries where they collect in a small chamber acting as seminal receptacle and separated from the ovary by a membrane (Fig. 41*B*). The ripe eggs pass through this membrane, are immediately fertilized, and then travel posteriorly along the ovovitelline ducts, becoming mingled with yolk cells emitted into these ducts from the yolk glands. Eggs and yolk cells collect in the male antrum (Fig. 48*D*) where a capsule (also called cocoon) is formed around them from droplets present in the yolk cells. When completed, the capsule containing several eggs and hundreds of yolk cells is laid through the common gonopore, receiving an adhesive secretion from the cement glands opening into the antrum or some adjacent part of the female system. In some genera (*Dugesia, Curtisia*) this adhesive secretion becomes drawn out into a stalk as the capsule is laid, and this serves to attach the capsule to objects, chiefly the underside of stones (Fig. 46*E*). At ordinary temperatures, the capsules hatch in two or three to several weeks into minute fully formed worms.

The triclads inhabit fresh and salt waters and humid terrestrial regions. There is a correspondence between ecological habitus and taxonomic classification, something very unusual among animals. Con-

---

[1] Formerly erroneously called "uterus" and still so labeled in old figures copied into textbooks. The egg capsule is formed in the male antrum, and positively never in the bursa.

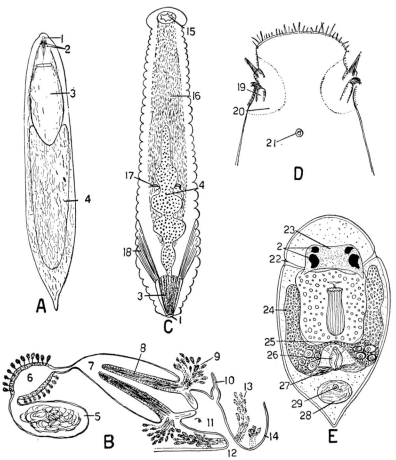

Fig. 60.—Alloeocoela (continued). *A. Plagiostomum album*, Maine (*after Hyman*, 1944). *B.* Scheme of the copulatory apparatus of the genus *Plagiostomum*. *C. Hypotrichina* (*after Graff*, 1903). *D.* Anterior end of *Otoplana intermedia* (*after Wilhelmi*, 1908). *E. Pseudostomum*, with ciliated groove (*after Graff*, 1882). 1, mouth; 2, eyes; 3, pharynx; 4, intestine; 5, seminal vesicle; 6, prostatic vesicle; 7, penis bulb; 8, penis papilla (introverted into bulb); 9, penis glands; 10, common ovovitelline duct; 11, common antrum; 12, common gonopore; 13, cement glands; 14, rear end of animal; 15, adhesive organ; 16, ciliated area; 17, excretory ampullae; 18, retractors of pharynx; 19, papillae bearing sensory bristles; 20, ciliated pits; 21, statocyst; 22, ciliated groove; 23, brain; 24, germovitellaria; 25, common gonopore; 26, penis; 27, spermiducal vesicles; 28, seminal bursa; 29, bursal pore.

sequently there are three suborders of triclads, marine, fresh-water, and terrestrial.

a. Suborder Maricola.—The marine triclads occur in the littoral zone, mostly on gravelly bottoms and under stones, in temperate and subpolar regions. The majority of the known forms are found along the Mediterranean, including the Black Sea, and in general the group prefers protected situations. Other localities where marine triclads occur

are north European coasts, the shores of Japan, the north Atlantic Coast
of North America, and arctic and antarctic situations. These worms
appear to be absent from tropical and subtropical shores, and none are
known to occur on the Pacific coasts of Africa and the Americas.

The marine triclads are of moderate size, from 2 to 20 mm. in
length, and are mostly white, gray, or brown. The anterior end varies
from truncate with auricles to pointed (Fig. 19*D*, *F*). An adhesive zone
with protrusible papillae encircles the ventral surface near the margin;
other adhesive structures are lacking. There is a pair of eyes, and
auricular grooves (page 91) appear to be of general occurrence in the
group. The submuscular nerve plexus has dorsal, lateral or marginal,
and ventral cords, connected by numerous ring commissures and also
by direct connectives between the dorsal and ventral cords (Fig. 25*C*).
The regular arrangement of the testes in some species has given rise to
unwarranted phylogenetic theories (page 25). All forms have a typical
penis papilla sometimes armed with a stylet. A large rounded copulatory
bursa is generally present, lying *behind* the male apparatus and attached
to the common antrum by a bursal canal, which receives the common
ovovitelline duct. However, in the Uteroporidae, the single median, and
in the Bdellouridae, the paired lateral bursae are situated anterior or
lateral to the male apparatus, and each has its own bursal pore to the
exterior, also connections with the ovovitelline ducts by insemination
canals (Fig. 61*A*). The round to oval brown capsules, to 1.5 mm. in
diameter, are fastened mostly without a stalk to stones, shells, etc., and
hatch in a month or more to two or three young worms. Sexual reproduction seems to be somewhat seasonal. The marine triclads are incapable of asexual reproduction.

The Maricola have been monographed by Wilhelmi (1909), whose
five families are now generally reduced to three. The Bdellouridae have
two bursae each with a pore. Members of the genus *Bdelloura* (Figs.
19*D*, *E*, 61*A*) with pointed anterior end and adhesive zone expanded
into a caudal adhesive disk are commensal on the horseshoe crab *Limulus*
along the New England Coast. The oval capsules containing two eggs
are attached by a stalk to the gill lamellae of the host (Fig. 46*G*). *Syncoelidium pellucidium*, without caudal disk, is also commensal on the
gill lamellae of *Limulus* (Wheeler, 1894). *Synsiphonium*, Antarctic,
South Africa, is peculiar in that the seminal bursae have the form of
long canals that run forward from the bursal pores to open into the
ovovitelline ducts near the ovaries (Hallez, 1913). The Uteriporidae
comprise one species, *Uteriporus vulgaris*, Swedish Coast, in which the
single bursa with separate pore lies anterior to the penis (Bergendal,
1890). The family Procerodidae includes the majority of marine triclads; the seminal bursa when present lacks a bursal pore and lies *behind*

the penis, opening into the female antrum by a bursal canal.   The typical genus is *Procerodes* (includes *Gunda*, *Fovia*), with a number of species, small dark-colored worms with a truncate head and more or less evident auricles (Fig. 19*F*, *G*).   The famous *Gunda segmentina* (page 25), notable for the regular repetitive arrangement of its testes, intestinal diverticula, etc., is really a species of *Procerodes*.   *Foviella* differs in the reduced or absent bursa (Bock, 1925).   *Ectoplana*, Japan, without adhesive disk, is commensal on *Limulus*.   The cercyrine Procerodidae, including the genera *Cercyra* and *Sabussowia*, are notable among the Turbellaria in that some species are dioecious.   *Micropharynx* is commensal on the back of skates in the North Atlantic (Jägerskiöld, 1896; Averinzev, 1925); it is a broad eyeless white worm adhering firmly to the host by the rear part of its adhesive zone.   In recent years several new genera of marine triclads have been discovered, and undoubtedly much remains to be learned of this group of planarians.

   b. Suborder Paludicola or Probursalia.—The fresh-water or paludico-lous triclads are familiar inhabitants of streams, springs, ponds, and lakes throughout the temperate zones of the earth.   Like the other groups of aquatic turbellarians, they appear to be scarce in tropical and subtropical regions.   A particularly rich development of species is seen in Lake Baikal and the Balkan peninsula.   The majority range from a few to 30 mm., but longer forms up to 10 cm. in length occur among the Lake Baikal planarians.   The coloration is mostly plain, white, brown, gray, or black, sometimes streaked, spotted, or striped (Fig. 15*B–D*). The anterior end ranges in shape from triangular with projecting auricles to truncate with scarcely noticeable auricles (Figs. 15, 38*A*), and the elongated flat body generally tapers to a more or less pointed caudal end. An adhesive organ of the glandulo-muscular type is often present in the center of the anterior margin.   The brain consists of two conjoined rounded masses or, in planarians with triangular head, of thick cords forming a V (Fig. 26).   There is a pair of large ventral cords, but the other longitudinal cords are generally absent (Fig. 25*D*).   The copu-latory apparatus is of rather uniform construction throughout the group, presenting as its distinguishing character a large sacciform copulatory bursa situated *in front* of the penis and connected to the female antrum by a long bursal canal passing dorsal to the penis (Fig. 38*G*).   The bursa may also be connected to the intestine.   The bursa was formerly erro-neously termed uterus and was supposed to be the site of fertilization and formation of the capsule.   Numerous observations prove that the bursa functions only to receive the sperm at copulation and to digest excess sex products (Burr, 1912; Cernosvitov, 1931).   Fertilization occurs at the head of the ovovitelline ducts (page 153), and the capsules are formed in the male antrum.   The ovovitelline ducts enter the bursal canal or the female antrum or most commonly the male antrum. The usual eosinophilous cement glands surround the terminal parts of the ovovitelline ducts and the antrum. The penis consists of a powerful bulb and usually also of a large muscular penis papilla, reduced or wanting in some genera. Not uncommonly one or more prostatoids, also called adenodactyls, are associated with the copulatory apparatus (Fig. 45D). The fresh-water planarians never fertilize themselves (Gelei, 1924; Goetsch, 1925). The spherical or oval brown capsules may or may not have an attachment stalk. They are usually to be found on the underside of stones and in many species are probably laid at definite seasons of the year. During the breeding season, each individual may copulate repeatedly and lays a succession of capsules at intervals of a few days. These hatch at ordinary temperatures in 2 or 3 weeks, cracking open to release several tiny worms.

The Paludicola have never been monographed, but valuable suggestions concerning their classification have been published by Meixner (1928) and Kenk (1930). They fall into three families, Planariidae, Kenkiidae, and Dendrocoelidae, distinguished by their adhesive organs and the arrangement of the muscle fibers of the inner wall of the pharynx (Fig. 61D, E). The Planariidae lack adhesive organs and are colored or white with triangular to truncate heads. Formerly it was usual to throw almost any two-eyed member of this family into the genus *Planaria*, but this genus has now been restricted according to taxonomic rules to that species to which the name was first applied (*Planaria torva* by O. F. Müller in 1776) and close relatives thereof. As *P. torva* happens to have a peculiar type of adenodactyl (Kenk, 1930), very few planarians remain in the genus *Planaria* (Fig. 45C, D). The typical textbook planarian with triangular head, projecting auricles, two eyes, and dark coloration belongs to the genus *Dugesia* (= *Euplanaria*) with many species, all of very similar appearance, in Europe, Asia, and the Americas (Fig. 15B–D). *Dugesia* reproduces by fission and is devoid of a reproductive system except during the seasonal breeding period. Some species are rarely found in the sexual state, and others have sexual and asexual races probably of genetic origin. *Dugesia tigrina* (= *Planaria maculata*) is the most common fresh-water planarian of the United States, found everywhere in streams and ponds (Fig. 15C, D), exhibiting considerable color variation. It breeds from early spring through summer, laying many stalked capsules under stones; the copulatory apparatus then disappears and the worms remain in a nonsexual state reproducing by fission until the following spring (Kenk, 1937, 1940). Sexuality is induced by a rising temperature following a sojourn at a cold temperature (Hyman, 1941b). This species is peculiar in that in some localities it remains permanently asexual (Curtis, 1902). The reason for this has not been

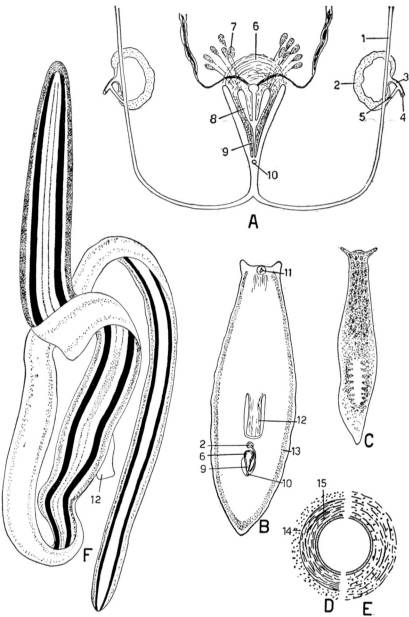

FIG. 61.—Tricladida.   *A.* Copulatory apparatus of *Bdelloura candida*, with two bursae.
B. Sphalloplana percoeca, white eyeless planarian of the family Kenkiidae, from Mammoth
Cave.   *C. Crenobia alpina*, European planarian of alpine streams (*after Micoletzky*, 1907).
D, E. Diagrams of arrangement of fibers of the inner muscular zone of the pharynx to show
diagnostic family characters.   *D.* Arrangement in the families Planariidae and Kenkiidae,
circular and longitudinal layers distinct.   *E.* Family Dendrocoelidae, circular and longitudinal fibers intermingled.   *F. Dolichoplana striata*, common land planarian of the Indo-

ascertained but Kenk (1941) was able to induce testes and the copulatory apparatus in the posterior two-thirds of an individual of such an asexual stock by grafting it to the anterior third of a sexual individual. *D. gonocephala*, a common Eurasian species, is very similar to *D. tigrina*, also occurring in sexual and asexual strains (Benazzi, 1936, 1937, 1938, 1940). It appears, however, that in *D. gonocephala* asexual individuals may arise from sexual stocks, and further that members of asexual stocks sometimes become sexual, although producing very few young. *D. dorotocephala* (Fig. 15*B*) is another common planarian of the United States, widely distributed in springs and spring-fed marshes. These species appear to be "polytypic," i.e., to occur in many geographical races. *Curtisia* with low triangular head and a few prepharyngeal testes has one species *C. foremanii* (= *Planaria simplissima*) in the eastern United States and some in South America. *Phagocata* (= *Fonticola*), with truncate head, common ovovitelline duct entering the male antrum, and spermatophores, comprises mostly rather small gray or white planarians, often found in mountain streams. Some are polypharyngeal (Fig. 34*C*). *P. velata* has an interesting life history (Child, 1913a, 1914; Castle, 1927, 1928; Castle and Hyman, 1934). In the spring the worms grow to 12 to 15 mm. in length, then gradually fragment into small pieces, each of which encysts in a mucous cyst. Within these cysts the pieces reorganize into minute worms that emerge in a few weeks if the cysts remain submersed. In habitats that dry up in summer, emergence may not occur until the following spring, and such an asexual cycle may continue indefinitely. In permanent waters, mostly spring-fed marshes, worms hatched from cysts in the fall become sexually mature and breed in winter. Similar fragmentation and encystment occur in some European *Phagocatas*. *Crenobia alpina* (Fig. 61*C*), a European planariid found in mountain streams, requires cold temperatures and is extremely reactive to water currents (page 213). *Polycelis*, with several Eurasian species, and one, *coronata* (Fig. 32*D*), in our western mountains, is characterized by the numerous eyes in a band around the anterior margin.

The Kenkiidae are a family of cave planarians peculiar to North America (Hyman, 1937, 1939c); they are white, eyeless, and have a glandulo-muscular adhesive organ in the center of the anterior margin, reaching an extreme development in *Kenkia rhynchida* (Fig. 22*B*, *C*). The Kenkiidae have the same pharyngeal structure as the Planariidae (Fig. 61*D*) and seem to be derived from the genus *Phagocata*. European cave planarians do not show any such peculiarities but are mostly eyeless

Malay region. 1, ovovitelline duct; 2, copulatory bursa; 3, copulation canal; 4, bursal pore; 5, insemination canal; 6, penis bulb; 7, penis glands; 8, gland pockets in penis; 9, penis papilla; 10, common gonopore; 11, adhesive organ; 12, pharynx; 13, margin of rhabdite-forming glands; 14, longitudinal muscle fibers; 15, circular muscle fibers.

variants of epigean species. A number of species of the Kenkiidae have been found in our caves, and in fact there seems to be a different species in each locality. The best known kenkiid, *Sphalloplana percoeca* (Fig. 61*B*) from the Mammoth Caves, Kentucky (de Beauchamp, 1931), showed surprisingly little response to light, although killed by direct sunlight, or to temperatures warmer than those of cave waters (Buchanan, 1936).

The Dendrocoelidae are mostly white planarians with two to many eyes (or none) and truncate anterior end often with a central adhesive organ. This family is represented abundantly in Eurasia by *Dendrocoelum, Sorocelis, Bdellocephala*, and other genera, but is poorly exemplified in the Americas where in fact there is only one common dendrocoelid, *Procotyla fluviatilis*, the familiar white planarian of the northeastern United States (Figs. 21*C*, 22*A*, 38*A*). *Polycladodes* and *Sorocelis* have numerous eyes in two clusters; the latter, though mainly Asiatic, has one species in Oklahoma caves (Fig. 32*E*). *Dendrocoelum* and *Bdellocephala* are not represented in the Americas; the former has an adenodactyl, the latter lacks a penis papilla.

The foregoing classification does not take account of some of the remarkable Lake Baikal[1] triclads described by Korotneff (1912), for the information furnished about them is inadequate for taxonomic purposes. These planarians are not only larger than any other Paludicula, but they show an excessive development of sucker-like adhesive organs (page 82, Fig. 21*A*, *B*).

c. Suborder Terricola.—The land planarians inhabit the forest floor of tropical and subtropical jungles, although a few species occur in humid habitats in temperate zones. Although they require a highly humid environment, the land planarians cannot endure submersion in water. They have nocturnal habits, remaining under leaf mold, fallen logs, stones, etc., during the day and coming out at night to seek prey. Mucous secretion plays an important role in their activities, forming a slime trail for locomotion, slime threads by which they can cross spaces or drop from heights, and a protective coat against drying. The land planarians are mostly of long and slender form, varying from 10 mm. or less to over 60 cm. in length. They are usually colored, either more or less uniformly green, gray, brown, or black, less often blue or violet, or else striped or barred with contrasting colors. A very frequent color pattern consists of dark or black stripes or bars on a light, often yellow or orange,

[1] Lake Baikal, in the mountains of eastern Siberia, is the largest fresh-water lake in Eurasia, having an area about equal to that of Switzerland, and is the deepest lake in the world, being at some points nearly a mile in depth. It has a rich and highly peculiar fauna, mostly endemic and probably in many cases relicts of ancient forms.

ground or vice versa (Figs. 14*D*, 61*F*). There are two to many eyes and other sense organs in the form of ciliated grooves and a sensory margin. One or two adhesive cushions on the ventral surface of the anterior end occur in some genera, as *Cotyloplana*, *Artiocotylus*, and *Choeradoplana*. The peculiarities of the nervous system of the Terricola were noted above (Fig. 25*E*).

The Terricola were monographed by von Graff in 1899, and in this work beautiful colored plates showing the characteristic appearance and color patterns may be seen. There are three principal families, Geoplanidae, Rhynchodemidae, and Bipaliidae, and some minor ones. The Geoplanidae have a flattened body tapering to a narrowed anterior end and numerous eyes along the body margin. They creep upon the entire ventral surface as they lack a creeping sole. The chief genus *Geoplana* (Fig. 32*A*) without adhesive organs or prostatoids has hundreds of species, centering in the jungles of tropical South America. Two species brought in with tropical plants have become established in Californian gardens (Fig. 32*A*). The Rhynchodemidae have two eyes on the narrowed anterior end and lack adhesive organs. *Rhynchodemus* and the related genera *Dolichoplana* and *Platydemus* have slender more or less flattened bodies, strongly developed subepidermal musculature and simple copulatory apparatus. Species of *Rhynchodemus* occur sparingly in the United States (Fig. 62*C*, *D*) and Europe in moist woods and in gardens (Hyman, 1943), and large numbers are found in the tropics. *Dolichoplana striata* (Fig. 61*F*) to 20 cm. long, is one of the most common land planarians of the Indo-Malay region and may be introduced into greenhouses. Another group of rhynchodemids, exemplified by *Geodesmus* (= old *Rhynchodemus* in part) and *Diporodemus*, are of short plump cylindroid form with a creeping sole, weak subepidermal musculature, and complicated copulatory apparatus, often including a seminal bursa. Species of *Geodesmus* (Fig. 62*A*) are endemic to Europe and the United States; the best known one is *Geodesmus terrestris*, a plump black worm discovered in 1774. *Diporodemus*, with species in the Appalachians (Fig. 62*B*), Mexico, and the Canal Zone, differs in the separate external pore of the seminal bursa (Fig. 62*E*). The Bipaliidae are readily recognized by the expanded lunate head (Fig. 14*D*) having numerous minute eyes along its borders. There is probably but one genus *Bipalium* (includes *Placocephalus*) with numerous tropical species, especially in the Indo-Malay region. *Bipalium kewense* (Fig. 14*D*), a large worm to 25 cm. or more in length, with five dark stripes on a lighter ground, is the best known member of the genus. It was discovered in the greenhouses of the Kew Gardens, near London, by Moseley in 1878 and has since been found widely distributed in greenhouses in temperate regions and outdoors in many tropical and subtropical localities, having been carried

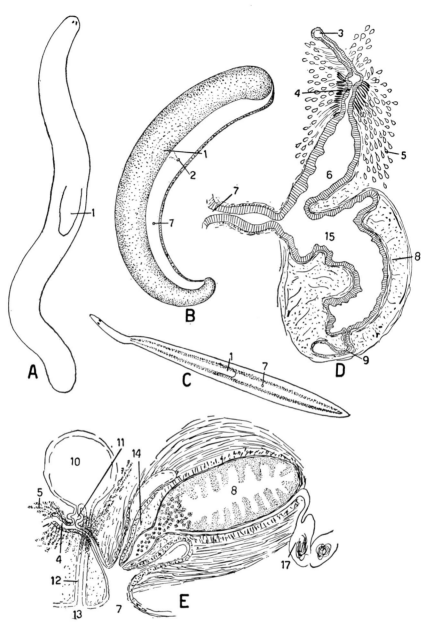

FIG. 62.—American land planarians. *A. Geodesmus atrocyaneus*, eastern United States. *B. Diporodemus indigenus*, Appalachians. *C. Rhynchodemus sylvaticus*, eastern United States. *D.* Sagittal section of the copulatory complex of *Rhynchodemus sylvaticus*. *E.* Sagittal section of the copulatory complex of *Diporodemus plenus*, Canal Zone. (*After Hyman, 1941a, 1943.*) 1, pharynx; 2, mouth; 3, common ovovitelline duct; 4, glandular part of female canal; 5, cement glands; 6, female antrum; 7, common gonopore; 8, penis bulb; 9, common sperm duct; 10, copulatory bursa; 11, bursal canal; 12, copulation canal; 13, bursal pore; 14, penis papilla; 15, male antrum; 16, common antrum; 17, spermiducal vesicle.

about the world at an early date with plant shipments. It is now established in gardens in California, Louisiana, Florida, and the West Indies. Its original habitat is unknown. It owes its colonizing success to extensive ability to propagate by fragmentation, for it never becomes sexual in temperate regions. In general, tropical land planarians are unable to mature sexually in temperate zones and hence soon die out unless they have some means of asexual propagation. Another *Bipalium, B. adventitium,* of unknown source, has become acclimated to Californian gardens where it breeds sexually (Hyman, 1943).

18. Order Polycladida.—The polyclads are common inhabitants of the ocean littoral in all zones of the earth. They are typically bottom dwellers, unable to swim or swimming only briefly, but some species are pelagic, having been taken from surface waters to depths of nearly 1000 m. Some of these apparently swim about freely in the open water whereas others are confined to the floating *Sargassum.* The group includes only one fresh-water species, *Limnostylochus borneensis* from Borneo (Stummer-Traunfels, 1902), although many endure some brackishness. There are no parasitic polyclads, but several species live in constant association with other animals, especially mollusks and hermit crabs.

The polyclads are mostly of considerable size, ranging from 2 or 3 mm. to several centimeters in length. They are greatly flattened animals and although sometimes of elongated form as *Cestoplana* (Fig. 35*G*) are mostly broadly oval, widest through the anterior third or the middle (Figs. 63*B*, 64*A*). The pelagic species tend to be translucent or transparent; the bottom dwellers are often white, brown, or gray, especially in northern waters, but bright colors and patterns also obtain, particularly in the polyclads of warmer waters and of coral reefs. Plates illustrating the colors may be seen in Lang's monograph (1884). The body contour is simple, although the margins may be ruffled, and the surface is generally smooth but there are a number of species with dorsal tubercles or papillae (Fig. 15*A*). Tentacles are frequent, either as a *nuchal* pair (Fig. 63*B*) over the brain region or a *marginal* pair at the anterior margin (Fig. 14*A, B*). The polyclads lack frontal glands, statocysts, and adhesive areas or organs except for the ventral disk of the Cotylea, the genital disk in *Leptoplana,* and adhesive cells in *Emprosthopharynx.* Numerous eyes are present, usually as a pair of cerebral clusters in the brain region and a tentacular cluster on or near each tentacle or at the sites where tentacles would be expected (Figs. 35*F–J*, 63*A, B*). Eyes may also occur strewn over the anterior end (Fig. 63*A*) or as a band along all or part of the body margin (Fig. 63*A, B*). The body is clothed in a completely ciliated cellular epidermis containing numerous gland and rhabdite-forming cells. Muscular and nervous systems were described above (pages 77, 85). The plicate pharynx is either an oval

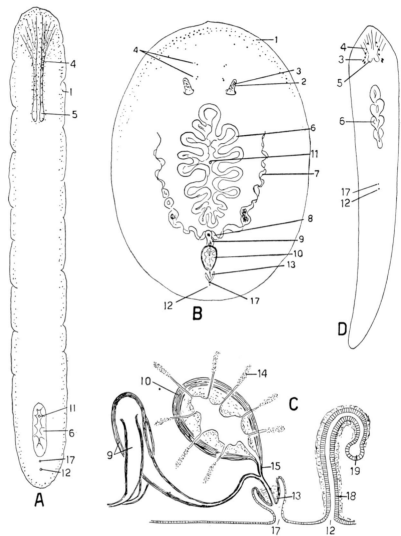

Fig. 63.—Polycladida.   *A. Latocestus whartoni*, Florida.   *B. Stylochus ellipticus*, most common polyclad of the United States Atlantic Coast.   *C.* Schematic sagittal view of the copulatory apparatus of the genus *Stylochus*, illustrating free type of prostatic vesicle; simple vagina without bursa is diagnostic of the genus.   *D. Euplana gracilis*, common lepto-planid polyclad of the United States Atlantic Coast.   1, marginal band of eyes; 2, tentacle; 3, tentacular eyes; 4, cerebral eyes; 5, cerebral ganglia; 6, pharynx; 7, sperm duct; 8, spermiducal vesicle; 9, seminal vesicle; 10, prostatic vesicle; 11, mouth; 12, female gonopore; 13, penis papilla; 14, prostatic glands; 15, prostatic duct; 16, ejaculatory duct; 17, male gonopore; 18, vagina; 19, entrance of oviduct into vagina.

ruffled curtain hung vertically or a cylindrical tube directed forward. The pharynx leads into a median main intestine lying above or behind it (Fig. 35*F–J*) and extending part or most of the body length. From this intestine branches radiate to the periphery, often subdividing and anastomosing. The form of the branching is correlated with body shape (Fig. 35*F–J*). Little is known of the excretory system beyond the fact that flame bulbs occur. There are numerous small ovaries and testes scattered throughout the lateral body regions; each ovary consists of ovocytes and nutritive follicle cells. Yolk glands are absent. The distal parts of the sperm ducts are usually expanded to form spermiducal vesicles, sometimes very muscular. Usually present are a muscular seminal vesicle and a large and muscular prostatic vesicle, of either the interpolated (Fig. 64*B*) or free type (Fig. 63*C*). When interpolated the prostatic vesicle may be incorporated into the muscular penis bulb (Fig. 39*E*) from which continues the penis papilla, often provided with a simple stylet, that is sometimes very long (Fig. 64*B*). Some polyclads, especially the Planoceridae, have a cirrus, often of complicated construction, instead of a penis (Fig. 39*E*). The frequent multiplication of male apparatus and prostatoids in the polyclads was noted above (page 117). The oviducts generally act as reservoirs of ripe eggs and hence are termed uteri; they sometimes bear uterine vesicles of unknown function (Pseudoceridae, Euryleptidae). The oviducts enter the terminal female canal or vagina, often very muscular, and usually having a glandular region or chamber (Fig. 65*D*) that receives the numerous cement glands. A seminal bursa termed Lang's vesicle is of common occurrence, opening from behind into the vagina by a long bursal canal (Fig. 64*B*). There is a common gonopore or separate male and female pores of which the latter is nearly always behind the former.

The polyclads practice both hypodermic impregnation and regular copulation; they do not fertilize themselves. In copulation, the sperm pass into the seminal bursa (Lang's vesicle) when this is present and later migrate up the oviducts, or they are ejaculated directly into the oviducts. Fertilization occurs in the oviducts or in the vagina, immediately before laying. In laying, a continuous adhesive gelatinous thread containing a row of eggs issues and is woven back and forth or in a spiral to make a gelatinous egg mass or ribbon (Fig. 46*H*). The sticky gelatinous material comes from the cement glands, and additional secretion is added from ventral mesenchymal glands (Kato, 1940). As soon as the egg reaches the exterior a surface layer of egg spherules coalesces to form a thin shell that elevates from the egg surface and hardens. This capsule encloses one egg (Fig. 46*J*) or sometimes several. Cleavage begins at once and hatching ensues in several days to weeks. In the northern hemisphere breeding usually occurs in the summer months, and an individual may lay several egg masses, containing thousands of eggs.

The best modern work on the systematics of the polyclads is that of Bock (1913), who has corrected and extended the pioneer monograph of Lang (1884). Lang's work, further, was more or less limited to Mediterranean species. Although a large number of species have been described, the polyclads are as yet imperfectly known. The species of the Atlantic Coast of the United States have been treated by the author (Hyman, 1939a, 1940). Those of our Pacific Coast are poorly known, although several papers needing revision have been published about them (Boone, 1929; Freeman, 1930, 1933; Heath and McGregor, 1912; Plehn, 1896a, 1897). Japanese polyclads have been well studied by Kato (1934–1939) and Yeri and Kaburaki (1918). Pelagic polyclads have been the object of several papers (von Graff, 1892; Hyman, 1939b; Palombi, 1924; Plehn, 1896b). Very little has been issued of the projected account of the polyclads by Stummer-Traunfels (1933) in Bronn's *Klassen und Ordnungen des Tierreichs*.

a. Suborder Acotylea and Section Craspedommata.—The acotylean polyclads lack a glandulo-muscular adhesive disk behind the female pore. The pharynx is usually a vertical ruffled curtain, tentacles when present are of the nuchal type, and eyes never occur as a pair of clusters on the anterior margin. The copulatory apparatus lies posteriorly as a rule, and from it the oviducts (uteri) extend forward alongside the pharynx. The section Craspedommata includes those acotylean families that have eyes in a band around all or the anterior part of the body margin (in addition to cerebral and tentacular clusters). Of these the Discocelidae, Latocestidae, and Stylochidae tend to occur in warmer waters. The Discocelidae lack a typical prostatic vesicle, but the penis papilla and antral wall bear numerous small prostatoids (Fig. 40D, E). The Latocestidae, with numerous species in the main genus *Latocestus* (Fig. 63A), are of long slender form with posterior pharynx, long main intestine, and numerous small eyes strewn over the anterior end. The Stylochidae have thick oval or oblong bodies and a free prostatic vesicle (Fig. 63B, C). There are a number of genera (see Bock, 1925), of which *Stylochus* with prominent nuchal tentacles containing eyes and simple female apparatus is the most common and best known (Fig. 63B, C). Several species of *Stylochus* occur along the Atlantic Coast of the United States (described in Hyman, 1940) of which *S. ellipticus* is the most common (Fig. 63B). Another, *S. zebra*, with a pattern of alternate brown and flesh crossbars, often occurs inside shells inhabited by hermit crabs. *Stylochus* often feeds on oysters; and one species, *S. frontalis*, has this habit to such an extent that it is deleterious to the oyster industry on the Florida Coast, where it is known as the "oyster leech" (Pearse

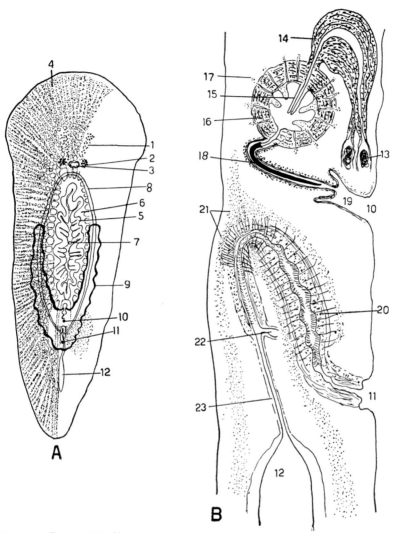

Fig. 64.—Polycladida: *Notoplana*. *A. Notoplana atomata*, common leptoplanid polyclad of North Atlantic shores. *B.* Sagittal view of the copulatory apparatus of *Notoplana
atomata;* only distal part of the bursa is shown; projection of ejaculatory duct into the
prostatic vesicle is diagnostic of the genus *Notoplana.* 1, cerebral eye clusters; 2, tentacular
eye clusters; 3, brain; 4, intestinal branches; 5, pharynx; 6, main intestine; 7, mouth; 8, oviducts (uteri); 9, sperm ducts; 10, male gonopore; 11, female gonopore; 12, seminal bursa
(Lang's vesicle); 13, spermiducal vesicles; 14, seminal vesicle; 15, ejaculatory duct; 16,
prostatic vesicle; 17, prostatic glands; 18, penis stylet; 19, male antrum; 20, vagina; 21,
cement glands; 22, entrance of oviducts into vagina; 23, bursal canal.

and Wharton, 1938).   It creeps into the oyster while the latter's valves
are open and gradually devours the oyster's flesh, although the latter
may put up a defense by secreting chitinous partitions around the polyclad.   Stylochids are often very large, and the largest polyclads of our
coasts, broad flat forms over 50 mm. long, belong to this family: *Stylochus
oculiferus*, Florida, and *Kaburakia excelsa*, Puget Sound.

Some other craspedommatous families are the Plehniidae and Polyposthiidae, characteristic of northern and boreal waters, and the Empros-
thopharyngidae.   The Polyposthiidae are mainly pelagic and have
numerous penes or prostatoids (Palombi, 1924, 1929, Fig. 40*A*).   *Emprosthopharynx opisthoporus*, Panama, commensal in shells occupied by
hermit crabs, is unique among polyclads in having a marginal adhesive
zone like that of triclads (Bock, 1925).

b. Suborder Acotylea: Section Schematommata.—The polyclads of this
section lack marginal eyes and generally have four clusters of eyes in the
brain region (Fig. 64*A*).   The chief family, Leptoplanidae, comprises
worms of moderate size, oval or oboval shape, and brown or gray coloration.   Formerly it was customary to throw almost any schematommatous polyclad without tentacles into the genus *Leptoplana*, but this
genus must be limited to the species first assigned to it and related species,
characterized by a genital adhesive disk between the male and female
pores and some other peculiarities.   Most of the species formerly called
Leptoplana fall into the genus *Notoplana*, a genus of many species common on all rocky shores and impractical to distinguish except by section
of the copulatory apparatus (Fig. 64*B*).   *Notoplana atomata* (Fig. 64*A*,
B) occurs on North Atlantic shores from Massachusetts to Scandinavia,
and many species are found on the Pacific Coast of North America.
Stylochoplana, another common genus with many species, differs in a
minor detail of the male apparatus; *S. parasitica* inhabits the mantle
groove and gills of chitons on Japanese coasts (Kato, 1935a).   *Euplana*
(= *Discoplana*), devoid of a prostatic vesicle, is represented on the
Atlantic Coast of the United States by the small planaria-like *E. gracilis*
(Fig. 63*D*).   *Euplana takewakii*, Japan, infests the genital bursae of
serpent stars (Kato, 1935b).   The Hoploplanidae, without seminal
vesicle, have highly muscularized spermiducal vesicles and a penis
stylet borne directly by the prostatic vesicle.   *Hoploplana inquilina*
(Fig. 65*A*), a small rounded polyclad, inhabits the mantle chamber of
snails along the Atlantic Coast of the United States, and *H. grubei* is one
of the common polyclads of the Sargassum.   The Planoceridae usually
have tentacles and are characterized by the cirrus armed with spines,
teeth, etc. (Fig. 39*E*).   They are often of thin transparent texture and
pelagic habits, as exemplified by the widely distributed *Planocera pel-
lucida*.   *Gnesioceros* (= *Pelagoplana*) with conch-shaped cirrus armed

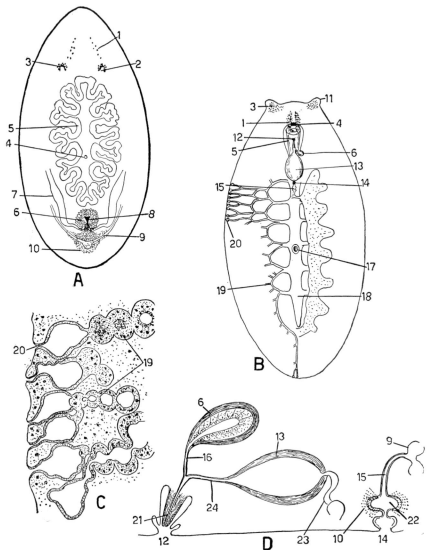

Fig. 65.—Polycladida (continued). *A. Hoploplana inquilina*, commensal in snail shells. *B. Cycloporus*, cotylean polyclad, simplified after Lang, 1884; has numerous anal pores around the margin. *C.* Part of margin of *Cycloporus*, showing anal pores (*after Lang*, 1884). *D.* Scheme of the copulatory apparatus of the Cotylea in general, with free prostatic vesicle. 1, cerebral eye cluster; 2, nuchal tentacle; 3, tentacular eye cluster; 4, mouth; 5, pharynx; 6, prostatic vesicle; 7, spermiducal vesicles; 8, penis stylet; 9, oviducts (uteri); 10, cement glands; 11, reduced marginal tentacles; 12, male gonopore; 13, seminal vesicle; 14, female gonopore; 15, vagina; 16, prostatic duct; 17, adhesive disk; 18, main intestine; 19, intestinal branches; 20, anal pores; 21, penis papilla; 22, cement pouch; 23, sperm duct; 24, ejaculatory duct.

with toothed bands (Fig. 39*E*) has one species, *sargassicola*, common on the *Sargassum* (Fig. 39*D*) and another, *floridana*, abundant among sea-weeds on the south Atlantic Coast of the United States. In the Diplo-soleniidae with free prostatic vesicle the most common genus is *Pseudo-stylochus* with several species in the North Pacific.

The two following schematommatous families have a tubular pharynx directed forward. The Apidioplanidae comprise only the curious species *Apidioplana mira* (Fig. 40*B*, *C*) with numerous prostatoids throughout the ventral surface, found on gorgonian colonies in the Fiji Islands (Bock, 1927). *Enantia*, sole genus of the Enantiidae, is unique among Turbellaria in having marginal spines (page 68, Fig. 17*A*, *B*).

c. Suborder Acotylea: Section Emprosthommata.—This section includes one family, Cestoplanidae, with one genus *Cestoplana* (Fig. 35*G*), very similar to *Latocestus* except that it lacks marginal eyes.

d. Suborder Cotylea.—The cotylean polyclads have a glandulo-muscular adhesive organ, commonly but erroneously called sucker, behind the female gonopore. They have a pair of marginal tentacles bearing eyes (Fig. 35*H*) or else a cluster of eyes where such tentacles should be (Fig. 65*B*) or a band of eyes across the anterior margin (Fig. 35*J*). The pharynx is ruffled or tubular. A seminal bursa is absent, and the prostatic vesicle when present is of the free type (Fig. 65*D*). The cotyleans are most common in less cold waters and are often of striking form and coloration. The principal families are the Pseudoceridae, Euryleptidae, and Prosthiostomidae. The first are large, often brightly colored polyclads with a pair of marginal tentacles, ruffled pharynx, and net-like intestinal branches. *Thysanozoon* (Fig. 15*A*) is covered with papillae, each containing an intestinal branch; *Pseudoceros*, very similar, is smooth or tuberculate, but the tubercles contain no intestinal diverticulum (Fig. 14*A*). In the similar *Yungia* many of the intestinal branches open dorsally by anal pores. The Euryleptidae have a tubular pharynx directed forward. *Prostheceraeus* with numerous lateral anastomosing intestinal branches, and *Eurylepta* and *Oligocladus* with three to five nonanastomosing branches (Fig. 35*H*) are the chief genera with well-developed tentacles. *Stylostomum* and *Cycloporus* have reduced tentacles, and the latter has a number of anal pores along the dorsal periphery (Fig. 65*B*, *C*). *Acerotisa* (= *Aceros*) lacks tentacles altogether, having an eye cluster in place of each. This genus contains some very small polyclads, as *A. notulata*, from the Sargassum, barely 1 mm. long. Even smaller, however, is the curious *Graffizoon lobata*, California, which resembles a Müller's larva but is fully mature sexually (Heath, 1928); it is probably a neotenic larval stage of a euryleptid. The Prosthiostomidae are rather small polyclads of elongated form, with long tubular pharynx, no tentacles, and a band of eyes along the anterior margin (Fig. 35*J*). The chief genus *Prosthiostomum* has numerous species in warmer waters, mostly pale or white, and very much alike externally. *Euprosthiostomum* differs in the posterior location of its adhesive disk, apparently as an adaptation to commensal life in the shells occupied by hermit crabs (Bock, 1925).

Some other cotyleans that may be mentioned are the Anonymidae with numerous copulatory apparatus in a curved row on each side and the Boniniidae in which many prostatoids encircle the male copulatory organ (Bock, 1923).

19. Embryology.—The embryonic development of the majority of the Turbellaria is modified by the fact that the yolk supply is contained in the yolk cells, not in the eggs. Hence for the study of the original, unmodified course of development, entolecithal eggs must be used. These occur in the Acoela and Polycladida, groups devoid of yolk glands. The development of polyclads is usually regarded as the original mode for the class and has been worked out in a number of species of different genera by Lang (1884), Surface (1907), Bresslau (1933), and Kato (1940). Practically nothing is known of the development of those Rhabdocoela and Alloeocoela that have entolecithal eggs.

a. Entolecithal Development of Polyclads.—In polyclads the cleavage is of the spiral determinate type and so closely resembles that of annelids and mollusks as to leave no doubt of some phylogenetic connection between these three groups. The egg undergoes total unequal spiral cleavage after the pattern described in Chap. IX (Fig. 3). Three quartets of micromeres are given off, and the macromeres then divide into a fourth quartet of large micromeres, and a quartet of small macromeres (4*A*–4*D*) that occupy the vegetal pole. Traces are sometimes seen of the rosette and the cross. The offspring of the first quartet of micromeres form the ectoderm of anterior dorsal regions and the pigment cells of the eyes and give off into the interior a mass of cells that differentiates into the brain and the entire nervous system (Fig. 66*D*, *E*). From the same invagination that produces the nervous system there is differentiated a cluster of frontal glands that in some species forms a long tuft of sensory hairs (Fig. 67). Although this frontal organ of polyclad larvae had been seen by earlier workers, it was first correctly interpreted by Kato (1940). It soon degenerates and no trace remains in the adult. It may be taken to correspond to the apical sense organ of some cnidarian larvae and of the trochophore. The descendants of the second quartet contribute to surface ectoderm, and some of them pass into the interior as the ectomesoderm from which the muscular and mesenchymal elements of the pharynx arise. The third-quartet cells also furnish surface ectoderm and may possibly contribute to the ectomesoderm. Three of the large yolky fourth-quartet cells, namely,

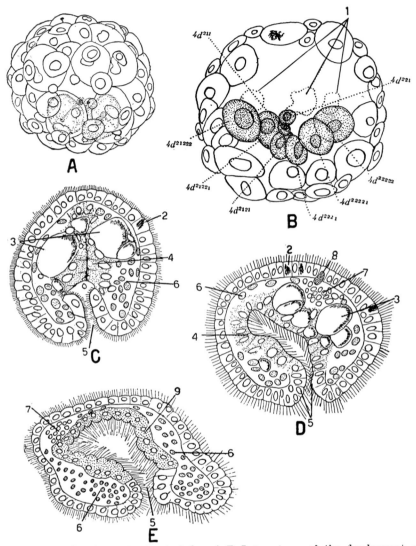

Fig. 66.—Development of polyclads. *A–E.* Later stages of the development of *Hoploplana inquilina (after Surface,* 1907); for general type of earlier cleavages see Fig. 3. *A.* Beginning gastrulation, showing offspring of 4d (stippled) in the interior. *B.* Section of a slightly later stage, showing offspring of $4d^2$ proliferating in the interior. *C.* Later stage, stomodaeum forming, intestine organizing; yolk has run together to form large droplets. *D.* Later stage, axis shifting forward, intestinal lumen formed, cerebral ganglia and eyes forming. *E.* Larval stage, axial shift completed. 1, degenerating 4a, 4b, and 4c; 2, ectoderm; 3, yolk masses; 4, intestine; 5, stomodaeum; 6, mesenchyme; 7, cerebral ganglia; 8, beginning of eye; 9, completed intestine.

$4a$–$4c$, plus the four macromeres, $4A$–$4D$, apparently serve only as food material while the single cell $4d$ furnishes the entire entoderm and ento-mesoderm and hence is the mesentoblast cell. It sinks into the interior and divides (Fig. 66A, B), and the offspring of $4d^2$ produce the entomeso-derm from which originate the mesenchyme, the subepidermal and mesen-chymal muscles, the mesenchymal glands, and the reproductive system. The offspring of $4d^1$ give rise to the intestine.

Gastrulation occurs chiefly by epiboly. A stereogastrula is formed, having a ciliated surface ectoderm, an apical frontal gland sometimes bearing a sensory tuft, a blastopore but no archenteron, and an interior mass composed of the cells of the brain, the ectomesoderm, and the off-spring of $4d$. The yolk droplets fuse into large globules (Fig. 66C, D). Near the original blastopore (which closes and disappears), an ecto-dermal invagination forms a pharynx simplex (Fig. 66C) that connects with the entodermal mass derived from $4d^1$; this mass hollows out to become the intestine (Fig. 66C–E). The axial relations meantime have shifted; the apical pole bearing the frontal gland moves forward and becomes the anterior end and the mouth region shifts backward (Figs. 66D–E, 67). The embryo flattens and in the majority of the Acotylea develops directly into a small worm that escapes from the egg capsule. In the Cotylea and some Acotylea (species of *Hoploplana*, *Planocera*), the flattened ciliated embryo puts out eight posteriorly directed lobes or lappets edged with especially long cilia and swims about for a few days in this stage, known from its discoverer as *Müller's larva* (Fig. 67). This may have a caudal sensory tuft opposite the apical one. The finding of a Müller's larva with mature reproductive system was noted above (page 170). In some species of *Stylochus*, the larva has only four lobes, and this is termed Götte's larva. This was regarded by Lang as a developmental stage of Müller's larva but incorrectly so, according to Kato, who finds that Götte's larva does not put out additional lobes. It appears that, in the genus *Stylochus*, some species develop directly and others by way of a Götte's larva. Kato has further found that a modified Müller's larva stage may be passed inside the egg capsule (*Planocera reticulata*). In any of the three cases, the larval lobes are absorbed after a few days, the sensory tufts disappear, additional eyes differentiate, and the larva flattens out as a young polyclad.

The adult plicate pharynx arises from the larval simple pharynx by a secondary ring-shaped ectodermal invagination that becomes the pharyn-geal chamber. A circular mesodermal mass that has separated from the rest of the mesoderm provides the muscle and glandular layers of the adult pharynx. The mouth is often closed during embryonic and larval life. There are usually at first only one or two eyes. The protonephridia

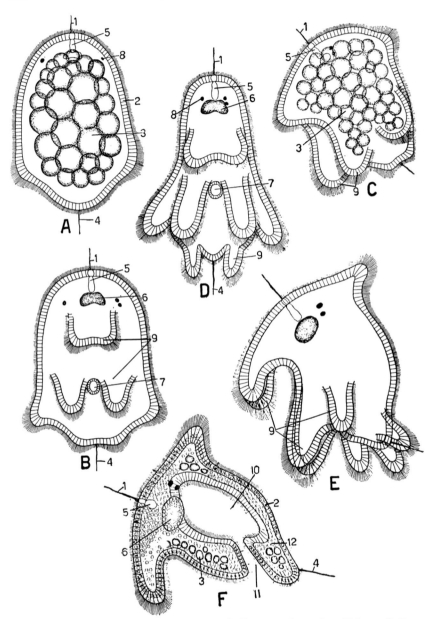

Fig. 67.—Development of Müller's larva. *A.* Beginning formation of lobes. *B.* Later stage of lobes. *C.* Side view of *B*; forward shift of axis has begun. *D.* Completed Müller's larva seen from above. *E.* Same from the side. *F.* Same in sagittal section. (*All after Kato*, 1940.) 1, apical sensory tuft; 2, ectoderm; 3, yolk masses; 4, caudal tuft; 5, frontal gland; 6, brain; 7, mouth; 8, eyes; 9, ciliated lobes; 10, intestine; 11, stomodaeum; 12, mesenchyme.

are believed to originate from paired ectodermal cords that grow into the interior.

b. Entolecithal Development of Acoels.—The development of the Acoela has been studied chiefly in *Polychaerus caudatus* by Gardiner (1895) and for *Convoluta roscoffensis* by Georgievitsch (1899) and Bresslau (1909). The development is of the spiral determinate type and resembles that of polyclads except that the egg undergoes only one meridional cleavage, giving rise to but two blastomeres, A and B (Fig. 68). The usual four sets of micromeres are given off, but as these consist of only two cells each, they are termed *duets* instead of quartets. In *Convoluta* $3A$ and $3B$ move into the interior before giving off the fourth duet; in *Polychoerus* emboly occurs after this event (Fig. 68C). The resulting four cells, $4A$, $4B$, $4a$, $4b$, are the source of most of the interior mass; the remainder is ectomesoderm derived from the second, possibly also the third, duet. A stereogastrula (Fig. 68D) arises in which the interior mass is not definitely separable into entoderm proper and entomesoderm. The blastopore closes and the surface cells separate as epidermis (Fig. 68E). The nervous system is derived from the first duet. The mouth (and pharynx when present) originate by ectodermal invagination near the former blastopore. A free larval stage is lacking, and the animal remains permanently in a stereogastrula stage. There is no trace of a digestive cavity, and hence the stereograstrula construction is primary.

c. Ectolecithal Development of Rhabdocoels and Alloeocoels.—Development with yolk cells is highly modified, and although traces of spiral cleavage are seen in some cases there is no possibility of following the fate of the various cells, and germ-layer formation is omitted. The egg surrounded by yolk cells undergoes total cleavage (Fig. 69A) into a mass of blastomeres that often become strewn throughout the yolk, later reassembling. The development of several rhabdocoels and alloeocoels has been investigated by Bresslau (1904); that of *Paravortex* by Hallez (1909) and Ball (1916). The following account is based chiefly on Bresslau's work on *Mesostoma*. The blastomere mass moves to one side of the mass of yolk cells which have united into a syncytium (Fig. 69B). This side is the future ventral side of the embryo while the other half occupied by yolk is dorsal. The blastomere mass often shows a bilateral arrangement along a plane which is the future median sagittal plane, and becomes divided anteroposteriorly into three masses (Fig. 69D). Its peripheral cells arrange into a surface epithelium, which is the ventral epidermis and which gradually spreads dorsally to enclose the dorsal yolk mass. The anterior of the three embryonic masses develops into the paired cerebral ganglia (Figs. 69E, G) which later become united by commissures and from which the rest of the nervous system grows out. Both pigment and retinal cells of the eyes come from this brain mass. The middle embryonic mass represents the musculature, glands, and parenchyma of the pharynx.   The epithelia of the pharynx, the lining of the pharyngeal cavity, and the epithelium of the esophagus come from a solid epidermal ingrowth that later hollows out (Fig. 69E–G).   The posterior embryonic mass forms the posterior end of the worm and apparently the reproductive system.   The intestine and general parenchyma come from those cells of the embryonic masses that are nearest the yolk (Fig. 70).   Some of

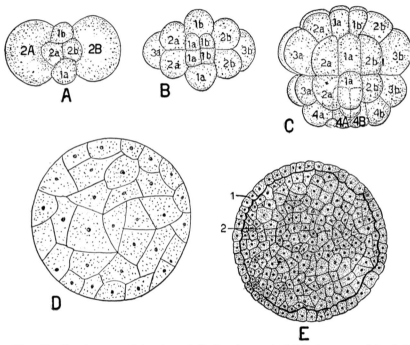

Fig. 68.—Development of Acoela.   A–E. Development of *Polychoerus caudatus* (*after Gardiner*, 1895).   A. 6-cell stage seen from above.   B. 16-cell stage seen from above. C. 38-cell stage seen from the side; 4A and 4B are passing into the interior.   D. Early stereogastrula stage.   E. Late sterogastrula stage; surface cells separated as epidermis.   1, epidermis; 2, interior mass.

these work into and absorb the yolk mass and then aggregate to form the intestine, solid at first, later hollowing out.   Other indifferent cells of the embryonic masses differentiate into parenchyma and subepidermal and parenchymal musculature.

    d. *Ectolecithal Development of Triclads.*—The development of triclads, known through the work of Metschnikoff (1883), Ijima (1884), Mattiesen (1904), and Fulinski (1914, 1916), is somewhat similar to that of rhabdocoels but is still more modified with relation to the yolk.   Certain blastomeres flatten to form an outer membrane that encloses a fluid yolk mass containing the remaining scattered blastomeres (Fig. 71*A–C*), and such embryonic spheres are surrounded by a yolk syncytium (Fig. 71*E*). Some of the scattered blastomeres aggregate at one point in contact with the outer membrane (Fig. 71*D*) and there form a temporary *embryonic pharynx* (Fig. 71*F–H*) and a small sac, the *temporary intestine* (Figs. 71*F–H*, 72*A*). The embryonic pharynx by sucking movements swallows the whole of the yolk syncytium into the temporary intestine (Fig. 72*B*, *C*). The latter distends until it approaches the outer membrane pushing the remaining blastomeres before it so that a spherical hollow embryo results having a cavity full of yolk cells, an embryonic pharynx, and a wall composed of free blastomeres floating in yolk and bounded externally by the original outer membrane, internally by the distended membrane of the temporary intestine (Fig. 72*C*). This embryonic wall forms the whole of the future worm. The blastomeres in it begin to proliferate rapidly especially on the future ventral side where they aggregate into three masses (Fig. 72*D*) whose fate is substantially the same as in rhabdocoels. The embryo flattens out, and the embryonic pharynx and inner and outer membranes disappear. The innermost cells of the embryonic masses correspond to entoderm, and they invade and devour the yolk cells. Eventually they form the intestine, at first a simple sac, later becoming branched by the invasion of mesenchyme at various points. The rest of the embryonic masses represent the ectoderm and the mesenchyme. The anterior mass, believed from its close association with the epidermis to be largely ectodermal, forms the cerebral ganglia as separate masses that later unite and from which the remainder of the nervous system grows out. The central embryonic mass produces the pharynx by forming cavities that become the pharyngeal chamber and the lumen of the pharynx (Fig. 72*E*). From the different appearance of the cells, the linings of these cavities are taken to be ectodermal while the remaining pharyngeal structure is mesenchymal. A definite stomodaeal invagination is wanting. The remaining indifferent cells of the embryonic masses are mesenchymal and give rise to the subepidermal and parenchymal muscles, the gland cells (probably) and other cells of the general mesenchyme, and eventually to the reproductive system. The mode of origin of the protonephridia of triclads has not been ascertained.

The embryos hatch in two or three weeks as complete minute worms by the rupture of the capsule, often along a predetermined line. In most cases as soon as the young worms have reached a certain size, the reproductive system appears, formed from the free cells of the mesenchyme. Some of these gather into little clusters that differentiate into ovaries and testes. The copulatory complex arises from a mass of mesenchyme that aggregates in the appropriate location, hollows out to form

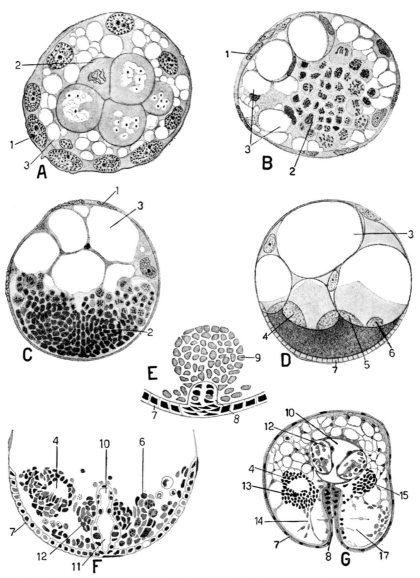

Fig. 69.—Development of rhabdocoels. *A.* Early cleavage. *B.* Later cleavage; mass of blastomeres moving to future ventral side. *C.* Mass of blastomeres at ventral side; epidermis forming. *D.* Three embryonic areas differentiating. *E.* Beginning stage of pharynx formation, showing stomodaeal ingrowth. *F.* Later stage of differentiation; brain and pharynx formed. *G.* Pharynx and stomodaeum completed. (*All after Bresslau,* 1904.) 1, covering membrane; 2, mass of blastomeres; 3, vacuoles; 4, anterior mass to form brain; 5, middle mass to form mesodermal mass of pharynx; 6, posterior mass to form rear parts of worm; 7, epidermis forming; 8, ectodermal invagination to form lining of pharynx and pharyngeal cavity; 9, mesoderm cells to form mesodermal part of pharynx; 10, lumen of pharynx; 11, pharyngeal cavity; 12, wall of pharynx; 13, beginning of eye; 14, ventral nerve cords; 15, primordium of copulatory complex; 17, mesenchyme.

the appropriate cavities, and differentiates into the lining epithelia, muscle layers, and gland cells characteristic of this complex.

Little was known of the embryology of land planarians until the recent study of Carlé (1935) on *Geoplana notocelis*, Brazil, that lays capsules 8 to 9 mm. in diameter, containing five to eight eggs. The development followed through the formation of the provisional pharynx and intestine is similar to that of fresh-water planarians.

There is no trace whatever in the development of any turbellarian of archenteron or coelom. All the evidence indicates that the stereogastrula is the primary embryonic form of the Turbellaria and that entoderm and entomesoderm arise by the mesenchymal method. The development affords no support for the belief that certain embryonic cells persist undifferentiated in the mesenchyme as "formative" cells set aside to function later in the formation of gonads and in regenerative processes. In the triclads and most rhabdocoels and alloeocoels, germ layers are not indicated, and the organ-systems of these animals cannot therefore be assigned to any particular germ layer. In those groups with determinate development it is seen that the mesenchyme and its derivatives are ecto- and entomesodermal; and what may be presumed to be entoderm in the Acoela also participates in the mesenchyme.

20. Asexual Reproduction.—Asexual reproduction occurs in the rhabdocoel families Catenulidae and Microstomidae, in fresh-water triclads of the family Planariidae, and in some land triclads. The rhabdocoels mentioned undergo transverse fission into chains of zooids which become well differentiated before breaking from the chain (Figs. 9, 29). The place where a fission plane is to form is first marked by the appearance of an indentation, soon followed by the differentiation of the ciliated pits. In *Microstomum* (Fig. 50*B*) an internal septum also develops. Pharynx and cerebral ganglia soon form from masses of mesenchyme cells. The order of formation of successive fission planes was already discussed (page 30). In general the time of appearance and locus of a new fission plane are controlled by the degree of development of the nearest fission plane anterior to the site; the more differentiated this plane, the farther away will the new plane appear (Fig. 9). These rhabdocoels multiply extensively by fission until sexual maturity comes on, usually in autumn, whereupon fission ceases and regenerative power is lost, at least in the female phase.

Multiplication by transverse fission is of common occurrence among fresh-water planarians, especially the genera *Dugesia*, *Phagocata*, and *Polycelis*. Fission is not preceded by morphological indications except in two species, "*Planaria*" *fissipara*, Trinidad (Kennel, 1889) and *Dugesia paramensis*, Colombia (Fuhrmann, 1914), in which pharynx and eyes of the new animal appear prior to fission (Fig. 73*C*). The fission process occurs when the animal has attained a certain size and when other factors are suitable. The rear end suddenly adheres firmly while the anterior region continues to advance so that the fission region is pulled out to an elongated shape and quickly ruptures (Fig. 73B). The isolated rear end soon regenerates into a complete small worm. Locomotion and adhesion are essential to the fission process, and fission can be prevented or delayed by interference with these prerequisites as by greasing the container whereupon very long worms can be obtained. On the other hand, rise of temperature and decapitation induce fission (Child, 1910b; Vandel, 1922). Fission usually occurs at a rather definite level shortly behind the pharynx but may take place at other levels, through or anterior to the

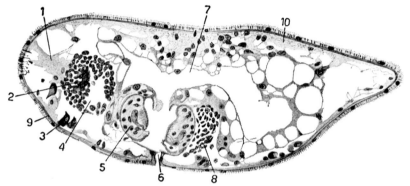

Fig. 70.—Embryology of rhabdocoels; completed embryo of *Mesostoma* (*after Bresslau*, 1904). 1, sensory nerve; 2, retinal cells; 3, rhabdite-forming cells; 4, brain ganglia; 5, muscular mass of pharynx; 6, pharyngeal cavity; 7, intestine; 8, primordium of copulatory complex; 9, epidermis; 10, mesenchyme.

pharynx in some species. The work of Child (1911d) indicates that the fission plane is predetermined physiologically and that the part of the animal behind this plane already has physiological characteristics of a new individual. In nature asexual reproduction of planarians is generally related to the seasonal cycle. Most commonly fissions occur at frequent intervals during the summer and sexual reproduction takes place in winter and spring. Fissions may cease during sexual activity but not necessarily so. As already noted, some species, especially of the genera *Dugesia* and *Phagocata*, exist in sexual and asexual strains (page 157), and also differ as to seasonal cycles in different localities. Some species propagate exclusively by the asexual method and are seldom or never seen in the sexual condition. Certain *Phagocatas* in place of regular fission fragment into a number of pieces (page 159) that encyst; within the cyst reorganization and regeneration of the piece ensue. Some land planarians, especially *Bipalium kewense* and *Dolichoplana striata*, also multiply asexually by fragmentation.

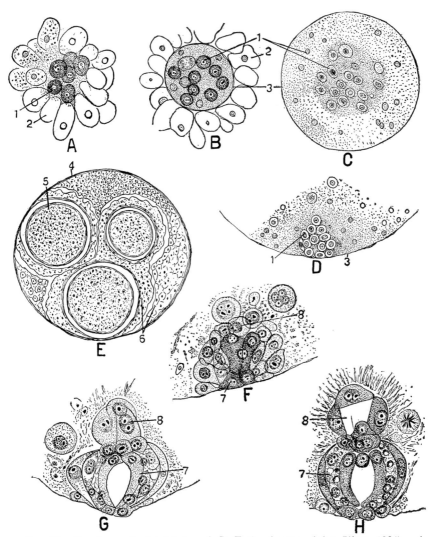

FIG. 71.—Development of triclads. *A–D.* Early cleavage (*after Ijima*, 1884). *A.* Several bastomeres surrounded by yolk cells. *B.* Later cleavage; some blastomeres have formed a surface membrane. *C.* Later; embryo expanding; yolk hereafter omitted. *D.* Mass of blastomeres moved to future ventral surface. *E.* Section through a capsule showing three embryos of about the stage of *C* embedded in the yolk syncytium (*after Metschnikoff*, 1883). *F–G.* Development of the embryonic pharynx (after *Mattiesen*, 1904). 1, blastomeres; 2, yolk cells; 3, bounding membrane; 4, capsule wall; 5, embryo; 6, yolk syncytium; 7, primordium of embryonic pharynx; 8, embryonic intestine.

21. Regeneration and Transplantation.—Those Turbellaria that reproduce asexually also possess high powers of regeneration and consequently have served as material for innumerable studies on regeneration. In other Turbellaria regeneration of a head is limited to pieces from anterior regions or to pieces containing the cerebral ganglia; or else the animals are incapable of regenerative processes beyond wound healing. Many forms can replace posterior regions, including the pharynx and the copulatory apparatus, when the cuts are made posterior to the cerebral ganglia. The region anterior to the ganglia is incapable of regeneration in any case. Polarity is strongly retained in pieces, i.e., the anterior cut surface regenerates a head, the posterior cut surface, a tail; but alterations of polarity occur or may be induced or increased by experimental means. The capacity to regenerate, the rate of the process, the amount of new tissue produced, and often the type of anterior regenerate are markedly related to level, being greatest or most normal anteriorly and declining posteriorly (Fig. 73D–L). In short, the flatworm body like the coelenterate (P–C, page 492) is a polarized system; the polarization consists in some sort of physiological gradation along the anteroposterior axis. The characteristics of and evidence for the existence of such an axial gradation have recently been summarized by Child (1941). Regeneration involves two processes: regeneration proper, or *epimorphosis*, in which new tissue grows out from the cut surface in partial replacement of the part removed; and *morphallaxis*, or the working over of the old tissue and organs to fit into the new animal. The relative roles of the two processes vary with different species and with size and level of the piece; but in any event reorganization of the old parts is necessary.

The Acoela have limited powers of regeneration, as illustrated by experiments on *Polychoerus* (Child, 1907; Keil, 1929; Stevens and Boring, 1905) and *Aphanostoma* (Peebles, 1913). Portions removed anterior to the cerebral ganglia or rear portions are replaced perfectly; in pieces cut posterior to the ganglia the amount of anterior tissue formed is less the more posterior the level, but in no case is a normal anterior end regenerated, for ganglia and statocyst are not replaced. Longitudinal halves replace the missing half.

Those rhabdocoels that form chains of zooids naturally regenerate readily, and the regeneration of *Stenostomum* has been much studied (Child, 1902, 1903; Van Cleave, 1929). Pieces from almost any region reorganize into complete new worms. In some species the anterior cut end forms the new head while in others preexisting fission planes or planes formed after cutting absorb the part anterior to them and become the head (Fig. 73A); or in cut pieces containing fission planes, these planes may continue to differentiate and fission may ensue, leaving a piece anterior to the fission plane that may or may not be able to regenerate a

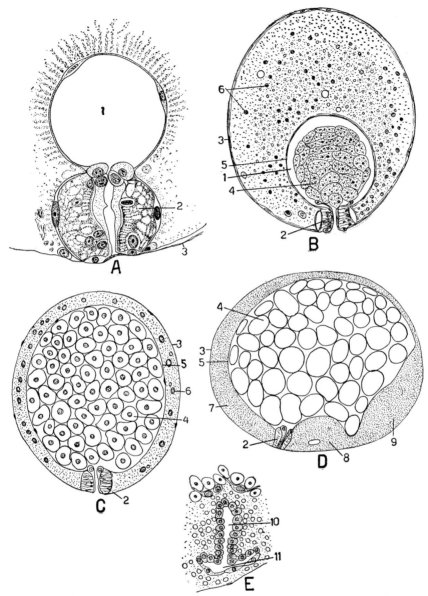

Fig. 72.—Development of triclads (continued). *A.* Embryonic pharynx and intestine completed (*after Mattiesen*, 1904). *B.* Embryo beginning to ingest the yolk (*after Metschni-koff*, 1883). *C.* Ingestion of yolk completed. *D.* Three embryonic masses formed. *E.* Formation of definitive pharynx by appearance of spaces. (*C–E after Fulinski*, 1916.) 1, embryonic intestine; 2, embryonic pharynx; 3, bounding membrane; 4, mass of ingested yolk; 5, inner bounding membrane; 6, blastomeres; 7, anterior mass to form brain; 8, middle mass to form definitive pharynx; 9, posterior mass to form mesenchyme and reproductive system; 10, pharynx lumen; 11, pharyngeal cavity.

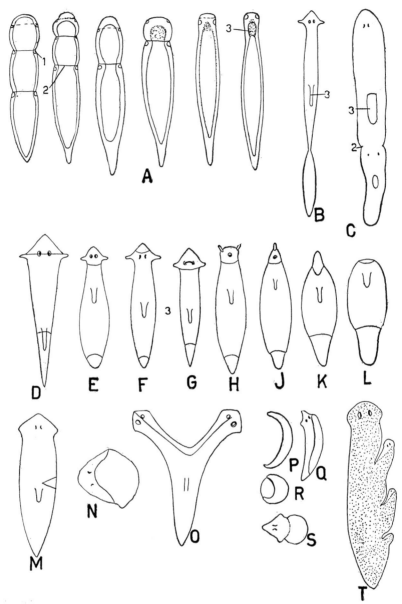

Fig. 73.—Asexual reproduction and regeneration. *A.* Six stages in the regeneration of a piece of *Stenostomum* containing fission planes *(after Child,* 1903); the best developed zooid absorbs parts anterior to it and becomes a new worm. *B. Dugesia* in fission, *(after Child,* 1910b.) *C. Planaria fissipara,* Trinidad, triclad that forms fission planes prior to fission *(after Kennel,* 1888). *D, E.* Effect of level on regeneration *(after Child,* 1911a). *D.* Regenerate from anterior piece; has large head, posteriorly located pharynx. *E.* Regenerate from postpharyngeal piece; has small head, more anterior pharynx. *F–L.* Series to show decline of head regeneration in *Dugesia dorotocephala* with decreasing size and more

head. The regeneration of *Microstomum* is similar to that of *Stenostomum* (Ruhl, 1927). Some other rhabdocoels may regenerate the tail tip (*Macrostomum*, Ruhl, 1927) but in general rhabdocoels that lack asexual reproduction and alloeocoels are incapable of any regeneration (Fulinski, 1922; Hein, 1928; Ruhl, 1927), although wounds are healed by epidermal migration.

Fresh-water planarians of the genera *Dugesia, Phagocata, Polycelis*, etc., display remarkable powers of regeneration and have been the object of numerous researches. In general, pieces of moderate size from any level form a complete new worm. With reduction in size of piece, complete worms may regenerate from even very short pieces in some species, while in others short pieces tend to regenerate reduced or imperfect heads or may remain headless, and this tendency is greatest the more posterior the level (Fig. 73F–L). The size and normality of the regenerated head, the rate of anterior regeneration, and the length of tail produced are generally greater the more anterior the level from which the piece was cut and decline in posterior levels. In *Dugesia dorotocephala* (Fig. 15B), extensively studied by Child, a series of anterior regenerates ranging from normal heads through several types of reduced heads to headlessness (Fig. 73F–L) occurs in relation to level and shortness of piece (Child, 1911a, b, c). This series shows increasing suppression of the middle region with consequent approximation and fusion of eyes and auricles. These facts constitute some of the evidence for the existence of the axial gradation mentioned above.

Reconstitution also involves the formation of a new pharynx. Pieces that do not regenerate anteriorly may form a pharynx if they were cut from postpharyngeal regions of the original worm; but pieces cut anterior to the pharynx will not regenerate a pharynx unless some sort of head first regenerates. The new pharynx may arise in either the new or old tissue and is nearer the anterior end the more posterior the level from which the piece was cut and the less normal the anterior regenerate (Fig. 73D, E). If a head has regenerated the old portions of the intestine are worked over so as to reproduce in the regenerated worm the typical three-branched pattern. In general, the ability of a piece to regenerate into a complete worm of typical morphology depends upon the regeneration of a

---

posterior location of piece (*after Child*, 1911c). *F*. Normal regenerate. *G*. Teratophthalmic regenerate with fused eyes. *H*. Teratomorphic regenerate with one eye and auricles shifted anteriorly. *J*. Extreme teratomorphic type with fused auricles. *K*. Anophthalmic regenerate without eyes or auricles. *L*. Headless, no anterior regeneration. *M*, *N*. Regeneration of lateral triangular piece at right angles to original polarity (*after Olmsted*, 1918). *O*. Double heads produced by keeping open an anterior split. *P, Q*. Regeneration of a narrow side piece, polarity retained. *R, S*. Alternative method of regeneration of a narrow side piece, polarity at right angles to original. (*O–S after Morgan*, 1900b.) *T*. Head regenerated on each of three anteriorly directed oblique cuts (*after Li*, 1928). Line in each case separates new from old tissue. 1, ciliated pit; 2, fission plane; 3, pharynx.

head at the anterior cut surface.   This means that the head controls the
pattern of the morphology, i.e., the spatial arrangement and proportions
of parts.   This control is an expression of the dominant position of the
head in the axial gradation already mentioned.

Some other points in planarian regeneration may be touched on
briefly.   Very short pieces especially from anterior regions may regenerate biaxial heads, i.e., form a head at each cut surface.   Isolated heads
cut off just behind the eyes also often regenerate a reversed head at the
cut surface (Fig. 74G).   In some species short posterior pieces produce
biaxial tails.   After oblique cuts, a head usually forms at the most
anterior point, a tail at the most posterior point, of the cut surfaces (Fig.
74A–C).   Lateral longitudinal pieces usually regenerate with reference to
the original polarity (Fig. 73P, Q); but short lateral strips (Fig. 73R, S),
or those cut lateral to the ventral nerve cords, or small triangular lateral
pieces (Fig. 73M, N) tend to regenerate the new head at the cut surface,
i.e., at right angles to the original polarity (Morgan, 1900b; Olmsted,
1918; Beyer and Child, 1930).   By means of appropriate splits, double
(Fig. 73O) or multiple (Fig. 74E) heads or tails may be induced at will;
heads will grow out from the body sides behind forwardly directed gashes
(Fig. 73T), tails behind posteriorly directed ones (Li, 1928); one or more
"crotch" heads (Fig. 74D) may arise in the angle of posterior longitudinal
splits if these are carried far enough forward (Beissenhirtz, 1928; Silber
and Hamburger, 1939; Hull, 1940); heads will form along the edges of
windows through the body (Hull, 1940, Fig. 74F); and in fact an endless
variety of bizarre forms can be produced by appropriate cuts.[1]   Regeneration is also affected by external factors such as temperature, osmotic
pressure, and chemical composition of the medium; many experiments
have been performed on the effect of various salts, anesthetics, radiations
(see below), etc., on regeneration.

If a sexually mature planarian is cut in two between the pharynx and
the copulatory apparatus, the latter degenerates and the piece regenerates
into an asexual worm.   The large anterior piece regenerates a new copulatory apparatus if active testes are present.   The presence of ovaries is
not pertinent (Vandel, 1920).   This result indicates that the formation
and maintenance of the copulatory apparatus depend on the presence of
testes.

The Dendrocoelidae are incapable of asexual reproduction and have
limited powers of regeneration.   Anterior pieces retaining the head regenerate the missing posterior parts, but decapitated pieces can reform the
head only when taken from anterior levels, in our common dendrocoelid,
Procotyla fluviatilis, only from the anterior third (Lillie, 1901; Curtis and

[1] As cuts and splits in the planarian body heal rapidly, they must be kept open
by repeated cutting if regenerates are wanted.

Schulze, 1934). Similar conditions obtain in marine triclads (*Procerodes*, *Cercyra*), some of which cannot regenerate a head when the cut lies behind the cerebral ganglia whereas in others prepharyngeal pieces may regenerate a head (Lloyd, 1914a; Lus, 1926; Steinmann, 1908). Pieces from pharyngeal and postpharyngeal regions are incapable of head regeneration but may regenerate a tail at the anterior cut surface. In marine triclads slight dilution of the sea water accelerates regeneration; other osmotic changes retard (Lloyd, 1914b). Some land planarians, as *Bipalium kewense*, regenerate very well (Morgan, 1900a); others, as *Geoplana* (Goetsch, 1933), regenerate perfectly when the pieces are large, less so in short pieces.

The polyclads in general have poor powers of regneration (Child. 1904a, b, c, 1905a, b, c, d, 1910a; Levetzow, 1939; Olmsted, 1922b). Pieces containing the cerebral ganglia regenerate perfectly. Pieces cut behind the cerebral ganglia are incapable of anterior regeneration but can regenerate parts behind their level of section.

Grafting experiments may also be performed with suitable fresh-water planarians; species of *Dugesia* are generally used. When crosspieces are fused in normal or reversed orientation, the result is similar to that found with hydroids (P–C, page 491), i.e., regeneration occurs according to the original polarity of each piece except that the polarity of very short pieces fused to larger pieces may be altered. Triangular or rectangular pieces may be excised and grafted into windows made into other parts of worms (Miller, 1938; Okado and Sugino, 1937; Santos, 1931) in normal or altered orientation. Such grafts from the cephalic region containing much nervous tissue are more effective in inducing a head-like outgrowth and causing reorganization of adjacent parts of the host with production of one or more pharynges, the more posteriorly they are grafted into the host (Fig. 75*A–C*). Similar grafts from tail regions implanted anteriorly are influenced by the host to develop into a tail regardless of their original polarity (Fig. 75*D*).

Heads regenerated from grafts or at a cut influence adjacent regions for a certain distance, reorganizing them to a greater or less degree into postcephalic regions (with pharynx and intestinal branches), and prevent the formation of another head at a cut surface or otherwise within a certain distance.

The histology of the regenerative process has been repeatedly studied in planarians with not entirely concordant results; the differences are probably real, depending on the species employed. The wound is considerably closed by muscle contraction (this contraction is omitted if the cutting occurs in an isotonic medium) and the adjacent epidermal cells flatten, become syncytial, and creep over the cut surface. If the exposed surface is sufficiently large, regeneration cells may participate in the

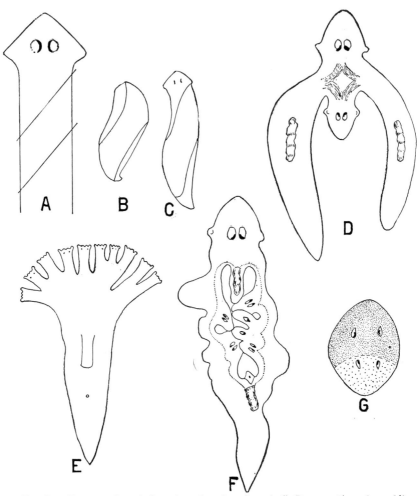

Fig. 74.—Regeneration of planarians (continued). *A–C.* Regeneration of an oblique piece (*after Morgan*, 1900b). *D.* Crotch head, produced at anterior end of posterior split that extends far forward (*after Hull*, 1940).   *E.* Numerous heads produced on *Dendrocoelum lacteum* by repeated splits (*after Lus*, 1924). *F.* Many heads regenerated along the sides of a central long window (*after Hull*, 1940). *G.* Head regenerated at posterior cut surface of head piece of *Curtisia foremanii* (*after Morgan*, 1900b).

formation of this covering membrane, which later differentiates into the typical epidermis. A mass of cells, variously known as regeneration cells, formative cells, etc., accumulates beneath the covering membrane and differentiates into the various missing parts (Bartsch, 1923; Lang, 1912; Bandier, 1936; Steinmann, 1926).   In the case of anterior regeneration strands of these cells attach to the cut nerve cords and differentiate into brain and eyes.   They also adhere to the cut intestinal branches and build on appropriate terminations, and differentiate into muscle cells and gland cells in appropriate locations. It appears, however, that in some species or with regard to some systems, the new parts may be formed by proliferation of the adjacent cells of the old parts, i.e., Bandier (1936) states that in the regeneration of land planarians both cut nerve ends and intestinal branches grow from their own cells. The source of these regeneration cells is still under dispute. There is little doubt that they comprise preexisting cells that migrate to the cut surface either with or without multiplying by mitosis. According to some authors, they consist entirely of the free cells of the mesenchyme; others state that, after cutting, various body cells, such as gastrodermis, yolk glands, gland cells, etc., undergo dedifferentiation into amoeboid cells and join the free mesenchymal cells to form the mass of regeneration cells (Lang, 1912; Steinmann, 1926). An extreme view is to the effect that the regeneration cells are persistent embryonic cells held as a reserve to function in regeneration and formation of the reproductive system (Curtis, 1936; Curtis and Schulze, 1934). It appears to the author that there is no evidence in support of such a view and that some of the evidence cited above opposes it. Curtis and Schulze have found that there are conspicuously fewer free mesenchymal cells in planarians with poor powers of regeneration, as *Procotyla fluviatilis*, than in those with high powers, as species of *Dugesia;* but their tabulation fails to show any marked decline in number of free mesenchymal cells in those regions of *Procotyla* that cannot regenerate a head as compared with regions that can. Further regions unable to regenerate a head can regenerate a tail and also can produce (from free mesenchymal cells) the entire complicated copulatory apparatus.

Attempts to shed some light on these problems have been made by studying the effect of X rays and radium on regeneration (Bardeen and Baetjer, 1904; Gianferrari, 1929; Meserve and Kenney, 1934; Schaper, 1904; Strandskov, 1937; Weigand, 1930). The subject has been reviewed by Curtis (1936) who has researched extensively on the matter. In general, exposure to sufficient dosage of X rays and radium inhibits regeneration altogether in most species, although *Dugesia dorotccephala* will regenerate after any exposures that do not kill.[1] The failure to regenerate is caused, according to some of the above workers, by the killing off of the free mesenchyme cells, according to others by the inability of these cells after radiation to migrate or to differentiate. The result therefore only proves what was already known, namely, that cells of the type of free mesenchymal cells are responsible for regeneration. It does

[1] It is very difficult to reconcile the results of Curtis using *D. agilis*, which he says does not regenerate after X-ray treatment, with those of Strandskov and Meserve and Kenney using *D. dorotocephala*, since, in the author's opinion, *D. agilis* is only a geographic variant of *D. dorotocephala* and cannot with certainty be distinguished from it by morphological criteria.

not settle the questions whether these cells are in fact embryonic rests and whether they get contributions from dedifferentiated tissues. The difference in susceptibility to radiation between the mesenchyme cells and other body cells evidently varies with different species.

22. Ecology, Physiology, and Behavior. *a. General Ecology.*—The Turbellaria are in general marine animals; only the Catenulida and

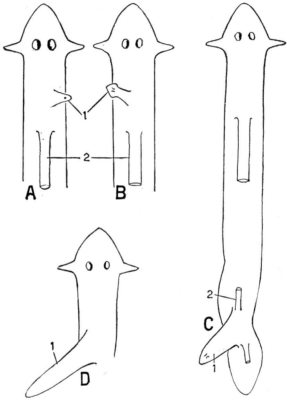

Fig. 75.—Grafts of planarians. *A, B.* Types of outgrowth produced by grafts of small pieces from the brain region into the prepharyngeal region of *Dugesia. C.* Same kind of graft grafted into the postpharyngeal region; produces larger head that has induced two pharynges in relation to itself. *D.* Postpharyngeal piece grafted into the prepharyngeal region of *Dugesia;* becomes a tail. (*All after Santos,* 1931.)   1, regenerate induced by graft; 2, pharynx.

Temnocephalida are typically fresh-water groups without evident marine relatives or forebears. The Turbellaria have obviously spread from marine into fresh-water habitats and from thence into humid terrestrial regions. There has also been a considerable amount of return invasion of brackish and even salt water by fresh-water turbellarians, notably among the Catenulida, Macrostomida, triclads, and such rhabdocoel genera as *Dalyellia, Castrada,* and *Phaenocora.* The Turbellaria are characteristic and constant members of a variety of habitats. They are typically bottom dwellers. The larger forms, as the triclads and polyclads, are generally found on hard bottom, under rocks and among shells and gravel, etc.; the small and microscopic members are more apt to occur on sandy and mucky bottoms. A characteristic assemblage of sand-dwelling rhabdocoels and acoels has been found on north European coasts (page 144). These have certain adaptive characteristics in common: long, slender muscular body, long sensory hairs, tail appendages, eyelessness, loss of rhabdites, especial development of food-catching devices, overdevelopment of adhesive organs including girdles of adhesive papillae in a number of species, some reduction of the reproductive system, posterior displacement of the gonopores (Fig. 76). The species of such sand communities appear to have a very limited distribution, i.e., those of the north German Coast are different from those of the west French Coast, although ecologically similar. Whether such sand-dwelling turbellarian communities occur along American coasts has not been ascertained but is highly probable. The benthonic Turbellaria are mostly limited to the littoral zone of the ocean, although some occur at considerable depths; however, there are no abyssal species. Some acoels (Fig. 49A) and polyclads have pelagic habits and show some adaptation to pelagic life by transparency and broadly oval form; many polyclads also have pelagic larvae or juvenile stages. Acoels and polyclads are regular components of the animal association of the floating Sargassum and may have the adaptive brown-and-white color pattern characteristic of Sargassum animals. Nearly all pelagic Turbellaria are limited to tropical or subtropical waters; the chief exception is the rhabdocoel *Alaurina composita* in the

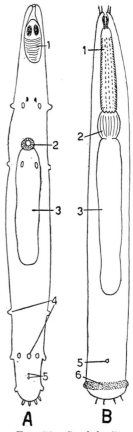

Fig. 76.—Sand-dwelling types: two kalyptorhynchid rhabdocoels from the Bay of Kiel (*after Meixner*, 1928). *A. Acerina remanei*, with five bands of adhesive papillae. *B. Rhinepera remanei*, with a caudal adhesive girdle. 1, proboscis; 2, pharynx; 3, intestine; 4, adhesive papillae; 5, gonopores; 6, adhesive girdle.

North Atlantic (Fig. 32B) of which large numbers may be found in late summer in the Zuider Zee and adjacent waters (Hofker, 1930). Although the ocean is in general a very constant habitat, turbellarians that live along shores in the tidal zone are subject to wide changes of

temperature and salinity.   The alloeocoel *Monocelis fusca* lives in tide
pools on the Welsh Coast where the natural temperature range is -1 to
28°C. and can recover from exposure to 44.5°C. (Rees, 1941).   This
species and the marine triclad *Procerodes ulvae* also endure great changes
in salinity (see further below).

    The fresh-water Turbellaria are chiefly inhabitants of lentic waters
and often have seasonal cycles related to such habitats, especially in the
case of planarians and rhabdocoels that inhabit vernal pools (pages 135).
Some turbellarians are *rheophilous*, i.e., limited to flowing water, such as
springs and hill and mountain streams.   Outstanding examples of stream
planarians are the European *Dugesia gonocephala*, *Polycelis felina* (= *cor-
nuta*), and *Crenobia alpina* (Fig. 61*C*) which occur along streams with
increasing altitude and decreasing temperature in the order named.
Crenobia alpina requires cold temperature and running water.   No alpine
planarians are known for North America, but the species *Phagocata
morgani*, Appalachians, and *Polycelis coronata* (Fig. 32*D*), western mountains, seem limited to flowing waters.   Our common *Dugesia dorotocephala* (Fig. 15*B*) appears to live only in springs or spring-fed waters,
probably because of the high calcium content of such habitats.   Although
some turbellarians are *stenothermous* (enduring only a limited temperature
range) as *Crenobia alpina*, most fresh-water forms are *eurythermous*, i.e.,
indifferent to wide changes of temperature.   An extreme case is *Microstomum lineare* found in a variety of habitats ranging from alpine lakes to
hot springs at 40 to 47°C.   Rhabdocoels are characteristic parts of the
fauna of alpine lakes, but most of these are common species with a wide
distribution in fresh waters.   More specific are the rhabdocoels, chiefly
of the genera *Phaenocora* and *Mesostoma*, found in *shallow* waters in high
altitudes and latitudes, and having in common a very dark coloration.
Several *Mesostomas* occur in such pools in the mountains of Tibet at
elevations of over 15,000 feet (Ruebush, 1939), and the author described
Mesostoma arctica from a pool on the Canadian tundra near the arctic
circle and from swamps in the Wyoming Mountains at 10,500-foot altitude
(Hyman, 1938).   A considerable number of fresh-water planarians occur
only in cave or subterranean waters; they are generally white, eyeless, and
provided with adhesive organs.   The most notable cave planarians are
the North American ones, of the family Kenkiidae (page 159).   The
turbellarian fauna of tropical fresh waters appears to be very scanty, consisting chiefly of a few widely distributed or cosmopolitan species (Reisinger, 1933) that tolerate a broad range of conditions.

    The terrestrial Turbellaria, comprising the land triclads, and a few
rhabdocoels and alloeocoels, being devoid of protective armor, require
high humidity and most seem unable to mature their sex organs except in
warm temperatures.   Hence they are mostly limited to tropical and sub-

tropical jungles with high rainfall where they live by day surrounded by mucus under stones, fallen logs, and leaf accumulations, in earth burrows, or between the leaf bases of tropical plants, coming forth at night to hunt food. *Bipalium*, subjected to desiccation, lost water according to the simple laws of evaporation and could recover if the water loss did not exceed 45 per cent of its weight (Kawaguti, 1932). However, mucous secretion plus aggregation into the most humid spot should furnish some protection against drying.

b. Relations with Other Organisms: *Symbiosis, Commensalism, Parasitism, Parasitic Infections, Enemies.*—Most acoels and some rhabdocoels and alloeocoels harbor symbiotic chlorellae and xanthellae; these occur in the mesenchyme chiefly just inside the subepidermal musculature and appear to be of the same nature and function as in other animals. They are absent in the eggs and newly hatched young, and it is known that they are acquired during juvenile stages by ingestion with food. They pass into the gastrodermis whence they are ingested by free mesenchymal cells that convey them into the mesenchyme (von Haffner, 1925). Much study has been devoted to the chlorellae of the acoel genus *Convoluta*, especially *Convoluta roscoffensis*, which occurs on the channel coast of France in such vast numbers as to color large areas green. Keeble and Gamble (1907) have shown that the green cells in this worm are flagellates of the chlamydomonad group and that they occur abundantly in the habitat and on the egg masses of *Convoluta*. These authors state that this acoel feeds while young but after attaining sexual maturity subsists entirely by digesting its chlorellae. A number of fresh-water rhabdocoels of the families Dalyelliidae and Typhloplanidae (Fig. 36*A*) contain green cells that can be cultivated apart from the worms and appear to be green algae of the genus *Chlorella* or close to this genus (von Haffner, 1925). It is notable that the *Dalyellia* species harboring these symbionts are much larger (2 to 5 mm.) than other *Dalyellias*. Sojourn in darkness almost but not entirely eliminates the green cells of *Dalyellia*. *Dalyellia* digests senile and degenerating green cells but does not damage healthy ones. The green and brown symbionts of Turbellaria contain starch, fats, and other lipoids and undoubtedly possess some nutritive value for their hosts. Their chief advantages are, however, that they utilize in their metabolism waste products of their hosts (it will be recalled that the Acoela have no excretory system) and that they give off oxygen enabling the host to endure stagnant conditions. Thus the acoel *Amphiscolops langerhansi* will survive enclosure in small airtight bottles of sea water for 2 weeks or more in the light but succumbs in the dark under otherwise similar conditions (Welsh, 1936); in the light, oxygen is added to the water by the photosynthetic activity of the brown cells of the worm.

As already noted, all groups of Turbellaria, except the fresh-water and terrestrial triclads, contain members that inhabit other animals in a relation that appears to be commensal rather than parasitic. Here may be recalled the acoels that live in the interior of echinoderms (page 131); the rhabdocoel families Graffillidae and Umagillidae, entocommensals of mollusks, echinoderms, and some other invertebrates (page 140); the wholly ectocommensal group Temnocephalida (page 145); the marine triclad ectocommensals of *Limulus* (page 155) and of skates (page 156); and the polyclad habit of dwelling in shells of live snails or in dead snail shells occupied by hermit crabs (page 166). The epizoic or ectocommensal forms are characterized by loss of pigment, cilia (especially dorsally), rhabdites, and often eyes, and especially by the strong development of adhesive areas and organs. The entocommensals, on the other hand, usually lack adhesive organs and are generally completely ciliated although they also tend to lose rhabdites and eyes; their most outstanding feature is the enlarged female system, exemplified by the branching yolk glands, elongated ovaries, etc. Such adaptation for increased egg production is a common feature of genuine parasites and no doubt indicates a tendency toward true parasitism among the entocommensal Turbellaria. However, probably the only genuine entoparasites among the Turbellaria are the Fecampiidae (page 140) and *Oekiocolax* (page 140).

The Turbellaria are themselves hosts to commensals and parasites. Euglenoid flagellates of the genera *Astasia* and *Euglena* occur in catenulids (de Beauchamp, 1911; Hall, 1931). A trypanosome-like flagellate, *Cryptobia* (= *Trypanoplasma*) *dendrocoeli*, inhabits the digestive tract and copulatory bursa of *Dendrocoelum lacteum* (Gelei, 1913). Holotrichous ciliates of the mostly free-living genera *Holophyra* and *Ophyroglena* may occur in *Stenostomum* (Kepner and Carroll, 1923) and planarians. Members of the parasitic ciliate group Astomata (P–C, page 189) are also represented, as *Hoplitophyra uncinata* with an anterior hook in the intestinal branches of marine triclads and *Sieboldiellina* (= *Haptophrya*) *planariarum* with an adhesive disk in fresh-water planarians (Bishop, 1926). *Coleps* (P–C, page 50) and *Trichodina* (P–C, page 199) species are often epizoic on fresh-water planarians. The most common endoparasites of planarians are gregarines, chiefly of the genus *Lankesteria* (P–C, page 149; Vandel, 1921). Encysted stages of larval trematodes are sometimes found in Turbellaria but probably represent accidental penetrations of wrong hosts. Land triclads seem much subject to nematode infestations.

The Turbellaria are seldom eaten by other animals as their surface secretions appear to be distasteful if not actually toxic (see below). Planarians, if taken into the mouth by fish and salamanders, are usually quickly ejected with signs of distaste. Bolen (1938) saw dragonfly and damsel fly nymphs eat planarians. The worst enemies are other turbellarians for the group is highly cannibalistic, promptly attacking weak or injured members or new fission products; the larger species may also eat the smaller ones.

c. *Duration of Life, Cycles, Senescence, Rejuvenescence.*—The length of life of turbellarians is known chiefly from laboratory cultures. The smaller forms, except those capable of fission, probably live but a short time, a few weeks or months, usually dying in summer or autumn after laying dormant eggs. Some, however, may survive a year or more by encysting during unfavorable seasons (Sekera, 1926). Species capable of fission can presumably under favorable conditions propagate indefinitely by the asexual method. Thus Nuttycombe and Waters (1938) cultivated *Stenostomum tenuicauda* for 11 years during which there were over 1000 asexual generations without the appearance of sexuality. They also had male specimens of *S. grande* that reproduced continuously by fission for 4 years. Sekera (1926) kept a *Microstomum* colony going for 3 years. Similar facts are known for asexually reproducing species of fresh-water planarians. Child (1914) maintained *Phagocata velata* in asexual culture for nearly 3 years during which there were 13 cycles of fragmentation, encystment, and hatching of small worms from the cysts (page 159). Individuals of the larger turbellarians survive in laboratory cultures 2 or 3 years (de Beauchamp, 1935; Vandel, 1922) and may have several periods of sexual propagation alternating with periods of fission or lack of any reproduction.

Something has been said in the preceding pages concerning sexual reproduction in relation to season. This matter has been studied in fresh-water planarians by several workers (de Beauchamp, 1931, 1935a, 1935b; Curtis, 1902; Kenk, 1937, 1940; Vandel, 1922). In general sexual reproduction is intermittent, alternating with periods of fission or of lack of any reproduction; the periods of capsule laying correspond in nature with external factors, chiefly temperature. In laboratory cultures, sexual reproduction is also intermittent but does not recur with the regularity noted in nature. Kenk, Vandel, and others believe there is an inherent cyclic reproductive rhythm in these planarians, but the author found that the same species used by Kenk (*Dugesia tigrina*) can, when fully grown, be caused at will to develop a copulatory apparatus and lay viable capsules by exposure to low temperature followed by rise of temperature. In some individuals even 2 or 3 days of exposure to lowered temperature is sufficient to bring on sexuality. Some time must elapse before another sexual period can be induced in the same individual by temperature manipulation. This time is much less than a year, mostly a few months, so that the alleged inherent rhythm is probably only an expression of such a "refractory" period following a period of reproductive activity.

After continued laboratory culture or after sexual reproduction in nature, turbellarians often evince signs of senescence such as loss of pigment, sluggish behavior, unwillingness to feed, and disintegrative processes in the eyes, head, or pharynx. Death by general disintegration frequently follows such changes. In species with high regenerative powers, however, rejuvenescence may be brought about experimentally or occurs naturally. Thus fission products or animals emerging from cysts are physiologically like young animals. Through starvation, adult worms may be reduced to the size of very young worms and so far as can be tested have actually become young again. Adult worms may be cut into small pieces, and these after regeneration are also indistinguishable from young worms. The already much mentioned *Phagocata velata* has in temporary pools a natural cycle of senescence and rejuvenescence; the worms grow to mature size, show the above symptoms of senescence, then fragment into small bits, each of which inside a cyst regenerates to a tiny worm that in all respects is identical with young worms hatched from capsules. Apparently this cycle is repeated in nature indefinitely with no loss of vitality. By underfeeding this species so that it does not grow, senescence and fragmentation are prevented, and the worms remain in a state of perpetual youth (Child, 1913a, 1914).

d. Osmotic Relations.—As already noted, both fresh- and salt-water turbellarians may invade brackish habitats. In a fresh-salt-water gradient as the entrance of a river into the sea, there is generally a barren zone, poor in animals, lying between the limits of increasing salinity endurable by the fresh-water animals and of decreasing salinity endurable by the marine forms. To endure changes of salinity animals must have some mechanism for regulating loss or entrance of water and salts. Generally fresh-water forms invading brackish water show reduction in size and greater tissue density as a result of water loss, and the reverse changes occur in marine forms adapting to lowered salt content. The best-studied case is that of the marine triclad *Procerodes ulvae* living on the English Coast at the mouth of streams (Pantin, 1931; Beadle, 1934). This animal is subject in nature to changes lasting several hours from the fresh stream water (salt content, 0.03 g. per liter) to sea water (salt content, 35 g. per liter). It can live indefinitely in all dilutions of sea water to 5 per cent; it swells and loses salts in the greater dilutions but not at all in proportion to the decreased osmotic pressure. In pure fresh water (i.e., without salts), it swells to nearly twice its volume, loses salts, and survives only 1 to 3 days. The worm can recover after loss of 85 to 90 per cent of its salts. In the natural stream water, swelling and salt loss are much less and survival better than in pure water. Osmotic pressure appeared not to be an important factor in the effect of the various media tried. It was found that calcium, in which the stream where *Procerodes* lives is rich, is the most effective factor in reducing swelling and salt loss in diluted media. Hence it appears that the presence of calcium in fresh waters enables marine animals to invade such waters. The cause of the protective action of calcium is not clear, although probably calcium makes the epidermis resistant to the passage of water and salts. Beadle (1934) studied sections of *Procerodes ulvae* that had been exposed for varying periods to diluted sea water and found that water, passing through the epidermis, at first accumulates in the mesenchyme but later is transferred to the gastrodermis where it accumulates in numerous vacuoles. Through this vacuole formation swelling is reduced, the mesenchyme is restored to normal, and the animal regains more normal appearance and behavior. In time the epidermis develops resistance to further water intake, although the gastrodermal vacuoles remain as long as the worms are kept in diluted media; i.e., there is no discharge of excess water through the mouth.

A number of other littoral turbellarians live under conditions in which they are exposed daily to large changes in environmental salinity. Thus *Monocelis fusca* inhabits tidal pools subject to evaporation and hence concentration of the sea water. The salinity of these pools was found to vary from 26 to 64 parts per thousand; the alloeocoel endured in tests a range from 5.6 to 76.8 parts per thousand but began to show sluggish behavior at 80 parts per thousand. It can, however, form a mucous cyst within which it can survive exposure to salinities of 298 parts per thousand, or over eight times the salinity of sea water (Rees, 1941).

Fresh-water planarians when exposed to solutions hypertonic to natural waters lose water and weight but not in proportion to the increased osmotic pressure, and they show some ability to resist water loss (Adolph, 1925; Gresens, 1928). *Dendrocoelum lacteum* was studied by Gresens (1928) in a stream opening into the Danish Wiek where it lives in a salt gradient from pure stream water (salt content, 0.01 to 0.04 per cent) to the Wiek water (0.5 per cent salt). Individuals from the more brackish water proved more resistant to high salinities than stream individuals. Worms could be acclimated by gradual changes so as to live normally and reproduce in 1.5 per cent salinity. Low temperature is an important factor in enabling planarians to resist increased salinity.

Some data are available on the salt content of the turbellarian body. According to the work of Pantin (1931), the salt content of *Procerodes ulvae* is about half that of sea water, or about 1.7 per cent. In *Stylochus frontalis*, the salt content is a little over 2 per cent (Pearse and Wharton, 1938). Hence the osmotic pressure of the body fluids of marine turbellarians is considerably less than that of sea water and the epidermis must be able to resist water loss or salt intake or some other regulating mechanism must be present. Dilution of the sea water causes increased oxygen consumption in marine invertebrates (Beadle, 1931), and this represents energy consumed in resisting water intake. The osmotic pressure of fresh-water turbellarians is greater than that of fresh water, and they require some mechanism to resist water intake and salt loss or to eliminate excess water. Murray (1927), seeking a medium suitable for growing planarian cells in tissue culture, found that the balanced salt solutions (e.g., Locke's, salt content, 0.9 per cent) in use for vertebrate tissues are far too concentrated for fresh-water planarians and require one-tenth to one-twelfth or more dilution. This indicates that the osmotic pressure of the species used (*Dugesia dorotocephala*) is equal to about a 0.08 per cent solution of sodium chloride. This species also requires a higher ratio of calcium to potassium than is customary in salt solutions made up for vertebrate tissues (Murray, 1928).

The water content of the polyclad *Stylochus frontalis* is 76.2 per cent (Pearse and Wharton, 1938); that of the land triclad *Bipalium* averages 81.5 per cent, grading from 80.7 per cent in the anterior third to 82.9 per cent in the posterior third (Kawaguti, 1932); and that of a fresh-water planarian, *Dugesia dorotocephala*, is 78 per cent (Buchanan, 1931).

e. Hydrogen-ion Concentration.—Turbellarians are in general indifferent to the pH of their environment, enduring without evident effect wide changes in this factor. *Dendrocoelum lacteum* will live indefinitely in a range from pH 4.2 to 9.5 (Gresens, 1928); greater acidities or alkalinities are fatal. The toxicity of acids for *Dugesia dorotocephala* depends on the acid used, being less for mineral acids such as hydrochloric and nitric, which kill in 2 to 3 hours at pH 3.0 to 3.4, than for organic acids, especially butyric, which is fatal in the same time at pH 5.0 (Hyman, 1925a). Similarly alkalinity caused by ammonium hydroxide is more toxic (lethal at pH 9.0) than that caused by sodium hydroxide (lethal at 9.2) (Anderson, 1927). In alkalinities and acidities less than those mentioned, *D. dorotocephala* survives indefinitely, although it is to be noted that planarians are able to reduce the alkalinity and acidity of the medium and it is very difficult to maintain a constant pH in solutions in which they are immersed. In general, alkalies accelerate (Anderson, 1927) and acids depress (Hyman, 1925a) the rate of oxygen consumption of planarians, but the acid effect results, not from the pH as such, but from the carbon dioxide set free when natural water is acidified.

f. Locomotion.—The smaller Turbellaria, including juvenile stages of the larger forms, probably move entirely by ciliary action. Although they probably can swim, few of them habitually do so, but for the most part they glide along the substratum or the underside of the surface film. The ciliary waves pass from anterior to posterior, thus driving the animal forward, and appear to be independent of the nervous system. Forms exceeding 2 to 3 mm. in length mostly crawl along a substratum with a characteristic gliding movement. Although the ventral cilia probably play some role in this gliding, if the worm is not too large, this type of locomotion is caused largely or wholly by muscular waves that pass from the anterior end backward either across the whole width (monotaxic) or alternately along the two sides (ditaxic). Triclads have mostly monotaxic, polyclads ditaxic waves (Stringer, 1917; Crozier, 1918; Olmsted, 1922a). The waves are mostly invisible to the naked eye in planarians, more noticeable in polyclads. The relative roles played by cilia and by muscular waves in locomotion can be determined by treating worms with lithium chloride which paralyzes ciliary action and with magnesium chloride which paralyzes the muscles. The first chemical does not stop locomotion in triclads and polyclads, whereas the second does. A number of polyclads swim by means of body undulations; these also may be monotaxic or ditaxic depending on the body shape.

Most turbellarians are capable of a more hasty type of locomotion which they employ when stimulated. This consists of large evident muscular contractions and expansions accompanied in those forms with adhesive organs or areas by alternate attachments of these, so that a leech-like form of progress results. Usually such an effort lasts but a short time and the usual gliding is soon resumed.

Mucous secretion probably plays an important role in gliding, even in aquatic turbellarians, and is obviously indispensable to terrestrial forms. The slime trail lubricates and smooths out the substratum on which progression occurs. The land triclads and some other Turbellaria also use slime threads in dropping from one level to another or in bridging gaps in a substratum (Kew, 1900).

The role of the nervous system in locomotion has been investigated by several workers (Bardeen, 1901a; Levetzow, 1936; Moore, 1923; Olmsted, 1922a). In general, turbellarians from which the cerebral ganglia have been removed tend to cease locomotion and to remain quiescent. They can, however, be stimulated to locomotion by mechanical or chemical means and are able to execute the usual creeping. Levetzow (1936) found that even quite small postcerebral pieces of *Thysanozoon* and *Eurylepta* are able to crawl. Such experiments indicate that the more simple muscular waves are independent of the brain and are mediated by the general nerve plexi. Most polyclads, however, are unable to swim following decerebration, and some cannot even execute the regular ditaxic crawling (Olmsted, 1922a). Therefore, the more complicated types of locomotion depend on initiation from the brain, also on transmission along the main nerve cords, since cuts through these inhibit swimming waves posterior to the cuts.

g. Food and Feeding Behavior.—The Turbellaria are as a class carnivorous. A few acoels and rhabdocoels are said to eat diatoms and other algae, but the vast majority of turbellarians eat other animals of suitable size or ingest bits of flesh of intact, damaged, or dead larger animals as fish and mollusks. Favorite items of food of the smaller species are rotifers, copepods, cladocerans, nematodes, annelid worms, etc., and the larger species feed on earthworms, snails, insect larvae, isopods, amphipods, other crustaceans, fish, oysters, and so on. Although the Acoela lack a digestive cavity, they are on the whole strictly carnivorous, ingesting copepods and similar small animals whole and digesting them in their interior cells. Aquatic and land triclads can attack and subdue intact animals of considerable size such as snails, earthworms, and insect larvae, and polyclads often devour bit by bit live sessile, helpless animals such as oysters, barnacles, ascidians, and the like. Turbellarians often gather, often in numbers, on animal corpses if these are not too decayed. Insects falling into the water constitute a regular food supply for pond turbellarians. Although most turbellarians will eat almost any kind of animal flesh, some appear limited to particular items. Thus *Stylochus frontalis* (= *inimicus*) of the southern Atlantic Coast of the United States seems to eat nothing but oysters, slipping between the shell valves and devouring the oyster bit by bit despite shell partitions erected against it (Pearse and Wharton, 1938), and *Pseudoceros crozieri* apparently feeds exclusively on ascidians (Crozier, 1917). In laboratory cultures, turbellarians can be fed on chopped or crushed earthworms or other annelids, mealworms and other insects, clams, snails, isopods, amphipods, clotted blood, or, most conveniently, bits of beef liver, although some species will not eat the last. Some species require live prey such as *Daphnia*. In general, turbellarians from lentic waters are most easily kept in the laboratory. Polyclads are usually difficult to maintain under laboratory conditions. Turbellarians may often be captured in numbers by baiting suitable habitats with pieces of beef or dead fish; at short intervals the bait is examined and any worms present shaken off into jars.

The presence of intact prey (not emitting juices) is detected either by direct contact with chemoreceptors or by the disturbance created in the water by the prey. The turbellarian then quickly grips the prey with the anterior end, especially the anterior adhesive organ when this is present, and wraps its body about the prey, holding the latter firmly against the substratum. Adhesive margins, disks, etc., are used by the worm to maintain a firm hold on the substratum while subduing the prey. Mucous and adhesive secretions assist in entangling the prey and rendering it helpless. Crustaceans and baby fish living in the same habitat with planarians may become coated with the slime left by planarians so as to be unable to move and are then attacked. Some turbellarians use the penis stylet to damage prey.

Food emitting juices is sensed in still water at a distance varying with species from 1 or 2 to 10 to 15 cm. or more. A turbellarian, previously gliding aimlessly about, when coming within the radius of diffusing juices exhibits a characteristic behavior (Pearl, 1903; Koehler, 1932; Müller, 1936). The worm pauses, swings the raised head about, then turns toward the food and goes to it in a direct line. Planarians living in running water detect food juices coming downstream at considerable distances, and if such places are baited with meat or fish the worms can be seen emerging in hordes from under stones and leaves and traveling in processions upstream to the bait. The European stream planarian *Crenobia alpina* is in fact more or less incapable of directing itself toward the food in the absence of a current (Doflein, 1925; Koehler, 1932) and even if it finds the food may often fail to feed in still water. Having reached the food, planarians test it with the anterior margin, then grip it with the head and move the body along until the pharynx can be brought into play. The protruded pharynx is inserted into the food, and ingestion begins. During feeding the worm keeps some part of its body firmly attached to the substratum.

The extirpation experiments of Koehler (1932) and Müller (1936) have shown that the lateral sensory organs of the head—the ciliated pits of *Stenostomum*, the ciliated grooves of *Phaenocora* and *Bothromesostoma*, the auricles including the auricular sense organs of planarians, or the corresponding lateral angles of the head in planarians that lack definite auricles—are the chief or only sensory areas involved in chemical perception of dissolved juices. *Stenostomum* after extirpation of the ciliated pits cannot detect the presence of food or find it, and planarians deprived of their auricles or corresponding regions show great loss in their food reactions. However, fresh-water planarians appear to have some chemoreceptors over the entire body and after such operations may in time find food. The testing of the suitability of food after finding it is vested chiefly in the anterior margin, which also functions to release the feeding reaction of the pharynx. After extirpation of this margin, planarians find the food as readily as before but fail to test it or grip it and often glide away without ingestion. The tip of the pharynx is, however, sensitive to food, and the pharynx may protrude on contact with food in the absence of anterior sensory regions. The pharynx tip can discriminate between normal food and the same food mixed with deleterious chemicals; but, after removal of both the anterior margin and the pharynx tip, the pharynx loses this discriminatory ability and may protrude into such treated food. The presence of fluid nutrients such as bouillon or blood in the water may induce repeated pharynx protrusions of intact planarians. According to some workers, headless pieces containing the pharynx or isolated pharynges will not feed when placed in contact with food, but according to others such reactions do occur in some species (page 101).

According to the available experiments, then, the ciliated pits, auricles, auricular sense organs, and corresponding head areas have sensory functions similar to smell in higher animals, and the anterior margin and pharynx tip function like taste.

After the prey has been subdued and firmly gripped, ingestion ensues. Turbellaria with simple and doliiform types of pharynx generally swallow their prey whole by means of muscular waves in the distended but not very protrusible pharynx. The rosulate pharynx is not distensible, and hence the contents of the food are sucked in. The triclads also do not swallow their food whole, but the highly protrusible plicate pharynx is inserted into the food or into the prey and the contents sucked in bit by bit through the peristaltic action of the pharynx. In polyclads the food is usually taken whole into the interior of the voluminous ruffled pharynx. Even those polyclads that have a cylindrical pharynx like that of triclads appear to swallow their prey whole, apparently limiting themselves to small animals. Whether the secretions of the pharyngeal glands have a softening and digestive action on the food cannot be answered categorically. These secretions possibly have such action in some species, but in general they function only to lubricate the food and facilitate its ingestion. Even in those cases where food is held in the pharynx and seen to undergo digestion, it does not necessarily follow that the enzymes involved are of pharyngeal origin.

Extirpation of the brain (without disturbance of the main chemoreceptors of the head) may greatly retard or altogether abolish the food-finding and food-ingesting reactions. The result, however, varies with species. The most marked effects of brain removal appear in *Crenobia alpina* which will not ingest food after this operation (Koehler, 1932), but other species may show little alteration of food reactions after decerebration.

Whether the surface and pharyngeal secretions of turbellarians have a toxic and paralyzing as well as an entangling effect on prey is a question often raised but never satisfactorily answered. In reviewing this question, Arndt and Manteufel (1925) note that large land planarians may produce an unpleasant astringent effect on the human tongue and that a South American land planarian, *Polycladus gayi*, is believed by the natives to be fatal when eaten by horses and cattle. These authors found that water extracts of ground fresh-water planarians were toxic or even fatal when injected into the coelom of small mammals. Later Arndt (1925) located this toxin in the surface secretions of planarians and found that it exercised its effect by stopping the heart. Mattes (1932) observed that the cercariae of flukes are damaged and killed by the surface slime of planarians. However, students of planarians, including the author, in general fail to see any toxic or paralyzing action of planarian slime on the usual prey, such as crustaceans and insect larvae.

The nutritional requirements of planarians are not definitely known, although attempts in this direction have been made by Wulzen, Bahrs, and others (Wulzen, 1923, 1926, 1929; Bahrs, 1929, 1931; Wulzen and Bahrs, 1931, 1935; Bahrs and Wulzen, 1936; Pettibone and Wulzen, 1934; Greenberg and Schmidt, 1936). Vertebrate liver, kidney, thymus, adrenal, and gray matter of the brain support excellent growth, whereas little or no growth is obtained with egg white, egg yolk, lean beef and other muscle, thyroid, pancreas, gelatin, beef fat, and the white matter of the brain. Tissues from animals fed on deficient diets also have an adverse effect on planarian growth and may cause a pathological condition in which the worms shrivel and turn black. Raw egg white alone or in high proportions in the food is very deleterious, causing disintegrating protrusions on the worms. Refrigeration at 0°C. or heating decreases the growth-promoting power of vertebrate tissues. Greenberg and Schmidt failed to find any favorable effect on planarian growth of adding vitamins and auxins to inadequate foods, although yeast addition was effective. Of all vertebrate tissues, liver has about the best growth-promoting power for planarians, and it contains an ether-soluble heat-labile growth factor of unknown nature.

h. Digestion, Assimilation, and Food Storage.—It was discovered by Metschnikoff in 1866 for *Convoluta* and later verified for rhabdocoels and triclads (Metschnikoff, 1878) that digestion in the Turbellaria is largely intracellular. As already indicated, it is improbable that the pharyngeal secretions have any digestive action, at least in planarians. Westblad (1922) failed to find any digestive action on protein or fat of extracts of 50 pharynges of *Dendrocoelum lacteum* and 100 pharynges of *Polycelis nigra.* It is also improbable that any digestion occurs in the lumen of the intestine in planarians (Westblad, 1922; Willier, Hyman, and Rifenburgh, 1925). The granular clubs (page 104), usually regarded as enzymatic cells emitting enzymes into the intestinal lumen, are in the author's opinion protein reserve cells (see below).

The details of intracellular digestion are best known for fresh-water triclads where the most complete studies are those of Westblad (1922) and Willier, Hyman, and Rifenburgh (1925). The latter fed planarians, starved 2 weeks, on beef liver and studied sections of worms fixed at varying intervals after the beginning of feeding. The liver torn into minute bits by the suctorial action of the pharynx fills first the anterior, then the posterior rami of the intestine. Some 45 to 60 minutes were required for complete filling of the intestine in the species used (*Dugesia dorotocephala*), but the phagocytic cells of the gastrodermis begin to engulf the food as soon as this comes in contact with them. These cells swell through intake of water, bulge into the lumen, often fuse into syncytia, and take in food particles in amoeboid manner by putting out pseudopodial processes.   The food particles together with fluid are formed into typical food vacuoles like those of Protozoa.   About 8 hours were required for all the food in the lumen to be phagocytized by the phagocytic cells which at this time are found packed with food vacuoles in various stages of digestion (Fig. 77).   The food in the vacuoles, at first loose and faintly stainable, gradually condenses to a strongly staining (eosinophilous)

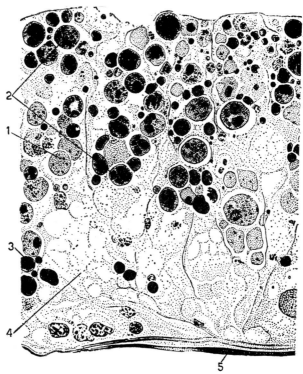

FIG. 77.—Intracellular digestion.   Gastrodermis of *Dugesia dorotocephala* 6 hours after feeding beef liver showing various stages of food vacuoles (*after Willier, Hyman, and Rifenburgh*, 1925).   1, early stage of digestion; 2, later stage with homogeneous areas forming; 3, final stage, vacuole becomes a homogeneous eosinophilous ball; 4, fat vacuoles; 5, muscle fibers.

homogeneous ball (Fig. 78) shown by chemical tests to be of protein nature.   About 8 hours are required for food vacuoles to reach the homogeneous ball stage.   These balls then gradually disappear, presumably as a result of the breakdown of their protein into soluble substances; about 5 days are required for the complete disappearance of the food balls from the phagocytic cells.   In a few phagocytic cells, the food balls do not disappear but subdivide into small spherules, and such cells then become granular clubs.   Westblad, using indicator dyes with the food, was unable to detect any change of hydrogen-ion concentration in the food vacuoles so that digestion appears to take place in a neutral medium. He found evidence of proteolytic and lipolytic enzymes but not of diastatic ones; in fact it appears that planarians are unable to digest carbohydrates.

In *D. dorotocephala*, the basal halves of the phagocytic cells are normally packed with fat, which largely disappears during the early stages of intracellular ingestion and digestion. It is also known that, during this period, the oxygen intake is doubled or tripled (Hyman, Willier, and Rifenburgh, 1924). It thus appears that the phagocytic activities of the gastrodermis consume extra energy and that this energy is supplied by the oxidation of the fat reserves. During the later stages of digestion fat reappears in the phagocytic cells and increases to its former amount. The indications are that the protein of the food is transformed into fat, without the intervention of carbohydrate stages, and that this fat is stored in the gastrodermis as a reserve. Fat droplets also occur sparingly in the mesenchyme of planarians. As already noted, planarians cannot digest carbohydrates and no carbohydrate reserve (glycogen) has been detected in most species studied, although von Brand (1936) found 3 per cent by weight in *Planaria torva* in autumn, less in winter.

The available researches indicate, then, that in fresh-water planarians practically the entire processes of digestion, assimilation, and storage of food occur within the phagocytic cells of the intestine. Nothing is known of the manner in which the food reserves are transported to and utilized by other body tissues.

In those Turbellaria that swallow their food whole one infers that considerable digestion must take place in the lumen before phagocytosis can occur. Metschnikoff (1878) and Westblad (1922) claim that digestion is wholly extracellular in those rhabdocoels having a ciliated gastrodermis (Catenulida, Macrostomida). Westblad saw protein and fat particles undergo digestion in the intestinal lumen of *Stenostomum* while starch grains remained unaltered. However, Jacek (1916), also using *Stenostomum*, found that digestion is wholly intracellular and that protein particles (egg white) and oil droplets are digested in vacuoles in the gastrodermis; during protein digestion the vacuolar fluid changed from an acid to an alkaline reaction and protein was converted into and stored as fat. Starch grains were ejected unaltered. Some observations of the author confirm the occurrence of intracellular digestion in *Macrostomum*. It may be assumed that in rhabdocoels small enough particles are ingested at once by the gastrodermis whereas larger ones must first undergo some extracellular digestion. Extensive storage of glycogen in temnocephalids was reported by Fernando (1945). Nothing is known of digestive processes in polyclads, which, it may be recalled, also have a ciliated gastrodermis.

Defecation has been witnessed by several observers. The worm first takes in water through the pharynx, then by vigorous muscular contractions expels indigestible remnants. Those polyclads that possess them use the anal pores as well as the mouth for defecation.

i. Starvation.—The fresh-water planarians can endure prolonged starvation, from 6 to 14 months, depending on species (Schultz, 1904; Stoppenbrink, 1905; Berninger, 1911). During this time they may reduce to $\frac{1}{10}$ to $\frac{1}{13}$ the original length and $\frac{1}{300}$ of the original volume. This

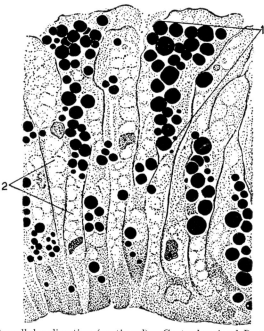

FIG. 78.—Intracellular digestion (continued). Gastrodermis of *Dugesia dorotocephala* 3 days after feeding beef liver; all food vacuoles have reached the stage of homogeneous eosinophilous balls (*after Willier, Hyman, and Rifenburgh, 1925*). 1, food ball; 2, fat vacuoles.

reduction results from tissue degeneration and does not involve any alteration of cell size. The nervous system undergoes no alteration so that greatly starved animals have disproportionately large heads. Epidermis and musculature are also practically unaltered, but the mesenchyme degenerates and disappears for the most part. The digestive system retains its form, and there appears to be no reduction in the number of diverticula, but the volume of the intestine is greatly diminished through degeneration of large numbers of the phagocytic cells. The gastrodermis loses food inclusions and reduces to a flattened syncytial state. In the later stages of starvation the fat stored in the phagocytic cells begins to be utilized but Willier, Hyman, and Rifenburgh

(1925) found that the surviving gastrodermis still contained considerable fat after 3 months' starvation in *D. dorotocephala*. However, the complete breakdown of most of the gastrodermis must furnish a large amount of fat and protein to the planarian. The greatest degeneration in starving worms is seen in the reproductive system. The copulatory apparatus, sex ducts, and yolk glands entirely disappear, and the gonads reduce to small clusters of cells. The oxygen consumption of planarians per unit weight declines during early starvation but rises continuously later, an indication that starvation in these worms acts as a rejuvenating factor (Hyman, 1919a, 1920).

The ability of other Turbellaria to endure prolonged starvation is not well known, but the smaller forms are probably able to survive for only short periods in the absence of food.

j. Respiration.—The Turbellaria are devoid of any special respiratory structures; the exchange of respiratory gases takes place by simple diffusion through the body surface. So far as known, respiration is of the ordinary aerobic type, comprising the intake of free oxygen and the emission of carbon dioxide. Exact measurements of respiratory rate have been made chiefly on fresh-water planarians. The rate of oxygen consumption of *Dugesia dorotocephala* is about 0.2 to 0.3 cc. per gram per hour in adult worms; the rate per unit weight is higher the smaller (younger) the worms, and is also increased by regeneration, during the early stages of intracellular digestion (see above), and during later stages of starvation (Hyman, 1919a, b, c, 1920; Hyman, Willier, and Rifenburgh, 1924). The oxygen consumed is also affected by the osmotic pressure of the medium as well as by the kind of salts in the medium (page 197; Buchanan, 1931; Hess, 1930). The rate of oxygen consumption of *Dugesia* species is constant at different oxygen concentrations in the water until this concentration falls below about one-third saturation (Hyman, 1929; Lund, 1921). The cutting of planarians into pieces accelerates the rate of oxygen consumption, and this increase is greater the smaller the pieces, i.e., if planarians are cut into six or eight pieces the rate of oxygen intake of the combined pieces is greater than that of intact worms (Hyman, 1923). This stimulatory effect of cutting declines with time and disappears within 24 hours. After allowance has been made for this effect, an axial series of pieces of *D. dorotocephala* shows an antero-posterior decline in rate of oxygen intake (Hyman, 1923), another expression of the axial gradation already mentioned several times.[1] Some

---

[1] The existence of such an axial gradient in respiratory rate in planarians has been disputed by others (e.g., Parker, 1929) for other species, but the author feels that in their experiments insufficient account was taken of the stimulating effect of section and of the sexual condition of the animals. Only nonsexual animals should be employed.

experiments on the carbon dioxide production of the polyclad *Stylochus ijimai* are also available (Watanabe and Child, 1933). Here, too, the rate of carbon dioxide production was found to decline with increasing size and to show an axial gradation in the form of a U, i.e., a decrease from the anterior end toward the middle and an increase again toward the posterior end. Unfortunately sexual worms were used, and as the reproductive system is not evenly distributed throughout the worm, a factor incapable of evaluation was present.

The oxygen consumption of planarians is depressed in the presence of potassium cyanide (Hyman, 1919d). It can be depressed as much as 90 per cent without injury to the worms. This indicates that the oxidative mechanism of planarians is chiefly of the cyanide-sensitive type, that it belongs to the "Warburg-Keilin" system, involving an iron-containing oxidase, a cytochrome complex, and a dehydrogenase. The dehydrogenase enzyme attacks the substance furnishing the energy, oxidizing it, and reducing the cytochrome complex which in turn becomes reoxidized by reducing the oxidase enzyme. The latter is restored by means of the free oxygen in the air or water, and so the system continues indefinitely as long as free oxygen is available (Commoner, 1940). Cyanide acts by preventing the oxidase from taking up free oxygen. The cyanide-stable respiration, which constitutes only a small part of the respiration of planarians, operates by way of enzymes other than oxidases.

k. Excretion.—Nothing whatever is known of the form in which turbellarians eliminate their nitrogenous wastes. From the fact cited above (page 205) that protein food is stored chiefly as fat in planarians, it seems evident that a process of deaminization must occur and hence that ammonia or some related substance must be given off. Several attempts have been made by use of vital dyes to determine what tissue is involved in elimination. Such experiments rest on analogy with conditions in vertebrates where it is known that vital dyes introduced into the body are treated like waste products and ejected by way of the kidneys.

When the Acoela (which have no protonephridial system) are exposed to vital dyes, the dyes collect in the central or digesting mesenchyme and are ejected through the mouth (Löhner, 1911). In triclads, also, the gastrodermis serves as the chief means of elimination of vital dyes (Westblad, 1922); the dye granules collect in mesenchymal vacuoles which are then passed to the intestine. In a number of kalyptorhynchid and typhloplanid rhabdocoels, also in *Stenostomum*, the dye collects in certain portions of the protonephridia, mostly the more proximal portions, and in the paranephrocytes (page 111) which also pass it into the protonephridia (Westblad, 1922; Reisinger, 1922, 1923), so that in these forms some evidence is available of an excretory function of the protonephridia, aided by paranephrocytes. No evidence has been seen of any passage of substances through the flame bulbs in any turbellarian. It seems probable that in Turbellaria the necessity of eliminating nitrogenous wastes is avoided by converting them into insoluble granules ("concrements") that are held permanently in the mesenchyme and in pigment cells.

Regulation of water content is in all probability one of the chief functions of the protonephridial system and the only function of the flame bulbs. This view is supported by the fact that the protonephridia are much better developed in fresh-water than in marine Turbellaria. Atrophy of the protonephridium of *Stenostomum* is followed by edema and general degeneration (Hess, 1937). New flame bulbs were formed by the evagination of capillaries in response to the accumulation of water in the worm. In a comparison of specimens of *Gyratrix hermaphroditus* from fresh, brackish, and salt water, Kromhout (1943) noted a gradual reduction in the protonephridial system with increasing salinity of the medium. Probably influx of water into the turbellarian body evokes activity of the flame bulbs, resulting in a current of water along the protonephridial tubule.

l. Chemotaxis.—This was already discussed in connection with finding of food, which is in effect a chemotactic reaction. Experiments have also been performed on the behavior of planarians to chemical substances in capillary tubes placed in the same dish with them. Pearl (1903) tested in this manner various concentrations of several acids, alkalies, and salts, and found that in general a positive response is given to weak concentrations of all the substances tried, and a negative one to stronger concentrations. A positive reaction is the same as that toward food, i.e., the planarian on perceiving the diffusing chemical turns toward and then proceeds directly to the capillary. In the negative response, the animal turns away from the capillary. Weak acids proved especially attractive, and planarians would often grip the capillary and extend the pharynx into its orifice. Koehler (1932) also employed the capillary method, using snail blood or crushed planarians, and found highly positive responses in some species, which can be caused to follow such a capillary around. Reactive species will also take a median course between double capillaries. Planarians with one auricle removed may show "circus movement" in a dish of diluted snail blood, circling toward the intact side. By adding india ink to snail blood diffusing from a capillary, it can be seen that response occurs when the carbon particles have passed along the auricular sense groove.

m. Reactions to Contact; Thigmotaxis.—The reactions of fresh-water planarians to mechanical stimuli have been investigated in detail by Pearl (1903). To a light touch on the side of the head, the worm may give a positive response, pausing, turning the raised head toward the stimulus, and moving to it. A similar stimulus along the body sides causes usually a small local contraction and may evoke the positive turning if not too far posterior. A positive reaction is never exhibited by postpharyngeal regions. Stronger tactile stimulation of the anterior end evokes the typical negative response, a turning of the head away from the stimulus and a gliding off in the new direction. Very strong or repeated prodding of the head causes jerking back by means of longitudinal contraction and turning through a larger angle. Moderate to strong mechanical stimulation of the sides of the body or the posterior region evokes local contraction and the hurried type of locomotion (page 199) for a short time, followed by the usual gliding.

If a planarian is cut in two, the anterior piece reacts as to strong posterior stimulation, i.e., moves by the hurried method for a short time, then returns to the usual gliding. The posterior piece generally crawls backward immediately after the cut and continues for some time to give this response to mechanical stimulation of the cut surface. To such stimulus elsewhere it gives either the negative turning away or the hurried crawling. A positive reaction to contact is not obtained in the absence of a brain.

The Turbellaria are markedly thigmotactic; the dorsal surface is negatively, the ventral surface positively thigmotactic. This is another way of saying that flatworms strive to keep their ventral surface in contact with a substratum, regardless of gravity, and their dorsal surface freely exposed to the medium. Pearl (1903) notes that if a light object is gently placed on the dorsal surface of a resting or moving planarian, the worm will promptly move away from under the object. Planarians will not come to rest in a situation where both surfaces are in contact. When placed on their backs, planarians, polyclads, and probably all flattened Turbellaria give a characteristic *righting reaction*. The worm twists into a spiral in such a way that the ventral surface of the head finally comes in contact with a substratum. The head then glides away and the spiral unwinds as the rest of the body follows. Planarians dropped through water (planarians cannot swim) give the righting reaction, usually several times, as they fall. Pieces of planarians also give the righting reaction although more slowly than when the head is present. Brainless pieces of polyclads also right themselves, but the reaction differs from the normal in that any part of the piece, not always the anterior end as in the case of intact worms, may attach first (Levetzow, 1936). However, this may also occur in pieces of planarians.

The entire body of planarians is sensitive to contact, but in general tangoreceptivity is highest on the auricles or sides of the head and decreases in an anteroposterior direction. In the absence of the brain, the auricles are no longer more sensitive than other parts of the body margin (Koehler, 1932).

n. Phototaxis.—Although some Turbellaria are positive to light, especially pelagic types, larval and juvenile stages of polyclads, acoels, and rhabdocoels that contain holophytic symbionts, and the rhabdocoels of Lake Baikal (Nasonov, 1935), the members of the class as a whole avoid light and unless other factors are operative seek the darkest areas of their environment. Many studies have been made on the response of turbellarians, chiefly fresh-water planarians, to light (Parker and Burnett, 1900; Walter, 1907; Taliaferro, 1920; Erhardt, 1932; Lemke, 1935; Ullyott, 1936). Exposure to light increases the activity of planarians and causes resting individuals to start locomotion; the rate of locomotion may also be more rapid in the light (Pearl, 1903; Werner, 1926). This stimulating action of nondirective light has been termed *photokinesis.* After a time the effect decreases, and the worms slow down and finally come to rest in the least illuminated region of the container, if such exists. The avoidance of light by planarians is an example of a phobotactic or phobic response (P–C, page 67), that is, the darkened area is found by random movements, a negative reaction when passing into more lighted areas and a lack of reaction when passing into more darkened regions. The most careful test of the phobic nature of light avoidance in planarians is that of Ullyott (1936). In a light gradient in which all possibility of directed rays from reflections, etc., was avoided, the planarians eventually came to rest in the darker part of the gradient. This phobic response to light is given equally well by specimens from which the eyes have been removed; these also show no change in rate of locomotion. Decapitated specimens also avoid light, although they move more slowly. In most species light is perceived by the entire surface, although in some the posterior region shows no reaction to light (*Procotyla fluviatilis*, Lillie, 1901; *Bdelloura candida*, Walter, 1907; *Bipalium*, Kawaguti, 1932). Both dorsal and ventral surfaces are sensitive to light (Walter, 1907), although planarians tend to keep their dorsal surfaces toward the light (Bock, 1936).

Planarians perceive changes in light intensity and may give evidence of such perception by hesitation, head swingings, and change of path when encountering a new intensity. Various experiments that have been performed on the possibility of color perception by planarians are really tests of intensity discrimination according to the more critical papers (Erhardt, 1932; Lemke, 1935). On contrasting backgrounds of black and white or dark and light colors, planarians come to rest on the darker ground and in general on colors of longer wave lengths. Such reactions are probably merely avoidance of light of higher intensity. A very exact phobic reaction was reported by Lemke (1935) for *Dugesia lugubris* on a background of alternate black and white circles; the planarian follows the black circles, turning back at the boundary with the white circles (Fig. 79). Eyeless specimens lose the reaction. Other species may not give such exact response to intensity boundaries and may in fact exhibit no change of behavior to considerable changes of intensity.

To directed light, planarians give a fairly precise negative response, turning away from the light and proceeding in a direction approximately opposite to the incidence of the light rays. The path of a planarian can therefore be directed by means of light rays. This phototopic reaction is mediated primarily by the eyes, for in worms from which the eyes have been removed (without injury to the brain) the response is much less definite and precise (Taliaferro, 1920), although still elicitable. If a spot of light is shone upon the eyes or head the negative turning away results, but if it is shone on middle or posterior regions there is no such response. Hence the topic reaction is mediated by the anterior end only, whereas the phobic response to light is mediated by the entire body in most species, with sensitivity decreasing in an anteroposterior direction.

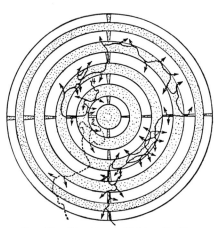

FIG. 79.—Reaction to light. Continuous line gives path of normal *Dugesia lugubris* on background of alternate white and black circles; worm gives avoiding reaction to white circles. Broken line gives path of individual of which the eyes have been extirpated. (*After Lemke*, 1935.)

The sense organs responsible for the phobic reaction have not been identified, but the eyes are evidently the chief receptors for the topic response.

According to the generally accepted analysis of Taliaferro (1920), directed light affects only those retinal cells whose long axes are parallel to the light rays. Because of the curvature of the planarian eye, only a few such cells would be affected in any given position of the planarian. The pigment cup also acts to shade retinal cells except those parallel to the light rays. This mechanism accounts for the highly directive effect of light on planarians, i.e., their ability to perceive rather exactly the direction of light, and it also makes it rather probable that planarians can see movement, although not objects. The decrease in intensity of light as a moving object interrupts light rays would affect a succession of retinal cells. Probably perception of movement is the function of the numerous eyes of land planarians and polyclads since a moving decrease of intensity would affect successive eyes rather than successive retinal cells of the same eye. According to Kawaguti (1932) the rear part of *Bipalium* is insensitive to light because it lacks eyespots.

Planarians can perceive ultraviolet radiations; they react negatively to them but move more slowly than in visible light (Werner, 1926). The behavior is the same in normal and eyeless specimens. Short exposures to ultraviolet and to direct sunlight are fatal to planarians (Merker and Gilbert, 1932). White species appear to be more sensitive to sunlight than colored ones.

Some data are available on the behavior to light of cave planarians that live in perpetual darknesss. *Sphalloplana percoeca* from Kentucky caves showed no avoidance of light or seeking of dark areas but would writhe on exposure to direct sunlight and might be killed by less than 2 minutes of such exposure (Buchanan, 1936). *Phagocata subterrannea* from an Indiana cave, however, was negative to light but less exact and more given to wandering than epigean species (Walter, 1907). Whether this different behavior is correlated with the fact that the first species is eyeless and the second has eyes cannot be stated.

o. Rheotaxis.—In general fresh-water turbellarians inhabiting still waters fail to react to water currents. Strong currents usually elicit only a "clamping" reaction, contraction and increased adhesion to the substratum. Weak currents may, however, call forth a positive rheo- tactic response, a turning of the anterior end toward the current and placing of the body in line with it. This has been reported for planarians (Pearl, 1903) and the rhabdocoel *Bothromesostoma* (Müller, 1936). In the latter animal, extirpation experiments indicated that the eight groups of sensory bristles along the lateral body grooves are rheoceptors (page 93). The reaction of still-water species to *weak* currents is probably part of the food-catching mechanism, since turbellarians are able to detect the presence of intact prey by water disturbances created by them. Pond planarians may develop a rheotactic response after being kept for some time in a rather strong water current (Koehler, 1932). Planarians that habitually live in flowing water usually exhibit a positive rheotaxis, for obviously without such a reaction they could not maintain themselves in their habitat. Thus, *Dugesia dorotocephala*, a spring-dwelling species, was found to show positive rheotaxis (traveling upstream) in nature and in the laboratory (Allen, 1915); but the positive reaction could be altered to a negative one (traveling downstream) by change of water or lowering the temperature. The outstanding example of a positively rheotactic planarian is *Crenobia alpina*, inhabitant of rapid alpine streams. As already noted, this animal is more or less incapable of finding food in the absence of a water current. It is highly positive to currents and will follow a tube from which a water current is issuing. In case of two currents of equal velocity opposite or at right angles to each other, it will take a resultant path between them, and of two currents of unequal velocity it will select the faster one (Koehler, 1932). The rheotactic reaction is given by all parts of the body, although most readily and to weaker currents by the head. Loss of the entire body margin does not eliminate the reaction so that rheoreceptors must be distributed over the entire body surface being, however, most numerous on the head. After being kept for long periods (6 months to a year) in still water this species retains its rheotactic response undiminished (Koehler, 1932). Beauchamp (1933) worked with a British stream planarian[1] in which the rheotactic response showed a definite seasonal cycle. In winter when temperatures were low and the reproductive system developing, the animal was positively rheotactic and accumulated at the head of hill streams; after the breeding season, negative rheotaxis ensued and the worms traveled downstream and even into the lake into which the streams flow.

p. Thermotaxis and Temperature Relations.—The majority of the Turbellaria are undoubtedly eurythermous, enduring wide ranges of temperature, but some species appear to be somewhat stenothermous. The behavior to temperature changes is considerably dependent on the temperature at which the worms had been living prior to the tests. Available data are limited to fresh-water planarians (Mast, 1903; Koehler, 1932). For local application of temperature change, a narrow hairpin-shaped tube is used through which water of the desired temperature is circulated. Planarians react to temperature change of 2 to 3°C. from that at which they have been living. To moderate increase applied to the anterior end a positive reaction may be given at first; the worm turns toward the tube and may test it with the anterior end, before turning away. Usually a negative reaction is eventually given. If the tube is very hot, a negative reaction may occur at once. Reactions to lowered temperatures are similar but less definite, and often no reaction is given. Localized heat applied to posterior regions results in local contraction, more rapid gliding away, or the hurried type of crawling. The lower limit of reaction to increased temperature was found by Koehler to be 24°C. for the anterior end of *Crenobia alpina*, 32 for its posterior part, 28 to 30 and 40, respectively, for *Dugesia lugubris*. The ventral surface of planarians is also sensitive to temperature, so that thermal perception is evidently distributed over the whole body. When placed in a temperature gradient, *D. dorotocephala* which had been living at 22°C. aggregated in a zone ranging from 17 to 26 (Mast, 1903); *Phagocata gracilis* aggregated at 0 to 10°C., whether taken directly from its natural

[1] Said to be *Crenobia alpina* but this seems improbable.

habitat at 9.5°C. or kept for a month in the laboratory at 20 to 22°C. (Eddy and Gleim, 1932). The thermal death point of the former species is about 42°C., of the latter 30°C.

The most interesting behavior to temperature is that of *Crenobia alpina*. This animal when presented with two streams of different temperature selects the cooler one and follows this about, being able to distinguish a difference of 3°C.

Planarians possess a high capacity for acclimation to temperature, being able when kept at high temperature (27 to 30°C.) to lower their rate of metabolic activity below and when kept at low temperature (8 to 10°C.) to raise it above that expected for such temperatures (Behre, 1918).

q. Geotaxis.—The Turbellaria in general show perception of gravity for when the oxygen supply of the medium decreases below requirements they come to the surface, i.e., exhibit negative geotaxis. This is not a response to an oxygen or other gradient for it is given by worms in a closed vessel completely filled with water of uniform constitution and turned upside down. Unfed planarians in water of good oxygen content in the dark tend to seek the bottom of the vessel, but after feeding they tend to come to the surface (Olmsted, 1917) probably because of the increased oxygen demand during intracellular digestion. The outstanding example of geotactic response among Turbellaria is seen in the acoel *Convoluta roscoffensis* (Bohn and Drzewina, 1928; Fraenkel, 1929). This animal is negatively geotactic when undisturbed, positively so when disturbed. On the sandy tidal zone on the channel coast of France, where it lives in countless numbers, it comes to the surface of the sand at low tide, and disappears into the sand when the tide returns or on any other disturbance. This rhythmic geotactic behavior with reference to the tides is retained for about a week by *Convoluta* when kept in the laboratory in vessels of still water (Martin, 1907; Bohn and Drzewina, 1928). It is independent of day and night. That the tidal response is really a geotactic one was proved by Fraenkel (1929) who showed that when *Convoluta* is simultaneously exposed to centrifugal force and gravitation it takes a resultant path between the two forces.

Although Turbellaria without statocysts react to gravity, it appears that the statocyst is of some importance in the geotactic reactions of the Acoela. The anterior tip of *Convoluta*, which contains the statocyst, reacts normally to gravity, but the rest of the body has lost the geotactic response. In regeneration experiments on Acoela it has been noticed that pieces without the statocyst have difficulty in righting themselves and in general react poorly to stimuli (Peebles, 1913; Keil, 1929).

r. Galvanotaxis.—The reaction of turbellarians to the direct constant electric current has been ascertained by a number of workers. All forms tested are cathodic, i.e., they turn their anterior ends toward the cathode and may swim or crawl toward this pole. *Stenostomum* (Pearl, 1903) in an electric current behaves exactly like ciliate Protozoa and its cilia also beat with reference to anode and cathode as in ciliates (P–C, page 68). *Convoluta* is highly cathodic (Bohn and Drzewina, 1928). Fresh-water planarians turn the anterior toward the cathode and may place the body in line with the current and proceed toward the cathode (Pearl, 1903; Alverdes, 1922; Hyman, 1932), or the body may curve into a C-, U-, or W-shape with ends and often ventral surface facing the cathode (Hyman and Bellamy, 1922; Robertson, 1927; Hyman, 1932). This cathodic orientation of posterior as well as anterior end may be attributed to the presence in such species of a fission region or some region of especial activity, such as an adhesive area, in the posterior part of the animal. Decapitated planarians show the same response as entire ones, and middle pieces move anterior end first to the cathode or backward to the anode. The land planarian *Bipalium* is likewise cathodic, moving by loops to the cathode, and pieces obtained by cutting the body in thirds also loop to the cathode. The one polyclad tested (Hyman and Bellamy, 1922) behaved like planarians, turning toward the cathode and usually also curving its body into a U-shape toward this pole.

The various explanations of galvanotaxis that have been advanced are based chiefly on the idea of a compulsory effect of the current directly on the ciliary or neuromuscular mechanism. This type of explanation appears unsatisfactory to the author, for it fails to explain reversals that occur under different physiological conditions. It can hardly be supposed that the neuromuscular mechanism also undergoes reversal during temporary changes of conditions. The fact that individuals facing the anode at the time the current is made also turn and proceed to the cathode is further difficult to explain on any such theory. According to the author's theory of galvanotaxis (Hyman, 1918, 1932; Hyman and Bellamy, 1922) also expressed independently by Robertson (1927), the flatworm takes that position with reference to the electric current which best corresponds with its own electrical currents. For at least the lower animals, as has been shown by numerous experiments (for flatworms, see Hyman and Bellamy, 1922), have inherent electrical currents related to their anteroposterior axiation. These currents presumably originate from different rates of chemical activity along this axis. In general, the anterior or head end is electropositive to lower levels, and hence it orients so as to face the cathode. The rear end of flatworms through the presence of a fission plane or other active region may also be electropositive with reference to the middle; hence the C or U attitude taken by such species in the current.

s. Desiccation.—The Turbellaria have no surface protection against evaporation and hence require an aquatic or humid environment. Some species secrete a mucous cyst or covering when exposed to desiccation and some land planarians can endure relatively dry environments as the South American pampas by habitually dwelling under cattle dung. In general, however, exposure to desiccation results in death. Fresh-water planarians when subjected to drying curl up so as to expose as little surface as possible (Pearl, 1903) and from time to time attempt to escape by extending the head in seeking movements or giving backward crawling waves but are unable to progress on a dry surface. When placed on a wet spot in a dry environment they give a phobic reaction whenever the head extends outside the wet spot. The land planarian *Bipalium* was found by Kawaguti (1932) to lose water according to the simple laws of evaporation in relation to the humidity and temperature of the environment. Water was lost even in an atmosphere of 100 per cent humidity. Recovery occurred if the water loss did not exceed 45 per cent of the fresh weight.

t. Mass Protection.—Following the discovery by Bohn and Drzewina (1920) that a number of *Convoluta* are more resistant to fresh water or much diluted sea water than single specimens in the same (limited) volume of fluid, much work was done by these authors and also by Allee and his students (reviews in Bohn and Drzewina, 1928, and Allee, 1931) on such mass protection in various turbellarians (and other animals) against adverse conditions and agents, such as toxic chemicals, ultra-violet radiation, salinity changes. In general, resistance to such agents and conditions is much greater when there are a number of individuals as contrasted with single or a few individuals in the same quantity of medium. The protection is not caused primarily by the fact that, in the case of a toxic chemical, for instance, there is less of the chemical per worm in the mass experiment, but it does result from the greater quantity of animal in a limited amount of medium. The French authors postulate the secretion under these conditions of a special protective substance of which of course more would be emitted by the larger number of animals, but the experiments of Allee indicate rather that the normal secretions and exudates of the animals furnish the protective materials. Protective action is furnished by disintegrated animals or the water in which the same or other animals had lived. In the case of turbellarians the mucous and other glandular secretions emitted from the surface are probably the chief means of protection. Such secretions, exudates, or disintegrated remains neutralize toxic chemicals and, in some unknown way, probably not by adding salts to the medium, also protect marine turbellarians against fresh water.

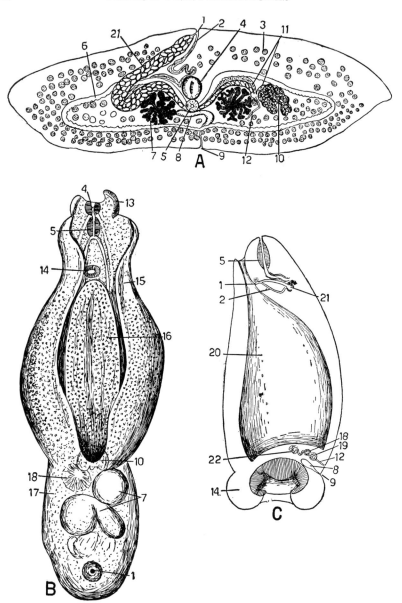

Fig. 80.—Variants of trematode shape. *A. Transversotrema (after Witenberg,* 1944)
fish trematode from the Red Sea. *B.* Strigeid fluke *Alaria alata (after Krause,* 1915).
C. Longitudinal section of the amphistome fluke *Gastrothylax (after Fischoeder,* 1903),
showing deep ventral pit. 1, gonopore; 2, sperm duct; 3, yolk glands; 4, oral sucker; 5,
pharynx; 6, intestine; 7, testis; 8, excretory bladder; 9, nephridiopore; 10, ovary, 11;
yolk ducts; 12, Laurer's canal; 13, lateral suckers; 14, acetabulum; 15, forebody; 16, holdfast; 17, hindbody; 18, ootype; 19, seminal receptacle; 20, ventral pit; 21, uterus; 22, beginning of uterus.

u. Learning.—The Turbellaria are capable of associative memory. *Stenostomum* can be trained to turn back into the dark at a light-dark boundary if punished by an electric shock when entering the light area (Soest, 1937). As *Stenostomum* is negative to light only a very weak light to which it does not react can be employed. The reverse experiment, training it to avoid the dark and remain in the light, requires longer training and gives a less definite result. Retention is poor. Similar experiments have been performed with the fresh-water planarian *Dugesia gonocephala* (Dilk, 1937), using shaking and electric shock as punishments, and rough versus smooth substratum, weak light versus darkness, and vertical versus horizontal surfaces as contrasting conditions. In general, the planarian could be taught by repeated punishment to avoid that condition to which it normally gives a negative response, as light and rough substratum, i.e., to turn back at the boundary in the absence of punishment, but the reverse attempt, to teach it to turn back into conditions that it normally avoids, gave poor or no results. The experiments of Soest and Dilk came from the same laboratory as the experiments with the formation of associations in Protozoa reported in P–C (page 181). Much more convincing is the work of Hovey (1929) on the formation of an association in a leptoplanid polyclad. These worms were subjected for hours to alternating periods of light lasting 5 minutes and darkness lasting 30 minutes. Light induces movement, darkness a quiescent state as is general in Turbellaria. Whenever a worm started to move on exposure to light it was stopped by being touched on the anterior margin. The number of touches required to cause the worms to cease movement in the light decreased notably with repeated trials although no worm learned to remain entirely motionless when exposed to light. Possibility of motor fatigue, injury to the anterior margin, or adaptation to light was ruled out. Following extirpation of the cerebral ganglia, worms did not learn to move less in the light, and repeated hindrance to such movement had no effect. Evidently the brain is involved in associative learning in polyclads.

V. CLASS TREMATODA

1. Definition.—The Trematoda are ecto- or entoparasitic Platyhelminthes with a digestive system but without an epidermis, being covered externally by a cuticle devoid of cilia and resting directly on the mesenchyme.

The class name refers to the cavity of the suckers (Greek, *trema*, a hole) with which most members are provided as adhesive organs. The trematodes are commonly known as *flukes*, apparently from the Anglo-Saxon *flok*, referring to the flat shape. The class is divided into three orders (considered subclasses by some) to which it is constantly neces-

sary to refer: the Monogenea or Heterocotylea, the monogenetic trematodes, chiefly ectoparasitic and with simple life histories; the Aspidobothria or Aspidocotylea, mostly entoparasitic and with simple cycles;
and the Digenea or Malacocotylea, the digenetic trematodes, entoparasitic
and with complicated life cycles, involving two to four hosts.

2. External Characters.—The trematodes are commonly of short to
elongated oval form (Fig. 82A), but a few are rounded or disk-like, one or

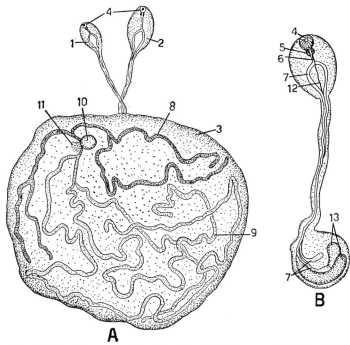

Fig. 81.—Peculiar trematodes (continued). *A*. Didymozoonid fluke *Wedlia* (*after
Ishii*, 1935), showing female body with male and female forebodies protruding from the
female hindbody. *B*. Male removed from depression in female hindbody. 1, male forebody; 2, female forebody; 3, female hindbody; 4, oral sucker; 5, pharynx; 6, esophagus; 7,
intestine; 8, ovary; 9, yolk gland; 10, seminal receptacle; 11, ootype; 12, sperm duct; 13,
testes.

two are broader than long (Fig. 80A), and the blood-inhabiting flukes
tend to be slender (Fig. 123). The body usually tapers to the anterior
end, which is not marked off as a head. The flukes are mostly much
flattened dorsoventrally with flat ventral and convex dorsal surfaces,
but some are rounded in cross section. Peculiar shapes obtain in the
digenetic families Strigeidae in which the body is divided into the flattened, concave, or cup-like *forebody*, bearing the adhesive organs, and
the narrower, cylindroid *hindbody* (Fig. 80B); and the Didymozoonidae,
some members of which have a slender forebody and a rounded sac-like

hindbody (Fig. 81A). A few Digenea are dioecious, and in these the males and females differ in size, shape, and general appearance (Fig. 123D). The trematodes are mostly of small, even minute, size, ranging usually between 0.5 and 10 mm. in length, but some Digenea are larger, 1 or 2 to several cm. long. The body is usually colorless or slightly tinted, although parts of the reproductive system may be dark or the intestine may be colored by food.

The adhesive organs furnish the most striking external feature and as in the Turbellaria vary from glandulo-muscular disks, projections, and pits to true suckers. The true sucker or *acetabulum*, highly characteristic of the trematodes, is a bowl-shaped depression set off or not by a constriction and separated internally from body tissues by a muscular stratum paralleling the concavity of the bowl (Fig. 82C). The sucker is highly muscular (Fig. 82C) and although usually provided with adhesive glands works primarily on the vacuum principle. The adhesive organs reach their highest and most varied development in the Monogenea which are usually also provided with claws and hooks for attachment. In the Monogenea, adhesive structures occur at both body ends and for them Dawes (1946) has suggested the useful terms *prohaptor* and *opisthaptor*. The mouth of the Monogenea is seldom encircled by a sucker, but instead the prohaptor consists of a pair of adhesive areas, disks, pits, or suckers. The principal clinging structure is the opisthaptor at the posterior end, consisting in its original form as seen in the Gyrodactylidae of an adhesive disk bearing two or four large hooks or claws (anchors), usually accompanied by smaller hooks (Fig. 83A). Next the disk alters more or less into a large circular sucker often divided by radial ridges into several sucking depressions (*Monocotyle, Tristoma*, Figs. 83B, 93A). This condition leads to the complete division of the originally single disk into a number of separate suckers, often six in a circle as in *Polystoma* (Fig. 94A) or eight bilaterally arranged (*Octocotyle, Diplozoon*, Fig. 93C) or six larger ones and two small ones on a terminal appendage (*Rajonchocotyle*, Fig. 83C) or two lateral suckers (*Sphyranura*, Fig. 93B). Another line of development is seen in *Microcotyle* (Fig. 84B) and *Axine* where the margin of the expanded rear is provided with a row of numerous (to 240) minute suckers resembling clamps. The suckers of the Monogenea are usually accompanied by hooks and are often supported by a complicated cuticularized framework (Fig. 83C).

The Aspidobothria have a characteristic adhesive organ in the form of a large oval to circular sucker divided by cross and longitudinal ridges into three or four longitudinal rows of depressions (Fig. 84A). An oral sucker is usually absent.

The adhesive apparatus of the Digenea is less developed than in the preceding orders, lacks hooks and spines, and commonly consists of two

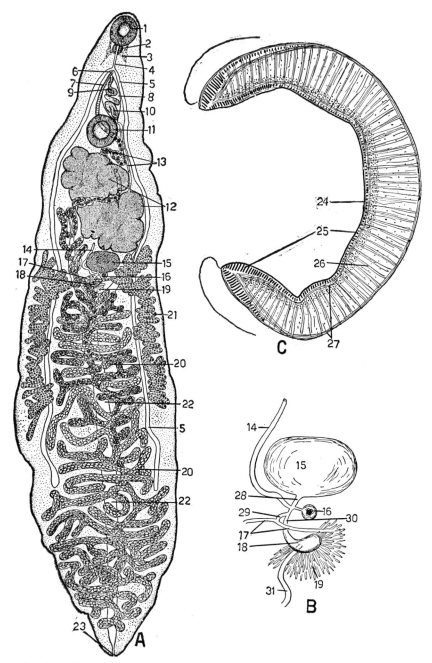

Fɪɢ. 82.—Trematode structure.   *A.* A typical distome fluke, *Dicrocoelium dendriticum* showing general structure of the Digenea (*after Neuhaus,* 1938).   *B.* Details of the female apparatus of the same.   *C.* Structure of an acetabulum (*after Näsmark,* 1937).   1, oral

suckers (either or both of which may be absent), an anterior or *oral sucker* encircling the mouth, and a ventral or posterior sucker, usually called the *acetabulum*, on the ventral surface (Fig. 82A). In the family Bucephalidae (= Gasterostomidae), the mouth occurs in the middle of the ventral surface (Fig. 84C) and lacks a sucker, as the anterior sucker retains its position at the anterior end. The acetabulum is a typical bowl-like sucker and may attain a very large size. The position and presence and absence of the acetabulum formerly served as a family character and still furnish convenient descriptive terms. Thus digenetic flukes with the acetabulum at or near the posterior end, probably the original location, are termed *amphistomes* and constitute the family Paramphistomidae (Fig. 107). Those in which the acetabulum has the usual position near or anterior to the middle of the ventral surface, often quite close to the oral sucker, are called *distomes* (Fig. 82A) and constituted the old family Distomidae, now scattered among many families. In a number of cases, the acetabulum has been secondarily lost; and such flukes, having only an oral sucker, are referred to as *monostomes*, although this character does not indicate relationship (Fig. 87C). Flukes that occupy very sheltered positions as blood flukes tend to have weak suckers or none at all (*Sanguinicola*, Fig. 123A). In the distome family Echinostomidae, the *echinostomes*, the anterior end bears a collar-like ridge edged with a single or double row of thorns (Fig. 119A). The family Rhopalidae can protrude two spiny processes at the anterior end. In the curious family Strigeidae, also called *holostomes*, the modified forebody already mentioned bears besides the usual two suckers a large adhesive organ of varied shape, the *holdfast*, situated behind the acetabulum (Figs. 119, 120).

The mouth of the trematodes is usually situated at or near the anterior end except in the Bucephalidae as noted above. The common gonopore, although often not far behind the mouth, may have almost any other location on the ventral surface or may be located laterally or even dorsally.

3. Cuticle.—The trematodes lack an epidermis and are clothed instead with a resistant cuticle (Fig. 85). The homology and origin of this cuticle have been long disputed, and several theories have been advanced: (1) that the cuticle is an altered and degenerated epidermis; (2) that it is the basement membrane of the former epidermis; (3) that it is the outer layer of an insunk epidermis, the cells and nuclei of which have sunk beneath the subcuticular musculature; (4) that the cells in

sucker; 2, pharynx; 3, brain; 4, esophagus; 5, intestinal crura; 6, gonopore; 7, uterus; 8, cirrus sac; 9, cirrus; 10, seminal vesicle; 11, acetabulum; 12, testes; 13, sperm ducts; 14, Laurer's canal; 15, ovary; 16, seminal receptacle; 17, yolk ducts; 18, ootype; 19, Mehlis's glands; 20, coils of uterus; 21, yolk glands; 22, bladder; 23, nephridiopore; 24, cuticle; 25, circular muscles; 26, radial muscles; 27, longitudinal muscles; 28, oviduct; 29, common yolk duct; 30, ovovitelline duct; 31, beginning of uterus.

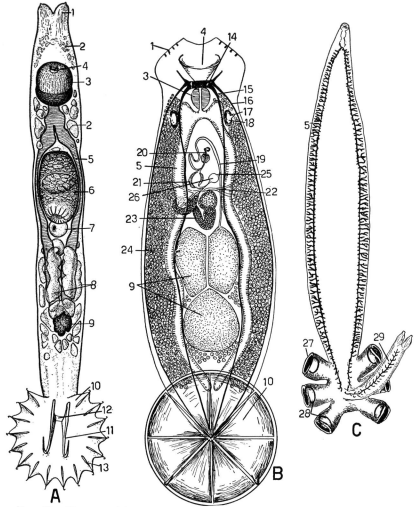

Fig. 83.—Types of Monogenea, showing especially various kinds of haptors. *A. Gyrodactylus (after Mueller and Van Cleave*, 1932). *B. Monocotyle (after Goto*, 1894). *C. Rajonchocotyle*, from a skate, from life, Pudget Sound. 1, anterior adhesive organ; 2, adhesive glands; 3, pharynx; 4, mouth; 5, intestine; 6, embryo; 7, uncleaved egg; 8, testis; 9, ovary; 10, opisthaptor; 11, anchors; 12, bar; 13, marginal hooks; 14, brain; 15, ventral nerve cords; 16, lateral nerve cords; 17, nephridiopore; 18, bladder; 19, sperm duct; 20, penis; 21, uterus; 22, yolk ducts; 23, ovary; 24, yolk glands; 25, copulation canal; 26, seminal receptacle; 27, suckers; 28, supporting piece in suckers; 29, appendage.

question are not epidermal but are mesenchymal (parenchymal) cells that secrete the cuticle; and (5) that the cuticle is secreted by the ordinary mesenchyme, not by special cells. Theories 1 and 2 have been discarded and seem to be definitely erroneous. Theory 3 has received much acceptance since the work of Hein (1904), who confirmed previous investigators that in many adult Digenea there exist beneath the musculature clusters of gland-like cells that send processes to the cuticle and seem to be secreting it (Fig. 85). However, the question obviously cannot be settled by study of adult flukes, and therefore Roewer (1906) undertook to shed light on the matter by a study of cercarial development. He found that in early stages the cercaria forms an epidermis by the same process as does the miracidium, i.e., by the separation of surface cells from the general mass, but that this epidermis later degenerates and is absorbed and the definitive cuticle is secreted by cells that differentiate in the general interior mass of the embryo. Further, cells supposed to be insunk epidermal cells are wanting in some flukes, especially Monogenea. Therefore theories 4 and 5 are the most acceptable, i.e., that the cuticle is a mesenchymal secretion, either of special cells or of the general mesenchyme. The chemical nature of the cuticle appears not to have been investigated, but doubtless the cuticle is a scleroprotein; it is definitely not chitinous.

The cuticle is thin and usually smooth in the Monogenea except for the hooks, spines, and supports of the adhesive apparatus which are of the same composition as the cuticle. In the Digenea, the cuticle is thicker and often bears minute spines, scales, or bristles that clothe the body in whole or part.

4. Musculature.—Beneath the cuticle occurs a typical muscle sheath like that of the Turbellaria, which may be termed the subcuticular musculature. It consists usually of an outer circular, middle longitudinal, and inner diagonal layer (Fig. 85); or the diagonal layer may lie between the other two, as in most Monogenea. The musculature is very weak in some forms, well-developed and even strengthened by additional layers, in others. The parenchymal musculature is usually poorly developed except for dorsoventral strands in lateral regions. Special muscle bands operate the hooks of the Monogenea. The musculature of the suckers derived from the subcuticular musculature consists chiefly of powerful bundles of radial fibers that give the sucker a striated appearance; in addition circular and longitudinal layers occur next to both inner and outer walls (Fig. 82C). The muscles are elongated fibrils with a persistent myoblast which may be connected to several fibrils by strands.

5. Mesenchyme and Gland Cells.—The mesenchyme or parenchyma consists in the Monogenea of discrete cells closely packed together; or sometimes the central mesenchyme has this structure while the peripheral mesenchyme is a fibrous syncytium. In the Digenea, the mesenchyme is mostly a syncytial meshwork with fluid-filled spaces containing free cells that give rise to lymphocytes and gonads (Fig. 85). Gland cells are scanty as compared with the Turbellaria. They are practically always of an adhesive nature. They are present in both ends of Monogenea in connection with adhesive structures and in relation to the oral sucker of Digenea. Some Digenea have clusters of gland cells on the ventral surface opening onto ridges or into pockets that are protrusible (families Paramphistomidae, Notocotylidae, Fig. 118D).

6. Nervous System and Sense Organs.—The nervous system entirely resembles that of the Turbellaria and consists of a pair of cerebral ganglia and a submuscular plexus concentrated into longitudinal cords and transverse connectives (Fig. 87A). The principal articles on the nervous system and sense organs are those of Looss (1894), Bettendorf (1897), and Zailer (1914). The two cerebral ganglia connected by a broad commissure lie dorsally, above or behind the pharynx in the Monogenea, between the oral sucker and the pharynx in the Digenea. From them several nerves, usually three pairs, proceed anteriorly, and three pairs of cords—dorsal, lateral, and ventral—proceed posteriorly (Fig. 87A). The ventral cords are the best developed; the dorsal cords are lacking in most Monogenea (Fig. 92D), and the lateral cords may be absent in elongated types. The adhesive organs and the pharynx receive a rich nerve supply (Fig. 86).

The trematodes like most parasitic animals are not well provided with sense organs. Eyes occur in most Monogena and in larval stages of some Digenea. They are closely related to the brain and consist in the cases investigated of a pigment cup containing a single rounded retinal cell with a rod border (André, 1910; Faust, 1918a; Hesse, 1897); sometimes the pigment cell is wanting. Bulb-shaped nerve endings, that may send a bristle to the surface have been found in abundance in trematodes, especially in the suckers, and are regarded as tangoreceptors (Fig. 86). The edge of the large sucker of the Aspidobothria bears sense organs in the form of little bulbs that apparently can be protruded (Fig. 97D).

7. Digestive System.—The digestive system closely resembles that of the dalyellioid rhabdocoels. The mouth, situated at or ventral to the anterior tip (except in the gasterostomes, as already noted) and encircled by the oral sucker in most Digenea, leads into a funnel-like mouth cavity which in many Monogenea connects with the pits of the adjacent lateral suckers. The mouth cavity is followed directly or after the intervention of a short buccal tube ("prepharynx") by a rounded or elongated doliiform pharynx whose strong radial musculature gives its wall a cross-striated appearance. In Monogenea, the distal end of the pharynx often projects free into the buccal tube. The pharynx has lateral pockets in some cases (Fig. 108A). Both internal and external pharyngeal glands may be present. The pharynx is reduced or absent in some Digenea, as some blood flukes (Fig. 123). Following the pharynx either with or without the intervention of an esophagus, usually short,

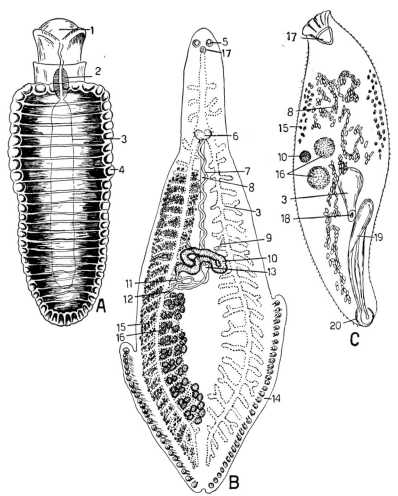

FIG. 84.—Types of trematodes. *A. Cotylogaster*, order Aspidobothria. *B. Microcotyle*, from life, Puget Sound, order Monogenea. *C.* Gasterostome fluke *Rhipidocotyle* (*after Nicoll*, 1914), order Digenea. 1, mouth funnel; 2, pharynx; 3, intestine, 4, sucker with three rows of alveoli; 5, lateral suckers; 6, gonopore; 7, sperm duct; 8, uterus; 9, yolk ducts; 10, ovary; 11, oviduct; 12, genitointestinal canal; 13, yolk reservoir; 14, opisthaptor with small suckers; 15, yolk glands; 16, testes; 17, anterior sucker; 18, mouth; 19, cirrus sac; 20, genital antrum.

sometimes long, comes the intestine, a simple rhabdocoel-like sac in some Monogenea, in the Aspidobothria, and in the digenetic family Bucephalidae (Fig. 84C). In the great majority of trematodes, however, the intestine forks at once into two branches, called *crura* or *caeca*, that extend posteriorly as blind tubes (Fig. 82A), usually to the rear end of the animal. These are usually simple in the Digenea; but in most Monogenea (Fig. 84B) and some Digenea, i.e., liver flukes, they give off a few to many lateral branches (Fig. 116*A*) that may anastomose to a network. The two crura may be confluent at their posterior ends (Fig. 87*C*) or may be very short (Fig. 88*A*), or sometimes one is lacking. In several Digenea, the posterior ends of the crura open into the excretory bladder, and in a few species of fish trematodes, they open directly to the exterior either separately or after union, so that one or two anal pores are present (La Rue, 1926; Ozaki, 1928a; Odhner, 1928; Stunkard, 1931; Fig. 87*B*).

The digestive system up to the intestine is lined by cuticle. The intestinal wall is composed of a cuboidal to columnar epithelium which in

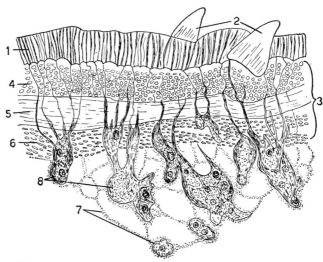

FIG. 85.—Histological structure. Longitudinal section through the surface of *Fasciola hepatica* (*after Hein*, 1904). 1, cuticle; 2, cuticular scales; 3, subcuticular musculature; 4, circular layer; 5, longitudinal layer; 6, diagonal layer; 7, mesenchyme; 8, mesenchymal cells secreting the cuticle.

the Digenea is usually underlain by a delicate muscle layer of circular and longitudinal fibers. In some Monogenea, the intestinal epithelium consists of scattered separated cells (Goto, 1894).

8. Excretory System.—This system likewise resembles that of rhabdocoels, consisting of a protonephridial tubule on each side that commonly recurves on itself. In the Monogenea, the two tubules are completely separate; each begins anteriorly, runs backward to the posterior end, and there bends upon itself, running forward again to terminate near the mouth on the dorsal side by a nephridiopore usually preceded by a small contractile bladder. The Aspidobothria are similar except that the nephridiopores are near the posterior end, and fusion to a single pore may occur. In the Digenea the two tubules unite to a median oval or elongated or Y-shaped bladder (Fig. 88*A*) opening by a single pore at the

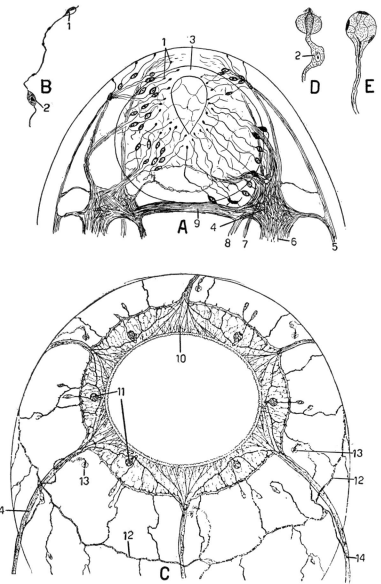

FIG. 86.—Nervous system and sense organs. *A.* Innervation of the oral sucker of a digenetic fluke (*after Bettendorf,* 1897), ventral view; right side of animal shows dorsal sensory cells, left side ventral ones. *B.* Tactile bulb of the same, enlarged. *C.* Innervation of the acetabulum of a digenetic fluke (*after Zailer,* 1914); three nerves from each ventral cord form a strong ring plexus at the margin of the sucker and a less developed deeper ring; each ring has six special sensory bulbs. *D.* Sensory bulb of deeper ring. *E.* Sensory bulb of outer ring. 1, tactile bulb; 2, sensory nerve cell; 3, oral sucker; 4, brain ganglion; 5, lateral nerve cord; 6, ventral nerve cord; 7, dorsal nerve cord; 8, nerve cord to pharynx; 9, connective between two brain ganglia; 10, marginal nerve ring of acetabulum; 11, sensory bulbs of same; 12, deeper nerve ring of acetabulum; 13, sensory bulbs of same; 14, nerves to sucker from ventral cords.

middle of the posterior end or near this location, usually dorsal, but sometimes ventral. Study of the development of the Digenea shows that the
two protonephridial tubules are separate at first and later fuse terminally
(Fig. 105). From the anterior end of the bladder, the two tubules run
forward and either extend to the anterior end, there recurving on themselves, or very often they fork near the body middle into an anterior and
a posterior branch (Fig. 88A). In some Digenea there are several main
tubules instead of the usual two, and these anastomose to a network.
The family Heronimidae differs from all other Digenea in that the
nephridiopore is near the anterior end (Fig. 125B).

The terminal flame bulbs are attached to the recurved portions of the
tubules or to the branches, not to the main trunks. In the trematodes,
each flame bulb is always a nucleated cell. It usually sends off delicate
processes into the mesenchyme. Extra flames, apparently originating
by division of the original flame, may be present, and lateral flames also
occur. In the Digenea, the terminal flame bulbs and capillaries occur in
clusters of two to four attached to a single collecting tubule (Figs. 88A,
102E) and the arrangement of the flame bulbs is held by many helminthologists to constitute an important taxonomic character (Faust, 1932).
The arrangement begins in the cercaria and can be traced through to the
adult so that it may constitute an important means of linking larval with
adult flukes. The flame-bulb pattern is also employed to determine
familial placing of adult flukes as related forms usually show the same
pattern. However, members of the same family may have different
flame-bulb arrangements (Stunkard, 1929), and in general caution is
necessary in basing taxonomic relationships on flame-bulb patterns.
These patterns are recorded by a formula devised by Faust (1919) which
expresses the number of flame bulbs in each group and the number of
groups on each main branch of the tubule. Thus the flame-bulb formula
for Fig. 88A would be $2[(2 + 2) + (2 + 2)]$ and that for Fig. 102E would
be $2[(3 + 3 + 3) + (3 + 3 + 3)]$.

9. Lymphatic System.—In a number of Digenea, particularly in the
Paramphistomidae, but also in the Angiodictyidae, Cyclocoelidae, and
Heronimidae, there is a system of mesenchymal vessels that seems to
represent a primitive circulatory system. It consists on each side of one
to four blind longitudinal tubes, unconnected with each other, that give
off blind branches to the intestinal crura and reproductive organs and
into the suckers (Fig. 88B). These lymph channels are lined by flattened
mesenchyme and contain a fluid in which float free cells closely resembling primitive vertebrate blood cells (haemocytoblasts, Jordan and
Reynolds, 1933). These free cells are mesenchymal cells that have
wandered into the lymph channels where they eventually disintegrate.
A center of formation of the lymph cells also exists at the forking of the

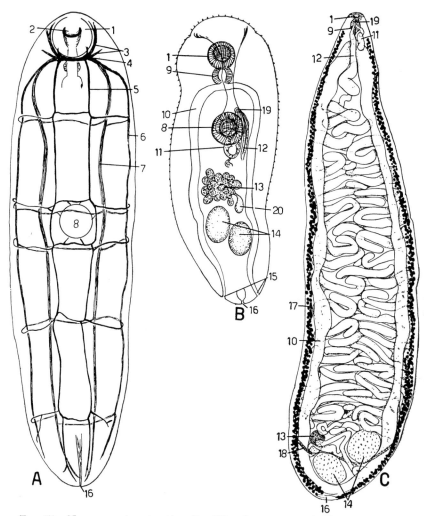

FIG. 87.—Nervous system (continued). Digestive system. *A.* Nervous system of a distome (*after Looss,* 1894). *B. Diploporus,* distome with two anal pores (*after Ozaki,* 1928). *C. Cyclocoelum,* monostome with confluent intestinal crura (*after Harrah,* 1922). 1, oral sucker; 2, mouth; 3, anterior nerves; 4, brain ganglia; 5, ventral cords; 6, lateral cords; 7, dorsal cords; 8, acetabulum; 9, pharynx; 10, intestinal crura; 11, cirrus sac; 12, uterus; 13, ovary; 14, testes; 15, anal pores; 16, nephridiopore; 17, yolk glands; 18, yolk ducts; 19, gonopore.

intestinal crura. In the mesenchyme the haemocytoblasts may also differentiate into cells resembling the eosinophils of vertebrate blood. The lymph channels seem to function in the distribution of food, respiratory gases, and excretory products.

10. Reproductive System.—This is built along the same lines as in the Turbellaria and similarly exhibits multitudinous variations, taxonomically important, of a few fundamental parts. The trematodes are hermaphroditic except for the digenetic families Didymozoonidae and Schistosomatidae. Some of the former are functionally dioecious in that one or the other system fails to mature (Fig. 81A), and the latter occur only as easily distinguishable males and females (Fig. 123D). The trematode reproductive system differs from that of turbellarians mainly in the utilization of the common ovovitelline duct as a uterus in which the capsules are stored before laying. Whereas in the Turbellaria, a uterus is infrequently present as a blind sac from the genital antrum, in the Trematoda the uterus is the main female canal and constantly present, being usually greatly elongated and coiled. Nearly all trematodes have yolk glands distinct from the ovary. Many trematodes possess as part of the female system a single or paired copulation canal, variously named, with its own external pore or pores. The male copulatory organ is generally a cirrus.

a. *Monogenea.*—The reproductive system of the Monogenea strikingly resembles that of rhabdocoels. There are usually several to many testes (Figs. 83B, 84B) posteriorly located but sometimes only one or two (Figs. 89B, C, 92D, 94A). The sperm duct runs forward to the copulatory organ before which it may widen to a spermiducal vesicle. The copulatory organ, essentially a penis bulb, is of varied construction. The muscular bulb may receive single prostatic glands or a single or paired prostatic vesicle (Fig. 89C). From the bulb projects the penis, consisting of a muscular or fibrous papilla (Fig. 89B) often armed with hooks or of a hard tube or stylet or a complex cuticularized apparatus (Fig. 89C) similar to that of the Dalyelliidae. Where the penis is unarmed the genital antrum may bear copulatory hooks.

There is a single ovary, usually of elongated form (Figs. 83B, 84B) and even often extensively coiled, and a pair of follicular yolk glands lying in lateral body regions. Yolk glands are said to be absent from *Gyrodactylus* (Fig. 83A), which seems to have a germovitellarium, and in some forms yolk glands occur on one side only. From the main yolk duct of each side a transverse duct arises and meets its fellow of the opposite side to form a *yolk reservoir* from which the short common yolk duct extends to the oviduct. The oviduct shortly after leaving the ovary receives the common yolk duct, may receive a long-stalked seminal receptacle, often connects with the right intestinal crus by a genitointestinal canal (Fig. 84B), and then presents a small widening commonly known as the *ootype* which is encircled by numerous gland cells, the so-called shell glands, also termed Mehlis's glands. Beyond the ootype, the common ovovitelline duct continues as a widened but relatively short tube, the uterus, that extends to the common genital antrum. In the majority of the Monogenea there occur single or paired copulation canals (usually called vaginae[1]) whose outer ends open independent of the gonopore on dorsal, lateral, or ventral surfaces. The inner end of these canals may open into the oviduct before the latter receives the common yolk duct or into the latter or into the yolk reservoir or into the transverse yolk ducts (Fig. 89B, C). When paired, the copulation canals may be united for

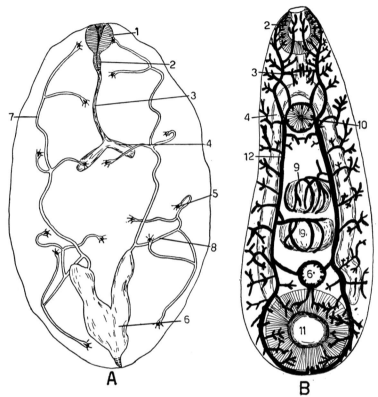

A   **B**

Fig. 88.—Excretory system; lymphatic system. *A*. Excretory system of *Microphallus* (*after Wright*, 1912); the flame-bulb pattern on each side is (2 + 2) + (2 + 2). *B*. Lymphatic system of the amphistome *Cotylophoron cotylophorum* (*after Willey*, 1930). 1, oral sucker; 2, pharynx; 3, esophagus; 4, intestinal crura; 5, flame bulbs; 6, bladder; 7, anterior branch; 8, posterior branch, excretory system; 9, testes; 10, gonopore; 11, acetabulum; 12, lymphatic system.

part of their course. They receive the penis in copulation and may have a widened portion or a pouch (Fig. 89C) serving as seminal receptacle; and it appears that in some cases the seminal receptacle is a copulation canal that has lost its surface connection.

The egg after leaving the ovary is immediately fertilized, becomes surrounded by yolk cells (not in *Gyrodactylus*), and enters the ootype where

[1] As the term vagina has been defined as the terminal part of the main female canal, it cannot be used in this connection.

234 PHYLUM PLATYHELMINTHES

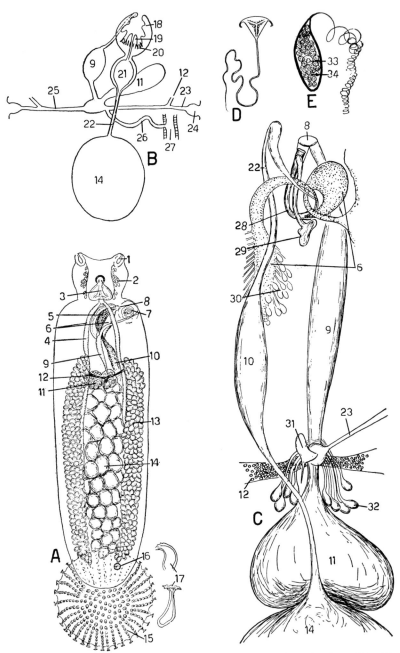

Fig. 89.—Reproductive system, Monogenea. A. *Acanthocotyle*, from life, Puget Sound, showing general features of reproductive system. B. Polystomoid type of reproductive system with penis papilla (*after Stunkard, 1917*). C. Gyrodactyloid type of reproductive system with penis stylet (*after Goto and Kikuchi, 1917*). D. Capsule of *Benedenia*

it pauses while the shell is formed. The shell or capsule is formed chiefly or wholly from droplets in the yolk cells. The so-called shell glands appear to play no role in its formation in most cases, although Dawes (1940) observed that in *Hexacotyle* these glands secrete a rudimentary capsule on which the yolk cells deposit their droplets. The secretion of Mehlis's glands probably functions mainly to lubricate the passage of the capsules along the uterus. The shell has an operculum at one end and often bears at one or both ends a long filament for attachment to the host (Fig. 89D, E). The capsules are usually held for some time in the uterus, which, contrary to the condition in the Digenea, contains only one or a few at a time.

The uterus and male apparatus open into a common genital antrum that exits by a common gonopore constantly situated on the ventral surface near the anterior end close to the crural fork.

b. *Aspidobothria.*—The reproductive system of the Aspidobothria is similar to that of the Monogenea (Fig. 97C). The male system comprises one or two testes and a straight or sinuous sperm duct that runs to the copulatory organ, usually a cirrus sac. The female system differs from that of the Monogenea chiefly in that the uterus may be long and coiled. A copulation (Laurer's) canal is frequently but not always present. In some forms, the beginning of the oviduct is provided with valves of unknown purpose. Sperm duct and uterus unite to a common antrum and gonopore on the ventral surface near the anterior end; the terminal part of the uterus may be thickened muscularly to form a *metraterm.*

c. *Digenea.*—The Digenea usually have two rounded testes situated side by side (Fig. 114D) or one behind the other (Fig. 82A); but some have one testis and others several testes (*Gorgodera*, Fig. 112A; *Schistosoma*, Fig. 124B). The testes may be lobed or branched as in the liver flukes (Fig. 116A) and *Opisthorchis* (Fig. 114A) or long and tubular (Didymozoonidae, Figs. 111, 112C; *Heronimus*, Fig. 125A). From each testis a sperm duct extends to meet its fellow, forming the common sperm duct. This pursues a straight or sinuous course, may enlarge as a spermiducal vesicle, and enters the copulatory apparatus, which varies from a simple muscular tube to an enlarged highly muscular *cirrus sac.* The distal portion of this, unarmed or armed with spines, scales, thorns, etc., is eversible as a cirrus (Fig. 90A, B). A seminal vesicle and also prostatic

(after *Jahn and Kuhn*, 1932). *E.* Capsule of *Diplozoon* (after *Zeller*, 1872b). 1, lateral suckers; 2, adhesive glands of same; 3, mouth; 4, intestinal crura; 5, cirrus sac; 6, prostatic vesicles; 7, termination of uterus; 8, gonopore; 9, uterus; 10, spermiducal vesicle; 11, ovary; 12, yolk ducts; 13, yolk glands; 14, testes; 15, pseudohaptor; 16, larval haptor; 17, haptorial hooks, enlarged; 18, penis bulb; 19, penis papilla; 20, thorns; 21, seminal vesicle; 22, sperm duct; 23, copulation canal; 24, opening of same on surface; 25, common genitovitelline canal; 26, genitointestinal canal; 27, crus of intestine; 28, penis stylet; 29, accessory piece of stylet; 30, prostatic glands; 31, seminal receptacle; 32, Mehlis's glands; 33, egg; 34, yolk cells.

glands with or without a prostatic vesicle may be contained within the cirrus sac (Fig. 90*A*). A cirrus is lacking in a number of families as the Paramphistomidae (Fig. 107*C*), Didymozoonidae (Fig. 111), Schistosomatidae (Fig. 124*B*), and others. A true penis papilla is occasionally present as in the family Microphallidae (Fig. 115).

The single ovary is usually of rounded form but may be lobed (*Prosthogonimus*, Fig. 113*B*) or branched (*Fasciola*, Fig. 116*A*) or tubular (Didymozoonidae, Figs. 111, 112*C*). The oviduct very shortly after leaving the ovary receives the common yolk duct and the copulation (Laurer's) canal, then widens slightly (Fig. 90*C*) to form the ootype, encircled by Mehlis's glands (also called shell glands), and then continues to the genital antrum as a widened, usually very long coiled tube, the uterus, full of capsules. The vitellaria usually occur as numerous clusters on each side extending most of the body length (Fig. 109*C*) but may take the form of simple or branched tubes (Fig. 118*A*) or of small branched bodies, and some flukes possess only one vitellarium. Where the yolk glands consist of clustered follicles, small ducts from the clusters join a longitudinal yolk duct on each side that at the level of the ovary gives off a transverse yolk duct toward the median line. These two join with or without the formation of a small enlargement, the *yolk reservoir*, and from this or the junction the short common yolk duct extends to the oviduct, which thereafter should be termed ovovitelline duct (Fig. 90*C*). The yolk cells contain shell-forming droplets in at least many cases. A seminal receptacle (Fig. 90*C*) may be attached to the oviduct near the ovary or may occur along the course of Laurer's canal, or rarely the oviduct itself may be widened to serve as a seminal receptacle.

The homology of Laurer's canal has been the subject of much debate. This muscular tube leaves the oviduct between the ovary and the entrance of the common yolk duct and proceeds directly to the dorsal surface where it opens in the middorsal line or to one side. The opening has no relation to the gonopore. Laurer's canal seems to correspond to the copulation canal of Turbellaria which extends from the copulatory or seminal bursa to the surface with or without the concomitant disappearance of the bursa. It is found in some polyclads and a few land and marine planarians. Laurer's canal in flukes was formerly considered to serve as exit for superfluous sperm and yolk cells but is now known to function in copulation. It is absent in a considerable number of flukes.

The uterus (= ovovitelline duct), whose beginning may serve as a seminal receptacle in the absence of any other, is a simple tube, usually greatly coiled and much longer than the body length, that fills the spaces between the other organs, often concealing them from view (Fig. 82*A*). When the gonopore is anterior, the uterus usually runs to the posterior end, then turns and proceeds anteriorly; if the gonopore is posteriorly

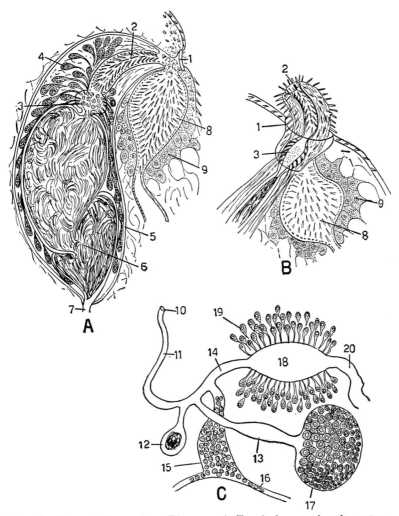

FIG. 90.—Reproductive system, Digenea. *A.* Terminal part of male system. *B.* Same, with cirrus everted. (*A, B after Looss*, 1894). *C.* Scheme of female system of the Digenea. 1, gonopore; 2, cirrus; 3, prostatic vesicle; 4, prostatic glands; 5, cirrus sac; 6, seminal vesicle; 7, sperm duct; 8, metraterm armed with spines; 9, gland cells of same; 10, pore of Laurer's canal; 11, Laurer's canal; 12, seminal receptacle; 13, oviduct; 14, ovovitelline duct; 15, yolk reservoir; 16, yolk ducts; 17, ovary; 18, ootype; 19, Mehlis's glands; 20, beginning of uterus.

located, the uterus often runs forward and then backward. This development of the ovovitelline duct into a long coiled uterus is the chief difference between the reproductive systems of the trematodes and the turbellarians. The formation of the uterus is correlated with a characteristic feature of entoparasitism, namely, the production of enormous quantities of eggs. Where the uterus contains but one capsule at a time as in blood flukes, it is a short enlarged tube as in the Monogenea (Figs. 123*A*, 124*A*). The terminal part of the uterus in flukes that lack a Laurer's canal functions to receive the cirrus in copulation and for this purpose may be greatly strengthened by a layer of circular muscles, armed with spines, scales, etc., and provided with gland cells.   Such an altered termination of the uterus is called *metraterm*.

The sperm duct and uterus may open separately to the exterior (*Sanguinicola*, Fig. 123*A*), but usually they enter a common genital antrum (or atrium), either separately or after fusion to a common canal. The antrum is usually a small chamber but may be a large shallow to deep pit or pocket (Fig. 119*B*), or a muscular tube into the bottom of which the genital ducts open.   The gonopore commonly occurs anteriorly in the mid-ventral line between mouth and acetabulum but can be situated laterally (Fig. 113*A*) or even dorsally and in some families occurs at or near the posterior end (Bucephalidae, Figs. 84*C*, 106*D;* Strigeidae, Figs. 119*B*, 120*A*).   The gonopore is sometimes encircled by a sucker-like structure, the *genital sucker* (Fig. 107*C*), or sometimes by the acetabulum itself.   The terminal parts of the reproductive system are lined with cuticle.

Upon leaving the ovary the eggs are fertilized and become surrounded in the ootype by yolk cells that thereupon emit their shell-forming droplets.   These harden into the characteristic shell or capsule, usually yellow or brown, of oval shape, and mostly with an operculum at one end or sometimes a filament or spine (Figs. 110*E*, 114*C*).   Stephenson (1947) has shown for the liver fluke that the shell-forming droplets of the yolk cells contain protein and a phenol, that this phenol is oxidized to a quinone in the beginning coils of the uterus, and that the quinone then acts to tan the protein, producing a hard resistant combination termed sclerotin similar to leather.   Probably these findings apply to all platyhelminth capsules as shown for Turbellaria by Vialli (1933).   The function of the clear secretion of Mehlis's glands discharged into the ootype is very uncertain; some think this fluid lubricates the passage of the capsules along the uterus (Goldschmidt, 1909; Ujiie, 1936; Kouri and Nauss, 1938).   As the capsules proceed along the coils of the uterus they undergo more or less alteration and eventually are discharged into the digestive or urinary tract of the host (although they can be emitted otherwise as through the gills of fish) whence they reach the exterior in the feces or urine, examination of which for capsules constitutes the usual method of diagnosis of the presence of flukes.   The capsules of the various flukes of economic and medical importance are recognizable through differences in size, shape, and other features.   It is customary in the literature of helminthology to talk about "eggs" when the capsules are meant.   As development has usually already begun, even the contents should not be termed "egg"; they will here be called *encapsulated* or *ovic embryos*.

11. Copulation.—Although self-fertilization is possible in flukes through sperm wandering from the male into the female canal or through autocopulation, cross-fertilization is the usual method. Monogenetic flukes in copulation hang onto the substratum by their opisthaptors and entwine their anterior ends (Fig. 91*A*), bringing the gonopores in contact with mutual insemination; or the gonopore of one makes contact with the opening of the other's copulation canal when this is present and a probably

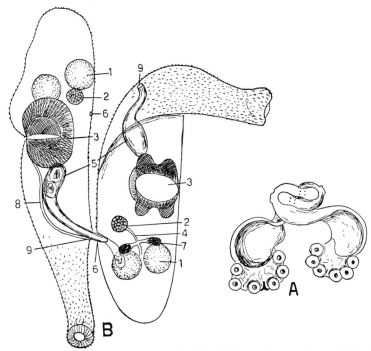

Fig. 91.—Copulation. *A.* Monogenetic fluke *Polystoma* in copulation (*after Zeller,* 1876). *B.* Digenetic fluke *Diphterostomum* (family Zoogonidae) copulating one-sidedly by way of Laurer's canal (*after Palombi,* 1932a). 1, testes; 2, ovary; 3, acetabulum; 4, oviduct; 5, cirrus sac; 6, opening of Laurer's canal; 7, yolk glands; 8, uterus; 9, gonopore.

one-sided insemination ensues (MacCallum, 1913). In the Digenea, copulation is either one-sided by way of Laurer's canal (Fig. 91*B*) or reciprocal by way of the metraterm (Leon, 1927; Palombi, 1932a). The sperm are stored in the seminal receptacle.

12. Order Monogenea.—The monogenetic trematodes are mostly ectoparasites that typically inhabit the gills, sometimes the skin, of fresh-water and marine fishes; a few occur on crustaceans or cephalopods. Some tend to entoparasitism, going into structures that open to the exterior, as the nasal and pharyngeal cavities and the urinary bladder and ureters of fish, amphibians, and reptiles. Only one is known to inhabit the interior of the host, *Dictyocotyle*, found in the coelom of a ray (Nybelin, 1941). The Monogenea move about on their hosts by looping in a leech-like manner, alternately attaching pro- and opisthaptors. They feed on slime, epithelial cells, and blood exuding from places damaged by their hooks and may seriously and even fatally injure the gills of the host, especially in the case of young fish.

The Monogenea have been monographed by Price (1937–1943) with special reference to the North American species. His arrangement and synonymy are followed here.

a. Suborder Monopisthocotylea.—In this suborder an oral sucker is generally absent but may be weakly developed. The prohaptor consists of a pair of small lateral suckers or pits supplied by adhesive glands or simply of a cluster of adhesive glands on each side opening singly or through one to several thickened bulbous ends known as *head organs* (Fig. 92*A*). These head organs often shape the anterior margin into two or more lobes. The opisthaptor is a simple or subdivided disk usually provided with one to three pairs of large hooks (*anchors*) and 2 to 16 marginal hooks (*hooklets*) (Fig. 92*B*). The two anchors of a pair may be connected by a crosspiece termed *bar*. The opisthaptor in this suborder always lacks separated suckers. Eyes are usually present. A genitointestinal canal is absent.

The Monopisthocotylea consist of two groups (superfamilies), the *gyrodactyloid* and *capsaloid* Monogenea. The former are worms of elongated form in which the prohaptor consists of glands opening through head organs (Fig. 92*A*) and the opisthaptor is armed with one or two pairs of anchors nearly always supported by bars (Fig. 92*B*). Some representative genera are: *Gyrodactylus*, viviparous, with one pair of anchors and 16 hooklets (Fig. 83*A*); *Dactylogyrus* with one pair of anchors and 14 hooklets (Fig. 92*A*, *B*); *Tetraonchus* with two pairs of anchors supported by one bar and 16 hooklets; *Ancyrocephalus*, similar but with 2 bars and 14 hooklets; *Amphibdella* with stalked lobed opisthaptor bearing two pairs of anchors without bars and 14 hooklets; *Diplectanum* (Fig. 92*C*) with a dorsal and a ventral *squamodisk* (these are disks near the opisthaptor bearing concentric circles of spines, scales, or ridges); and *Calceostoma* with greatly lobed anterior end. In the capsaloid Monogenea, the prohaptor may consist of glands with head organs (Fig. 83*B*) as in the gyrodactyloid group but more usually takes the form of a weak oral sucker or a pair of lateral pits or suckers (Fig. 92*D*). The opisthaptor is generally a large muscular disk with or without hooks and divided or not by septa. Some capsaloid genera are: *Monocotyle* (Fig. 83*B*) and *Heterocotyle* with an armed opisthaptor divided into one central and eight marginal depressions; *Microbothrium* with prohaptor of two adhesive pits opening into the oral cavity and a very reduced opisthaptor; *Acan-*

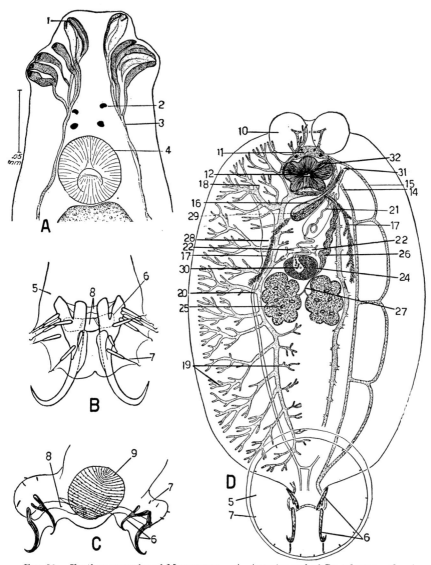

Fig. 92.—Further examples of Monogenea. *A*. Anterior end of *Dactylogyrus*, showing the head organs. *B*. Posterior end of *Dactylogyrus*, showing the opisthaptor. (*A, B, after Mueller and Van Cleave*, 1932.) *C*. Opisthaptor of *Diplectanum*, showing a squamodisk (*after Johnson and Teigs*, 1922). *D. Benedenia* (= *Epibdella*) *melleni* (*after Jahn and Kuhn*, 1932) showing general structure. 1, head organs; 2, eyes; 3, ducts of adhesive glands; 4, pharynx; 5, opisthaptor; 6, anchors; 7, marginal hooks; 8, bars; 9, squamodisk; 10, prohaptor; 11, brain; 12, mouth; 13, pharynx; 14, ventral cords; 15, lateral cords; 16, cirrus sac; 17, prostatic glands; 18, nephridiopore; 19, branches of intestine; 20, nephridial tubule; 21, uterus; 22, yolk reservoir; 23, oviduct; 24, ovary; 25, testes; 26, spermiducal vesicle; 27, sperm duct; 28, bladder; 29, seminal vesicle; 30, seminal receptacle; 31, gonopore; 32, oral sucker.

thocotyle in which the original opisthaptor has been replaced by a very large *pseudohaptor* bearing radiating rows of spines (Fig. 89*A*); *Udonella* with two anterior suckers and a large unarmed undivided opisthaptor; *Benedenia* (= *Epibdella* in part), similar to *Udonella*, but with armed opisthaptor (Fig. 92*D*); and *Capsala* and *Tristoma* (Fig. 93*A*) with a pair of conspicuous anterior suckers and a large armed opisthaptor with one central and seven marginal depressions.

b. *Suborder Polyopisthocotylea.*—In this suborder, the prohaptor has the form of an oral sucker encircling the mouth or of two suckers opening into the oral cavity or of two pits. The opisthaptor is armed or not but always bears separate suckers or else sucker-like projections containing cuticularized supports resembling clamps. Eyes are generally absent and there is a genitointestinal canal. The suborder is also divisible into two superfamilies: the *polystomoid* forms with an oral sucker, and the *diclidophoroid* forms with two small anterior suckers opening into the oral cavity. The polystomoid Monogenea are characterized by an opisthaptor bearing six armed suckers. In *Polystoma* and related genera the circular opisthaptor with six suckers lacks an appendage (Fig. 94*A*). Only two suckers are present in *Sphyranura* (Fig. 93*D*). In another group of genera exemplified by *Hexabothrium* (= *Onchocotyle*), *Erpocotyle* (= *Squalonchocotyle*), and *Rajonchocotyle* (Fig. 83*C*), the opisthaptor in addition to the six suckers has a tail-like appendage that bears a pair of terminal suckers also provided with hooks. These types are found mostly on elasmobranch fishes. The diclidophoroid Monogenea usually have two rows of suckers or of sucker-like projections supported by a complicated framework of cuticularized pieces. In this group belong the curious *Diplozoon* (Fig. 93*C*) with eight suckers (see below) and types like *Microcotyle* (Fig. 84*B*) with two rows and *Axine* with one row of many small adhesive clamps.

13. Development and Life History of the Monogenea.—The capsules of the Monogenea are mostly of fusiform shape and generally provided at one or both ends with short to long filaments for attachment to hosts (Fig. 89*D*, *E*). The egg develops into a ciliated larva of gyrodactyloid appearance and with a gyrodactyloid opisthaptor (Fig. 95*B*) that quickly fastens to a host of the same sort, where it grows and alters to the adult form; hence the name Monogenea in reference to the simple life history which does not involve a change of host. The details of the embryology are known in only a few cases, best in *Polystoma integerrimum* (Halkin, 1901). This fluke inhabits the urinary bladder of frogs and breeds in spring, exuding its eggs into the bladder whence they exit into the water with the feces. Inside the shell are found one egg and a number of yolk cells. The egg undergoes total unequal cleavage into a mass of blastomeres in which the smaller cells enclose the larger ones by a sort of

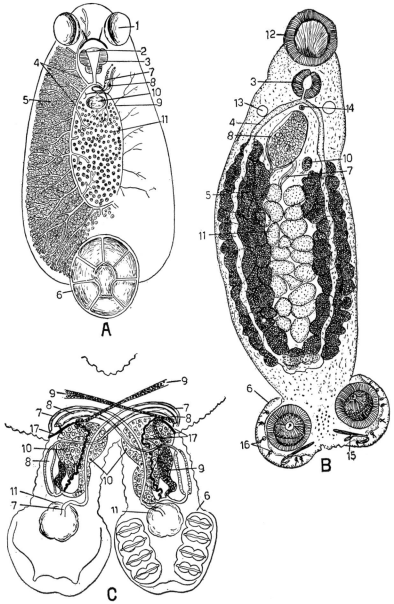

FIG. 93.—Types of Monogenea (continued). *A. Tristoma (after Goto,* 1894). *B. Sphyranura (after Alvey,* 1936). *C.* Rear end of two *Diplozoon* in permanent copulation *(after Zeller,* 1888). 1, prohaptor; 2, mouth; 3, pharynx; 4, branches of intestine; 5, yolk glands; 6, opisthaptor; 7, sperm duct; 8, uterus; 9, yolk ducts; 10, ovary; 11, testes; 12, oral sucker; 13, bladders; 14, gonopore; 15. anchors; 16, marginal hooks; 17, copulation canal.

epiboly (Fig. 94B). Some of the peripheral cells flatten out to an epidermis (Fig. 94C) that later develops a ciliation. In the interior mass of cells a cavity arises by cell degeneration beginning at a posterior dorsal point where an opening to the exterior is established and progressing anteriorly. This cavity is the lumen of the intestine, and the cells bordering it become the intestinal epithelium (Fig. 94D). In the mid-ventral region a ball of cells differentiates into a pharynx and establishes with the ventral surface a connection that becomes the mouth. Cells in contact with the pharynx differentiate into the cerebral ganglia (Figs. 94D, 95A). The remaining cells of the interior mass furnish the mesenchyme, muscles, gland cells, etc., and later the reproductive system. The embryo elongates, and at its posterior end appears a gyrodactyloid opisthaptor, in the form of a disk armed with a circle of 16 hooklets (Fig. 95A). Each hooklet originates as a secretion between two cells. The resemblance of this embryology to that of the Rhabdocoela with its lack of germ layers and formation of organs from cell masses is obvious. The formation of an anal pore (this soon closes) is, however, puzzling and has not been explained.

The development requires four or more weeks, after which the embryo hatches as a larva with four eyes, cilia in transverse bands, a pair of protonephridia, and a hooked opisthaptor as described above (Fig. 95B). It soon attaches to the gills of a late tadpole and there slowly grows and alters. When the tadpole metamorphoses into a frog, the young flukes pass down the digestive tract into the bladder where they lodge and complete their development; or possibly may infect the frog by way of the anus (Paul, 1938). The alteration to the adult state includes loss of the eyes, disappearance of the ciliated epidermis, and transformation of the opisthaptor to the *Polystoma* type. The six suckers appear two at a time, some of the larval hooks become incorporated into the suckers, and one or two pairs of anchors appear (Fig. 95C–E). Ordinarily up to 3 years are required for the attainment of sexual maturity but if the fluke larvae attach to younger tadpoles, they may develop sexually, although otherwise immature, to a condition in which they lay eggs in a few weeks after attachment (Gallien, 1932, 1934; Paul, 1938). Such neotenic forms never mature further nor do they get into the bladder. In the American variety of *P. integerrimum*, it seems probable that the neotenic branchial form alternates with the mature bladder form, i.e., that the latter are produced from larvae of the branchial form that invade the frog directly by the anus (Paul, 1938). The close correlation between the maturing and egg laying of the bladder form and that of its host suggests some hormonal control by the latter.

In *Gyrodactylus*, common on the gills of fresh-water fishes, the naked egg lacks yolk cells, obtaining yolk by fusing with sister eggs, and develops

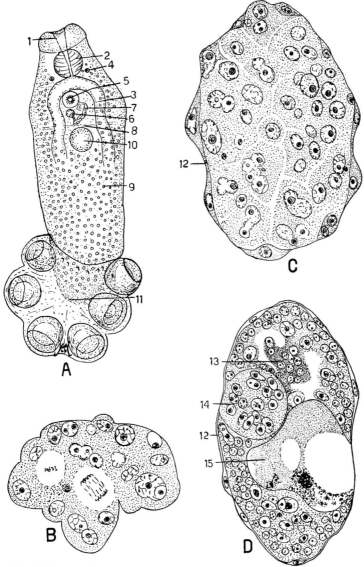

FIG. 94.—Polystomoid Monogenea, development. *A. Polystomoides (after Stunkard, 1917). B–D.* Development of *Polystoma (after Halkin, 1901).* *B.* Early stage showing epiboly. *C.* Later stage, epidermis separating from cell mass. *D.* Organs forming from cell masses, cavity becomes digestive lumen. 1, mouth funnel; 2, pharynx; 3, intestine; 4, nephridiopores; 5, gonopore; 6, ovary; 7, uterus; 8, yolk ducts; 9, yolk glands; 10, testis; 11, opisthaptor with six suckers; 12, epidermis; 13, brain ganglion; 14, primordium of pharynx; 15, lumen of intestine.

in the uterus (Fig. 83*A*). The development is remarkable in that very early a second embryo appears inside the first one, a third inside the second, and even a fourth inside the third. Only the early embryology has been described, and this resembles that of *Polystoma* through the epiboly process (Kathariner, 1904). The successive embryos appear to arise by a kind of polyembryony. When the first embryo has completed its development it passes to the exterior, still enclosing the other embryos, and attaches directly to a host fish.

In the curious genus *Diplozoon*, the capsule attached by a long tangled filament (Fig. 89*E*) to the host gills hatches into a ciliated larva provided with two eyes, digestive system, and a pair of suckers at each end. This larva soon loses cilia and eyes and becomes a *Diporpa* larva that must attach to fish gills for further development. The Diporpa develops a small sucker near the mid-ventral region and a dorsal papilla; two Diporpae then unite into an X-shape through the grasping of the dorsal papilla of one by the ventral sucker of the other (Fig. 96*A*). The two animals grow permanently together in this position and apparently can survive only as such fused pairs. When the reproductive system develops, the sperm duct of each opens directly into the yolk duct of the other by a connection probably representing a copulation canal, so that the two flukes are in a permanent state of copulation (Zeller's account, 1872a). Meantime additional suckers have been added to the opisthaptor which in the adult consists of paired ovals, each bearing a row of four suckers supported by cuticularized pieces (Fig. 93*C*).

Life cycles have been described for a number of other Monogenea: *Dactylogyrus* (Wilde, 1936; Gröben, 1940), *Benedenia* (= *Epibdella*, Jahn and Kuhn, 1932), *Ancyrocephalus* (Siwak, 1931), *Acolpenteron* (Fischthal and Allison, 1941), *Sphyranura* (Alvey, 1936), *Polystomoides* (Paul, 1938), and *Microcotyle* (Remley, 1942). In general the mature fluke lays capsules throughout its life singly at the rate of one every 5 to 10 minutes or at least a few daily. These hatch, usually in several days but requiring up to a month in some species, to a free-swimming larva provided with eyes, cilia usually in the form of three or more incomplete transverse bands, and an opisthaptor of the gyrodactyloid type (Figs. 95*B*, 96*B*). The larvae of *Sphyranura* are not ciliated, however, and creep about to find their host (*Necturus*); they also already have indications of the two adult suckers (Fig. 96*C*). The larva must locate and attach to a host of the same kind within a few hours or it perishes. After attachment, the larva sheds the ciliated epidermis and gradually alters to the adult state. The larval opisthaptor generally alters into the adult opisthaptor but in *Microcotyle* is shed and the adult opisthaptor is a new development. The same probably applies to other Monogenea with complicated type of opisthaptor (Fig. 89*A*). The adult worm probably has a short existence.

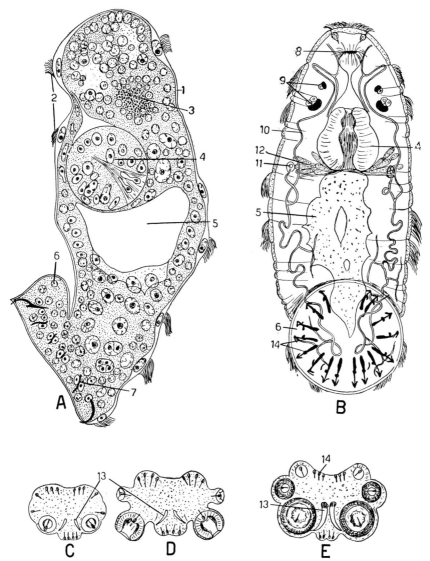

FIG. 95.—Development of *Polystoma* (continued). *A.* Late stage (*after Halkin*, 1901).
B. Larva of *Polystoma* (*after Halkin*, 1901). *C–E.* Stages in the development of the opisthaptor of *Polystoma* (*after Zeller*, 1872). 1, epidermis; 2, ciliary rings; 3, brain; 4, pharynx;
5, intestine; 6, opisthaptor; 7, haptorial hook developing between two cells; 8, mouth; 9, eyes;
10, nephridium; 11, nephridiopore; 12, pharyngeal glands; 13, anchors; 14, marginal hooks.

Gröben estimates the duration of life of *Dactylogyrus* from egg to death at 10 to 12 days, but other forms probably live a month or two, and as noted above *Polystoma* from the frog bladder may have a cycle lasting 3 years.

14. Order Aspidobothria.—The members of this order have long been of uncertain status, being included by some workers in the Monogenea, by others in the Digenea. They were separated from both these groups as early as 1856 by Burmeister under the name Aspidobothrii. The same separation under the name Aspidocotylea was made by Monticelli in 1892, but later authors again incorporated them into the Digenea. However, recent work (Faust and Tang, 1936; Williams, 1942) again favors regarding them as a distinct group of trematodes, and hence they are here considered an order coordinate with Monogenea and Digenea under Burmeister's name slightly altered.[1]

The order comprises two families, Aspidogastridae and Stichocotylidae, of which the former includes the more typical and best known members.

The Aspidogastridae are characterized by the enormous circular, oval, or elongated sucker divided by septa into one, three, or four longitudinal rows of depressions termed *alveoli* (Figs. 84*A*, 97*A*, *B*). This sucker occupies the greater part of the ventral surface and is somewhat set off from the body. The narrowed anterior end of the body has a terminal or slightly subterminal mouth, usually a large funnel-like opening, not provided with an oral sucker although sometimes with muscularized walls (Fig. 97*A*). It leads usually by way of a small pharynx into the simple rounded or elongated intestinal sac. Between mouth and pharynx there may be a long buccal tube ("prepharynx"). The protonephridia have separate bladders and separate or a common nephridiopore situated dorsally near the posterior end. The reproductive system resembles that of the Digenea except that usually there is a single testis; a Laurer's canal may be present (Fig. 97*C*). Characteristic sense organs occur along the margins of the sucker embedded between the outer ends of the alveoli. They are protrusible flask-like bodies with a canal leading to the surface (Fig. 97*D*); each consists of a granular oval mass embedded in fibrous tissue and supplied by a nerve bundle. In the genus *Lophotaspis* the septa of the sucker bear numerous projecting papillae presumably of sensory nature (Fig. 98*A*, *B*).

---

[1] Faust and Tang have proposed a new name Aspidogastraea for the group on the ground that the name has to be derived from the genus *Aspidogaster*. This ground is mistaken. There are no rules governing the formation of names of higher taxonomic categories, and the creator of an order or class is at liberty to select any name he pleases. The author is strongly opposed to the invention of new names for groups for which names already exist.

The members of this family are entoparasitic in the mantle and pericardial and renal cavities of clams and snails and in the digestive tract of
fish and turtles and the bile passages of fish, occurring in both fresh-water
and marine hosts. The best known genus *Aspidogaster* has four rows of
alveoli; *A. conchicola* is common in the pericardial and renal cavities of
fresh-water clams (Fig. 97*A*). *Cotylaspis* (Fig. 97*B*) with three rows of
alveoli occurs in the branchial cavity of clams and the intestine of turtles.
Cotylogaster from the intestine of fishes also has three rows of alveoli of
which the middle row is much elongated transversely (Fig. 84*A*); in this

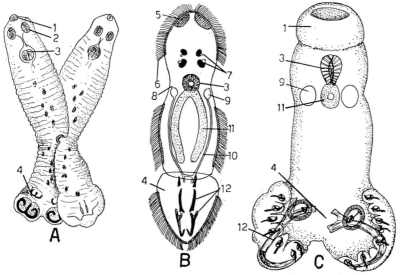

Fig. 96.—Other larval types of Monogenea. *A*. Diporpae larvae of *Diplozoon* (after
Zeller, 1872). *B*. Larva of *Benedenia* (= *Epibdella*) (after Jahn and Kuhn, 1932). *C*.
Larva of *Sphyranura* (after Alvey, 1936). 1, oral sucker; 2, lateral suckers; 3, pharynx; 4,
opisthaptor; 5, anterior adhesive areas; 6, ciliary rings; 7, eyes; 8, nephridiopore; 9, bladder;
10, protonephridium; 11, intestine; 12, anchors.

genus there are also two testes. Other genera are the very long slender
Macraspis with a single row of alveoli, *Lobatostoma* with lobed mouth rim,
and *Lophotaspis* (Fig. 98*A*, *B*) with the papillae mentioned above.

The life cycle of the Aspidogastridae is generally simple, without
alternation of hosts. The egg hatches into a fluke-like larva with both
oral and posterior suckers or only the latter (Nickerson, 1902; Williams,
1942; Fig. 97*E*). This larva develops directly into the adult by expansion
of the posterior sucker into the adult sucker (Fig. 97*F*) and makes its way
into other individuals of the same kind of host. Probably aspidogastrids
get into fish and turtles through the eating of clams and snails by these
vertebrates; but the vertebrate host is not necessary for the completion of
the life cycle, for several aspidogastrids occur in the mature state in both

clams and cold-blooded vertebrates. However, *Lophotaspis* apparently has a digenetic type of cycle with a young stage in a marine snail and the adult stage in turtles (Wharton, 1939).

The family Stichocotylidae comprises the single genus *Stichocotyle*, very elongated slender worms around 10 cm. in length that inhabit the bile passage or spiral valve of skates. Of the two known species, one, *S. nephrops*, has a row of up to 30 separated alveoli along the ventral surface. In the other species, *S. cristata*, there is a short row of alveoli anteriorly, and then the rest of the ventral surface bears a continuous longitudinal row of alveoli thrown into ridges and depressions (Faust and Tang, 1936, Fig. 98*C*). The life cycle is partly known for *S. nephrops;* immature worms occur encysted on the intestine of lobsters and presumably develop to maturity only when ingested by skates (Cunningham, 1887; Nickerson, 1894; Odhner, 1910). The cycle is therefore a complex one, involving at least two hosts.

15. Order Digenea: Embryology and Life Cycle.—The digenetic trematodes comprise a bewildering array of families, genera, and species that differ in shape and size, number, location, and size of suckers, length of intestinal crura, flame-bulb arrangement, and especially details of the reproductive system. New species are described almost daily, and investigation of almost any vertebrate not hitherto examined for this purpose is certain to yield new forms.

The Digenea with rare exceptions are entoparasites of vertebrates, fresh-water, marine, and terrestrial. In the adult stage they occur primarily in the digestive tract, particularly the intestine, and in various appendages of the digestive tract, such as lungs, liver, gall-bladder and bile passages, and urinary bladder; other sites are the kidneys and ureters, air sacs of birds, other parts of the respiratory system, coelom, eye, and various head cavities. Several families represented by the genera *Sanguinicola*, *Spirorchis*, and *Schistosoma* (old name, *Bilharzia*), flukes of elongated form, inhabit the blood of fish, turtles, birds, and mammals. A tendency to ectoparasitism is exhibited by a few Digenea that live on the gills of fishes or in the mouth and pharyngeal cavities, or around the anus, etc. In the adult stage, the Digenea are capable of little movement and remain at the site of attachment.

As the main features of the anatomy were given above, it remains here to consider the life cycle. The Digenea, as the name implies, have complicated life cycles, involving typically four larval forms and three, sometimes four, different hosts. That the life cycle of the Digenea involves an alternation of hosts and that cercariae, previously considered to be adult animals, are a larval stage of the Digenea, was first recognized by Steenstrup in 1842. Many contributions to digenetic life cycles followed (for an annotated bibliography of this period see Braun, 1879–

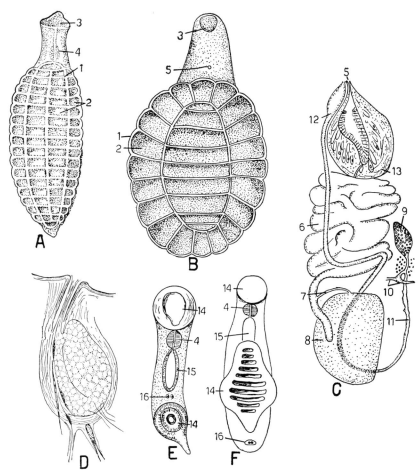

FIG. 97.—Types of Aspidobothria. *A. Aspidogaster conchicola (after Monticelli, 1892). B. Cotylaspis (after Osborn, 1903). C.* Reproductive system of *Cotylaspis (after Stunkard, 1917). D.* Longitudinal section of sense organ of sucker margin of *Cotylogaster (after Nickerson, 1902). E, F.* Larval stages of *Aspidogaster (after Voeltzow, 1888). E.* Newly hatched larva. *F.* Later stage, definitive sucker developing from larval posterior sucker. 1, sucker; 2, alveoli; 3, mouth funnel; 4, pharynx; 5, gonopore; 6, seminal vesicle; 7, sperm duct; 8, testis; 9, ovary; 10, yolk ducts; 11, ovovitelline duct; 12, uterus; 13, cirrus sac; 14, larval suckers; 15, intestine; 16, nephridiopore.

1893), but the first complete account of the cycle was that of the liver fluke of the sheep by A. P. Thomas in 1883, an article that has become a zoological classic. Following the lead given by Thomas many life cycles were worked out, and research on trematode life histories constitutes today an active branch of investigation throughout the world.

a. *Embryology.*—Development usually proceeds while the capsules are passing along the uterus and out of the host but may be deferred until the exterior is reached. Hence newly laid capsules may contain any stage from the uncleaved egg to the finished larva, and hatching of capsules may require a few hours or less up to several weeks. Sometimes the larva has already hatched within the parent uterus (Cyclocoelidae). Although the embryonic development of the Digenea was described in several older papers (Schauinsland, 1883; Looss, 1892; Goldschmidt, 1905; Schubmann, 1905; Ortmann, 1908), the best and most exact accounts are those of Ishii (1934), P. D. Chen (1937), and Rees (1940). As these are in substantial agreement although concerned with different species, they may be taken as generally applicable to the group.

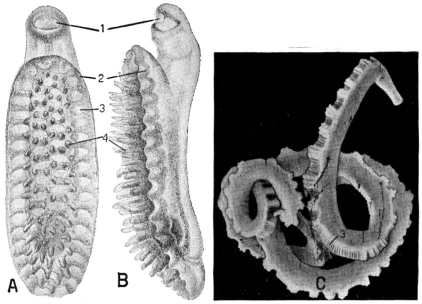

Fig. 98.—Aspidobothria (continued). *A. Lophotaspis*, ventral view. *B. Lophotaspis*, lateral view. (*A, B, after Ward and Hopkins*, 1931.) *C. Stichocotyle cristata* (*after Faust and Tang*, 1936). 1, mouth; 2, sucker; 3, alveoli; 4, papillae.

The egg cleaves into a *propagatory* cell and a slightly larger *somatic* cell (Fig. 99*A*). The latter divides to form a ball of unequally sized cells (Fig. 99*B*) of which certain small cells pass to the periphery forming just inside the capsule a vitelline membrane that encloses embryo and yolk cells (Fig. 99*C*). The propagatory cell, distinguishable by certain cytological details, now divides repeatedly and at each division one daughter retains the characteristics of the propagatory cell while the other is a somatic cell contributing to the embryo. The ball of cells elongates and differentiates into the first larval form, the *miracidium* (Fig. 99*D*). Its surface cells differentiate into an epidermis, later ciliated. An anterior mass of cells produces the brain and other parts of the nervous system. From a strand of cells arises a pair of protonephridia. The propagatory cell remaining after the divisions mentioned above retires into the rear part of the embryo (Fig. 99*D*) where it divides to form a number of cells that produce the next larval type. It will be perceived that there is no formation of germ layers in this development and that the embryology in general resembles that of ectolecithal Turbellaria.

b. Miracidium.—As just noted, the embryo differentiates directly into a ciliated larval form, termed the *miracidium*. This escapes from the capsule by butting against the operculum until the latter opens; gland secretions probably also aid the escape. As the miracidium is a swimming larva requiring an aquatic environment it occurs in typical form only when the capsules are shed into water as is usually the case.

The miracidium (Fig. 100) is a minute oval creature that darts about rapidly seeking a suitable host. It is clothed in a flattened ciliated epidermis consisting of a definite number of cells, usually 18 to 21, arranged in four or five tiers (Fig. 99*E, F*). A table of the known arrangements is given by Bennett (1936); the most common types are 6, 8, 4, 2 for amphistomes; 6, 6, 4, 2 for echinostomes; 6, 8, 4, 3 for strigeids; and 6, 6, 3, 4, 2 for liver flukes. The numbers give the number of cells in each tier from the anterior end backward. The anterior tip of the larva is devoid of cilia and forms a mobile protrusible *apical papilla* or *terebratorium* (Fig. 100) that in some cases is sufficiently firm and muscular to constitute a *rostrum*. This papilla may be armed with a protrusible stylet and also bears the openings of glands, all structures associated with host penetration. Two, sometimes three, eyes are often present over the brain. In the groove between the first and second tiers of epidermal cells there usually occurs on each side a *lateral papilla*, presumably sensory, although some observers have seen drops of secretion exuding from them. In some miracidia there are additional sensory papillae (up to 24) in a circle in this groove (Fig. 99*F*), and similar papillae may occur in the groove between the third and fourth tiers (Rees, 1940).

Beneath the epidermis is found a thin subepidermal musculature of outer circular and inner longitudinal fibers, and beneath this is a layer called the subepithelium. This in some miracidia forms a definite one-layered epithelium (Fig. 100*A*) but in others is more like mesenchyme; probably it represents the mesenchyme. The interior of the larva contains glands, the nervous system, the nephridia, and the propagatory cells and balls (Fig. 100). Attached by a stalk to the center of the apical papilla is a large rounded multinucleate sac of coarsely granular cytoplasm. This was formerly considered to be a rudimentary gut but is now regarded as a gland. Probably this *apical gland* is homologous with the frontal gland of the Turbellaria. There also often open on the apical papilla one to several pairs of large unicellular *cephalic* or *penetration* glands. The brain is a large mass behind the apical gland; usually nerves

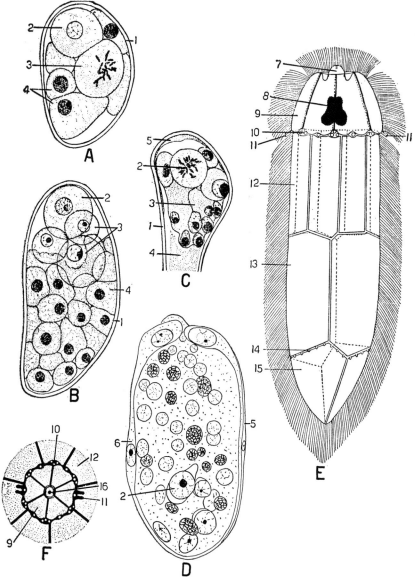

Fig. 99.—Development of Digenea. *A–C.* Early development of *Parorchis* (*after Rees,* 1940). *A.* First cleavage of fertilized egg into propagatory cell and somatic cell, entire capsule shown. *B.* Entire capsule showing stage of four blastomeres. *C.* Later stage, only part of capsule shown. *D.* Late embryo, *Paragonimus,* epidermis differentiated (*after Chen,* 1937). *E.* Miracidium of *Parorchis,* showing epidermal cells. *F.* Anterior end of miracidium of *Parorchis.* (*E, F, after Rees,* 1940.) 1, capsule; 2, propagatory cell; 3, somatic cell; 4, yolk cells; 5, vitelline membrane; 6, epidermis; 7, apical papilla; 8, eyes; 9, first tier, 6 cells; 10, ring of sensory papillae; 11, lateral papilla; 12, second tier, 7 cells; 13, third tier, 3 cells; 14, ring of papillae between third and fourth tiers; 15, last tier, 3 cells; 16, opening of apical gland.

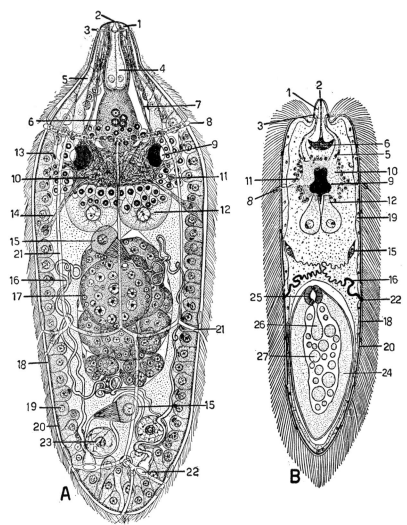

Fig. 100—Structure of the miracidium. *A*. Miracidium of *Heronimus* (*after Lynch*, 1933). *B*. Miracidium of *Parorchis* (*after Rees*, 1940), type containing fully developed redia. 1, apical papilla; 2, opening of apical gland; 3, opening of penetration glands; 4, additional glands of uncertain nature; 5, duct of penetration glands; 6, apical gland; 7, anterior nerve; 8, lateral sensory papilla; 9, eyes; 10, brain; 11, nerve cells; 12, penetration glands; 13, lateral nerve; 14, posterior nerve; 15, flame bulb; 16, nephridium; 17, germ balls; 18, epidermis; 19, subepithelium; 20, subepidermal musculature; 21, boundary of epidermal cells; 22, nephridiopore; 23, athrocyte; 24, redia; 25, pharynx of redia; 26, intestine of redia; 27, germ balls of redia.

may be seen proceeding from it. There is a pair of protonephridia, each with one or two flame bulbs; each is a sinuous tube proceeding to a nephridiopore situated laterally between the last two tiers of cells or penetrating the third or fourth tier. In the rear part of the larva are found a number of propagatory cells, some or all of which may have divided to form balls of cells known as *germ balls;* these are in reality embryos.

Very peculiar miracidia occur in the families Bucephalidae (= Gasterostomidae) and Brachylaimidae. In these the epidermis lacks cilia, and instead the cilia are borne on projecting rods (Fig. 106*B*, Woodhead, 1929; Allison, 1943).

Further details of miracidial structure with figures will be found in such articles as those of Coe (1896), Cort (1919), Lynch (1933), the Hunters (1935b), Bennett (1936), Yamaguti (1940), and Willey (1941).

Unless the miracidium finds a suitable host within a few to 24 hours it perishes. This host, called the first intermediate host, is practically always a mollusk, usually a snail, less often a bivalve. Only one exception is known, a case in which the first intermediate host is a polychaete annelid (Linton, 1915; Martin, 1944). Host specificity varies greatly, i.e., in some flukes only one particular species of mollusk is suitable, but in most more than one species will serve; and trematodes transported into new countries may become adapted to new species of mollusks as intermediate hosts. The miracidium adheres to the mollusk by its apical papilla and with the aid of the flesh-dissolving secretions of its apical and penetration glands rapidly passes (Fig. 126) into the mollusk, often by way of the latter's branchial apparatus, and lodges in almost any organ or tissue, most commonly the digestive gland ("liver") or the gonads. The miracidium sheds its ciliated epidermis either during its passage through the host epidermis (Fig. 126) or shortly after attaining the interior of the mollusk where it undergoes extensive alteration into the next larval stage, the *sporocyst* or *germinal sac.*

c. *Sporocyst.*—This is a rounded, elongated, or vermiform (to 25 mm. long) hollow structure (Fig. 101) covered with a thin cuticle beneath which is the miracidial muscle layer and mesenchyme (Fig. 101*A*). Other structures of the miracidium generally disappear except the protonephridia. The hollow interior contains propagatory cells and germ balls (Fig. 101*C*) or else these are embedded in the mesenchymal layer of the wall. The germ balls may multiply by dividing up into other germ balls. In some families (Bucephalidae, Brachylaimidae), the sporocyst branches and ramifies through the host tissue (Fig. 101*E*). The sporocyst moves about more or less in the host tissue from which it absorbs nutrition and to which it is often highly destructive and its germ balls develop either into daughter sporocysts or into the next larval stage,

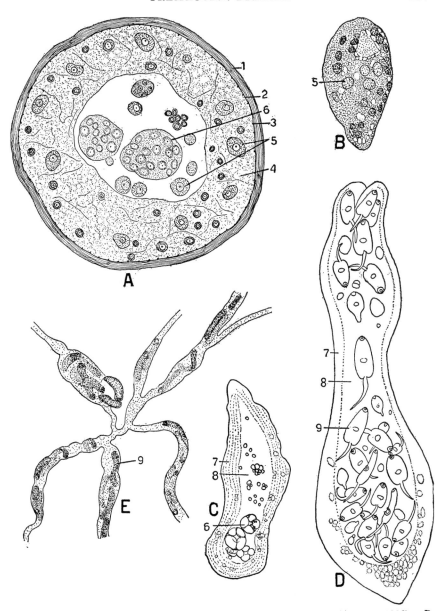

Fig. 101.—Sporocyst. *A.* Section through a sporocyst (*after Tennent*, 1906). *B.* Very young sporocyst (of the amphistome, *Cotylophoron, after Bennett*, 1936). *C.* Young sporocyst (plagiorchid fluke, *Renifer*). *D.* Mature daughter sporocyst (*Renifer*), filled with cercariae. (*C, D, after Byrd*, 1935). *E.* Branching type of sporocyst of the gasterostomes (*after Palombi*, 1934). 1, cuticle; 2, circular muscle layer; 3, longitudinal muscle layer; 4, mesenchyme; 5, propagatory cells; 6, germ balls; 7, wall; 8, hollow interior; 9, cercariae.

the redia. If daughter sporocysts are formed, then rediae are lacking from the life cycle and the final larval form, the cercaria, arises directly in the daughter sporocysts (Fig. 101*D*). Hence mature sporocysts may be filled either with daughter sporocysts or with rediae or with cercariae.

d. *Redia.*—The redia develops from a propagatory cell or germ ball in practically the same manner as the miracidium does from the egg and propagatory cells are again set aside for the formation of the cercariae or else germ balls for this purpose are split off from preexisting germ balls. The redia (Fig. 102*A*, *C*) is of elongated form usually with two ventral projections near the posterior end and a birth pore near the anterior end, where there also may be a collar-like welt (Fig. 102*C*). The body wall consists of the usual cuticle, muscular and mesenchymal layers. The mouth at the anterior end leads into a muscular pharynx followed by a simple sacciform intestine. Penetration glands are sometimes present. There is a pair of cerebral ganglia at the sides of the pharynx from which nerves extend. Protonephridia with flame bulbs are present (Fig. 102*B*). The hollow interior is filled with germ balls in process of development (Fig. 102*A*). The rediae escape from the sporocyst and move about in the host tissues on which they feed. They give rise either to a new generation of rediae, rarely more than one, or to cercariae and in any event cercariae are the final product of the redial generations (Fig. 102*C*). The cercariae are typically swimming larvae; they escape from the redia (by way of the birth pore when this is present) and exit from the molluscan host into the surrounding water. The time that elapses between the penetration of a miracidium into the host and the emergence of cercariae is naturally variable, depending on external factors, especially temperature, but generally occupies some weeks or even months.

e. *Cercaria.*—The development of a cercaria from a germ ball is similar to that of the preceding stages, and propagatory cells of direct descent from the original propagatory cell are again set aside to furnish the reproductive system of the adult fluke. As already noted, cercariae develop either in rediae or in daughter sporocysts; they sometimes leave the parent at an early stage and complete their development in the host tissues. The cercaria has a higher grade of organization than any of the preceding stages and already considerably resembles an adult fluke (Figs. 102, 103, 104). It consists of a broad to elongated oval body and a simple or forked tail. In early stages the cercaria is covered by a thin epidermis, but this is soon shed and replaced by a cuticle. This is often spiny in whole or in part or may bear bristles; a crown of larger spines may occur on the anterior tip. A shoulder girdle of spines is characteristic of echinostome cercariae but may be lacking in some species. Beneath the cuticle is found the usual muscle layer and a number of gland cells, the *cystogenous glands* (Fig. 103*A*). Oral sucker and acetabulum

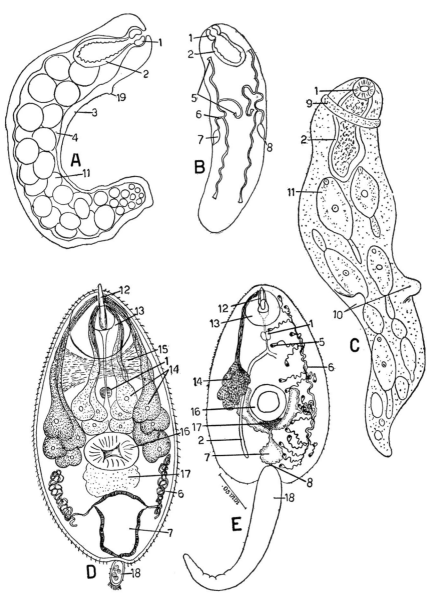

FIG. 102.—Rediae, types of cercariae. *A*. Redia of the amphistome *Cotylophoron*, type without collar or appendages. *B*. Same showing excretory system. (*A, B, after Bennett*, 1936.) *C*. Redia of the liver fluke (*after Ross and McKay*, 1929); birth pore does not show. *D*. Microcercous cercaria of *Paragonimus* (*after Ameel*, 1932). *E*. Stylet cercaria of a plagiorchid reniferine fluke (*after Byrd*, 1935). 1, pharynx; 2, intestine; 3, wall; 4, central hollow containing young cercariae; 5, flame bulbs; 6, protonephridia; 7, bladder; 8, nephridiopore; 9, collar; 10, lateral projections; 11, cercariae; 12, stylet; 13, oral sucker; 14, penetration glands; 15, brain; 16, acetabulum; 17, primordium of reproductive system; 18, tail; 19, birth pore.

are present except in monostome cercariae, which lack an acetabulum. The digestive system resembles that of adult flukes, consisting typically of buccal cavity encircled by the oral sucker, pharynx, esophagus, sometimes very long, and bifurcated intestine, but parts are often lacking. The anterior end may be armed with a protrusible stylet and bears the openings of the penetration glands, large gland cells occurring in a cluster in either side of the body with long necks running forward (Fig. 102D, E). There is a pair of protonephridial tubules, each provided with a number of flame bulbs (Fig. 102E) whose grouping has been considered in recent years of great taxonomic importance (Faust, 1932). However, it is probably not so diagnostic as considered by some, and the same arrangement may be found in unrelated forms. The two tubules meet at the posterior end of the body in a bladder from which a single stem proceeds along the tail; this then usually divides into two forks each of which opens by a pore on the side of the tail (Fig. 103E). In fork-tailed cercariae, the tubule divides where the tail forks and each branch then extends to the tip of the fork (Fig. 124D). The development of the tubules has been followed in a number of digenetic cercariae (Komiya, 1938; Hussey, 1941) and found to be similar in all. There first appear two tubules each with one or two flame bulbs and a pore as in the miracidium. As the tail develops the pores and terminal parts of the tubules are usually drawn into the tail, and fusion of the two tubules occurs at the rear end of the cercarial body where the fused portion also develops a bladder (Fig. 105). When the tail is shed the bladder is thus left at the rear end of the definitive fluke where a new common pore is established. The nervous system is similar to that of the adult; two, rarely three, eyes similar to those of the miracidium, are often present. The tail, formed by outgrowth, is of various shapes (see below) and is provided with muscles and often also with gland cells and hairs or spines.

Various types of cercariae occur, and these have been classified by Lühe (1909), Cort (1915b), Faust (1919), Sewell (1922), and others. They are broadly grouped into gasterostome, monostome, amphistome, echinostome, holostome, and distome cercariae on the same characters as give these names to adult flukes. The very numerous distome cercariae have been named on the basis of tail features, although these do not necessarily express taxonomic relationship. Distome cercariae with heavy broad tails are termed *rhopalocercous;* with very small tails, *microcercous* (Fig. 102D); with a cup-like tail, really a sucker provided with adhesive glands, *cotylocercous* or *cotylomicrocercous* (Fig. 103F, McCoy, 1929a; Palombi, 1938; Dobrovolny, 1939; Neuhaus, 1940; Hunninen and Cable, 1941, 1943); *furcocercous* with forked tails (Fig. 120C, H. M. Miller, 1926); *pleurolophocercous* when the tail has a fin (Fig. 103A, Lundahl, 1941; Cable and Hunninen, 1942a); *trichocercous* when the tail is beset with

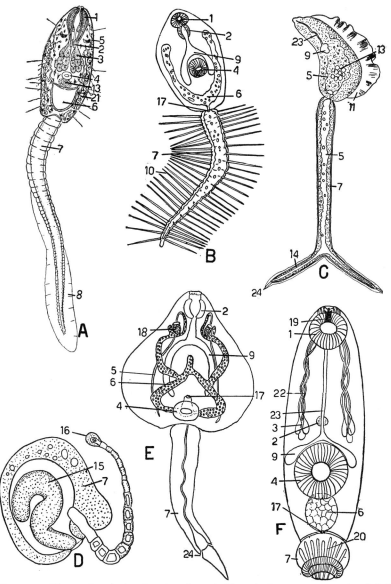

Fig. 103.—Types of cercariae (continued). A. Pleurolophocercous cercaria of *Opist-horchis sinensis* (*after Komiya and Tajimi*, 1940). B. Trichocercous cercaria (*after Palombi*, 1934). C. Lophocercous furcocercous cercaria of *Sanguinicola* (*after Ejsmont*, 1925). D. Cystophorous cercaria of *Halepegus* (*after Rankin*, 1944a). E. Amphistome cercaria of *Cotylophoron* (*after Bennett*, 1936). F. Cotylocercous cercaria (*after Palombi*, 1938). 1, oral sucker; 2, pharynx; 3, penetration glands; 4, acetabulum; 5, protonephridium; 6, bladder; 7, tail; 8, tail fin; 9, intestine; 10, bristles on tail; 11, body fin: 12, esophagus; 13, primordium of reproductive system; 14, tail forks; 15, body of cercaria; 16, appendage; 17, nephridiopore; 18, eyes; 19, stylet; 20, adhesive glands; 21, cystogenous glands; 22, ducts of penetration glands; 23, esophagus; 24, larval nephridiopore.

bristles (Fig. 103B, Palombi, 1932b; Martin, 1938; Cable and Hunninen, 1942b); and *cystocercous* when the proximal end of the tail contains a cavity into which the cercarial body can be withdrawn (Figs. 103D, 104). Furcocercous cercariae are characteristic of the families Strigeidae and Schistosomatidae; the stem may be long and the forks short (*brevifurcate*) or vice versa (*longifurcate*). The most peculiar of all cercariae are the cystocercous forms. These really consist of three types (Horsfall, 1934; E. L. Miller, 1936). In the cystocercous type proper, also called *mirabilis* type, the tail is large and thick with two anchoring flaps at the rear (Fig. 104B); this kind of cercaria belongs to the family Azygiidae (Ward, 1916; Faust, 1918c; Smith, 1932; Horsfall, 1934). The *macrocercous* or *gorgoderine* cercariae, typical of the family Gorgoderidae, have simple, often long tails (Fig. 104A, D) with or without a vesicular swelling containing the cercarial body (Krull, 1934a; E. L. Miller, 1936; Steelman, 1939; Baker, 1943). The most peculiar are the *cystophorus* types in which the tail consists of a rounded vesicle bearing various long appendages (Fig. 103D, Cort and Nichols, 1920; Thomas, 1939; Hunninen and Cable, 1943b; Rankin, 1944a). Cystophorous cercariae are characteristic of the family Hemiuridae and related forms. When the body of the cercaria bears a dorsal fin, the name *lophocercous* (Fig. 103C) is applied. A considerable number of cercariae are armed at the anterior end with a boring spine and are termed *stylet* or *xiphidiocercariae* (Fig. 102E). Cercariae that lack a tail are known as cercariaea (Fig. 104C). Special types of cercariae occur in the gasterostomes and holostomes (see later). Very curious are the marine *rattenkönig* cercariae which are united into a writhing ball by the tips of their long tails (Fig. 104E). While the family and even the genus to which a cercaria belongs may be recognizable through its structure, this is often not the case, and large numbers of cercariae have been described and named of which the adult is unguessed.

The number of cercariae produced is often prodigious. Infected snails may give off hundreds of cercariae daily over long periods of time. Thus Rothschild (1942) records an individual of the common shore snail *Littorina littorea* that gave off cercariae of *Cryptocotyle lingua* for 7 years at the rate of about 1,000,000 per year, or about 830 daily. This snail was presumably infected with more than one sporocyst, but reinfection was prevented. The number of cercariae coming from a single miracidium (hence from one fertilized egg) varies according to the details of the life cycle from as few as 50 to 200 up to a million in strigeids (discussion in Cort, 1944); probably the usual figure is ten to fifty thousand.

Innumerable studies of cercariae have been published; among the more extensive ones may be mentioned those of Cort (1915b), Faust (1918b, 1918d), H. M. Miller (1925–1928), Wesenberg-Lund (1934),

E. L. Miller (1936), Porter (1938), Palombi (1934, 1938, 1940), Brooks (1943).

When fully developed, the cercariae leave the redia or daughter sporocyst, bore through the host tissues, and escape into the water where they swim about for a few minutes to 2 or 3 days. They may encyst on plants or inert objects; but more often they penetrate or are eaten by a new host, the second intermediate host, in or on which they encyst. Unless the suitable host is found they perish. The second intermediate host may be a medusa, turbellarian, annelid, crustacean, mollusk, insect larva, or vertebrate, mostly fish and amphibians. Penetration into animals is accomplished by boring movements of the anterior tip aided by the stylet if present and particularly by the flesh-dissolving action of the secretion of the penetration glands. As the cercaria passes into the host it sheds its tail by a sudden jerk. The cyst is usually a thick-walled sphere (Fig. 106*A*) secreted by the cystogeneous glands but may consist wholly or partly of host connective tissue. Rarely encystment occurs by the tail coiling about the cercarial body (Palombi, 1937a). The encysted cercaria must be eaten by the final or definitive host before it can develop into the adult fluke. In rare cases there is a third intermediate host so that there are two successive encysted stages (*Alaria*, see under family Strigeidae).

f. Metacercaria.—The encysted larva, termed *metacercaria*, is a juvenile fluke. The typical larval organs such as eyes, stylet, cystogenous and penetration glands, etc., disintegrate gradually following encystment and the metacercaria develops the general structural features of the adult fluke (Fig. 106*A*). The reproductive system, however, remains rudimentary and its differentiation and other changes take place after the metacercaria has entered the definitive host. Following ingestion of the encysted metacercariae or of the animals containing them, the cyst wall dissolves in the host's digestive tract, chiefly in the intestine, and the young fluke migrates to the location typical of the species. During this migration and after attachment to the selected site the fluke continues to grow and mature; several to a number of days are required for the attainment of sexual maturity.

g. Variations of the Life Cycle.—The foregoing recounts the usual life cycle, but many variants occur as adaptive short cuts. Not uncommonly the miracidium does not lead a free existence but hatches only after the capsules have been ingested by the proper host; such miracidia may be devoid of cilia and may be provided with an apical crown of thorns for easier invasion of host tissue (Fig. 111*B*). Cycles of this type occur not only in flukes that have all their stages in terrestrial animals but are also found where aquatic hosts are involved. A few cases are known in which the miracidium already contains a fully developed redia (Fig. 100*B*),

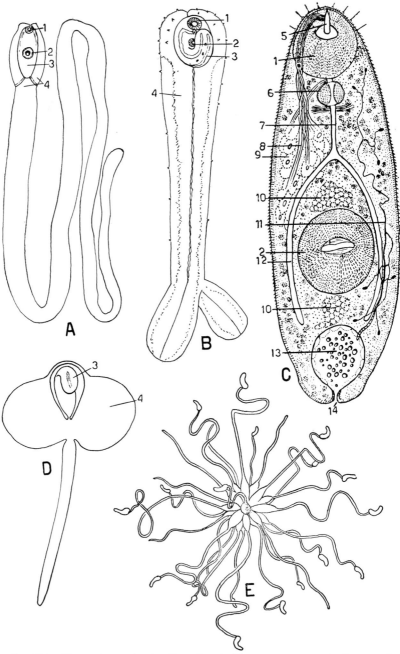

Fig. 104.—Types of cercariae (continued). *A.* Macrocercous cercaria of a gorgoderine fluke (*after Krull,* 1934a). *B.* Cystocercous cercaria of the Azygiidae (*after Horsfall,* 1934). *C.* Cercariaeum, Zoogonidae (*after Stunkard,* 1943). *D.* Another kind of macrocercous

sometimes provided with penetration glands, so that the sporocyst stage is skipped (*Typhlocoelum*, Szidat, 1932b; Stunkard, 1934; *Parorchis*, Stunkard and Cable, 1932; Rees, 1940; *Stichorchis*, Bennett and Humes, 1939). The cercariae of the Schistosomatidae and some other blood flukes penetrate the definitive host directly and omit the encysted stage, hence do not require a second intermediate host. Cercariaea (tailless cercariae) may occur in either aquatic or terrestrial hosts and may or may not be encysted; they usually do not lead a free existence but remain in the snail host without further development until the latter is eaten by the second intermediate or the definitive host.

  h. The Nature of the Digenetic Life Cycle.—The type of reproduction involved in the larval stages of the Digenea has been the subject of discussion for over a hundred years. The different views that have been held are reviewed by P. D. Chen (1937), Rees (1940), and Cort (1944) and as they are mostly of historical interest will not be recounted here. A widely accepted theory was that the reproductive processes in the sporocyst and rediae are parthenogenetic in nature, i.e., that the propagatory cells are eggs that undergo parthenogenetic development, and maturation processes were described by some authors. Under the influence of this theory, the following terms were introduced into the literature and received wide usage: *parthenitae* for the sporocysts and rediae, *adolescariae* for cercariae and metacercariae, and *maritae* for adult flukes. As it is now practically certain that the parthenogenesis theory is erroneous, these terms will pass out of the literature and hence have not been employed here. According to the best work on digenetic life cycles, that of Ishii (1934), Chen (1937), and Rees (1940), the reproductive processes in the sporocysts and rediae are of the nature of *polyembryony*, a simple multiplication of propagatory cells by mitosis or of germ balls by breaking up into other germ balls. The digenetic life cycle is therefore similar to that of hydroid coelenterates, comprising a period of asexual multiplication during immature stages followed by sexual reproduction in the mature stage. Although some regard this cycle as constituting an alternation of asexual and sexual generations it is better to view it simply as a continuous ontogeny involving asexual multiplication in larval stages.

  16. Some Families of the Digenea and Their Life Cycles.—The Digenea are classified into a large number of families, mainly on the basis of details of the reproductive system; only the more interesting and important of these can be considered here.

gorgoderine cercaria (*after Baker*, 1943). E. Rattenkönig (ball of cercariae attached by their tail ends) (*after Ward*, 1916). 1, oral sucker; 2, acetabulum; 3, body of cercaria; 4, tail of cercaria; 5, stylet; 6, pharynx; 7, esophagus; 8, ducts of penetration glands; 9, penetration glands; 10, primordium of reproductive system; 11, nephridium; 12, intestine; 13, bladder; 14, nephridiopore.

a. *Family Bucephalidae* (= *Gasterostomidae*).—This family, known as gasterostomes, is distinguished from all other Digenea by the location of the mouth at the middle of the body (Fig. 106*D*) and hence is often separated as a suborder Gasterostomata from the remaining digenetic families, constituting the suborder Prosostomata, in which the mouth is at the anterior end.   This classification is considered of doubtful validity at present.   The anterior end bears a simple (*Bucephalopsis*) or lobed (*Bucephalus*) oral sucker or has a generally lobed hood-like extension (*Rhipidocotyle*, Fig. 84*C*) or instead of a sucker has a protrusible piston-like muscular cushion (*Prosorhynchus*, Fig. 106*D*).   The mouth leads by way of a pharynx into a small sacciform intestine; this digestive system

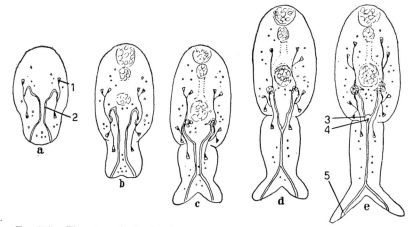

Fig. 105.—Five stages in the development of the excretory system and the forked tail of a strigeid cercaria (*after Komiya*, 1938).   1, flame bulbs; 2, protonephridium; 3, beginning of bladder; 4, definitive nephridopore; 5, nephridiopores of cercaria.

is considered by some as a primitive feature reminiscent of rhabdocoels while others maintain that the original digestive system has degenerated and the present one is a modified acetabulum.   An acetabulum is lacking; the genital pore is posterior.   The adults, under 1 mm. long, inhabit the digestive tract of carnivorous fish (Ozaki, 1928b; Eckmann, 1932). The peculiar miracidia (Fig. 106*B*, Woodhead, 1929) bear their cilia on projecting rods.   They penetrate fresh-water clams of the family Unionidae or marine bivalves such as the oyster and there grow into highly branched sporocysts (Fig. 101*E*) that produce cercariae directly (Woodhead, 1929, 1930; Tennent, 1906).   The cercariae, known as oxhead cercariae (whence the name *Bucephalus*) have a pair of long tails, often extremely long, that give them a resemblance to an oxhead with a pair of horns (Fig. 106*C*, Woodhead, 1936).   The cercariae have the typical gasterostome digestive tract and are hence easily recognizable as belonging to the family.   The second intermediate host, comprising small fishes, is attained by the entanglement of the cercarial tails in the fins. The cercariae encyst under the scales, mostly of the fins, and develop to adults when the fish carrying them are eaten by larger fish.

b. *Family Paramphistomidae* (= *Amphistomidae*).—This family comprises the amphistome flukes, i.e., those having the acetabulum, sometimes very large, at the posterior end of the body, considered to be the primitive position (Figs. 107, 108). In *Homalogaster* (Fig. 108*B*) and *Gastrodiscus* the ventral surface is papillate in whole or part, and in some genera the interior of the acetabulum is papillate (Fig. 108*A*). The anterior end, often provided with minute sensory papillae, is devoid of an oral sucker and bears the mouth; this leads into a very muscular pharynx often provided with two pouches (Fig. 108*A*). The posterior end of the slender esophagus is often thickened to form a muscular bulb (Fig. 109*A*). The family has a lymphatic system (page 230). The gonopore, situated in the anterior body half, and provided in some genera with a genital sucker (Fig. 108*A*), leads into a roomy antrum, often very muscular and provided with a sphincter, into which the sex ducts open on a protrusible papilla that may be encircled by a sphincter (Fig. 107*C*). In the genus *Gastrothylax* (Fig. 80*C*) there is a very deep ventral pouch considered by some to represent an enlarged antrum, into the anterior part of which the genital ducts open. The nephridiopore is dorsal in front of the acetabulum, and the mouth of Laurer's canal lies near by (Fig. 107*C*). This family has been treated extensively by Fischoeder (1903), Stiles and Goldberger (1910), Maplestone (1923), Fukui (1929), Travassos (1934), and Näsmark (1937). The adults, ranging from 3 to 20 mm., are parasites of the digestive tract of vertebrates, especially large herbivorous mammals. Some representative genera are *Microrchis* in fish, *Diplodiscus* (Fig. 109*A*) in the rectum of frogs, *Allassostoma* in the cloaca of turtles, *Ophioxenos* in garter snakes, *Zygocotyle* in ducks, *Stichorchis* in the beaver, *Cladorchis* (Fig. 108*A*) in tapirs, *Gastrodiscus* in the horse tribe, *Chiorchis* in aquatic mammals of the order Sirenia, *Nilocotyle* and *Buxifrons* in the hippopotamus, *Brumptia* and *Pseudodiscus* in elephants, *Watsonius* in man and monkeys, and *Paramphistomum* (Fig. 107), *Cotylophoron* (Fig. 88*B*), *Gastrothylax* (Fig. 80*C*) *Homalogaster* (Fig. 108*B*), *Gigantocotyle*, and others in ruminants (cattle, sheep, goats, antelopes, deer, etc.), especially in the rumen. *Gastrodiscoides hominis*, normally a parasite of pigs, is the only amphistome parasitizing man to any extent, inhabiting the colon; it occurs in India and Indo-China, where 40 per cent of the natives may be infected (Buckley, 1939). *Watsonius watsoni*, normally in monkeys, is rarely found in man (Stiles and Goldberger, 1910).

The life cycle is thoroughly known for only a few species. Miracidia, sporocysts, and rediae offer no peculiarities except that in *Stichorchis* the

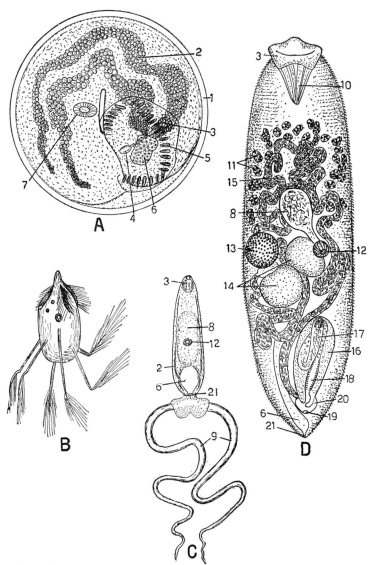

Fig. 106.   Metacercaria, family Bucephalidae.   *A.* Metacercaria of an echinostome (*after Palombi,* 1934).   *B.* Miracidium of the Bucephalidae (*after Woodhead,* 1929). *C.* Oxhead cercaria of the Bucephalidae (*after Palombi,* 1934).   *D.* A gasterostome fluke *Prosorhynchus* (*after Ozaki,* 1928b).   1, cyst wall; 2, protonephridia filled with excretory spherules; 3, oral sucker; 4, pharynx; 5, collar of thorns; 6, bladder; 7, acetabulum; 8, intestine; 9, tails; 10, rhynchus; 11, yolk glands; 12, mouth; 13, ovary; 14, testes; 15, uterus; 16, cirrus sac; 17, seminal vesicle; 18, cirrus; 19, gonopore; 20, genital antrum; 21, nephridiopore.

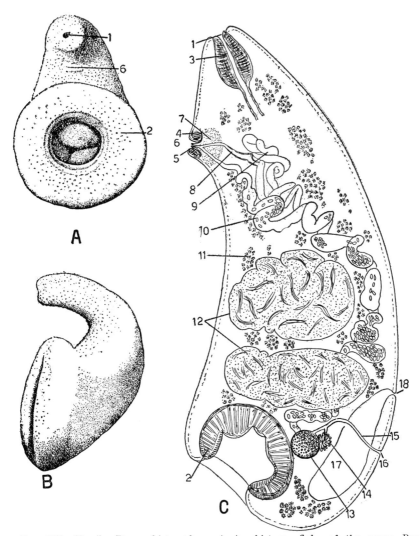

FIG. 107.—Family Paramphistomidae. *A.* Amphistome fluke of the genus *Paramphistomum,* ventral view. *B.* Same, seen from the side. (*A, B, after Fukui,* 1929.) *C.* Longitudinal section of *Paramphistomum* (*after Fischoeder,* 1903, *and Näsmark,* 1937). 1, mouth; 2, acetabulum; 3, pharynx; 4, genital sphincter; 5, genital papilla; 6, gonopore; 7, prostatic glands; 8, sperm duct; 9, seminal vesicle; 10, uterus; 11, yolk glands; 12, testes; 13, ovary; 14, ootype with Mehlis's glands; 15, Laurer's canal; 16, pore of same; 17, bladder; 18, nephridiopore.

miracidium contains a fully developed redia (Bennett and Humes, 1939). The cercariae have the amphistome construction (Fig. 103*E*) and hence are easily recognized as belonging to the family. They emerge from snails that harbor the sporocysts and rediae. In *Diplodiscus temperatus* (Fig. 109*A*) from American frogs, the cercariae encyst on bottom debris and on the surface of tadpoles and frogs. Infection ensues when debris or shed skin bearing the cysts is eaten by tadpoles or frogs (Krull and Price, 1932). According to Beaver (1929), the cercariae of *Allassostoma* encyst on tadpoles and crayfish which are then eaten by the definitive hosts (turtles, bullfrogs). In the case of amphistomes of large herbivorous mammals, the cercariae probably encyst on grasses and other vegetation, as was determined for *Cotylophoron cotylophorum* (Bennett, 1936) and *Paramphistomum cervi* (Szidat, 1936), both from ruminants.

c. *Family Zoogonidae.*—These are small distomes with spiny cuticle, short intestinal crura, and yolk glands reduced to one or two small masses so that the eggs lack proper shells, being enclosed in the vitelline membrane. At the time of laying, the miracidium is fully developed. Life cycles have been worked out for *Zoogonus lasius* and *Zoogonoides laevis* (Fig. 109B) from the New England coast (Stunkard, 1938a, 1943) and for *Diphterostomum brusinae* from the Mediterranean (Palombi, 1930). The miracidia penetrate marine snails such as *Nassa*, *Ilyanassa* and *Natica*, in which the sporocyst produces cercariae directly. These cercariae are of the cercariaeum type, i.e., without tails (Fig. 104C). In *Zoogonus* and *Zoogonoides* these are emitted and crawl about on the bottom until they make contact with the second intermediate host, chiefly the polychaete *Nereis*, in which they encyst. In *Diphterostomum*, they encyst within the mother sporocyst, and these cysts are then discharged from the snail and fall on various sessile animals or on plants. The definitive hosts are a variety of marine fishes.

d. *Family Allocreadiidae.*—These are small distomes that parasitize the intestine of marine and fresh-water fishes, being among the common parasites of salmon, trout, perch, pike, bass, sunfish, catfishes, etc. In the genera *Crepidostomum* and *Bunodera* the oral sucker has six muscular papillae (Fig. 109C). The known life cycles are of three different types (Hopkins, 1934). In *Crepidostomum* and *Allocreadium*, the rediae, found in small bivalves of the family Sphaeriidae, produce ophthalmoxiphidio-cercariae (i.e., with eyes and stylet) and the metacercariae encyst in May fly nymphs, amphipods, crayfish, or bivalves (Hopkins, 1934; Ameel, 1937; Crawford, 1943). A different cycle obtains for such genera as *Hamacreadium* (McCoy, 1929a, 1930) and *Plagioporus* (Sinitsin, 1931a; Dobrovolny, 1939); the sporocysts inhabit snails and produce cotylo-cercous cercariae (Fig. 103F) that encyst in various animals as crayfish, snails, or small fish or encyst directly in the sporocyst so that there is no second intermediate host. Still a different history is known for *Lepocreadium* and *Pharyngora*. The trichocercous cercariae (Fig. 103B), produced in rediae in snail hosts (Dollfus, 1925; Palombi, 1931, 1937b; Hopkins, 1937), attach to various hosts and transform into metacercariae without encysting. Thus *Pharyngora* metacercariae occur naked attached to medusae (Lebour, 1916) awaiting ingestion by the final fish host. The variability in the cycles indicates that the family is artificial and requires breaking up into several families.

e. Family Azygiidae.—These are flukes with opaque muscular bodies, found in the esophagus and stomach of fishes. The family is discussed by Odhner (1911a), Manter (1926), and Dickerman (1934). Some

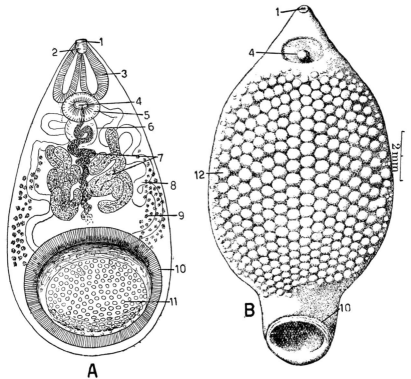

Fig. 108.—Paramphistomidae (continued). *A. Cladorchis* from the tapir, with pharyngeal sacs (*after Fischoeder*, 1903). *B. Homalogaster* from ruminants, with ventral papillae (*after Fukui*, 1929). 1, mouth; 2, pharynx; 3, pharyngeal sacs; 4, gonopore; 5, genital sucker; 6, cirrus sac; 7, uterus; 8, intestine; 9, yolk glands; 10, acetabulum; 11, papillae in acetabulum; 12, papillae on ventral surface.

genera as *Azygia* in fresh-water fishes and *Otodistomum* from elasmobranches (Fig. 110*A*, Mühlschlag, 1914; Manter, 1926) are of long slender form, up to 125 mm. in length; whereas *Proterometra* from centrarchid fishes is oval. Life cycles are known for *Azygia* (Szidat, 1932a) and *Proterometra* (Smith, 1934, 1936; Dickerman, 1934, 1945). The capsules containing the unciliated miracidia are eaten directly by snails; the miracidium is armed with four anterior bristle plates for penetrating the snail's intestinal wall. The cercariae are of the cystocercous type (Fig.

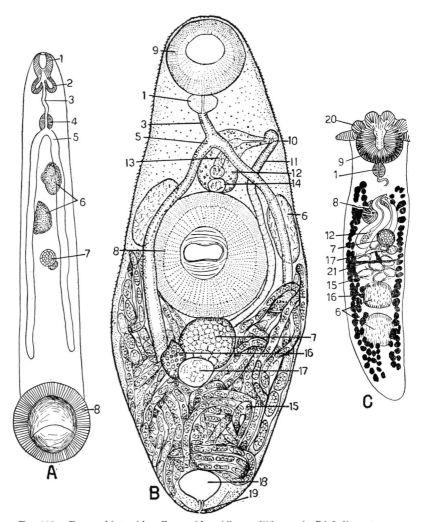

Fig. 109.—Paramphistomidae, Zoogonidae, Allocreadiidae. *A. Diplodiscus temperatus*, amphistome from the rectum of frogs, from life. *B. Zoogonoides (after Stunkard,* 1943), from fish intestine. *C. Crepidostomum cornutum (after Van Cleave and Mueller,* 1934), allocreadiid from the intestine of fresh-water fish. 1, pharynx; 2, pharyngeal sacs, 3, esophagus; 4, esophageal bulb; 5, intestine; 6, testes; 7, ovary; 8, acetabulum; 9, oral sucker; 10, gonopore; 11, metraterm; 12, cirrus sac; 13, cirrus; 14, seminal vesicle; 15, coils of uterus; 16, yolk gland; 17, seminal receptacle; 18, bladder; 19, nephridiopore; 20, papillae; 21, yolk ducts.

104*B*) and notable for their relatively gigantic size (up to 16 mm.); they are eaten directly by the definitive fish host.

f. Family Hemiuridae.—This is a distome family of varied appearance. The typical members, known as *appendiculate* flukes, are slender cylindroid forms, up to 15 mm. in length, that inhabit the esophagus and stomach, less often the pharynx and intestine, of marine fishes. The rear part of the body, up to one-half the body length, can be telescoped into the anterior part, from which it is demarcated by a constriction marking the ring of attachment of the retractor muscles accomplishing the withdrawal (Fig. 110B, C). The anterior part has a thick, often ringed, cuticle whereas the posterior part is thin-walled and hence supposed to serve for respiration, absorption etc. Some representative appendiculate genera are *Hemiurus* (Fig. 110B, C), *Dinurus*, *Sterrhurus* and *Lecithochirium* (Pratt, 1898; Lühe, 1901; Lander, 1904; Looss, 1908). The life cycle is not known except that metacercarial stages have been found in copepods (Pratt, 1898).

The nonappendiculate hemiurids, represented by such genera as *Derogenes*, *Hirundinella*, and *Halipegus* (Rankin, 1944a), are smaller and of normal form. *Halipegus* (Fig. 110D) differs from the rest of the family in parasitizing fresh-water hosts, frogs and salamanders, where it is found chiefly in the buccal cavity and related parts. The life cycle of *Halipegus*, worked out by Krull (1935) and Thomas (1939), includes a nonciliated miracidium escaping only after ingestion of the capsules by snails, sporocyst and redial stages in snails, and cystophorous cercariae (Fig. 103D) that are eaten by copepods or dragonfly and damsel fly nymphs; or possibly copepods are the second and these nymphs the third intermediate hosts.

g. Family Didymozoonidae.—The members of this curious family live in pairs in cysts on the surface, gills, operculum, or on the walls of the oral cavity or pharynx of marine fishes, seldom in the interior. Studies on the family have been made by Odhner (1907), the MacCallums (1916), Dollfus (1933), and Ishii (1935). Although some forms are hermaphroditic, there is a tendency in the family toward gonochorism through degeneration of the organs of one sex, and this is accompanied by sexual dimorphism and assumption of peculiar body shape. Characteristic of the family are the demarcation of a slender or spoon-like forebody from the cylindroid, plump, or rounded hindbody, and the long slender tubular shape of ovary, testis, and yolk gland (Figs. 81, 111). *Nematobothrium* is extremely long and slender up to a meter in length. In *Didymozoon* (Fig. 112C) the hindbody is plump and cylindroid, and in *Didymocystis* (Fig. 111) it has shortened to a reniform shape from which the slender forebody protrudes. These genera are hermaphroditic. *Wedlia* (Fig. 81) in which the peculiar body form reaches its climax is dioecious; the small male hindbody is lodged in a depression in the large rounded female hindbody from which the two small spoon-shaped forebodies protrude. Throughout the hindbody of the members of this family wind the coils of the long slender ovary, yolk gland (single), and uterus. The Didymozoonidae have an oral sucker, but an acetabulum is wanting so that they classify

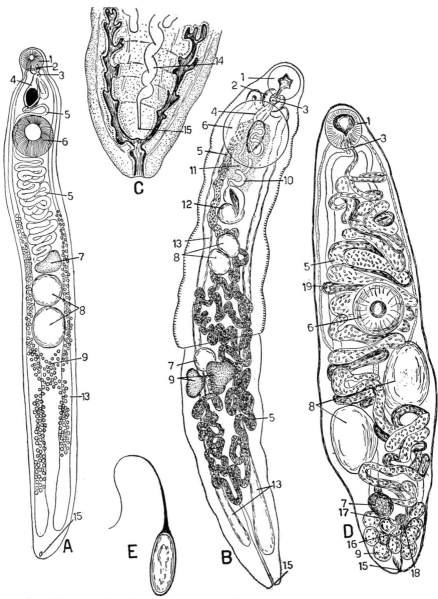

Fig. 110.—Azygiidae, Hemiuridae. *A. Otodistomum*, to 100 mm. long, from the stomach of a skate, from life. *B. Hemiurus* (after Looss, 1908) with rear end extended. *C.* Rear part of same with rear end telescoped into the interior (*after Looss*, 1908). *D. Halipegus*, nonappendiculate hemiurid, from the oral cavity of frogs. *E.* Capsule of *Halipegus*. (*D* and *E*, *after Krull*, 1935.) 1, oral sucker; 2, pharynx; 3, gonopore; 4, cirrus sac; 5, uterus; 6, acetabulum; 7, ovary; 8, testes; 9, yolk glands; 10, sperm duct; 11, prostatic glands; 12, seminal vesicle; 13, intestine; 14, bladder; 15, nephridiopore; 16, yolk duct; 17, oviduct; 18, ootype; 19, nephridium.

as monostomes. The pharynx is often reduced or absent. The life cycle is not known, but the miracidia lack cilia and are armed with an anterior crown of thorns (Fig. 111*B*), whence it may be inferred that the capsules hatch only after being eaten by the intermediate host, presumably a marine snail.

h. Family Gorgoderidae.—This is a distome family parasitic in the ureters and urinary bladder of fish, amphibians, and reptiles. The best known genera are *Gorgoderina* with two testes, *Gorgodera* (Fig. 112*A*) with nine testes, and *Phyllodistomum* (Fig. 112*B*, Lewis, 1935) with expanded rear part, all common in the urinary bladder of frogs and salamanders. The life cycle of these genera, first worked out by Sinitsin (1907), has been verified by Krull (1934a), Rankin (1939b), Crawford (1940), and Goodchild (1943). The laid capsules already contain the miracidium which enters small bivalves of the family Sphaeriidae. The cercariae, developing directly in sporocysts, are of the macrocercous type (page 262) with long broad tails or very long and slender tails (Fig. 104*A*, *D*). Wriggling of the tails induces ingestion by the second intermediate host, usually a damsel fly nymph or other aquatic insect larva, less often a snail or tadpole. Enclosure of the cercarial body in the tail base is believed to act as a protection from insect jaws. The metacercariae, after hatching in the definitive host, seem to inhabit the kidneys first, passing into the bladder as sexual maturity is attained (Odlaug, 1937).

i. Family Plagiorchidae.—These are small to moderate distomes, with a spiny cuticle, Y-shaped urinary bladder, and anterior, often lateral, gonopore (Fig. 113). The family, broadly conceived, is one of the largest digenetic families, with nearly 50 genera and hundreds of species, inhabiting the intestine of various vertebrates, chiefly those of aquatic habits; the oral cavity, esophagus, and respiratory tract of amphibians and reptiles; and less often the gall bladder and urogenital tract of reptiles and birds. The capsules on laying contain a fully developed miracidium but hatch only after ingestion by snails. The development of the sporocysts has been studied by Cort and Olivier (1943a) and Cort and Ameel (1944); the daughter sporocysts are covered with a special epithelial layer and contain a germ mass that continues to produce cercariae over a long period. The cercariae are of the stylet type (Fig. 102*E*), and have the flame-bulb formula $2[(3 + 3 + 3) + (3 + 3 + 3)]$, also occurring in the adults. By the scraping action of the stylet, the cercariae penetrate the surface of aquatic insect larvae, crayfish, or tadpoles in which they encyst to form metacercariae.

The family is divided into several subfamilies, of which the arrangement proposed by Travassos (1928) is probably the best. The plagiorchine group (Olsen, 1937), comprising the genera *Plagiorchis* (= *Lepoderma*), *Glyphthelmins*, *Styphlodora* (Byrd, Parker, and Reiber, 1940),

Opisthioglyphe, and others, generally inhabits the intestine of various vertebrates of aquatic habits but may be experimentally grown in mice, rats, and pigeons. The cercariae of *Plagiorchis* penetrate aquatic insect larvae (odonates, May flies, dipterans, McMullen, 1937b) or crayfish

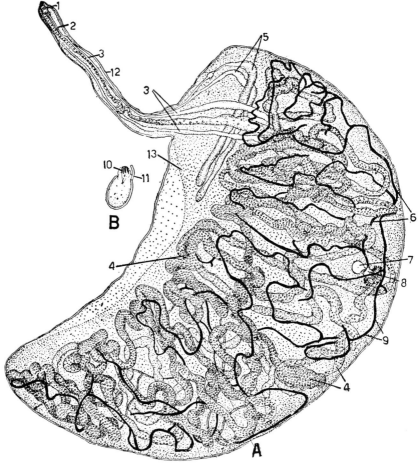

Fig. 111.—Didymozoonidae. *A. Didymocystis (after Nigrelli,* 1939). *B.* Capsule of same, shown crown of thorns on nonswimming miracidium. 1, oral sucker; 2, esophagus; 3, intestine; 4, uterus; 5, testes; 6, ovary; 7, seminal receptacle; 8, ootype; 9, yolk glands; 10, thorns; 11, operculum; 12, forebody; 13, hindbody.

(McCoy, 1928); those of *Glyphthelmins* encyst in the epidermis of frogs that when shed is eaten by the definitive frog host (Rankin, 1944b). Species of *Plagiorchis* occasionally occur in the human intestine (Philippines, Africa and Garcia, 1937; Java, Sandground, 1940) and *Plagiorchis muris,* naturally infecting the muskrat and aquatic birds, will take in man (McMullen, 1937c).

The reniferine plagiorchids, discussed by Talbot (1934) and Byrd and Denton (1938), include such genera as *Renifer* (Fig. 113*A*), *Neorenifer*, *Zeugorchis*, and *Dasymetra*, parasitizing snakes. The life histories of this group have been worked out by Ingles (1933), Talbot (1933), Byrd (1935), and Walker (1939). The cercariae encyst in tadpoles that are eaten by snakes in which the adults infect the oral cavity, esophagus, air passages, and lungs.

The saphaedrine group contains the familiar lung flukes of frogs, belonging to the genera *Haematoloechus* (= *Pneumoneces*,[1] Fig. 113*C*), with rounded testes and simple ovary, and *Pneumobites* with elongated testes and lobed ovary. The species of American frog lung flukes have been described and figured by Stafford (1902) and Cort (1915a). The life cycle has been elucidated by Krull (1930, 1931, 1934b). As in other plagiorchids, the capsules hatch only after ingestion by snails, and stylet cercariae are produced. These commonly encyst in dragonfly nymphs of the genus *Sympetrum* after being swept into the rectum of the nymph by its respiratory currents; but they also may employ other aquatic insect nymphs as second intermediate hosts. The metacercariae remain through the metamorphosis of the insect and attain the definitive frog host when the latter eats infected dragonflies. After hatching in the frog stomach, the young flukes travel up the esophagus to the oral cavity and then down the glottis into the lungs.

This ability of plagiorchid metacercariae to persist in an infective state through metamorphosis to the adult insect permits the spread of plagiorchid flukes to nonaquatic birds and mammals that have access to shores of ponds and lakes, and birds such as swallows that feed on insects over water. Thus plagiorchids of the genus *Prosthogonimus* (Fig. 113*B*) that have their metacercarial stage in dragonfly nymphs and adults are common in the intestine, bursa Fabricii, and oviducts not only of ducks and other aquatic birds but also of a great variety of land birds, including the domestic hen. Infection of the oviducts of the domestic hen by *Prosthogonimus* (Fig. 113*B*) in lake regions throughout the world (Macy, 1934) has become of economic importance, since it results in a great decline in egg production, formation of soft-shelled eggs, and deterioration of the health of the hen; not infrequently the flukes are found in the eggs laid by infected hens.

j. Family Dicrocoeliidae.—These are distomes of some size and of elongated flattened form with tubular excretory bladder and testes situated anterior to the ovary (Fig. 82*A*). They parasitize the liver and gall

---

[1] In 1902, Looss proposed to change the name *Haematoloechus* to *Pneumoneces* on the ground that the former name was too similar to the prior name *Haematoloecha*. Such similarity is not, however, a valid ground for changing generic names, and therefore *Haematoloechus* is the valid name of the common lung flukes of frogs.

bladder of reptiles, birds, and mammals, the pancreas of ruminant mammals, and the intestine of amphibians and reptiles.   *Dicrocoelium* (Fig. 82*A*), *Eurytrema*, and *Brachycoelium* are representative genera, and the lancet fluke, *Dicrocoelium dendriticum* (= *lanceolatum* or *lanceatum*),

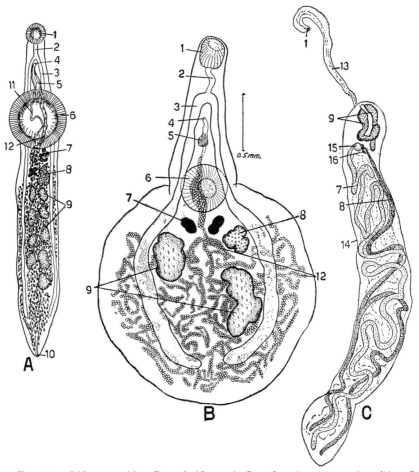

Fig. 112.—Didymoozonidae, Gorgoderidae.   *A. Gorgodera*, frog rectum, from life.   *B. Phyllodistomum* (after *Van Cleave and Mueller*, 1934).   *C. Didymozoon* (after *Ishii*, 1935). 1, oral sucker; 2, esophagus; 3, intestine; 4, gonopore; 5, cirrus sac; 6, acetabulum; 7, yolk glands; 8, ovary; 9, testes; 10, nephridiopore; 11, sperm duct; 12, uterus; 13, forebody; 14, hindbody; 15, seminal receptacle; 16, ootype.

found in the bile passages of sheep, cattle, and other herbivorous mammals, is one of the best known flukes.   Its life cycle was worked out by Mattes (1936) and Neuhaus (1936, 1938).   The capsules hatch only after ingestion by certain land snails in which two generations of sporocysts occur.   The cercariae exit through the pulmonary sac into the mantle cavity of the snail host where they form an adhesive cyst. These cysts stick together to form balls containing hundreds of metacercariae that fall on vegetation and debris. After ingestion by the definitive host, the metacercariae hatch in the intestine and bore through the intestinal wall

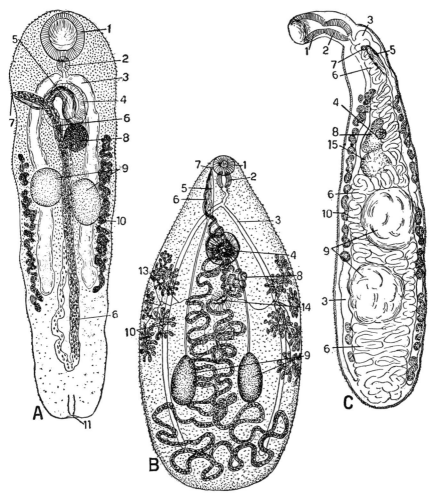

Fig. 113.—Plagiorchidae. *A. Renifer*, oral cavity of snakes, original. *B. Prostho-gonimus macrorchis*, oviduct of hen, original. *C. Haematoloechus* (= *Pneumoneces*), frog lung, original. 1, oral sucker; 2, pharynx; 3, intestine; 4, acetabulum; 5, cirrus sac; 6, uterus; 7, gonopore; 8, ovary; 9, testes; 10, yolk glands; 11, nephridiopore; 12, sperm ducts; 13, yolk ducts; 14, ootype; 15, seminal receptacle.

into the branches of the portal system which carries them to the liver; here they finally pass from the portal vein into the bile passages. Similar cycles obtain for *Eurytrema* from the pancreas and bile passages of mammals (Denton, 1944) and *Brachylecithum* from the bile passages of passerine birds (Denton, 1945), except that a second intermediate host seems to be required. *Dicrocoelium* and *Eurytrema* sometimes occur in man, probably as a result of eating infected mammalian livers.

k. Family Opisthorchidae.—These are distomes of small to considerable size with flat semitransparent bodies, small suckers, Y-shaped excre-·tory bladder, posterior testes, and gonopore just in front of the acetabulum. They inhabit the bile passages of fish-eating reptiles, birds, and particularly mammals. The best known members of the family are *Opisthorchis felineus* and *O.* (= *Clonorchis*) *sinensis* (Fig. 114*A*) from the bile passages of cats, dogs, man, and other mammals. These two species have very similar life cycles. The small oval capsules (Fig. 114*C*) contain a complete miracidium that hatches only after ingestion by operculate snails of the genus *Bythinia* and related genera. In the snail the mother sporocyst gives rise to one generation of rediae without birth pore or projections, and these produce cercariae of the pleurolophocercous type (Fig. 103*A*). The cercariae penetrate fresh-water fish of the family Cyprinidae in which they encyst under the skin or in the musculature. The definitive host becomes infected by eating raw or insufficiently cooked fish. The metacercarial cyst after partial dissolution by the gastric juice is finally dissolved in the small intestine, and the metacercariae make their way up the bile duct. *Opisthorchis sinensis* is an important human parasite in local areas of Japan, China, and French Indo-China and may cause serious symptoms through blocking the bile passages. A comprehensive study of this parasite was made by Faust and Khaw in 1927, but it appears they confused the larval forms of three different species of flukes. The cercariae (Fig. 103*A*) and metacercariae (Fig. 114*B*) have been well studied and figured by Yamaguti (1935) and Komiya and Tajimi (1940). *O. felineus*, whose cycle was fully elucidated by Vogel (1934), and other species of *Opisthorchis* occur in man in areas where raw fish are eaten. Some other genera of the family, found in fish-eating mammals, are *Amphimerus. Metorchis*, and *Pseudamphistomum* (Schuurmans-Stekhoven, 1931).

l. Family Heterophyidae.—This family comprises small distomes or monostomes, mostly not more than 2 to 3 mm. long, of oval or pyriform shape with motile contractile anterior region contrasting with the heavier rear containing the whole of the reproductive system. The cuticle, at least anteriorly, is spiny or scaly. Other characters are a long esophagus, the lack of a cirrus, and the presence in the genital antrum of a muscular protrusible cushion or tubercle termed the gonotyl (Fig. 114*D*). The acetabulum is often reduced and incorporated into the genital antrum and is altogether lacking in some genera (*Stictodora, Monorchitrema*). The heterophyids inhabit the intestine of birds and mammals, usually those of aquatic, fish-eating habits, and also occur commonly in the

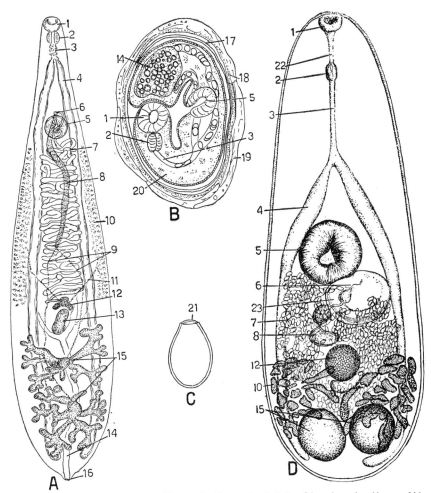

FIG. 114.—Opisthorchidae, Heterophyidae. *A. Opisthorchis sinensis (from slide, courtesy A. E. Galigher)*, human liver fluke. *B.* Metacercaria of *O. sinensis (after Komiya and Tajimi*, 1940). *C.* Capsule of *O. sinensis (after Looss*, 1907a). *D. Heterophyes heterophyes (after Witenberg*, 1929), intestinal fluke of mammals. 1, oral sucker; 2, pharynx; 3, esophagus; 4, intestine; 5, acetabulum; 6, gonopore; 7, uterus; 8, seminal vesicle; 9, sperm ducts; 10, yolk glands; 11, yolk ducts; 12, ovary; 13, seminal receptacle; 14, bladder; 15, testes; 16, nephridiopore; 17, inner cyst wall; 18, outer cyst wall; 19, host part of cyst wall; 20, metacercaria coiled in cyst; 21, operculum; 22, buccal tube; 23, gonotyl.

intestine of man, dogs, and cats. The family has been reviewed by Ransom (1920) and Witenberg (1929). The life cycle is similar to that of the Opisthorchidae; the capsules are eaten by operculate snails in which one generation of sporocyst and one or two generations of rediae develop, and the pleurolophocercous cercariae, distinguished from opisthorchid cercariae mostly by a spiny armature on the anterior end, encyst in fish. The genus *Heterophyes* is characterized by the occurrence of a

well-developed acetabulum adjacent to the gonotyl (Fig. 114*D*). Several
species of this genus, of which the most common is *Heterophyes heterophyes*
(Fig. 114*D*), occur in the intestine of dogs, cats, and man in Egypt,
Palestine, and other Asiatic regions. A similar distribution and host
relationship obtains for *Metagonimus yokogawai*. Man appears to be a
normal host for these two heterophyid flukes, and they evoke negligible
symptoms. But it appears that other heterophyids, not normal to man,
may develop in man from eating infected fish and may cause serious
damage (Africa and Garcia, 1935, Vazquez-Colet and Africa, 1940). The
genus *Euryhelmis*, parasite of the intestine of minks, differs from other
heterophyids in that the metacercariae occur in frogs and tadpoles
(Ameel, 1938).

m. *Family Microphallidae.*—These flukes resemble closely in general
appearance the Heterophyidae, of which family they were formerly considered a subfamily. Differences are the short intestinal crura and the
presence of a penis papilla (Fig. 115). *Microphallus* occurs in the intestine of fishes; other genera as *Spelotrema* (Fig. 115, Rankin, 1940a; Cable
and Hunninen, 1940), *Levinseniella* (Rankin, 1939a; Young, 1938), and
Maritrema inhabit the intestine of shore birds such as gulls, terns, and
sandpipers. The capsules containing the miracidium are eaten by littoral
snails in which sporocysts and rediae occur. The cercariae are simple
monostome stylet cercariae that encyst in crustaceans such as amphipods,
isopods, barnacles, sand crabs, and true crabs.

n. *Family Troglotrematidae.*—These are distomes or monostomes of
some size, mostly of shortened oval form, with scaly cuticle, that live
two or more in cysts in various organs of bird and carnivorous mammals.
The family includes the important genus *Paragonimus* (Fig. 118*A*), the
lung fluke of mammals, up to 20 mm. long, living in cysts about the size
of a hazelnut in the lungs of various mammals and of man. In North
America, where *Paragonimus* has been extensively studied by Ameel
(1934), the parasite occurs mainly in the Great Lakes region where the
mink is the usual definitive host, although muskrats, cats, rats, and pigs
may also be infected. In the Orient (China, Korea, Japan, Formosa,
Indo-Malay region, etc.), human infection, up to 50 per cent in some
localities, is common, from the habit of eating raw crayfish and crabs.
The capsules (Fig. 118*B*) are emitted with the sputum, and the miracidium develops in about 3 weeks if moist conditions obtain. After a
brief free existence, the miracidia penetrate operculate snails in which the
mother sporocyst and two generations of rediae occur. The cercaria
(Fig. 102*D*) is microcercous and does not swim, crawling about in a leech-
like manner and encysting in crayfish or fresh-water crabs, but not in
fresh-water shrimps. After ingestion by the final host, the young flukes
bore through the intestinal walls into the abdominal cavity and thence

through the diaphragm into the lungs. The number of species of *Paragonimus* has been repeatedly discussed (Ward and Hirsch, 1915; Ameel, 1934; H. T. Chen, 1940) but no agreement has been reached and it is probable that only one species, *P. westermani*, exists in man.

Some other genera of the family are *Collyriclum* and *Troglotrema*. Species of the former are rounded flukes without an acetabulum that occur in cysts in the skin of passerine birds (Cole, 1911; Jegen, 1917);

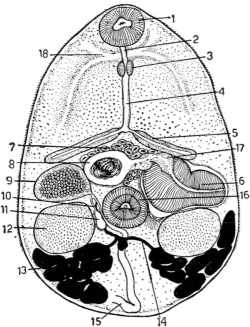

Fig. 115.—Microphallidae. *Spelotrema (after Rankin,* 1940a). 1, oral sucker; 2, buccal tube; 3, pharynx; 4, esophagus; 5, intestine (note short crura); 6, penis papilla; 7, prostatic gland cells; 8, seminal vesicle; 9, ovary; 10, Laurer's canal; 11, seminal receptacle; 12, testes; 13, yolk glands; 14, yolk ducts; 15, beginning of uterus (rest not shown); 16, acetabulum; 17, prostatic vesicle; 18, brain.

the life cycle is unknown. There is a tendency to sexual dimorphism, for of the two worms in each cyst, one is larger and with better development of the female system and the other smaller with male tendency (Jeger, 1917). *Troglotrema salmincola* with metacercariae in the salmon is the causative agent of a highly fatal disease of dogs termed salmon poisoning resulting from eating infected salmon (Simms, Donham, and Shaw, 1931; Witenberg, 1932). Presumably the fatal effect comes from some disease carried by the flukes, rather than from the flukes themselves.

o. Family Fasciolidae.—This family includes the well-known liver flukes of ruminants, large leaf-like flukes with acetabulum relatively close to the oral sucker, gonopore just in front of the acetabulum, and a branched condition of crura, gonads, yolk glands, and excretory tubules (Fig. 116*A*). These flukes inhabit the liver and bile passages of sheep, goats, cattle, deer, and other ruminants, often to the great detriment of the host's health. The principal liver flukes are *Fasciola hepatica*, to 30 mm., in ruminants in Europe and America; the even longer *Fasciola gigantica*, to 75 mm., in Africa and Asia; and *Fascioloides magna*, to 100 mm., in North America (Stiles, 1894, 1895; Swales, 1935). *Fasciola hepatica* is frequently used as a textbook and class type, but the branched condition of its organs is somewhat atypical for the Digenea (Fig. 116*A*). Stephenson (1947) has made valuable contributions to the anatomy and physiology of this species; he finds that an ootype is lacking and Laurer's canal enters the oviduct, not the common vitelline duct (Fig. 116*C*). The life cycle of the liver fluke as worked out by A. P. Thomas in 1883 has been confirmed for other Fasciolidae. The capsules at laying contain an uncleaved egg (Fig. 117*A*) that requires some weeks to develop to a miracidium (Fig. 117*B*). This penetrates pulmonate snails of the genus *Lymnaea* and related genera, in which the sporocyst produces two generations of rediae (Fig. 102*C*) and finally somewhat long-tailed cercariae (Fig. 117*C*). These encyst on grasses or aquatic plants (Fig. 117*D*), and after ingestion by the definitive host the cysts hatch into young flukes that bore through the intestinal wall into the peritoneal cavity and thence into the liver (Schumacher, 1938; Krull and Jackson, 1943). The chief fasciolid fluke of man is *Fasciolopsis buski*, to 70 mm., inhabiting the intestine, and common in China, India, Sumatra, and similar localities in pigs as well as in man. In China the cercariae encyst on the nutlike fruits of a certain aquatic plant (Nakagawa, 1922; Barlow, 1925) that are eaten raw by the natives.

p. Family Cyclocoelidae.—This is one of the principal families of monostome flukes, although a small acetabulum is sometimes present. They are large to moderate flukes, to 15 mm., with muscular bodies, reduced or nearly absent oral sucker, and intestinal crura confluent posteriorly (Fig. 87*C*). The adults inhabit the coelom, trachea, lungs, air sacs, and nasal and other head cavities of water birds. The family has been extensively treated by Kossak (1911), Harrah (1922), Witenberg (1926), and Joyeaux and Baer (1927). The last named authors reduce the number of genera to three: *Cyclocoelum*, *Typhlocoelum*, and *Ophthalmophagus*. The life cycle of *Typhlocoelum cymbium* from grebes and ducks has been worked out by Szidat (1932b) and Stunkard (1934). The miracidium contains a fully formed redia which escapes after penetration of snails. Within the snail the redia produces directly cercariae of the cercariaeum type that encyst in the same snail, and the eating of such infected snails by water birds completes the cycle. The cercariae are distome so that the monostome condition is here secondarily derived

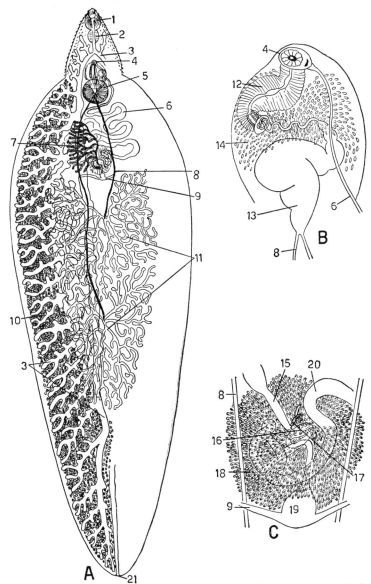

Fig. 116.—Fasciolidae. *A. Fasciola hepatica (from slide, courtesy A. E. Galigher).* B. Details of male system of *F. hepatica.* C. Details of the female system. 1, oral sucker; 2, pharynx; 3, intestine; 4, gonopore; 5, acetabulum; 6, uterus; 7, ovary; 8, sperm duct; 9, yolk duct; 10, yolk glands; 11, testes; 12, cirrus sac; 13, seminal vesicle; 14, prostatic glands; 15, oviduct; 16, beginning of uterus; 17, Laurer's canal; 18, Mehlis's glands; 19, yolk reservoir; 20, continuation of uterus; 21, nephridiopore.

from a distome ancestor.   The monostomes are clearly a heterogeneous assemblage of no taxonomic status.

q. Family Clinostomatidae.—These are distomes of some size with small oral sucker, large anteriorly placed acetabulum, scantily coiled uterus, and surface network of excretory vessels.   The adults inhabit the oral cavity, throat, and esophagus of fish-eating birds, especially wading birds.   The best known genus is *Clinostomum*, the metacercariae of

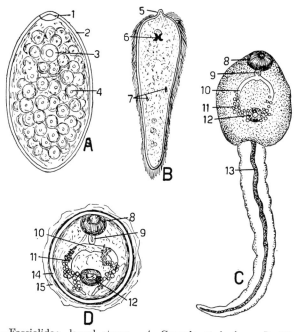

Fig. 117.—Fasciolidae, larval stages. *A*. Capsule at laying. *B*. Miracidium. *C*. Cercaria. *D*. Encysted metacercaria.   (All stages of the human intestinal fluke, *Fasciolopsis buski, after Nakagawa*, 1922.)   1, operculum; 2, capsule; 3, egg; 4, yolk cells; 5, apical papilla; 6, eyes; 7, flame bulbs; 8 oral sucker; 9, pharynx; 10, intestine; 11, spherules in nephridia; 12, acetabulum; 13, nephridium in tail; 14, inner cyst wall; 15, outer cyst wall.

which, known as "yellow grubs," occur encysted in the muscles throughout the body in fish and in the coelomic lining and lymph sacs of frogs (Fig. 118*C*).   These cysts, large enough to be obvious, have long been noticed by zoologists, students dissecting frogs, fishermen, and breeders of tropical fishes (Nigrelli, 1936); but the life cycle of *Clinostomum* was first elucidated in 1934 by the Hunters.   The capsules drop into the water from the mouths of the bird hosts as they are fishing, and the miracidium (the Hunters, 1935), provided with two pairs of flame bulbs, hatches at once or later and penetrates snails of the genus *Helisoma*.   The sporocyst produces two generations of rediae, and the cercariae are 'ophocercous with forked tails.   The metacercarial cyst is composed entirely of the host's connective tissue (Hunter and Dalton, 1939). It has been shown (Cort, 1913; the Hunters, 1933) that the species encysted in fish with herons as the definitive host is distinct from that encysted in frogs with the final stage in the bittern. The one is *C. complanatum* (= *marginatum*) and the other is *C. attenuatum*. The adult anatomy was extensively described by Osborn (1912).

r. Family Notocotylidae.—These are monostomes notable for the presence on the ventral surface of rows of eversible pouches into which glands open (Fig. 118*D*). The adults inhabit the intestine of aquatic birds and mammals. The majority of species belong to the notocotyline group, including the genera *Notocotylus, Quinqueserialis, Catatropis,* and *Paramonostomum*, of which the North American forms have been reviewed by Harwood (1939). The life cycle of the notocotylines comprises sporocysts and two generations of rediae in snails, cercariae of ordinary tailed type, and metacercarial encystment on vegetation and inanimate objects (Yamaguti, 1938; Herber, 1942).

s. Family Echinostomatidae.—This is a large and important distome family of mostly slender elongated form, with spiny or scaly cuticle, large acetabulum shortly behind the small oral sucker, and a collar of spines on the anterior end (Fig. 119*A*). The collar of spines is already present in cercarial and metacercarial stages (Fig. 106*A*) and serves to distinguish the family readily from all other digenetic families. The echinostomes inhabit chiefly the intestine of birds, less often the intestine of mammals. The echinostomes of birds were extensively treated by Dietz (1910), and many species were also described from Japanese birds by Yamaguti (1933–1941). Some representative genera are *Echinostoma, Echinoparyphium, Patagifer, Petasiger, Euparyphium, Himasthla, Echinochasmus,* and *Parorchis.* The life cycle of an echinostome was first worked out by Johnson (1920), and a number of cycles have since been described (Beaver, 1937; Johnston and Angel, 1941; Macy, 1942, for *Echinostoma;* McCoy, 1928; Rasin, 1933; Tubangui and Pasco, 1933, for *Echinoparphyium;* Stunkard and Cable, 1932, for *Parorchis;* Stunkard, 1938b, for *Himasthla;* and Beaver, 1939, for *Petasiger*). The capsules at laying contain an uncleaved egg that develops into a miracidium in 2 to 5 weeks. The miracidium penetrates snails in which the sporocyst and two redial generations are passed; but in *Parorchis* (Fig. 100*B*) the miracidium already contains a fully developed redia. The cercariae swim free and encyst chiefly in other snails, also in clams, planarians, tadpoles, and fish. Echinostomes appear not to be very particular as to either intermediate or definitive hosts, and several species may infect man in common with other hosts as a result of eating raw snails and clams, in China, Java, Philippines, etc. (Vogel, 1933; Tubangui and Pasco, 1933; Sandground and Bonne, 1940).

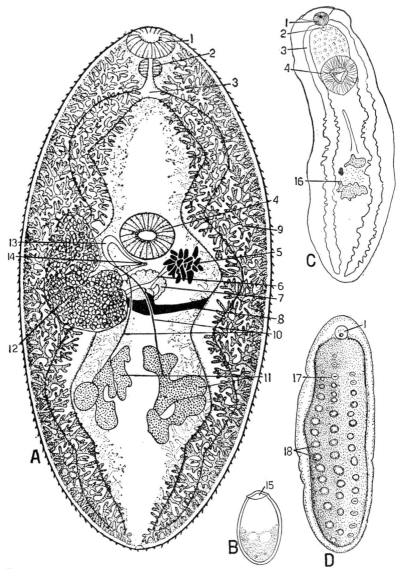

FIG. 118.—Troglotrematidae, Clinostomatidae, Notocotylidae. *A. Paragonimus (after Chen, 1940). B.* Capsule of *Paragonimus (after Ward and Hirsch,* 1915). *C.* Metacercaria of *Clinostomum* removed from cyst *(after Cort,* 1913). *D. Notocotylus (after Harwood,* 1939).   1, oral sucker; 2, pharynx; 3, intestine; 4, acetabulum; 5, ovary; 6, oviduct; 7, ootype; 8, yolk ducts; 9, yolk glands; 10, sperm ducts; 11, testes; 12, uterus, 13, cirrus sac; 14, gonopore; 15, operculum; 16, primordia of reproductive system; 17, gland pockets; 18, pockets everted.

t. Family Strigeidae (= *Holostomidae*).—This is also a large and important distome family, parasitic as adults in the intestine of birds and mammals, less often reptiles. The strigeids are flukes of small to considerable size (to 20 mm.) and of peculiar body shape, being typically (but not always) divided by a constriction into a flattened, concave, spoon-like, or cup-like *forebody*, and a cylindroid *hindbody* (Figs. 80*B*, 119*C*). The relative proportions of these two regions vary greatly in different members; thus in *Nematostrigea, Ophiosoma* (Fig. 119*B*), and *Cardiocephalus*, the forebody is short and the hindbody very slender and elongated, whereas in *Cyathocotyle* (Fig. 120*A*) the very small hindbody is not distinctly set off. The forebody bears the small oral sucker and acetabulum and behind the latter an accessory adhesive organ termed the *holdfast* (Figs. 80*B*, 119*C*) that is without counterpart in other Digenea. This holdfast is a rounded, mushroom-like, or elongated protuberance that is often cleft or lobed or may be subdivided (Fig. 120*B*) into dorsal and ventral parts; it contains gland cells whose secretion has been conjectured to exercise a corroding effect on host tissue (La Rue, 1932). The strigeids maintain a very strong attachment on the host intestine by grasping villi between the holdfast and the side walls of the forebody. In some strigeids, especially the genus *Diplostomum* (Fig. 119*C*) and related genera, the anterior end bears to either side of the oral sucker, a small accessory sucker or sucker-like depression or ear-like projection; these are called *pseudosuckers, sucking cups*, etc. Another peculiar feature of strigeids is the so-called *reserve bladder*, a peripheral system of excretory channels (Fig. 121*C*) that opens into the regular protonephridial system. The reproductive system is usually lodged chiefly in the hindbody and opens at the posterior end, often into a large antrum (Fig. 119*B*). Strigeids with cup-like forebody and holdfast divided into dorsal and ventral parts are often called *holostomes;* those with leaf-like or spoon-like forebody and undivided holdfast are termed *hemistomes* and *diplostomes;* the latter may have pseudosuckers.

Extensive articles on the family have been published by Brandes (1890), Krause (1915), Szidat (1929), and Dubois (1937), and numerous studies on North American strigeids have been made at the University of Michigan by La Rue, Hughes, and Van Haitsma (1926–1931). Dubois in 1938 issued a valuable monograph in which what is here considered a family was raised to the rank of supersuperfamily Strigeida and what are usually considered subfamilies were raised to family rank. Some of the principal genera of the Strigeidae (in the broad sense) are *Alaria* (= *Hemistomum*, Fig. 80*B*) and *Pharyngostomum* in dogs, cats, foxes, and other carnivorous mammals; *Braunina* in whales and dolphins; *Neodiplostomum* and *Strigea* (= *Holostomum*) in birds of prey; *Apatemon*, *Cyathocotyle* (Fig. 120*A*), *Cotylurus* (Fig. 120*B*), and *Diplostomum* (Fig.

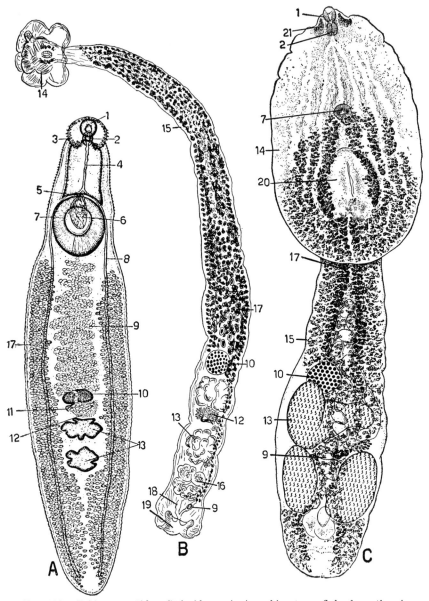

Fig. 119.—Echinostomatidae, Strigeidae. *A.* An echinostome fluke from the pigeon intestine (*after Yamaguti*, 1935). *B.* Strigeid *Ophiosoma*, intestine of the bittern. *C. Diplostomum*, gull intestine. (*B, C, after Dubois*, 1938.) 1, oral sucker; 2, pharynx; 3, collar of spines; 4, esophagus; 5, gonopore; 6, cirrus sac; 7, acetabulum; 8, intestine; 9, uterus; 10, ovary; 11, ootype; 12, Mehlis's glands; 13, testes; 14, forebody; 15, hindbody; 16, seminal vesicle; 17, yolk glands; 18, sperm duct; 19, genital antrum; 20, holdfast; 21, pseudosuckers.

119*C*) in ducks, other anseriform birds, and various other birds; *Postho-diplostomum, Apharyngostrigea, Cardiocephalus,* and *Tylodelphys* in gulls, terns, grebes, wading birds, etc.; and *Uvulifer* in kingfishers.

The strigeid life cycle was first worked out by Lutz (1920), and cycles have since been described for *Cotylurus* by Szidat (1924), Mathias (1925), Hughes (1929), Van Haitsma (1931), Olivier and Cort (1942); for *Diplostomum* by Hughes and Berkhout (1928) and Van Haitsma (1931); for *Apharyngostrigea* by Scheuring and Everbusch (1926) and Azim (1935); for *Uvulifer* by the Hunters (1934); for *Posthodiplostomum* by Hunter (1936) and Ferguson (1936); for *Pharyngostomum* by Wallace (1939); for *Cyathocotyle* by Yamaguti (1940b); and for *Apatemon* by Stunkard, Willey, and Rabinowitz (1941).[1] The miracidia, distinguished by 21 epidermal cells in tiers of 6, 6, 6, 3, and two pairs of flame bulbs, develop after the capsules are laid and penetrate snails, mostly lymnaeids, in which there occur two generations of sporocysts. The development of the sporocysts has been described by Cort and Olivier (1941) who find that daughter sporocysts and cercariae develop from multinucleate germ masses broken off from preexisting germ masses. The cercariae, of which many studies have been published (e.g., Cort and Brooks, 1928), are of characteristic appearance, being pharyngate furcocercous cercariae (Fig. 120*C*). These penetrate various aquatic animals, chiefly snails and fish, but also leeches, tadpoles, frogs, salamanders, and snakes, where they metamorphose into metacercariae, with or without encystment.

The metacercariae of the Strigeidae are of peculiar appearance, and several different types have been recognized. These metacercariae may be naked or encysted in a gelatinous cyst of parasite origin, or the outer part of the cyst may be furnished by the host. In the last case, the host part of the cyst is often permeated with black pigment, whence the name "black grub" often applied to these cysts by fishermen. All strigeid metacercariae have oral sucker, acetabulum, holdfast, and reserve bladder system. In the *tetracotyle* type (Faust, 1918e; Hughes, 1928, 1929a, 1929b, Fig. 121*A*), the body is pyriform, with or without a small hind-body, with well-developed pseudosuckers, and with the reserve bladder in the form of large spaces (Fig. 122*A*). The *diplostomulum* type (Hughes and Berkhout, 1928; Hughes and Holl, 1928; Hughes, 1929b, 1929e) has a foliaceous concave forebody, a small conical hindbody, pseudosuckers, and a reserve bladder of anastomosing tubules, and lacks a cyst wall of parasitic origin (Fig. 120*E*). *Tylodelphys* metacercariae are a variety of

[1] The generic names here employed follow Dubois (1938); in the articles cited various other names are used. The synonymy of the strigeids is in fact frightfully confused and the same species appears in the literature under many different names with also different names for its cercarial and metacercarial stages. The synonymy is thoroughly considered in Dubois's monograph.

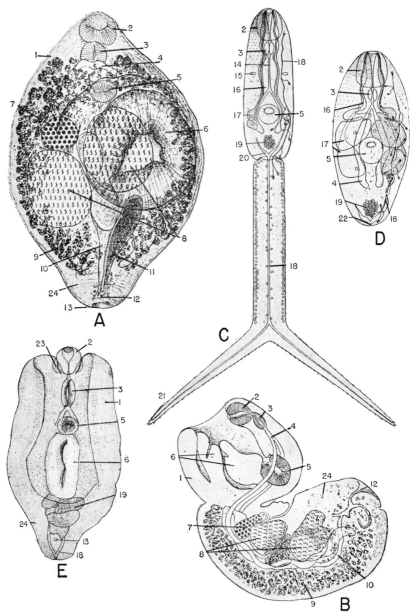

FIG. 120.—Strigeidae (continued). *A. Cyathocotyle*, duck intestine. *B.* Longitudinal section of *Cotylurus flabelliformis*, intestine of ducks and other water birds. (*A, B, after Dubois*, 1938.) *C–E*, larval stages of *Alaria* (*after Bosma*, 1934). *C.* Cercaria, note forked tail, pharynx. *D.* Mesocercaria. *E.* Metacercaria of the diplostomulum type. 1, forebody; 2, oral sucker; 3, pharynx; 4, intestine; 5, acetabulum; 6, holdfast; 7, ovary; 8, testes; 9, yolk glands; 10, uterus; 11, cirrus sac; 12, genital antrum; 13, gonopore; 14, esophagus; 15, eyes; 16, ducts of penetration glands; 17, penetration glands; 18, protonephridium; 19, primordium of reproductive system; 20, definitive bladder; 21, larval nephridiopores; 22, definitive nephridiopore; 23, pseudosuckers; 24, hindbody.

diplostomulae that are more elongate with less defined pseudosuckers and hindbody. Diplostomulum and tylodelphys metacercariae often occur in the eyes of fishes, in the lens or the vitreous humor, and if sufficient numbers invade the lens, blindness ensues (La Rue, 1926). A third kind of strigeid metacercaria, termed *neascus*, was defined by Hughes (1927); this has a cup-shaped forebody, well-developed hindbody, and a reserve bladder similar to that of the diplostomulum larva but lacks pseudo-suckers (Fig. 121*B*, *C*). Neascus larvae occur in *Crassiophila*, *Uvulifer*, and related forms. The *codonocephalus* metacercaria, described by Kopczynski (1907), is similar to the neascus type.

The genus *Alaria* (Fig. 80*B*) differs from all other Digenea in requiring three intermediate hosts (Bosma, 1934; Odlaug, 1940). The cercariae (Fig. 120*C*) penetrate tadpoles and frogs but do not develop very far, remaining in a stage termed *mesocercaria* (Fig. 120*D*). These, after their host has been devoured by a small mammal such as mice, rats, and raccoons, develop into metacercariae of the diplostomulum type (Fig. 120*E*) that become adult in the intestine of the definitive host, dog, cat, mink, weasel, etc. It has been shown that the mesocercaria stage cannot be omitted for the third intermediate host cannot be infected directly by the cercariae.

u. Family Brachylaimidae (= Harmostomidae).—This is a family of small to moderate distomes with well-developed suckers, posterior gono-pore, and seminal vesicle free from the cirrus sac (Fig. 122*B*). The harmostomes occur chiefly in the intestine of birds and mammals, less often of amphibians and reptiles. The systematics of the family have been treated by Witenberg (1925) and Sinitsin (1931b). The principal genera are *Brachylaima* (= *Harmostomum*) and *Leucochloridium* (Fig. 122*B*). The remarkable sporocysts of the latter have long attracted the attention of zoologists and are regularly mentioned in zoology texts. The life cycle of the European *Leucochloridium* was worked out by Zeller (1874) and Heckert (1889), and various observations on American species confirm the account (Magath, 1920; McIntosh, 1932; Woodhead, 1935; Bennett, 1942). The capsules dropped by birds on vegetation are eaten by terrestrial and amphibious snails, chiefly *Succinea*, in which the mira-cidia hatch, then penetrating the snail tissues. Two generations of sporocysts ensue; the daughter sporocysts are highly branched, and branches eventually push into the snail's head and tentacles where they enlarge to swollen sacs that are brightly pigmented with green, brown, or orange bands (Fig. 122*C*) and that undergo pulsations of about 70 per minute at summer temperatures (Wesenberg-Lund, 1931). These brightly colored pulsating sacs are noticeable at a distance of several feet and presumably simulate insect larvae, thus attracting the attention of birds. The swollen snail skin ruptures at the slightest touch, releasing

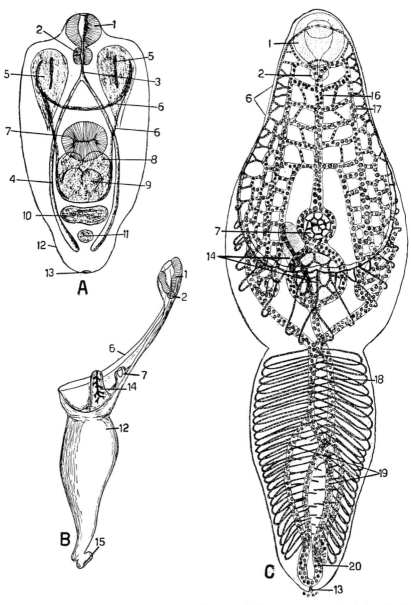

Fig. 121.—Strigeidae (continued). *A.* Tetracotyle from a garter snake (*after Hughes,* 1929). *B.* Neascus larva from the bass (*after Hughes,* 1927). *C.* Same, to show vessels of the reserve bladder (*after Hughes,* 1927). 1, oral sucker; 2, pharynx; 3, esophagus; 4, intestinal crura; 5, pseudosucker; 6, edge of cup-like forebody; 7, acetabulum; 8, anterior lobes of holdfast; 9, posterior lobes of holdfast; 10, glands of holdfast; 11, primordium of reproductive system; 12, hindbody; 13, nephridiopore; 14, holdfast; 15, gonopore; 16, median dorsal vessel; 17, main lateral vessel; 18, median dorsal vessel of hindbody; 19, median ventral vessel of hindbody; 20, excretory bladder.

the colored sacs, which continue to pulsate. The sacs are filled with encysted cercariaea (Fig. 122*D*) that are infective to various passerine birds. Although Zeller saw captive birds peck the sacs from the tentacles of infected snails and swallow them, it seems more probable that in nature the sacs are released through chance contacts and are then picked up by birds (Wesenberg-Lund, Woodhead). Juvenile birds are more susceptible to infection than adults, and probably the sacs are often fed to nestlings by parent birds.

  v. Family Sanguinicolidae.—This and the next two families are blood flukes, i.e., they live in the blood of vertebrates inside the blood vessels and hence are of slender shape with weak or degenerate suckers. The present family comprises the single genus *Sanguinicola* (Fig. 123*A*) which inhabits the blood of fishes of the families Cyprinidae, Siluridae, and Percidae. Three species are known from Europe (Odhner, 1911b 1924; Scheuring, 1922; Ejsmont, 1925) and one from North America (Van Cleave and Mueller, 1932). The animal is slender, pointed at both ends, about 1 mm. long, without suckers. The protrusible anterior tip contains the mouth armed with three hooks in some species and leading into a long tube provided or not with a poorly developed pharynx and terminating in a small lobed intestinal sac. The numerous testes occupy a central position, and from them the sperm duct runs to a posterior, dorsally located male pore before which it widens to a simple cirrus. From the bilobed ovary a long oviduct proceeds posteriorly and shortly after receiving the common vitelline duct widens to form an ootype. This is followed by a short vagina opening dorsally by a female pore. A uterus is lacking, and the curious triangular capsules (Fig. 123*F*) are formed and laid singly into the blood stream which carries them to the gills. Meantime the miracidium has already developed, hatches in the host blood vessels, and escapes through the gills (Scheuring, 1922; Ejsmont, 1925). It enters a snail in which sporocysts and cercariae develop. The cercariae are furcocercous without a pharynx and lophocercous (Fig. 103*C*) and were long known under the name of *Cercaria cristata*. Whether there is a second intermediate host is not known; it is supposed that the cercariae penetrate the definitive host directly.

  w. Family Spirorchidae.—These are flukes of small to moderate size, either distome or monostome, found in the blood of turtles, chiefly in the heart and larger arteries. They have been extensively discussed by Stunkard (1923) and Byrd (1939). The mouth provided with an oral sucker leads by a long esophagus, for a pharynx is lacking, into the intestine that may have the usual two crura, or may be wholly or partly single. The principal genera are *Spirorchis* (Fig. 123*B*) with a central longitudinal row of several (to 10) testes; *Hapalorhynchus* with two testes; and *Vasotrema* with a single elongate spirally coiled testis. The capsules are

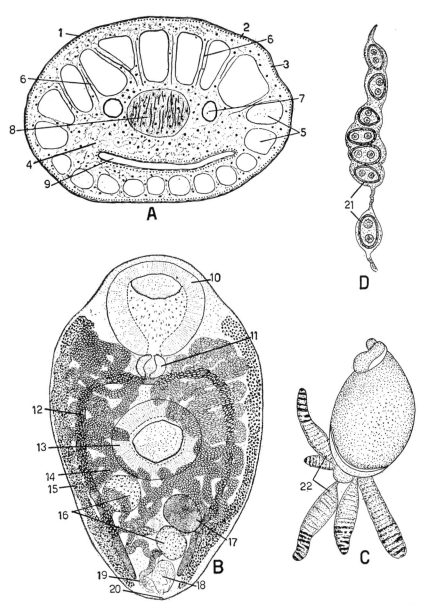

Fig. 122.—Strigeidae, Leucochloridium. *A.* Cross section of tetracotyle shown in Fig. 121*A*, at level of acetabulum, to show spaces of reserve bladder (*after Hughes*, 1929). *B.* *Leucochloridium* (*after McIntosh*, 1932). *C.* Snail *Succinea* with protruding sporocyst sacs of *Leucochloridium*. *D.* Small portion of branching sporocyst of *Leucochloridium* to show encysted cercariaea. (*C, D, after Wesenberg-Lund*, 1931.) 1, cuticle; 2, circular muscle layer; 3, longitudinal muscle layer; 4, mesenchyme; 5, spaces of reserve bladder; 6, mesenchymal muscle fibers; 7, section of intestinal crura; 8, section of acetabulum; 9, cavity of forebody; 10, oral sucker; 11, pharynx; 12, intestine; 13, acetabulum; 14, uterus; 15, yolk glands; 16, testes; 17, ovary; 18, cirrus sac; 19, metraterm; 20, gonopore; 21, cercariaea; 22, sporocyst sacs.

discharged into the tissues of the host whence they find their way into the digestive tract and so to the exterior. The life cycle has been worked out by Wall (1941a, 1941b). The miracidium, provided with two pairs of flame bulbs, hatches some days after the capsules are laid and penetrates lymnaeid snails where two generations of sporocysts occur. The cercaria as in the case of other blood flukes is apharyngeal and furcocercous; it penetrates directly into the definitive host.

x. Family Schistosomatidae (= Bilharziidae).—These are blood flukes that inhabit the hepatic portal system and pelvic veins of birds and mammals, including man. They are notable among flukes for their sexual dimorphism. The sexes are completely separate, and neither sex retains any part of the reproductive system of the other sex. The schistosomes are of long slender form; most species are below 10 to 15 mm. in length, but *Gigantobilharzia acotylea* from birds is 140 to 165 mm. long. The male is generally broader than the female; in some schistosomes the male is shorter, in others the female is shorter, and in some both sexes are about of the same shape and length. The usual thing is for the female to be slender and thread-like (Fig. 123D). The ventral surface of the male is usually incurved for a length varying in different species to form the *gynecophoric canal* in which the female remains (Fig. 123D) more or less permanently. The body surface is often spiny or papillose, or spines may be confined to the inner surface of the suckers. Both suckers may be present close together as in *Schistosoma* (= *Bilharzia*), or the acetabulum or both suckers may be wanting. The acetabulum is often better developed in the male than in the female (Fig. 123D). A pharynx is wanting, and a long esophagus leads to the intestinal crura which are fused posteriorly to form a single stem for a distance variable in different species. There are several to many testes in the male (Fig. 124B) and a long tubular ovary, voluminous yolk glands, long oviduct, ootype, and straight uterus containing relatively few eggs, in the female (Fig. 124A).

The capsules, laid one or a few at a time, may or may not be provided with a projecting spine (Fig. 123E, 124F). In laying them, the female leaves the gynecophoric canal of the male and pushes herself into the smallest possible vessels where she deposits the capsules. These work their way into the intestine or in *Schistosoma haematobium* into the urinary bladder and so reach the exterior, containing by this time fully developed miracidia (Fig. 124C). These hatch in the presence of water into miracidia with two pairs of flame bulbs that penetrate suitable pulmonate snails in which two generations of sporocysts ensue (development of schistosome sporocysts studied by Cort and Olivier, 1943b). Very large numbers of cercariae are produced. The cercariae as in other blood flukes are of the apharyngeal furcocercous type, distinguished from the similar strigeid cercariae by the lack of a pharynx (Fig. 124D, E). They

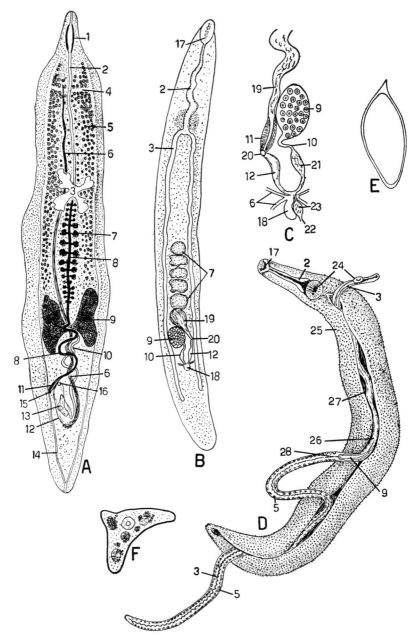

Fig. 123.—Blood flukes. *A. Sanguinicola* (*after Scheuring*, 1923). *B. Spirorchis* (*after Stunkard*, 1923). *C.* Reproductive system of *Spirorchis* (*after Wall*, 1941). *D. Schistosoma haematobium*, male and female in copulation (*after Looss*, 1900). *E.* Capsule of *S. haematobium;* note terminal spine (*after Looss*, 1900). *F.* Capsule of *Sanguinicola* (*after Ejsmont.* 1925). 1, pharynx; 2, esophagus; 3, intestine; 4, nervous system; 5, yolk

penetrate directly through the skin of the definitive host or through the mucous membranes of the mouth or throat if taken in with water. They do not survive in the stomach. They make their way into small vessels where they are carried to the heart and lungs and eventually to the portal system or bladder veins. An encysted metacercarial stage is lacking; the cercariae lose their tails on penetrating the host and during their passage to the portal system gradually transform to the adult condition.

The human blood fluke, *Schistosoma* (old name, *Bilharzia*[1]), is the most important trematode parasite of man and has therefore been the object of numerous investigations. There are three human species: *S. haematobium* (Fig. 123*D*), in Africa, particularly Egypt, and southwestern Asia; *S. japonicum* in China, Japan, Formosa, and the Philippines; and *S. mansoni* (Fig. 124*A*, *B*) in Egypt and other parts of central Africa from which it has been imported, probably in the days of slavery traffic, into the West Indies and northern South America. *S. haematobium* was extensively investigated by R. T. Leiper (1915–1918), *S. japonicum* was monographed by Faust and Meleney (1924), and *S. mansoni* in Puerto Rico was investigated by Faust and Hoffman (1933–1934). These species also occur in mammals other than man and laboratory mammals can be infected with them; additional species of *Schistosoma* parasitize large mammals, as *S. spindale* in cattle, sheep, and goats, and *S. bovis* in cattle, horses, sheep, and antelopes. The human species are distinguished by structural details and also by their capsules (Figs. 123*E*, 124*C*, *F*). Infection results from wading in or drinking water containing active cercariae.

The genera of the family have been reviewed by E. Price (1929) and McLeod (1940). Most of the genera are found in birds of aquatic habits, such as gulls, ducks, grebes, and blackbirds. Some with a gynecophoric canal are *Ornithobilharzia* (Odhner, 1912) and *Schistosomatium* (Tanabe, 1923; H. F. Price, 1931; Cort, Ameel, and Olivier, 1944) and some without a definite canal are *Gigantobilharzia* (Odhner, 1910; Brackett, 1942), *Bilharziella*, and *Pseudobilharziella* (Brackett, 1942; McLeod and Little, 1942). The life cycles of these forms so far as known are similar to that of *Schistosoma*. In the Great Lakes region of North America and around lakes in various parts of the world, bathers are annoyed by a severe itch shown by Cort in 1928 to be caused by the penetration into the skin of the cercariae of bird schistosomes. The itch

[1] *Bilharzia* has priority over *Schistosoma* but *Schistosoma* has been validated by a ruling of the International Commission on Zoological Nomenclature.

glands; 6, yolk duct; 7, testes; 8, sperm duct; 9, ovary; 10, oviduct; 11, cirrus sac; 12, ootype; 13, capsule in ootype; 14, protonephridia; 15, male gonopore; 16, female gonopore; 17, oral sucker; 18, yolk reservoir; 19, spermiducal vesicle; 20, common gonopore; 21, insemination chamber of oviduct; 22, Laurer's canal; 23, seminal receptacle; 24, acetabulum; 25, male; 26, female; 27, gynecophoric canal; 28, place of fusion of crura just behind ovary.

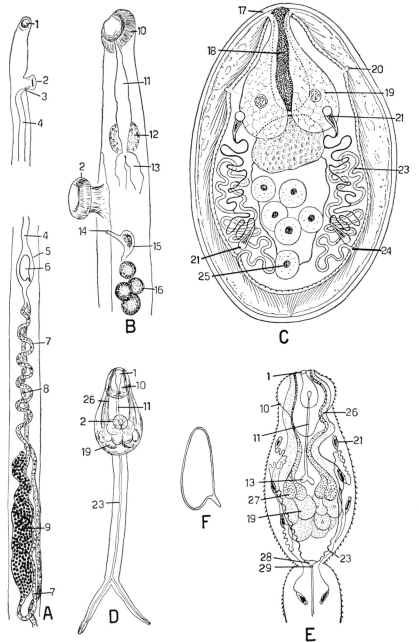

Fig. 124.—Schistosoma (continued). *A.* Female system of *Schistosoma mansoni. B.* Anterior part of male *S. mansoni*, to show male system. *C.* Miracidium of *S. japonicum* within the capsule (*after Cort,* 1919); note lack of spine on capsule. *D.* Cercaria of *S. mansoni.* (*A, B, D, from slides, courtesy Dr. H. W. Stunkard.*) *E.* Anterior part of cercaria of

is therefore now known as cercarial dermatitis and is, at least in part, of an allergic nature; it has been the subject of numerous studies (Cort, 1936; Talbot, 1936; McLeod, 1936, 1940; Brackett, 1941; McMullen and Brackett, 1941; McLeod and Little, 1942).

An interesting question concerns sex determination in the schistosomes. It was suspected by Cort in 1921 and demonstrated by Severinghaus (1928) and Niyamasena (1940) that all the flukes coming from one miracidium (of which there may be as many as 200,000) are of one sex. Sex is therefore determined at fertilization of the egg by a chromosomal mechanism. According to the work of Severinghaus on *S. japonicum*, using the mouse as experimental host, isolated male schistosomes develop normally but isolated females remain small and sexually undeveloped and complete their development only when given access to males.

y. Family Heronimidae.—This family comprises the single genus *Heronimus* distinguished from all other Digenea by the location of the nephridiopore (Fig. 125*B*) near the anterior end (on the dorsal surface). Another peculiarity is that the coils of the uterus traverse the body length four times. There is apparently only one species (Stunkard, 1919; Caballero, 1940), *Heronimus chelydrae*, to 15 mm. long, found in the lungs of turtles (Fig. 125).

17. Ecology of Developmental Stages.—The conditions suitable for the hatching of trematode capsules have been studied chiefly for fasciolid (Barlow, 1925; Mattes, 1926; Ross and McKay, 1929; Shaw and Simms, 1930; Krull, 1934c; Swales, 1935; Griffiths, 1939) and schistosome (Manson-Bahr and Fairley, 1920; Magath and Mathieson, 1945) flukes, forms developing in fresh water. Fresh capsules containing a mature miracidium hatch at once in a suitable medium, but those laid in the uncleaved state as in fasciolid flukes require several days or weeks up to 2 or 3 months before the miracidium is ready to hatch. Temperature is the chief factor controlling the rate of embryonic development, but great variability in hatching time may be shown by a lot of capsules kept under the same conditions. In general, fasciolid eggs do not develop at temperatures below 10°C. but remain viable at such temperatures for long periods (up to 2½ years) and can develop to infective miracidia when exposed to warm temperatures. Temperatures below freezing are fatal to later stages and to encapsulated miracidia but may not kill uncleaved eggs or early embryos if the exposure is short. Light and depth of water

S. mansoni (after Faust and Hoffman, 1934) to show structural details; note lack of pharynx. *F.* Capsule of *S. mansoni;* note lateral spine. 1, mouth; 2, acetabulum; 3, female gonopore; 4, uterus; 5, ootype, 6, capsule in ootype; 7, oviduct; 8, yolk duct; 9, ovary; 10, oral sucker; 11, esophagus; 12, brain; 13, intestinal crura; 14, male gonopore; 15, seminal vesicle; 16, testes; 17, capsule; 18, apical gland; 19, penetration glands; 20, lateral papillae; 21, flame bulb; 22, brain; 23, protonephridium; 24, nephridiopore; 25, propagatory cells; 26, ducts of penetration glands; 27, oxyphilic type of penetration gland; 28, definitive bladder; 29, definitive nephridiopore.

appear to be without effect upon development, but desiccation is fatal to all stages. Capsules remain viable in damp feces with a moisture content of at least 60 per cent, but less than 50 per cent is quickly fatal.

The hatching of mature miracidia is dependent on external factors. Cold and darkness inhibit hatching, which in fasciolid flukes usually occurs on bright warm mornings. Addition of fresh aerated water which must not be too acid or too alkaline favors hatching. A pH of about 7.0 to 7.5 is suitable. Lowering the salt content also favors hatching. Similar factors—aeration, change of water, lowering of salt content, moderate temperatures—also favor hatching of schistosome miracidia. In nature, the advent of rain would reproduce all these conditions and is probably the main natural stimulus to hatching. Schistosome capsules will not hatch under conditions prevailing in the human intestine—a temperature of 37°C. and a salt content of 0.9 per cent. The springing open of the operculum probably results from factors other than or in addition to the butting movements of the miracidium, such as swelling of the capsule contents through intake of water or dissolving action of miracidial secretions.

Miracidia resemble in appearance and behavior ciliate protozoans. They dart about in a restless aimless fashion or may spiral in a fairly steady path or may hang to the surface film or bottom and rotate. They show great flexibility and continual peristaltic changes of form. Their general behavior suggests that they are "seeking something with feverish haste" (Barlow, 1925). They may be positive to light and negative to gravity, reactions that bring about their escape from the bottom muck in which the capsules often lie. The miracidium does not feed. The question whether miracidia find the snail host by chemotactic attraction has been answered in the negative by most observers (Swales, 1935; Mattes, 1936; Griffiths, 1939). According to their statements, miracidia test with the anterior end and attempt to bore into almost any object, including various species of unsuitable snails and other animals such as planarians. They may keep on trying to enter an unsuitable host or an unsuitable part of the snail host as the shell until they die of exhaustion. They seem to find the right host by accident, and they succeed in penetrating this host simply because their boring mechanism is adapted to succeed only with that host. Barlow (1925), on the other hand, found that the miracidium of the human intestinal fluke is attracted to snail juice and does not try to penetrate a recently killed snail.

The penetration of the snail host by the miracidium has been repeatedly witnessed and is well described by Barlow (1925). When the miracidium has by chance made contact with a suitable soft spot on the snail, the apical papilla attaches and the miracidium executes boring movements accompanied by body contractions and expansions. Flesh-dissolving secretions from its glands undoubtedly aid the penetration process. The miracidium gradually squeezes through the minute opening made in the host (Fig. 126), shedding its epidermis in the process. It seems that successful penetration depends not only on the activities of the mira-

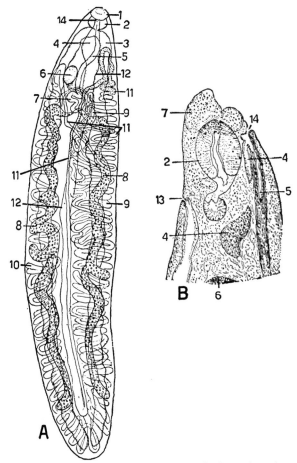

Fig. 125.—Heronimus. *A. Heronimus chelydrae*. *B.* Sagittal section of the anterior end of *Heronimus*, to show nephridiopore. (*Both after Stunkard*, 1919.) 1, oral sucker; 2, pharynx; 3, intestinal crura; 4, uterus; 5, cirrus sac; 6, ovary; 7, seminal vesicle; 8, testes; 9–12, the four successive parts of the uterus; 13, nephridiopore; 14, gonopore.

cidium but on unknown properties of the snail skin. It is generally noted that young and immature snails are more apt to be penetrated than old individuals. Although a given species of snail may serve as intermediate host for several different species of fluke (21 species in *Stagnicola*, see below), usually not more than two kinds of larval trematodes are found in any one individual snail. This indicates either that the presence of larval trematodes in a snail inhibits penetration by other species of miracidia or that different kinds of larval trematodes are antagonistic to each other.

Nothing seems to be known of the physiology of larval trematodes in the snail host. Sporocysts and rediae may be observed moving about in the snail. They absorb nutrition through the surface and the rediae also ingest bits of snail tissue.

The emergence of cercariae from the snail host is more or less dependent on external factors. In general, warm weather favors the emission of cercariae. Cort (1922) studied the emission of one species of cercaria from the snail *Planorbis trivolvis* during one summer month and found much fluctuation in the number emitted daily by any one snail, and of course much difference between different snails depending on the number of sporocysts with which they were infected. The maximum number of cercariae issuing from one snail in a 24-hour period was about 5000. Cercariae tended to emerge at a definite time of day, but this time differed for different individual snails. Seasonal peaks, mostly one in winter and one in summer, of cercarial emergence have been noticed by several workers (Miller and Northrup, 1926; Rankin, 1939c). In general, seasonal relations of cercariae are correlated with the habits of the definitive host. Thus in a given pond cercariae infective to constantly present fish showed no seasonal fluctuation but a species having its adult state in a summer resident bird passed the winter in snails and emerged only with the advent of warm weather (McCoy, 1929b).

The behavior of cercariae has been the object of several studies (Miller, 1925–1928; Miller and McCoy, 1928–1930; Miller and Mahaffy, 1930; Rankin, 1939c; Wheeler, 1939). Some cercariae swim continuously but many swim intermittently, moving upward by lashing the tail, then pausing and sinking, then jerking upward again. The active periods are generally much shorter than the rest periods. Sudden decrease of light as by casting a shadow often evokes a marked reaction—usually an accelerated rate of swimming or renewed swimming from a rest position. But in some cercariae sudden decrease of light intensity may result in stoppage and sinking and in others any change of light intensity evokes swimming. Agitation of the water also often also starts swimming activity. Many cercariae are positive to light and negative to gravity, thus seeking surface waters, but others show the reverse reaction, remaining near the bottom. Cotylocercous cercariae do not swim but stay on the bottom creeping about like a leech or attaching by the tail sucker and swinging the body about in the water. Fork-tailed cercariae (strigeids and schistosomes) swim tail forward by lashing the tails or opening and closing them scissor-fashion (Manson-Bahr and Fairley, 1920; Szidat, 1924; Miller and Mahaffy, 1930; Brackett, 1940). They generally swim upward and hang to the surface film by means of the spread tail forks, body down. The peculiar bucephalus cercariae swim to the surface tail foremost by alternately extending and contracting the long tails (Wunder, 1924; Bevelander, 1933; Folger and Alexander, 1938), at a rate of 55 to 70 contractions per minute at 20°C. Sudden increase of light or sudden shock evokes cessation of swimming and sinking with the tails contracted and curved inward. The reaction time of this response is shorter the greater the intensity increase or the strength of shock.

The behavior of cercariae is undoubtedly related to the nature and habits of the host on or in which they encyst. Thus the stimulating action of shadows or agitation is presumably related to the proximity of

Fig. 126.—Penetration of miracidium of *Fasciolopsis buski* through the epidermis of a snail (*after Barlow*, 1925). 1, snail epidermis; 2, shed epidermis of miracidium.

a possible host such as a fish. However, cercariae do not give evidence of any chemotactic attraction to hosts (Szidat, 1924; Ferguson, 1943). They are on the other hand excessively positive to contact, pausing by and testing almost any object. They apparently swim, float, and crawl about until chance contact with a suitable host occurs, whereupon they attach and penetrate. Ferguson found that numerous cercariae would attach to a fishtail dipped for only 1 second in a heavy suspension of them. Chemical properties of the host seem to play some role after contact is established. Thus Miller and McCoy (1930) noted that cercariae would come to rest on, penetrate, and start encystment on pieces of feathers smeared with fish mucus but showed no response to control feathers. The most interesting case of chemotactic attraction is that of the eye for diplostomulum larvae of strigeids (Ferguson, 1943). These cercariae after penetrating fish at any point migrate anteriorly chiefly by way of the blood vessels and enter the eye where they encyst in the lens. They will migrate to eyes from which the lenses have been removed but do not migrate anteriorly if the entire eyes are extirpated.

Although they give no chemotactic reaction to crushed fish tissues, including the parts of the eye, the conclusion appears inescapable that they reach the eyes by some chemotactic attraction. These cercariae appear incapable of developing into diplostomulae except in vertebrate lenses; they will develop normally in isolated lenses cultivated in sterile salt solution (Ferguson, 1943c).

The penetration of cercariae into host animals is accomplished partly by such aids as the stylet and spines but primarily, so it is believed, by the flesh-dissolving action of the secretion of the penetration glands. Evidence for this view has been brought forward by Davis (1936), who noted a dissolving action on tadpole skin and muscle of an aqueous extract of cercariae.

The metacercarial cyst wall undoubtedly affords some protection against desiccation and other adverse conditions, but its chief role appears to be protection from the gastric juice of the final host. Naked cercariae and metacercariae are destroyed and digested by gastric juice but the cyst wall is generally insoluble in this fluid. Usually the cyst wall dissolves in the upper part of the intestine, releasing the metacercariae which then migrate to their typical location.

Ferguson (1940) achieved the development of the metacercariae of the avian strigeid *Posthodiplostomum minimum* to the adult condition in a sterile medium composed of Tyrode's solution (balanced salts), chicken serum, and yeast extract, but the eggs and sperm of these flukes were abnormal.

18. Host-Parasite Relations; Immune Reactions.—Discussion of the symptoms and treatment of fluke infections of man and domestic animals lies outside the province of this book and will be found in works on parasitology. Suffice it to say that heavy infections with either larval or adult trematodes are usually highly damaging to the host, resulting in retardation of growth, loss of weight, emaciation, and a general unhealthy condition, often eventuating in death. Flukes that inhabit sites such as the bile ducts, blood vessels, and lungs are generally more deleterious than those that live in the digestive tract. Heavy infections of snails with larval trematodes often result in the partial or complete destruction of favored sites of infection as the gonads or digestive gland ("liver"). Snails may respond to heavy infections by considerable increases of size (Rothschild, 1936), and this has given rise to the erroneous impression that older individuals are more susceptible to infection than younger ones. Light infections with trematodes usually fail to produce any definite symptoms.

The presence of a trematode may evoke in the host body the same kind of reaction as does a foreign body or a wound, i.e., an inflammatory reaction consisting of the aggregation of leucocytes at the site, phagocytosis, and production of connective tissue. A study of the reactions of fish tissues to encysting metacercariae, especially strigeid and clinostomid forms, has been made by Hunter and associates (the Hunters, 1940, 1942; Hunter and Dalton, 1939; Hunter and Hamilton, 1941). The meta-cercarial cysts studied consisted wholly or in part of connective tissue of host origin, often with the addition of pigmented host cells.

Trematodes may also call forth in the host body an immune reaction, that is, the host produces one or more substances known as antibodies that are chemically antagonistic to the parasite or its products. These antibodies may stunt the growth of the parasite or kill it or prevent its attachment to the host tissues or they may precipitate or neutralize parasitic products. In general, trematodes inhabiting the digestive tract do not evoke immune reactions. Such reactions are called forth by the invasion of host tissues by the parasite and hence have been studied chiefly in liver flukes, schistosomes, and the like. For a general consideration of immune reactions to worm parasites the books of Taliaferro (1929) and of Culbertson (1941) may be consulted.

It was already noted that host specificity varies greatly among flukes, i.e., some will succeed in a wide range of hosts whereas others require a specific host. Even closely related flukes may exhibit great differences in host requirements. Thus *Schistosoma japonicum* is infective not only to man but to a great variety of other mammals, including the common laboratory mammals; *S. spindale* succeeds only in ungulates; and *S. haematobium* only in man. Usually, a given fluke is able to parasitize only one kind of host or a group of taxonomically related hosts. Feeding of or other exposure to infective stages of trematodes results in infection only with a particular host or hosts. The mechanism of such protection against flukes by hosts other than the normal ones is obscure and probably differs in different cases. It is usually supposed that the fluke requires a very specific environmental complex for its development, and this is found only in the proper host (discussion in Sandground, 1929). In some cases, however, failure to establish in an unsuitable host results from the development or presence of antibodies in the host that are fatal to the developing trematodes. Thus monkeys can be infected with the cercariae of human schistosomes, but their serum contains antibodies that soon kill the invaders (Fairley and Jasudasan, 1930). Another factor preventing infection of unsuitable hosts is the inability, noted above, of miracidia and cercariae to penetrate any but the appropriate host. This failure seems to rest on a very close adaptation between the penetrating mechanism of the larval trematode and the surface character-istics of the appropriate host.

Penetration of even the proper host by miracidia or development therein is inhibited to some extent if other species of flukes are already present.   Thus many snail species serve as host to several kinds of larval trematodes but all of these are never found simultaneously in the same individual snail.   The fresh-water snail *Stagnicola emarginata* harbors 21 kinds of larval trematodes (seven strigeids, six plagiorchids, two schisto-somes, one echinostome, one monostome, and four others) but usually only two kinds, sometimes three or four, occur simultaneously in any one snail (Cort, McMullen, and Brackett, 1937).   In other similar investiga-tions not more than two kinds of larval flukes have been found in snail individuals that are normal hosts to several species.   Very striking is the fact that the cercariae of the strigeid *Cotylurus flabelliformis* that encyst in the same snail species harboring the sporocysts are unable to penetrate snails that already contain sporocysts although metacercarial develop-ment is favored by the presence of sporocysts of other fluke species (Win-field, 1932; Cort, Brackett, *et al.*, 1945).

Animals may develop immunity to flukes to which they serve as normal hosts, as a result of repeated attacks.   The best case of this kind is that of the monogenetic fluke *Benedenia* (= *Epibdella*) *melleni* which infects the skin of a large number of species of marine fish (Jahn and Kuhn, 1932; Nigrelli and Breder, 1934).   Some fish species remain permanently susceptible while others develop partial or complete resist-ance to superinfection.   The resistance may be local in that the parasites do not or are unable to attach to skin areas previously parasitized.   The surface mucus of resistant fish was found to be fatal to the parasite (Nigrelli, 1935).   The presence of the amphistome *Zygocotyle lunata* in the caeca of the normal duck or rat host prevents superinfection by more specimens of the same species (Willey, 1941).   Man does not show any resistance to reinfection with schistosomes, but other mammals such as dogs, horses, and monkeys develop partial or complete resistance after being cured of an initial infection.   A careful study of the development of resistance to *Schistosoma spindale* by goats, which are normal hosts to the parasite, was made by Fairley and Jasudasan (1930).   In this case the formation of antibodies fatal to the cercariae was demonstrated, but it is not clear that the other cases mentioned of acquired resistance depend on such an immune reaction.

Age resistance to trematodes by their normal hosts also occurs, i.e., young animals are more susceptible to infection than older ones and as the animal ages, flukes already present may be ejected (*Parorchis*, Cable, 1937; heterophyids, Willey and Stunkard, 1942).   Human schistosomes usually infect young persons, and adults over thirty generally do not become infected on exposure; a similar age resistance to schistosomes occurs in other mammals (Ozawa, 1930).   Age resistance does not appear to depend on immune reactions but rather on changes in the host tissues that render them an unsuitable environment for the parasite.

Immune reactions against flukes are similar to those evoked in the animal body against foreign proteins, bacteria, and the like, and are detectable by the same means. Thus skin, precipitin, and complement-fixation reactions occur in liver fluke and schistosome infections and can be used to diagnose the presence of the parasite. As antigens[1] extracts of liver flukes or of snail digestive glands infected with larval schistosomes are used, although it has been shown that the antigen need not be particularly specific and extracts of other flukes than those tested for can be employed. When such antigens are applied to the skin a typical reaction (reddening, itching, formation of wheals) results in case of infected individuals (liver fluke, Sievers and Oyarzun, 1932; schistosomes, the Taliaferros, 1931; Fairley and Jasudasan, 1930; Culbertson and Rose, 1942). A precipitin test (see page 4) may also be obtained with the serum of persons infected with schistosomes (Taliaferro, Hoffman, and Cook, 1928). A complement-fixation test[2] is elicitable in schistosome infections (Fairley, 1933; Andrews, 1935).

19. Physiology of Adult Flukes.—Because of the difficulty of keeping flukes alive outside the host body, only fragmentary knowledge of their physiology is available. Van Cleave and Williams (1945) maintained *Aspidogaster conchicola* alive in tissue culture media and especially mussel blood for long periods at cold temperatures but this species is hardly a typical endoparasite. Digenetic flukes remain alive for a few hours in balanced salt solutions of proper osmotic pressure, pH, and temperature, much longer in such solutions plus sugars (Stephenson, 1947) or in the blood or tissue fluids of their hosts. Because of its large size, *Fasciola hepatica* is usually employed in experimental work.

Although some absorption of nutrients may take place through the body surface, flukes generally ingest food by the mouth; the food consists of blood, tissues cells, tissue exudates, or food particles from the host intestine (Hsu and Li, 1940). The liver fluke subsists mainly on bile duct epithelium according to Müller (1923) and Hsu (1939); mainly on blood according to Stephenson (1947). Such flukes as the schistosomes and the lung flukes of frogs feed almost entirely on blood. Digestion is probably chiefly extracellular; some flukes appear to exude enzymes into the host tissues, causing these to degenerate and dissolve into a nutritive

[1] Antigen: a substance or organism that when introduced into the animal body evokes the formation of antibodies against it.

[2] Complement fixation: vertebrate blood contains a substance or complex of substances termed complement that is a necessary constituent of certain reactions between antigen and antibody. Therefore the disappearance, or fixation as it called, of the complement from the fluids being tested is a proof that antibody was present. The fact that the complement has disappeared has of course to be determined by additional tests. Complement fixation is considered the most delicate of the various tests for antibodies.

fluid that is then ingested by the fluke.   This method of feeding is apparently characteristic of strigeids (Szidat, 1929) which grasp the host's intestinal villi between their holdfast and body wall, causing congestion and then rupture of the blood vessels of the villi.   The exuding blood is then ingested by the fluke, and later the villi dissolve, furnishing a nutritive pabulum for the parasite.

Food is stored chiefly in the form of glycogen.   In a number of flukes studied, the glycogen was found localized in the mesenchyme, musculature, including the suckers, and eggs or ovaries (Ortner-Schönbach, 1913; Wilmoth and Goldfisher, 1945; Axmann, 1947).   The last author reported glycogen present in miracidia and cercariae but not in the stages inhabiting snails.   Fine fat droplets may also be present in flukes (Vogel and Brand, 1933), mostly in the walls and lumen of the excretory system (Brand, 1928).   The liver fluke contains a variety of lipoid substances, including saturated and unsaturated fats, cholesterin, lecithin and other phosphatids, and soaps, and is able to make fats from carbohydrate (Brand, 1928).   According to the analysis of Flury and Leeb (1926), the liver fluke consists of 2.4 per cent fats, 3.7 per cent glycogen, 11 per cent protein, and 82 to 90 per cent water.   Glycogen constitutes 20 per cent of the dry weight.

The respiratory metabolism of the liver fluke is of the anoxybiotic type (Weinland and Brand, 1926; Harnisch, 1932).   Although the liver fluke will consume oxygen when this is available to an amount dependent on the oxygen tension of the medium, this oxygen does not appear to be utilized in metabolic processes, for the carbon dioxide emitted remains constant regardless of the amount of oxygen consumed.   It has been shown (Brand, 1938) that the oxygen content of the intestine and bile is extremely low and that therefore intestinal helminths in general are highly resistant to lack of oxygen and obtain their energy by anoxybiotic processes, especially if they are of some size.   In anoxybiotic respiration, glycogen is utilized and carbon dioxide and fatty acids are given off into the medium (Weinland and Brand, 1926).

Very little of a definite nature is known of the excretory function in flukes.   The bladder and main nephridial stems often contain conspicuous granules and spherules presumably of an excretory nature, especially in larval stages (Figs. 106*A*, 114*B*, 121*C*), but the chemical nature of these has not been definitely ascertained, except that some are fat droplets (Vogel and Brand, 1933).   Presumably the fatty acids mentioned above are the normal excretory products of flukes.   Reisinger (1923) observed that as long as the encapsulated miracidia of *Schistosoma haematobium* are kept in urine the flame bulbs remain inactive; but, if the urine is diluted with water, the flames begin to beat immediately, ceasing on return to undiluted urine.   This observation indicates a water-regulatory function of the flame bulbs. Various observers (references in Westblad, 1924) have obtained staining of the bladder, main tubules, and sometimes the capillaries of the nephridial system, but never the flame bulbs, with various vital dyes, such as alizarin and neutral red. Although such experiments frequently fail, it nevertheless seems probable that the tubular part of the system functions to secrete waste products.

Data on the longevity of flukes have been assembled by Sandground (1936). The liver fluke may persist in cattle, sheep, and goats 5 years or more. Schistosomes and the oriental liver fluke, *Opisthorchis sinensis*, may live 20 to 30 years in the human host. Lung flukes of the genus *Paragonimus* also live for a number of years. Probably most flukes survive in the adult state in their hosts from several months to a year or two.

VI. CLASS CESTODA

1. Definition and Introductory Remarks.—The Cestoda are entoparasitic Platyhelminthes devoid of epidermis, mouth, or digestive tract, with attachment organs limited to the anterior end, and usually with elongated jointed, though sometimes simple fluke-like, bodies.

The cestodes are commonly known as tapeworms from the long tapelike bodies characteristic of most members of the class. This body is typically divided up by transverse constrictions into joints or segments known as *proglottids* (Fig. 127*B*). A few tapeworms, however, have simple undivided bodies of moderate length and resemble flukes in general appearance (Fig. 127*A*). All such unsegmented tapeworms were formerly placed in a subclass Monozoa contrasted with the Merozoa or Polyzoa in which the body is divided into proglottids. It is now evident, however, that some of these unsegmented forms are closely related to and belong with the typical segmented tapeworms, and that the class consequently cannot be subdivided on the basis of the presence or absence of proglottids. Certain of the unsegmented forms differ from other tapeworms in adult and larval characters and are therefore separated into a subclass Cestodaria, including chiefly the genera *Amphilina* and *Gyrocotyle*, with a 10-hooked larva; and all other tapeworms, including all the segmented forms and a few undivided ones, constitute the subclass Eucestoda, in which the larva has six hooks. The terms *monozoic* and *polyzoic* are, however, convenient for descriptive purposes and may be retained. The original name of the class was Cestoidea (proposed by Rudolphi, 1809), and this form of the name is still preferred by some authorities. The name refers to the ribbon-like shape (Latin, *cestus*, a girdle).

The classification of the Eucestoda has been subject to the usual disputes and disagreements. Four chief orders are universally recognized:

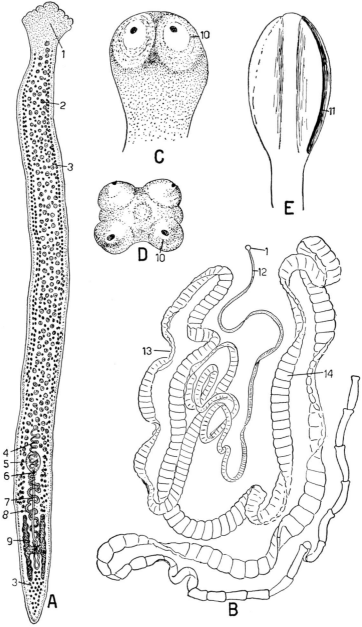

Fig. 127.—Types of cestodes and scolices. *A.* A monozoic tapeworm, of the family Caryophyllaeidae, with simple unarmed scolex and one set of sex organs (*after Yamaguti*, 1934). *B.* A polyzoic tapeworm, *Taenia saginata*, original. *C, D.* Lateral and front views of the scolex of *Taenia saginata*, showing the four acetabula (*after Stiles*, 1898). *E.* Scolex of a pseudophyllid, *Diphyllobothrium*, with bothria, original. 1, scolex; 2, testes; 3, yolk glands; 4, sperm duct; 5, cirrus sac; 6, gonopore; 7, vagina; 8, uterus; 9, ovary; 10, acetabula; 11, bothria; 12, neck; 13, strobila; 14, proglottid.

Tetraphyllidea, Trypanorhyncha, Pseudophyllidea, and Taenioidea. The erection of additional orders depends on whether the author in question thinks that certain forms should be separated off into distinct orders or not. The present work follows chiefly the classification of Southwell (1930) with the addition of two new orders that have been recognized since this publication. A thorough review of the taxonomic history of the Cestoda appears in Southwell's work. The names of the orders preferred in this book are the older ones. The following general account applies only to the Eucestoda; the Cestodaria are considered separately.

The cestodes are in the adult state parasites of vertebrates, nearly always of the intestine. They usually have complicated life cycles involving one or two intermediate hosts, which may be invertebrate or vertebrate.

2. External Characters.—The flat band-like body, opaque white or yellowish in color, ranges from 1 mm. to 10 or 12 m. (40 feet) in length and may be undivided (Fig. 127*A*) or consists of 4 (*Echinococcus*, Fig. 172*A*) to 4000 proglottids. The body typically comprises the small knob-like or clavate head or *scolex* bearing the organs of attachment, followed by a relatively short undivided region, the *neck*, in which the proglottids proliferate, succeeded by the long chain of proglottids, termed the *strobila*, that gradually increases in dimensions so that the rear end of the tapeworm has the broadest or longest proglottids (Fig. 127*B*). Neck and strobila are markedly flattened, but as the scolex is radially or biradially symmetrical (Fig. 129*B*, *F*) definition of surfaces is difficult. In many tapeworms the uterine pore defines the ventral surface, but often no external characters are present suitable for differentiating the surfaces and in such cases internal features may be employed. The testes are usually nearer one surface, then defined as dorsal, and the surface in proximity to the female system is considered ventral. In the absence of all criteria the term *surficial* is convenient to indicate the flat surfaces of the strobila.

The head or scolex of tapeworms is a very small enlargement at the anterior end of the body. Whether the scolex actually is the morphologically anterior end was much debated in the past, and some zoologists (e.g., Kofoid and Watson, 1907; Watson, 1911) have maintained that it is the posterior end. But it is now recognized that the larval hooks mark the posterior end of the tapeworm larva and that the scolex develops from the end opposite the hooks. Hence the scolex is really the anterior end of cestodes. As a digestive system is entirely lacking in cestodes, even in larval stages, the scolex has a solid muscular, mesenchymatous construction; it contains nephridial canals and the central part of the nervous system and bears the organs of attachment in the form of sucking depressions and hooks, sometimes also glandular areas. The sucking

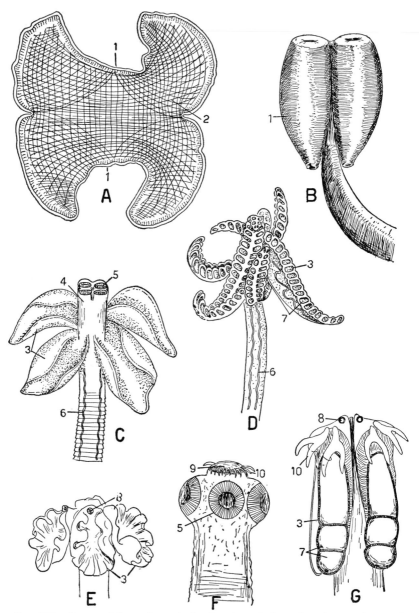

Fig. 128.—Organs of the scolex. *A.* Section through the scolex of a pseudophyllid to show the bothria and the musculature (*after Benham, 1901*). *B.* Scolex of *Bothridium pythonis*, from the python, showing bothria fused to tubes (*after Southwell, 1930*). *C.* Scolex of *Myzophyllobothrium* with four bothridia and a myzorhynchus with four suckers (*after Shipley and Hornell, 1906*). *D.* Scolex of *Echeneibothrium* with areolae (*after Linton, 1887*). *E.* Scolex of *Phyllobothrium*, with ruffled bothridia, each with an accessory sucker, from a skate, from life. *F.* Scolex of *Taenia solium* with armed rostellum and four acetabula (*after Southwell, 1930*). *G.* Scolex of *Acanthobothrium*, with areolae, hooks, and

depressions are of three sorts: *bothria, bothridia,* and true suckers or *acetabula.* Each type is more or less characteristic of a particular order of cestodes.

Bothria, typical of the Pseudophyllidea, consist typically as seen in *Diphyllobothrium* (= *Dibothriocephalus*) of a pair of elongated shallow sucking grooves (Fig. 127*E*). The distinguishing features of bothria are their shallow shape, weak muscularity, and absence of an inner bounding muscular layer (Fig. 128*A*). The margins may project or may be ruffled or may fuse to form a tubular cavity open at both ends (*Bothridium,* Fig. 128*B*); or the grooves may be obliterated by fusion from behind forward leaving apical cups (Fig. 156*C, H*).

Bothridia or phyllidia are characteristic of the order Tetraphyllidea where they occur four in number symmetrically placed around the anterior part of the elongated scolex (Fig. 128). Bothridia are broad leaf-like structures with thin and very flexible and mobile margins. They may be sessile or set off on short or long flexible stalks (Fig. 147*D*). The margins may be greatly ruffled as in some species of *Phyllobothrium* (Fig. 128*E*). Frequently each bothridium is divided by one or two ridges into two or three secondary depressions termed *areolae* or *loculi* as in *Acanthobothrium* (Fig. 128*G*) and *Trilocularia* (Fig. 129*C*); or by many ridges to form many (up to 50) small areolae as in *Echeneibothrium* (Fig. 128*D*). The upper end of a bothridium may form a small round sucker (Fig. 128*E*), or one or more such suckers may occur on the scolex just above each bothridium (Fig. 128*G*). Such *accessory* suckers are probably isolated areolae. Bothridia are much more muscular than bothria, being practically identical in muscular structure (Fig. 129*F*) with true suckers from which they differ chiefly in their projecting leaf-like form.

Acetabula or true suckers, characteristic of the Taenioidea, Lecanicephaloidea, and Proteocephaloidea, are hemispherical depressions, four in number, sunk into the sides of the scolex around whose circumference they are symmetrically placed (Fig. 129*B*). They are identical in structure with the suckers of the digenetic trematodes, being characterized by strong radial fibers and an inner muscular layer bounding them from the mesenchyme (Fig. 129*B*). Although usually unarmed they may bear hooks or spines marginally or in the concavity.

The apex of the scolex may be provided with additional attachment organs, such as a single protrusible sucker, or a glandular area (Fig. 149*F*), or a protrusible muscular mass, the *myzorhynchus,* that may itself bear additional suckers (Fig. 128*C*). The apex of the taenioid scolex frequently forms a highly mobile cone, the *rostellum,* usually armed with

accessory suckers (*after Southwell,* 1925). 1, bothrium; 2, muscle fibers; 3, bothridia; 4, myzorhynchus; 5, suckers; 6, excretory canals; 7, areolae; 8, accessory sucker; 9, rostellum; 10, hooks.

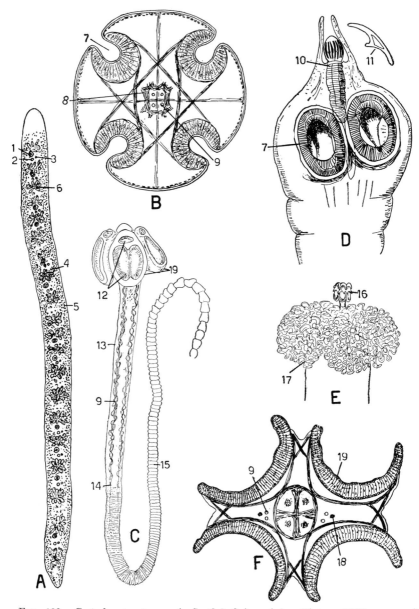

Fig. 129.—Cestode structure. *A. Spathebothrium* (*after Linton*, 1922), monozoic
cestode without scolex and with many sets of reproductive organs. *B.* Section through
the scolex of a taenioid tapeworm (*Nematobothrium*) showing muscular structure (*after
Fuhrmann*, 1895). *C.* A tetraphyllid tapeworm, entire, *Trilocularia*, with three areolae to
each bothridium, from the spiny dogfish, from life, Cape Cod. *D.* Scolex of taenioid tapeworm, *Choanotaenia*, with withdrawable armed rostellum (*after Fuhrmann*, 1932). *E.*
Thysanocephalum with metascolex, from life, Cape Cod. *F.* Section through the scolex of a
tetraphyllid showing muscle bands and muscular structure of the bothridia (*after Zschokke*,

hooks, and in many genera withdrawable into a sac-like cavity in the scolex (Fig. 129*D*).

The scolex in addition to the sucking apparatus may be armed with hooks. In tetraphyllids these occur at the upper ends of the bothridia (Fig. 128*G*). The rostellum of taenioids is usually encircled with one or more circles of hooks or spines (Fig. 128*F*), that are of taxonomic value. The entire scolex may be covered with minute spinules. The tetrarhynchid tapeworms are characterized by the fact that they are able to protrude from the summit of the scolex four eversible proboscides covered with spines; the details of this apparatus are discussed later.

The genus *Spathebothrium* (Fig. 129*A*) is devoid of a scolex or any organs of attachment. In certain taenioid genera (*Fimbriaria, Idiogenes*) the scolex is cast off or reduced in the mature worm and the neck and beginning of the strobila are altered to a crest-like shape and act as a *pseudoscolex* (Fig. 130*A*). In many trypanorhynchids the posterior end of the scolex projects as a collar-like fold, the *velum*, over the beginning of the neck, and various other folds may occur on the rear part of the scolex. In some tapeworms, especially the trypanorhynchids and *Echinobothrium*, the posterior part of the scolex is drawn out into a long neck-like region called the *head stalk* that in *Echinobothrium* is covered with spines (Fig. 152*A*). The head stalk is necessary in the trypanorhynchids to house the proboscides and related parts.

The term neck is properly applied to the unsegmented region behind the scolex in which proliferation of new proglottids occurs. It is typically a slender region of variable length well delimited from the broader scolex as in taenioids but is absent in many pseudophyllids and some tetraphyllids; in such cases the proglottids begin immediately behind the scolex. In a few tetraphyllids and pseudophyllids the neck bears a conspicuous ruff termed *metascolex* (*Thysanocephalum*, Fig. 129*E*).

The strobila or chain of proglottids follows after the neck or directly after the scolex. The proglottids arise by the formation of transverse constrictions, and typically the latest constriction appears anterior to the preceding one so that the youngest and smallest proglottid is nearest the scolex, the largest and oldest one at the posterior end. The young proglottids are always broader than long; the older ones may be broader than long as in *Moniezia* (Fig. 133*A*) or approximately squarish or longer than broad as in *Dipylidium* (Fig. 167*C, D*). The posterior end of each proglottid may enclose the anterior end of the succeeding one by a projecting region termed the *velum* that may be lobed or toothed (Fig. 165*A*).

1888). 1, male gonopore; 2, female gonopore; 3, uterine pore; 4, testes; 5, yolk glands; 6, ovary; 7, acetabula; 8, brain; 9, excretory vessels; 10, rostellum; 11, enlarged hook of same; 12, areolae; 13, head stalk; 14, neck; 15, strobila: 16. scolex: 17, metascolex; 18, nerve cords; 19, bothridia.

Proglottids with a velum are called *craspedote*, those without one, *acras-pedote*. As they increase in size, the proglottids differentiate and the reproductive system begins to develop in them, reaching maturity as one proceeds posteriorly in the strobila. Each proglottid contains at least one complete set of reproductive organs of both sexes and not infrequently two sets, bilaterally arranged (Fig. 133*A*). As new proglottids are continually forming in the neck region, the tapeworm increases greatly in length with age; but this process is eventually compensated in most cestodes by the dropping off of ripe proglottids full of capsules or embryos from the posterior end. Proglottids may, however, be shed while quite young and then move about in the host intestine, even developing an anterior spiny armature as an adhesive organ (some tetraphyllids). Tapeworms that shed their ripe proglottids are termed *apolytic;* those that retain them throughout life, as most pseudophyllids, are referred to as *anapolytic*. Anapolysis is usually associated with the absence of a proliferating neck and with a diffuse method of growth in which the segmentation is often obscured. Thus growth may occur by the subdivision of primary proglottids into secondary ones, or a number of successive reproductive sets may exist internally without corresponding external constrictions, or two to four external constrictions may cover a single set of reproductive organs. Often in these cases the successive genital complexes appear first and later constrictions form between them, beginning at the margin and often remaining incomplete.

Whether the tapeworms are segmented animals or not is a question usually settled in zoological textbooks by a categorical denial of the existence of "true" segmentation in this class of animals, but what is meant by "true" segmentation is not defined. It is to be noted that the segmentation of tapeworms differs from that of annelids and arthropods in that the zone of proliferation is situated behind the head and new segments arise from behind forward so that the most anterior proglottid is the youngest one. In annelids and arthropods, on the other hand, the zone of proliferation is posterior, just in front of the anal segment, and new segments arise there from before backward so that the youngest segment is the most posterior one, excepting the terminal segment. In order to make the mode of formation of cestode proglottids conform with that of annelid and arthropod segments it would be necessary to assume that the scolex is the posterior end of tapeworms. As already noted, this assumption has been made by some zoologists, but the facts of development prove that the scolex is the true anterior end. It therefore has to be admitted that the manner of formation of cestode segments differs from that of the segments of all other segmented animals, but merely as regards the direction in which the segments form. Unless such direction of segment formation is to be made a fundamental part of the definition

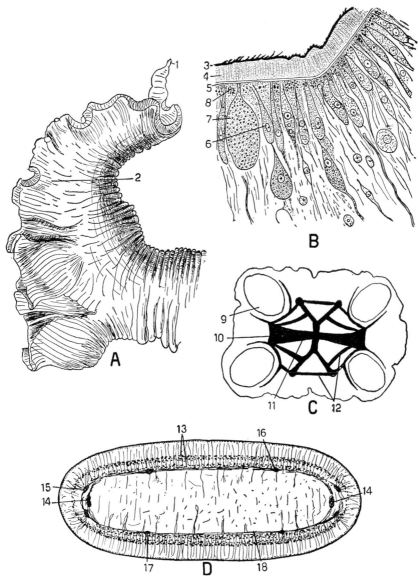

FIG. 130.—Cestode structure, nervous system. *A*. Anterior end of *Fimbriaria*, showing pseudoscolex (*after Wolffhügel*, 1900). *B*. Section through a taenioid (*Mesocestoides*), showing subcuticular cells and structure of the cuticle (*after Hamann*, 1885). *C*. Section through a taenioid scolex to show the central nervous system (*after Cohn*, 1898). *D*. Section through a proglottid of a taenioid (*Anoplocephala*) showing muscle arrangement and nerve cords (*after Becker*, 1922). 1, true scolex; 2, pseudoscolex; 3, comidial layer of cuticle; 4, homogeneous layer; 5, basement membrane; 6, subcuticular cells; 7, gland cell; 8, subcuticular muscle layer; 9, suckers; 10, main ganglia; 11, transverse commissure; 12, ring connections; 13, mesenchymal longitudinal muscle strata; 14, lateral nerve cords; 15, accessory lateral cords; 16, dorsal cords; 17, ventral cords; 18, ring connection.

of a segmented animal, then it follows that the tapeworms are segmented. The author takes the view that the direction of segment formation is unimportant and that therefore the cestodes must be listed among the segmented animals. They exhibit the fundamental characteristic of segmentation, namely, the serial repetition of structural parts at regular intervals along the anteroposterior axis. Presumably multiplication of the reproductive system was the initiating factor, and the formation of external constrictions followed.

3. Histological Structure.—The cestodes, like the trematodes, are devoid of an epidermis and clothed instead with a cuticle like that of trematodes. This cuticle rests directly on the mesenchyme and appears to be secreted by the long-necked subcuticular cells that occur in abundance beneath the subcuticular muscle layer (Fig. 130*B*). As to the nature of the cuticle and subcuticular cells, the same controversy exists as with regard to trematodes (see page 223), in the author's opinion the preponderance of the evidence supports the mesenchymal nature of both (discussion in Young, 1908; Pratt, 1909). The cuticle usually consists of three layers, an outer *comidial* layer, best developed in tetraphyllids and trypanorhynchids, which is fringe-like and may be extended into fine hairs, spines, or scales, a central and thickest homogeneous layer, and a basal membrane (Fig. 130*B*). The various hooks and spines of the scolex are cuticular specializations.

All space between internal parts is filled with a mesenchyme (parenchyma) about which the usual uncertainties exist. It generally appears as a meshwork inclosing fluid-filled spaces and believed to be a syncytium formed by the anastomosis of branched mesenchymal cells. In young proglottids and in the zone of proliferation, the mesenchyme is denser and richly nucleated and contains strands and groups of cells from which the reproductive system differentiates. The mesenchyme, especially in the Taenioidea, frequently contains calcareous bodies, round or oval masses composed of concentric layers of calcium carbonate; they are secreted by mesenchyme cells that eventually atrophy, setting the bodies free. Cestodes usually lack pigment.

The muscular system as in other flatworms consists of a peripheral stratum, the subcuticular muscle layer, and the mesenchymal musculature. The former, situated directly beneath the cuticle (Fig. 130*B*), and hence penetrated by the necks of the subcuticular cells, is composed of outer circular and inner longitudinal layers. The mesenchymal musculature is generally strongly developed and comprises dorsoventral, transverse, and longitudinal systems, seldom diagonal fibers. The longitudinal fibers predominate and usually occupy a broad peripheral zone leaving the central mesenchyme free. This peripheral zone consists of one to several layers of longitudinal fibers or bundles of fibers that may occupy

the peripheral mesenchyme up to the subcuticular muscle layer as in most
tetraphyllids and many taenioids; but in other tapeworms it fails to reach
this layer so that a zone of cortical mesenchyme free from longitudinal
fibers exists between the subcuticular and mesenchymal muscles (Fig.
130D). In many taenioids the longitudinal zone is stratified into two
layers with mesenchyme between. The transverse fibers when well
developed occur as dorsal and ventral sheets coursing from one side to
the other just inside the longitudinal zone and thus bounding the
central mesenchyme; but they may be more or less distributed throughout the proglottid or limited to one or both ends of the proglottid
or very feebly developed. They may intermingle with the longitudinal
fibers to produce a crisscross effect. The dorsoventral fibers are
much less developed than in Turbellaria; they may occur as fine
fibers throughout the proglottid but commonly are confined to the
margins. The mesenchymal muscles usually course throughout the
strobila as continuous systems that are not affected by the interproglottidal constrictions. They continue into the scolex where the muscle
arrangement is complicated and varies with the degree of development of
the organs of attachment. Usually longitudinal bundles are attached to
the sucking organs and transverse fibers course between adjacent and
opposite sucking organs making rhomboidal and crisscross patterns in
transverse sections of the scolex (Fig. 129B, F). Bothria scarcely differ
from the general body in muscular content (Fig. 128A), but bothridia and
acetabula have the same structure as the suckers of trematodes. They
consist of powerful radial fibers bounded on both inner and outer surfaces
by a crisscross muscle layer parallel to these surfaces (Fig. 129B, F).
The musculature atrophies in ripe proglottids, and these therefore readily
break loose from the strobila.

Gland cells are usually lacking except in the scolex where there may
be a well-developed apical glandular region, particularly in tetraphyllids
and tetrarhynchids, seldom in taenioids (Fig. 149F). These apical
glands are a constant feature of tapeworm larvae (Fig. 139C) and appear
to be homologous with the penetration glands of trematode cercariae;
they often disappear with maturity. Exceptional among tapeworms are
the *interproglottidal* glands of the taenioid genus *Moniezia*, a row of cell
clusters or of sacs provided with gland cells, situated along the posterior
margin of each proglottid (Fig. 133A, C).

4. Nervous System and Sense Organs.—The details of the nervous
system are known for relatively few tapeworms. The most important
articles are those of Cohn (1898) for several taenioids and pseudophyllids;
Tower (1900) for *Moniezia;* Becker (1921) for *Anoplocephala;* and Pintner
(1880, 1925), Johnstone (1912), and Rees (1941) for tetrarhynchids.
There is always present a pair of lateral longitudinal nerves situated near

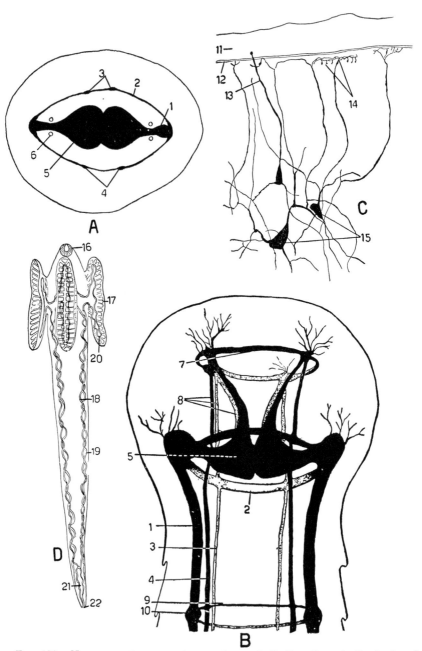

FIG. 131.—Nervous system, excretory system. A. Section through the brain of Moniezia at the level of the main nerve ring. B. Central nervous system of Moniezia seen from the side. (A, B, after Tower, 1900.) C. Subcuticular plexus of Ligula (after Zernecke, 1895), showing a tangoreceptor and two sensory nerve cells with free sensory endings. D. Larval tetraphyllid (Echeneibothrium), from the foot of a clam, showing basic type of

the excretory canals and running throughout the length of the strobila. Usually additional longitudinal trunks are present. Most typical are two accessory lateral nerves (absent, however, in *Moniezia*) accompanying each main lateral nerve, and in taenioids there are regularly also present a pair of dorsal and a pair of ventral longitudinal nerves, making a total of 10 longitudinal trunks in the strobila, readily seen in cross sections of proglottids (Fig. 130*D*). These 10 trunks also not infrequently occur in members of other orders of cestodes, but other numbers may also obtain. The longitudinal trunks are connected in each proglottid by at least one ring commissure (Fig. 130*D*) situated posteriorly near the transverse excretory canal; and two or three or even more ring commissures may occur in each proglottid. A ganglionic thickening may be present at the junction of ring commissure and each of the longitudinal trunks. The longitudinal trunks seems to be connected by a network in some cases. This nervous system of the strobila is situated in the central mesenchyme usually just inside the zone of mesenchymal muscles. The longitudinal nerves are really ganglionated cords. From them and from the ring commissures numerous branches are given off into the proglottids, especially into the genital complex.

The longitudinal nerves continue into the scolex where in the simpler cases the two main lateral nerves swell into a pair of ganglia connected in the transverse axis by a thick cross commissure. Usually, however, and typically in the taenioids, the outer ends of these ganglia are also united by a ring or polygonal commissure that receives the other longitudinal nerves by way of ganglionic enlargements (Fig. 131*A, B*). Other cross commissures between the main transverse commissure and the ring may be present (Fig. 130*C*). From this brain complex nerves pass anteriorly and laterally to the parts of the scolex, especially the rostellum and sucking organs, and in tetrarhynchids four nerves pass posteriorly, one to each proboscis apparatus (Fig. 154*A*). The anterior nerves from the brain complex are mostly four or eight in number in taenioids (Fig. 131*B*) and shortly become united by a second ganglionated ring commissure, the *rostellar ring;* and in many cases there is still a third nerve ring, the *apical ring,* at the apex of the scolex. Although the brain enlargements are generally spoken of as ganglia it appears that they contain few nerve cells; the nerve cells are mostly in the commissures.

The Cestoda lack special sense organs, but the body surface and organs of the scolex are richly supplied with free sensory nerve endings. Zern-

excretory system, from life, Puget Sound. 1, main lateral nerve; 2, nerve ring; 3, dorsal nerves; 4, ventral nerves; 5, ganglionated transverse commissure; 6, excretory vessels; 7, rostellar ring; 8, anterior nerves (8); 9, transverse connective in proglottid; 10, ganglion at origin of transverse connective; 11, cuticle; 12, basement membrane; 13, tangoreceptor; 14, free sensory endings; 15, sensory nerve cells; 16, apical sucker; 17, bothridia with areolae; 18, dorsal excretory vessel; 19, ventral excretory vessel; 20, loop in bothridium; 21, bladder; 22, nephridiopore.

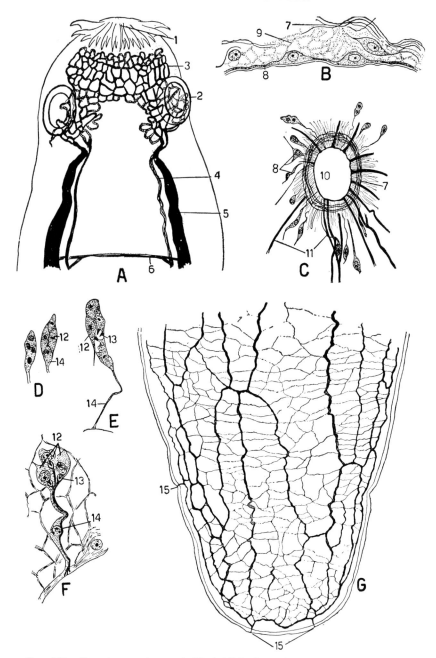

Fig. 132.—Excretory system. *A.* Nephridial plexus in the scolex of *Taenia* (*after Riehm*, 1881). *B, C.* Histological structure of the wall of the main tubules (*after Bugge*, 1902); *B,* longitudinal, and *C,* transverse section. *D–F,* Manner of development of new flame bulbs (*after Bugge*, 1902). *G.* Rear part of *Ligula* showing peripheral nephridial

ecke (1895) noted in pseudophyllids besides the free endings numerous tangoreceptors with bulbous or bristle endings (Fig. 131*C*) situated in a subcuticular nerve plexus.

5. Excretory System.—The excretory system consists of protonephridia provided with typical terminal flame bulbs (Fig. 133*B*) strewn throughout the mesenchyme. There are typically two protonephridial canals on each side, a dorsal and a ventral, of which the ventral is commonly the larger and either or both of which may be straight, sinuous, or coiled (Fig. 133*A*). Longitudinal canals in addition to the usual two pairs may occur, up to a total of 20 in various taenioids. In the pseudophyllids there are usually two or four main longitudinal canals but more, up to 16, in some forms as *Ligula* and *Schistocephalus;* in this group the canals are connected by a network that is further in communication with a peripheral network situated in the cortical mesenchyme between the subcuticular and mesenchymal muscle systems (Fig. 132*G*). The ventral canals, seldom the dorsal canals, may be connected in the posterior part of each proglottid by a transverse canal (Fig. 133*A*), as is usually the case in taenioid tapeworms. The main nephridial system is situated in the central mesenchyme just inside the zone of mesenchymal muscles.

The ventral vessels run the entire length of the strobila while the dorsal ones usually die out in the ripe proglottids. In anapolytic tapeworms or in young apolytic forms that have not yet shed any proglottids the excretory canals terminate in the last proglottid in a median excretory bladder that opens by a pore (Fig. 131*D*). After proglottids have been shed the bladder is lost and the broken ends of the longitudinal canals serve as pores. In pseudophyllids and proteocephalids but rarely in taenioids, the excretory system may open in each proglottid or in certain parts of the animal by two to many secondary pores (Fig. 132*G*).

The longitudinal canals continue into the scolex where they usually connect by cross branches or break up into a plexus (Fig. 132*A*) as in taenioids; but in the simplest cases the ventral and dorsal canal of a side are confluent in the scolex and form no cross unions (Fig. 131*D*). Such a condition shows that the two canals of each side really constitute a single canal that recurves on itself in the scolex and runs back as the dorsal canal (Fig. 131*D*), a point of view that harmonizes the cestode excretory system with that of rhabdocoels.

The histology of the excretory system has been investigated by Bugge (1902). The protonephridial canals are lined by a thin cuticle underlain by a flattened epithelium (Fig. 132*B*), or else the epithelial cells are

plexus and three accessory pores (*after Zernecke*, 1895). 1, rostellum; 2, sucker; 3, nephridial plexus; 4, dorsal vessel; 5, ventral vessel; 6, transverse vessel; 7, muscle fibers; 8, epithelium; 9, mesenchyme; 10, lumen of main excretory canal; 11, secondary canals; 12, cells to form flame bulbs; 13, beginning flames; 14, cell to form capillary; 15, accessory nephridiopores.

attached by strands to the cuticle (Fig. 132C); associated muscle fibers occur. The flame bulbs are single cells, hence properly called flame cells, and are of typical construction with a conical flame (Fig. 133B). New flame cells originate as follows. Cells of the lining epithelium sink into the mesenchyme and divide into four or five cells, all but one of which differentiate into flame cells (Fig. 132D–F). The remaining cell forms an intracellular channel and becomes the capillary connecting the cluster of three or four flame cells with the nephridial canal with which it has remained in continuity. In taenioids the ventral vessels at the place of origin of the connecting transverse canal are provided with a valve, a muscular fold projecting into the lumen (Koehler, 1894).

6. Reproductive System.—The cestodes are hermaphroditic with the exception of the taenioid genus *Dioecocestus* (Fig. 161C) which is not only dioecious but sexually dimorphic; the female is longer and broader than the male (Fuhrmann, 1900). Usually the reproductive system develops progressively from anterior to posterior end of the strobila. Rudiments of the system appear in young proglottids shortly behind the neck, then, as most tapeworms are protandrous, the male organs reach maturity, further posteriorly occur mature proglottids containing the fully developed systems of both sexes, and finally the rear end of the strobila is composed of ripe, or *gravid*, proglottids occupied by the uterus stuffed with capsules or embryos and showing only degenerating remnants of other sex parts. In many pseudophyllids, however, and other forms in which the strobila grows diffusely, there is no such definite succession of sex stages along the strobila and most of the proglottids may be simultaneously in the same sexual state. The reproductive system develops from mesenchyme cells. The gonads originate from groups of mesenchyme cells and the sex ducts from cords of such cells that hollow out and differentiate into epithelial and muscle cells. Later a cuticular lining of uncertain origin appears in the sex ducts.

In many taenioids each proglottid contains two complete reproductive systems bilaterally arranged (Fig. 133A); but this seldom occurs in other orders. Otherwise the system is single in each proglottid, and monozoic tapeworms usually have but one set of reproductive organs, although this is not necessarily the case.

The gonoducts usually open together into a common genital antrum that in the majority of cestodes is situated in the lateral margin, often at its center but also frequently nearer either end. The antrum is usually a hemispherical chamber narrowing to the gonopore and may be provided with a sphincter muscle. The gonopores, when lateral, may be all on the same side of the strobila or vary regularly or irregularly between the two sides; when the reproductive system is double there is an antrum and gonopore on each side of each proglottid (Fig. 133A). In most pseudophyllids, some tetraphyllids, *Echinobothrium*, *Haplobothrium*, and *Meso-cestoides*, the antrum and gonopore are situated on the ventral surface of the proglottids, sometimes on the dorsal surface. Very seldom does the gonopore occur at or near the posterior end of elongated proglottids, and this naturally happens only where proglottids are shed in an immature state.

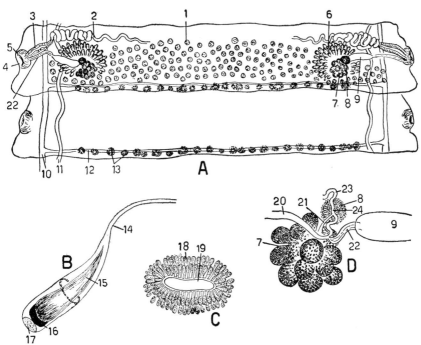

Fig. 133.—Excretory system, reproductive system. *A.* Two proglottids of *Moniezia*, showing excretory canals, interproglottidal glands, and double sex system, original. *B.* Flame cell of a tapeworm, original. *C.* Interproglottidal gland, enlarged. *D.* Details of the female ducts of *Moniezia*. 1, testes; 2, sperm duct; 3, cirrus sac; 4, gonopore; 5, antrum; 6, ovary; 7, yolk gland; 8, shell gland; 9, seminal receptacle; 10, ventral excretory vessel; 11, dorsal excretory vessel; 12, transverse excretory vessel; 13, interproglottidal gland; 14, capillary; 15, flame; 16, basal bodies of the cilia; 17, nucleus; 18, gland cells; 19, sac; 20, oviduct; 21, yolk duct; 22, vagina; 23, beginning of uterus; 24, ootype.

The testes are usually small and numerous rounded bodies, up to several hundred or even a thousand in number in each proglottid (Figs. 133*A*, 134*A*) but may be fewer and larger and even reduced to one to three in some taenioids (e.g., *Hymenolepis*, Fig. 135*C*). They are commonly strewn in the central mesenchyme, often in a layer nearer one surface, thereby defined as dorsal, and are commonly anterior to the ovary (Fig. 134*A*); but they may extend behind the ovary or be more or less grouped into two lateral fields as in many pseudophyllids (Fig. 135*B*) or rarely may lie in the dorsal cortical mesenchyme or sometimes may extend laterally to the outer side of the excretory canals. Fine sperm ductules that may anastomose to a network extend from the testes and join to form the sperm duct, a large much-coiled tube terminating in the cirrus sac. The latter is an elongated highly muscular body through which the terminal, usually coiled part of the sperm duct runs to open into the genital antrum (Fig. 135*B*). Inside the cirrus sac, the sperm duct consists of a noneversible proximal portion, often called ejaculatory duct, that may be enlarged to form a seminal vesicle, and a distal portion, the cirrus, usually lined with bristles, spines, or hooks that is eversible to the exterior as a finger-like copulatory organ. The cirrus is unarmed in pseudophyllids and trypanorhynchids. Before entering the cirrus sac the sperm duct may be enlarged to form a spermiducal vesicle (external seminal vesicle) and either inside or outside the cirrus sac may bear a muscular enlargement, the *propulsion vesicle* (found in some pseudophyllids and most trepanorhynchids). A definite prostatic vesicle is absent except in the genus *Andrya* (Fig. 164*B*), but prostatic glands are frequently present, opening into either the sperm duct or the cirrus sac (Fig. 135*B*). The cirrus sac presents many variations but is usually a rounded or tubular body with thick walls of generally inner circular and outer longitudinal muscle fibers (Fig. 135*B*). The ejaculatory duct and cirrus are often provided with muscle fibers, and special retractor muscles to retract cirrus or sac may be present.

The single ovary usually lies ventrally and posteriorly in the central mesenchyme, in or near the median line, except when the reproductive system is double, whereupon the ovary naturally has a lateral position. The ovary commonly consists of two lobes connected by a narrow bridge; often each lobe is dorsoventrally forked so that in a transverse section the ovary appears as an H- or X-shaped figure (Fig. 134*C*). Each lobe may be subdivided into subsidiary lobes. In many taenioids and some pseudophyllids, the ovary is a single, more or less lobulated body, seldom of simple contour or reticulated. An unusual position is seen in some genera of the tetraphyllid family Monticelliidae where the ovary lies wholly or partly in the dorsal cortical mesenchyme.

In the main orders except the Taenioidea, the yolk glands occur as numerous follicles, arranged in lateral bands or fields in tetraphyllids (Fig. 134*A*); in a superficial layer around the other sex organs in most pseudophyllids (Fig. 135*B*) and trypanorhynchids. In taenioids the yolk gland is reduced to a small body (Fig. 133*D*) near and usually behind the ovary but is lacking in certain genera (*Thysanosoma, Avitellina, Stilesia*). Where the yolk glands are follicular the numerous ductules from the follicles unite to a main duct on each side that runs transversely toward the median line and joins its fellow to form a common yolk duct (Fig. 135*A*). This usually enlarges to a small yolk reservoir and shortly

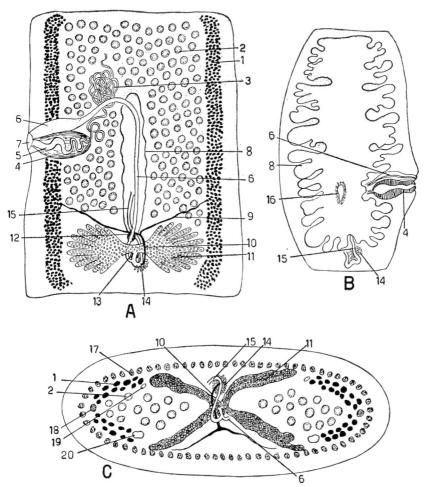

Fig. 134.—Reproductive system. *A.* Scheme of the reproductive system of a tetra-phyllid tapeworm. *B.* Ripe proglottid of a tetraphyllid tapeworm, showing mature uterus and uterine pore (*after Zschokke,* 1888). *C.* Section through level of the ovary of a tetraphyllid proglottid. 1, yolk glands; 2, testes; 3, sperm duct; 4, cirrus sac; 5, cirrus ; 6, vagina; 7, gonopore; 8, uterus; 9, yolk ducts; 10, common yolk duct; 11, ovary; 12, seminal receptacle; 13, ovicapt; 14, shell glands; 15, uterine duct; 16, uterine pore; 17, longitudinal muscle stratum; 18, lateral nerve cord; 19, dorsal excretory vessel; 20, ventral excretory vessel.

thereafter enters the oviduct. In the Taenioidea the very short yolk duct opens immediately into the oviduct.

The oviduct springs from the bridge between the two ovarian lobes or from the center of the ovary when the latter is a compact mass and except in the Taenioidea presents at once a muscular thickening, the *ovicapt,* said to suck eggs into the oviduct by peristaltic contractions. An ovicapt is present in a few taenioids but in this order is generally weak or absent.

The oviduct beyond the ovicapt very soon receives the vagina and then the common yolk duct after which it usually enlarges slightly to an ootype surrounded by the so-called shell glands. These as in other flatworms probably play little or no role in the formation of the capsules, the material of which comes from droplets in the yolk cells. In taenioids the shell glands are reduced to a small mass around the ootype but are seldom wanting, and in this order the yolk duct usually opens directly into the ootype. Beyond the ootype the ovovitelline duct sooner or later enlarges to form the uterus.

The vagina is a straight or slightly sinuous tube that leads from the common antrum to the oviduct near the exit of the latter from the ovary. The proximal part of the vagina is nearly always enlarged to a fusiform seminal receptacle, sometimes of great size, that harbors the sperm received in copulation.

In the majority of cestodes the cirrus sac and sperm duct lie anterior to the vagina and retain this relation at their openings into the common antrum, but in most tetraphyllids the terminal portions of the sex ducts cross (Fig. 134A). Where the gonopore is mid-ventral as in many pseudophyllids the vagina is usually posterior to the sperm duct (Fig. 135A) but a crossing may occur. The sperm duct may also lie dorsal to the vagina cr infrequently ventral to it. The vagina is degenerate distally and fails to open to the exterior in the taenioid family Acoleidae. Other aberrant taenioids are *Amabilia* and *Schistotaenia* in which the sperm duct opens laterally as usual while the vaginal opening is elsewhere, usually dorsal or ventral; and *Aporina* which lacks gonopores altogether.

The most characteristic feature of the cestode reproductive system, the uterus, begins to develop only after the gonads and their ducts have attained maturity. It is a continuation of the ovovitelline duct and takes the form of a sac, usually greatly lobed, or a coiled tube. The slender portion of the ovovitelline duct between the ootype and the uterine expansion is termed the uterine duct. In tetraphyllids and trypanorhynchids the uterus is a median tube (Fig. 134A) that as it fills with ripe capsules expands to a sac (Fig. 134B), often with lateral diverticula; it commonly opens ventrally by a pore or row of pores or an elongated slit. The sac-like uterus obtains in some pseudophyllids but more typically in this order the uterus is a large coiled tube (Fig. 135A); in either case the uterus opens ventrally (sometimes dorsally), mostly by a single pore. The uterus of taenioids typically lacks an aperture, and consequently the embryos are freed by the disintegration of the proglottid. In this order, the uterus is of varied form, mostly a central tube or sac with (Fig. 162D, E) or without lateral diverticula or a network (Fig. 162C), of which the meshes later become more or less confluent (*Moniezia*). In a number of taenioids the uterus eventually breaks up into many small portions

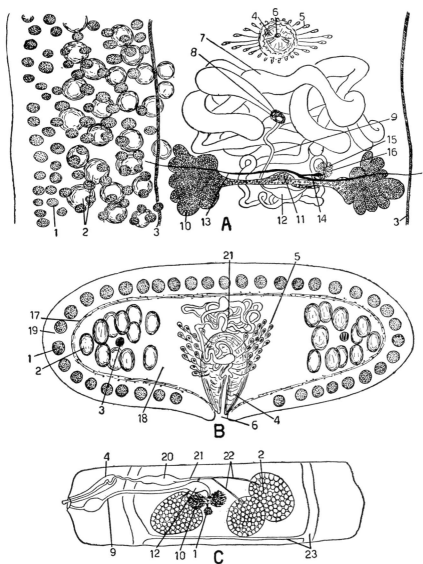

FIG. 135.—Reproductive system (continued). *A*. Pseudophyllid reproductive system (*after Nybelin*, 1922), right side omitted. *B*. Section through a pseudophyllid proglottid (*Cyathocephalus*) at the level of the cirrus sac (*after Nybelin*, 1922). *C*. Reproductive system of *Hymenolepis* with three testes (*after Southwell*, 1930). 1, yolk glands; 2, testes; 3, lateral nerve cord; 4, cirrus sac; 5, prostatic glands; 6, male gonopore; 7, uterus, 8, female gonopore; 9, vagina; 10, ovary; 11, oviduct; 12, seminal receptacle; 13, yolk ducts; 14, common yolk duct; 15, ootype; 16, shell gland; 17, muscle stratum; 18, central mesenchyme; 19, peripheral mesenchyme; 20, spermiducal vesicle; 21, sperm duct; 22, sperm ductules; 23, excretory vessels.

termed *uterine capsules* (Fig. 163*G*) each enclosing one to several embryos. In still other taenioid genera, one to many tough fibrous sacs, called *paruterine organs*, arise in the mesenchyme, establish connection with the uterus, and receive and retain the embryos (Fig. 165*C*). As the proglottids ripen the uterus spreads until it often fills the entire proglottid, and the rest of the reproductive system together with many other structures degenerates. In apolytic tapeworms such gravid proglottids stuffed with capsules or embryos are shed into the intestine, pass out with the feces, and disintegrate, freeing the embryos. Where uterine pores are present, as in anapolytic forms, the encapsulated embryos can be shed while the proglottids are retained.

The sex ducts are usually lined by an epithelium at first, but later this often disappears especially in the distal portions and is replaced by a cuticle, often hairy or fringed (Balss, 1908; Young, 1913; Schaefer, 1913). This is usually underlain by muscle fibers, often well developed. The uterus may or may not be lined by an epithelium.

The eggs are sucked into the oviduct by the ovicapt, then fertilized, and then receive yolk cells (except in those taenioid genera as *Avitellina* that lack a yolk gland). In the ootype the egg becomes enclosed with the yolk cells in a shell or capsule. Thick capsules with or without an operculum occur only in some pseudophyllids, particularly the family Diphyllobothriidae. Such capsules enclose one egg and a number of yolk cells and the egg develops only after reaching the exterior (Fig. 136*A*, *J*). In other pseudophyllids and in the other cestode orders the capsules are very thin and the egg receives only one to a few yolk cells that adhere to its surface and pass their yolk into its cytoplasm (Fig. 137*B*). These eggs develop to embryos within the uterus while still inside the host so that in the majority of tapeworms the shed proglottids contain fully developed embryos.

The reproductive system of cestodes is seen to follow the same structural plan as in the other classes of flatworms. The chief features of the male system are the absence of a prostatic vesicle and the occurrence of a cirrus instead of a penis papilla. The female system is very similar to that of the digenetic trematodes except as regards the correspondence of uterus and vagina. The vagina of cestodes has the same general relations as the Laurer's canal of trematodes except that it opens into the gonopore. Similarly the uterus of cestodes seems to be as in trematodes a specialization of the ovovitelline duct; but it fails to open into the gonopore. Although some authors therefore believe the uterus of cestodes is homologous with the Laurer's canal of trematodes it seems more reasonable to think that there has been a shift of the external openings and that therefore the uterus in both is the ovovitelline duct and the cestode vagina corresponds to Laurer's canal.

7. Copulation.—Self-fertilization by eversion of the cirrus into the vagina of the same proglottid is probably the most common method of impregnation in cestodes. Copulation between different proglottids of the same strobila or, when opportunity affords, of different strobila is probably frequent. The insemination in such cases may be mutual or the younger anterior male segments may inseminate the more posterior segments that have reached the female phase. Hypodermic impregnation also occurs in those genera that lack a vaginal opening (taenioid family Acoleidae); here the cirrus armed with large hooks is thrust anywhere into the mesenchyme (Wolffhügel, 1898, 1900).

8. Embryonic Development.—The details of the prelarval development are known for very few tapeworms, chiefly for pseudophyllids (Schauinsland, 1886) and a few taenioids (Janicki, 1907; Spätlich, 1925). In the former, the extruded capsules consist of a thick operculated or nonoperculated shell enclosing a single egg and a number of yolk cells that soon break up into yolk masses (Fig. 136A, J). The egg undergoes total and equal cleavage into several blastomeres, one of which situated at one pole takes no part in the formation of the embryo but spreads and flattens and together with one or two other cells becomes a membrane enclosing the yolk and the remaining blastomeres (Fig. 136B, C). The latter continue to cleave to a spherical mass of small cells some of which cover the others by a sort of epiboly and become the surface layer of the embryo (Fig. 136D, E). This surface layer is apparently the ectoderm and the interior mass is the mesentoderm. The ectoderm soon separates from the interior mass and becomes a second or inner embryonic membrane (Fig. 136F, G). The interior mass continues to cleave and forms an oval embryo, the *oncosphere*, composed of many small cells and showing little differentiation except for the formation of three pairs of hooks at one pole, which is posterior (Fig. 136H, L); it also has some muscle fibers and a pair of flame cells. The ectodermal membrane may or may not develop long cilia. The first or outer embryonic membrane thins and disappears. At this stage the capsules are extruded into water and the larva, known as a *coracidium*, escapes, still enclosed in the inner embryonic membrane. If ciliated, the coracidium swims about; if not, it falls to the bottom. In either case, the coracidium must be eaten by the first intermediate host, typically a copepod, before it can develop further. In the digestive tract of the host, the embryonic membrane is shed and the oncosphere is freed.

The taenioid capsule is a very thin delicate shell enclosing one egg and one yolk cell. The egg cleaves totally and unequally into a mass composed of two or three macromeres, three or more mesomeres, and a number of micromeres (Fig. 137A–C). The macromeres contain the yolk which has entered them as droplets and they soon fuse to a syncyt-

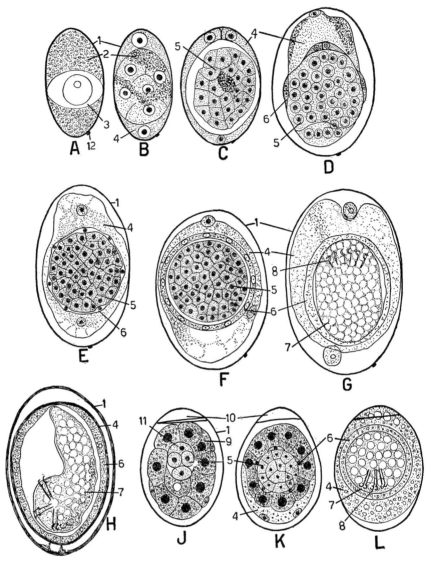

Fig. 136.—Embryonic development of pseudophyllids. *A–G.* Development of *Eubothrium (after Schauinsland*, 1886). *A.* Capsule (nonoperculated) containing egg and yolk mass. *B.* Cleavage stage, outer membrane formed by two cells. *C.* Further cleavage, outer membrane completed. *D.* Inner membrane forming. *E.* Inner membrane completed. *F.* Inner membrane separated from embryo. *G.* Embryo differentiated into a hexacanth larva. *H.* Mature hexacanth of *Eubothrium* inside membranes and capsule (after Rosen, 1917–1918). *J–L.* Development of *Diphyllobothrium latum (after Schauinsland*, 1886). *J.* Operculated capsule containing 4-celled embryo and yolk cells. *K.* Embryonic membranes formed. *L.* Hexacanth with two membranes. 1, capsule; 2, yolk mass; 3, egg; 4, outer membrane; 5, embryo; 6, inner membrane; 7, hexacanth larva; 8, hooks; 9, yolk cells; 10, operculum; 11, cell to form outer membrane; 12, knob on capsule.

ium that encircles the other blastomeres as the *outer* embryonic membrane of nutritive nature (Fig. 137*C–E*). The blastomere mass continues to cleave; and three to five of the larger cells, termed mesomeres by Spätlich, enclose the others as an *inner* embryonic membrane (Fig. 137*D–*

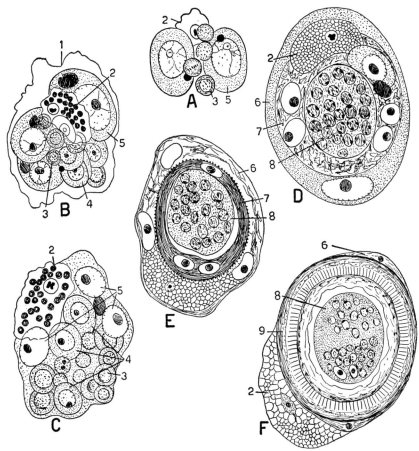

Fig. 137.—Embryonic development of *Taenia*. *A.* Cleavage, showing micromeres and macromeres. *B.* Later cleavage, mesomeres formed. *C.* Later stage, macromeres forming outer membrane. *D.* Outer membrane formed, mesomeres forming inner membrane. *E.* Embryo with both membranes. *F.* Outer membrane disappearing, inner membrane producing a striated shell. (*All after Janicki, 1907.*) 1, capsule; 2, yolk cell; 3, micromeres; 4, mesomeres; 5, macromeres; 6, outer membrane; 7, inner membrane; 8, embryo; 9, shell.

F). This later hardens to a thick cuticularized shell (Fig. 137*F*) that apparently corresponds to the ectodermal membrane of the bothriocephaloid coracidium. The inner mass of micromeres becomes an oncosphere in which little differentiation is to be seen except the three pairs of hooks that appear at its posterior end (Fig. 138).

In the taenioids the capsules reach the oncosphere stage in the uterus of the terminal proglottids which when shed are therefore filled with oncospheres (also called *hexacanth* larvae), that are enclosed in the embryonic membranes, often thicker than the diameter of the oncosphere itself. The original thin capsule may be retained but is often shed. Then comes the thick albuminous outer membrane that may be drawn out into a filament on each side (Fig. 138*B*). Within this is the hard inner membrane, usually spherical or oval but sometimes also extended into filaments (Fig. 138*B*). In *Moniezia* and other anoplocephalids the inner membrane may project as a *pyriform* apparatus, consisting of two adjacent crossed or straight spines, perhaps of aid in rupturing the embryonic membranes (Fig. 138*C*). In the genus *Taenia*, the capsule and outer embryonic membrane are lost and the oncosphere is enclosed only in the thick striated shell developed from the inner membrane (Fig. 138*D*). The oncosphere does not hatch from its membranes until eaten by an appropriate host.

Very little is known of the development of trypanorhynchids and tetraphyllids except that an oncosphere is produced enclosed in embryonic membranes that in tetraphyllids resemble those of taenioids.

9. General Account of the Cestode Life Cycle.—Like the digenetic trematodes, the cestodes require intermediate hosts for the completion of their life cycle. In the pseudophyllids and in the other orders so far as known except taenioids, two intermediate hosts are required, of which the first is apparently always a crustacean, while the second is generally a fish but may be some other vertebrate. The taenioid cycle usually includes only one intermediate host, generally an arthropod, but sometimes an annelid, mollusk, or vertebrate. In a few taenioids an intermediate host is lacking and the larva infects the final host directly. Cestode larvae do not bore actively into hosts but must be passively eaten. Multiplication of late larval stages by asexual methods is not uncommon in taenioids.

As already noted the first larval stage of eucestodes is termed an oncosphere. It is a rounded or oval mass of cells without a surface epithelium and provided with three pairs of hooks and a pair of flame bulbs; the presence of a pair of large penetration glands in taenioid oncospheres has been demonstrated by Reid (1947). The pseudophyllid oncosphere is enclosed in a one-layered ciliated or unciliated membrane and is then termed *coracidium* (Fig. 139*A*); the taenioid oncosphere is provided with one to three acellular membranes (Fig. 138). The oncosphere escapes from its membranes only after being eaten by an intermediate host, usually an arthropod, in whose digestive tract the membranes are digested; the oncosphere then bores through the intestinal wall into body spaces or various organs where its further development differs. In what may be supposed to represent the more primitive cycle, as illustrated in many pseudophyllids, the oncosphere develops into the second larval stage, the *procercoid* (Fig. 139*B*, *C*). The body elongates and becomes covered with a thick, sometimes bristly, cuticle, underneath which appears the subcuticular muscle layer. The posterior end including the six hooks

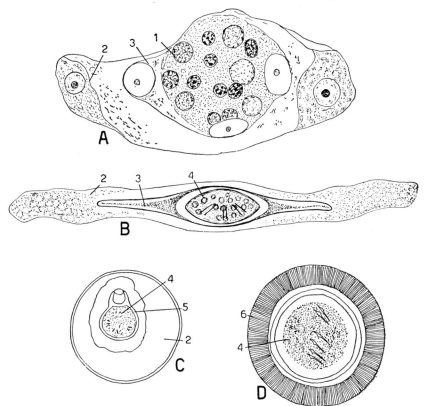

FIG. 138.—Membranated embryos ("eggs") of taenioids. *A.* Late stage of formation of embryo and membranes of *Diorchis*. *B.* Completed membranated embryo of *Diorchis;* inner membrane has formed an elongated shell. (*A, B, after Spätlich,* 1925.) *C.* Membranated embryo of *Moniezia* with pyriform apparatus (*after Stiles and Hassall,* 1893). *D.* Hexacanth of *Taenia saginata,* enclosed in striated shell formed of the inner membrane (*after Southwell,* 1930). 1, embryo; 2, outer membrane; 3, inner membrane; 4, hexacanth larva; 5, pyriform apparatus; 6, shell.

constricts as a rounded or elongated tail used as an organ of attachment. The anterior end may form a small muscular invagination on which open large gland cells of mesenchymal origin; these appear to be homologous with the frontal glands of Turbellaria (Fig. 139*C*). Additional flame bulbs arise and a network of excretory canals appears leading to a median bladder situated just anterior to the tail constriction. The mesenchyme frequently becomes filled with calcareous bodies. The resemblance of

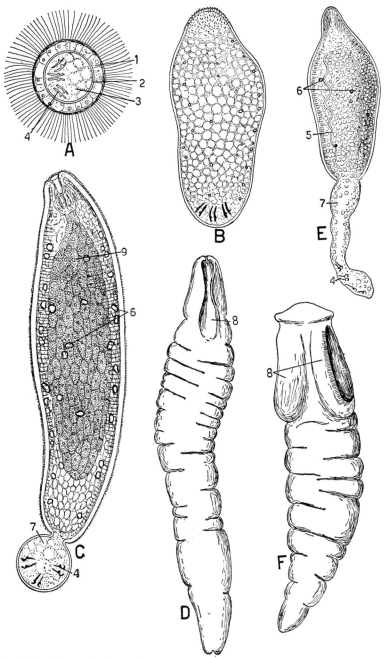

Fig. 139.—Life cycle of pseudophyllids. *A–D. Diphyllobothrium latum (after Rosen,* 1916–1917). *A.* Ciliated coracidium. *B.* Early procercoid in Cyclops. *C.* Mature procercoid; note enormous frontal glands. *D.* Plerocercoid. *E, F.* Stages of *Eubothrium*

the procercoid to a cercaria is obvious. The procercoid develops no further until its host is eaten by the appropriate second intermediate host, usually a fish, sometimes some other vertebrate. The tail is shed while the procercoid is still in the first host or after it has reached the digestive cavity of the second.

Freed in the intestine of the second host, the larva penetrates the intestinal wall with the aid of the secretion of its frontal glands and eventually reaches the coelom, liver, spleen, musculature, or other parts. Meantime it is gradually developing into the next larval stage, the *plerocercoid*, originally called *sparganum*, because the generic name *Sparganum* was current for plerocercoid larvae found in man of which the adults were then unknown. The plerocercoid grows and elongates, its anterior end develops into the scolex with adhesive organs typical of the species, the cuticle thickens, nervous and excretory systems develop toward the adult condition, and the larva is in fact a young tapeworm but does not begin to strobilate (Fig. 139*D*, *F*). The plerocercoid becomes encysted by the host tissues and develops no further until its host is eaten by the final host, generally a larger carnivorous fish, less often a carnivorous bird or mammal. Arrived in the intestine of the final host, the plerocercoid attaches to the wall and simply continues to develop into the mature tapeworm, growing many proglottids daily.

This pseudophyllid life cycle has been abbreviated and altered in the taenioids where the oncosphere, after being ingested by the intermediate host, is freed from its membrane and penetrates the intestinal wall into the coelom, liver, or other parts. Typical procercoid and plerocercoid stages are absent or but slightly indicated and the taenioid oncosphere usually develops into either a *cysticercoid* or a *cysticercus*. The oncosphere enlarges and elongates and develops more or less of a central cavity. In forming a cysticercoid, the anterior end either before (Fig. 140) or after (Fig. 141*A–D*) differentiating into a scolex withdraws but does not introvert into a cavity formed by the folding of the middle region of the larva around the scolex (Fig. 140*G*). The cysticercoid therefore usually consists of an anterior vesicle containing the scolex and a posterior tail-like region in which the larval hooks may persist for some time (Figs. 140*G*, 141*E*, 170*D*). Such taenioid cysticercoids are very common encysted in the body cavity of crustaceans, insects, millipedes, oligochaetes, and other invertebrates, less common in vertebrates. Various modifications of the cysticercoid occur depending on the transformations of the tail; this may branch or elongate greatly (Fig. 170*E*) or may fold up around the scolex as an additional enclosing wall (Fig. 140*G*).

(*after Rosen*, 1917–1918). *E*. Procercoid. *F*. Plerocercoid. 1, outer membrane; 2, inner membrane; 3, hexacanth; 4, hooks; 5, nephridial canals; 6, calcareous bodies; 7, tail; 8, bothria; 9, frontal glands.

If the last process is complete, the cysticercoid becomes a vesicle enclosing the scolex. The distinguishing feature of the cysticercoid is that the scolex is oriented normally in the cavity, not invaginated (turned inside out). The tissues of the cysticercoid other than the scolex become loose and vacuolated.

The most modified type of taenioid larva is the *cysticercus* or *bladder worm*, occurring in reptilian and mammalian, seldom avian, intermediate hosts. A central cavity appears in the oncosphere and this enlarges until the oncosphere is transformed into a fluid-filled vesicle with a wall composed of an outer cuticle and an inner mesenchymal layer. The latter thickens at one point (Fig. 141*F*) and invaginates into the vesicle as a hollow knob that differentiates into a scolex with its adhesive organs facing the cavity of the vesicle (Fig. 141*G–J*), i.e., the scolex is invaginated or introverted and this condition together with the absence of any structure representing the tail characterizes the cysticercus. These rounded or oval bladders each containing an introverted scolex (Fig. 142*A*, *B*) occur embedded in any part of the host but especially in the coelom, muscles, and liver, and attain considerable, even large, size. The occurrence of such bladders in mammals was known to the ancients, but the fact that they are a larval stage of tapeworms was first demonstrated in 1851 by a physician named Küchenmeister who fed cysticerci from rabbits, sheep, and pigs to dogs and man and recovered the adult tapeworms.

A type of cysticercus termed *tetrathyridium* or *dithyridium* occurs in certain taenioid genera as *Mesocestoides* and *Cylindrotaenia*. This is a long slender larva resembling a plerocercoid, but the enlarged anterior end contains an introverted scolex (Fig. 166*C*, *D*).

When animals infected with cysticercoids or cysticerci are eaten by the proper final host, the scolex emerges (Fig. 142*C*), attaches to the intestinal wall, and begins to proliferate proglottids, sooner or later casting off the bladder and other larval parts. Sometimes, however, eversion occurs and the scolex strobilates into a young tapeworm while still encysted in the intermediate host, as in the common *Cysticercus taeniaeformis* of rats and mice with adult stage in the cat. Such larval strobilae that still retain the bladder at their rear ends are called *strobilocerci* (Fig. 171).

10. Asexual Multiplication and Regeneration.—Although in general asexual multiplication is lacking from the tapeworm cycle and each egg produces only one adult, a few striking cases of such multiplication occur. Pseudophyllid plerocercoids often undergo fragmentation but only the fragment bearing the scolex can regenerate (Joyeaux and Baer, 1939). What seems to be a remarkable kind of asexual multiplication occurs in a rare human pseudophyllid termed *Sparganum prolifer*. Three cases of

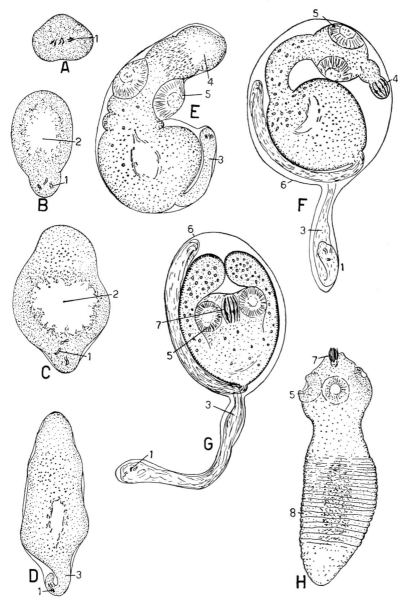

Fig. 140.—Development of a cysticercoid. *A–H*. Development of the cysticercoid of *Hymenolepis exigua* (*after Alicata and Chang*, 1939), type in which the scolex develops first, then withdraws into the middle region. *A*. Hexacanth in beach amphipod *Orchestia*. *B–D*. Growth of hexacanth, internal cavity forms. *E*. Scolex and tail differentiated. *F*. Further differentiation; tail folds up around body. *G*. Completed cysticercoid; scolex withdrawn, tail partly encloses scolex. *H*. Young tapeworm in fowl. 1, hooks; 2, cavity; 3, tail; 4, rostellum; 5, suckers; 6, cyst wall; 7, rostellar hooks; 8, young proglottids.

this parasite are known from Japan (Ijima, 1905; Yoshida, 1914) and one from Florida (Stiles, 1908). The victims were covered with nodules containing one or more, usually encapsulated but active, plerocercoid-like larvae, totaling thousands. These larvae appeared as slender unsegmented worms mostly 3 to 12 mm. in length, without a scolex, and often exhibiting lateral buds and branches or evidences of fission (Fig. 142*H*). The findings of Owata (1934) and Mueller (1938) suggest that "Sparganum prolifer" is a bothriocephaloid plerocercoid of which man is not the normal host and which therefore in man undergoes degeneration and abnormal growth and multiplication.

Better known are a number of cases of normal asexual multiplication in taenioid larvae that add complication to the life cycle. The asexual process consists of either exogenous or endogenous budding to form additional cysticercoids and cysticerci. Exogenous budding is seen in a form called *Urocystis* found in earthworms (Haswell and Hill, 1894) and myriapods (Joyeaux, 1922); a cellular mass presumably derived directly from an ingested oncosphere puts out external buds that develop into cysticercoids of an unknown taenioid (Fig. 142*D–F*). The bladder of *Cysticercus longicollis* of rats (larval stage of *Taenia crassiceps* of dogs and other canines) buds externally numerous cysticerci that can detach and themselves bud in the same manner. In internal budding the inner surface of the bladder wall puts out buds into the cavity that develop into cysticercoids or cysticerci. A simple case of this kind is the so-called *polycercus* larva (Metschnikoff, 1868; Villot, 1883) of earthworms, that buds off tailless cysticercoids into the interior cavity. It is now believed that this polycercus is the larval stage of a taenioid tapeworm of birds, *Paricterotaenia nilotica*, belonging to the family Dilepididae. More complicated cases of internal proliferation of scolices are seen in the *coenurus* and *hydatid* bladders of mammals described in detail later in which there is an enormous multiplication of scolices through budding processes (Fig. 172).

Proliferation of young strobili as outgrowths from the rear end of a parent strobilus appears to be occurring in a specimen described by Beddard (1912) under the name *Urocystidium gemmiparum* (Fig. 142*G*), but the normality of the specimen remains questionable. The normal formation of proglottids in tapeworms is a budding process, and therefore it is not surprising to find that proliferative processes resulting in complete or partial duplications of proglottids or of considerable regions of a strobila are of common occurrence. A number of such abnormalities in the common sheep tapeworm, *Moniezia expansa*, have been described by Child (1900, 1902).

The scolex and neck region of a tapeworm can regenerate the strobila, or perhaps more correctly speaking the neck region (as long as the scolex

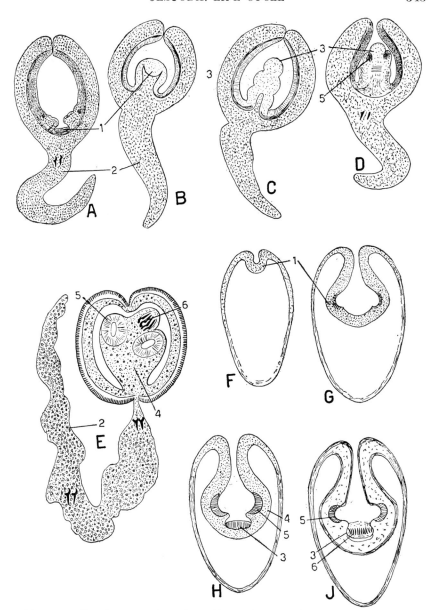

Fig. 141.—Development of cysticercoid, cysticercus. *A–E.* Development of the cysticercoid of *Hymenolepis tenuirostris* (*after Hamann*, 1899), in the amphipod Gammarus; scolex differentiates after invagination. *A.* Vesicle formed by invagination. *B.* Bud grows up from bottom of vesicle. *C, D.* Bud develops into scolex. *E.* Completed cysticercoid. *F–J.* Scheme of the formation of a cysticercus; invagination into vesicle develops into introverted scolex. 1, bud to form scolex; 2, tail with hooks; 3, rostellum; 4, scolex; 5, suckers; 6, rostellar hooks.

is retained) continues its normal process of proliferation so that a new strobila eventuates. The regenerative capacity of bothriocephaloid plerocercoids was tested by Iwata (1934) who made various cuts, incisions, and transections and then reimplanted the operated specimens into the appropriate host. A high regenerative capacity was revealed, including regeneration of the anterior end, and incisions and splits resulted in branched forms resembling the "Sparganum prolifer" described above.

11. Subclass Cestodaria.—The Cestodaria as here constituted are a small group of monozoic tapeworms that inhabit the coelom and intestine of lower fishes. They differ considerably from other tapeworms in structure and also in having a 10-hooked, instead of a 6-hooked, larva. The principal genera, *Amphilina* and *Gyrocotyle*, are themselves so different from each other that they are usually made the basis for separate orders, Amphilinidea and Gyrocotylidea.

a. Amphilinidea.—The amphilinids are flattened oval to elongate monozoic tapeworms ranging from a few to 30 to 40 cm. in length. They inhabit the coelom of the sturgeon and other fish. The anatomy of *Amphilina* (Fig. 143A) has been thoroughly expounded by Cohn (1904), Hein (1904), Poche (1925b), and Goto and Ishii (1936). A definite scolex is lacking, and instead the anterior tip bears a protrusible proboscis on which opens a cluster of large frontal glands (Fig. 143C). This proboscis is weakly developed in *Amphilina* but in some other genera is a powerful muscular organ resembling that of the kalyptorhynchid rhabdocoels. As regards the histology, the cuticle is thin and delicate and underlain by a fibrous mesh, the subcuticular cells are extremely large, and the mesenchymal musculature is often weakly developed. The nervous system consists of a commissure behind the proboscis; from this a pair of nerves proceeds anteriorly and a pair of main lateral nerves extends to the posterior end where they are united by a commissure (Fig. 143A). The excretory system, best known for *Amphilina*, takes the form of a peripheral network of vessels opening at the rear end by way of a small excretory bladder. Peculiar flame cells occur in the amphilinids; each cell encloses a rosette-like cluster of 18 to 30 flame bulbs (Fig. 143D). The numerous testes either are strewn throughout most of the body (*Amphilina*) or are arranged in a lateral band along the sperm duct on each body side (other genera). The common sperm duct is provided with a muscular propulsion region and receives prostatic glands; it opens at the posterior end of the worm by way of a penis papilla in some forms. The single rounded or lobed ovary is located in the rear part of the worm. The oviduct, after giving off the vagina and receiving the common yolk duct and the shell glands, becomes the uterus that pursues a winding course, traversing the body length three times, and finally opens at the anterior tip, alongside the proboscis (Fig. 143A). The poorly developed yolk glands occur in a lateral strand on each side. The vagina runs posteriorly and either joins the end of the sperm duct at the posterior end or opens independently in the posterior part of the body, sometimes after forking in two (Fig. 144*A*). A seminal receptacle is usually present as a widening of the vagina or as a large sac or long tube attached to it.

The Amphilinidea comprise six genera, all of which but *Amphilina* are represented by a single species. The genus *Amphilina*, characterized by the strewn testes, single lateral vaginal opening, and absence of a seminal receptacle, contains the only common member of the order, *Amphilina foliacea* (Fig. 143*A*), known since 1819, a parasite of the coelom of the sturgeon *Acipenser*. The other genera are of long strap-like shape with lateral testes (Fig. 143*B*), and all but *Austramphilina* inhabit the coelom of bony fishes. In *Gigantolina* (Southwell, 1915; Poche, 1926), *Nesolecithus* (Janicki, 1908; Poche, 1922), and *Schizochoerus* (Poche, 1925a), the vagina forks and one fork opens dorsally, the other ventrally (Fig. 144*A*); the last two genera have also a very long tubular seminal receptacle extending forward (Fig. 143*B*). In *Gephyrolina* (Woodland, 1923), without a seminal receptacle, and *Austramphilina* (Johnston, 1931), from the coelom of a fresh-water turtle, the vagina opens posteriorly close to the male pore.

The complete life cycle is known only for *Amphilina foliacea* (Janicki, 1928), although the characteristic larva has been seen in other species. The thin-shelled capsules, provided with a short tubular filament at one end (Fig. 144*C*) but no operculum, contain an egg and many yolk cells. During their passage along the long uterus the eggs develop into the typical cestodarian larva, termed a *lycophore* or *decacanth*. The lycophore of *Amphilina* (Fig. 144*D*) has a ciliated epidermis, a subcuticular muscle sheath, a cluster of huge frontal glands opening at the anterior end, a transverse nerve commissure near this end, and 10 large hooks at the posterior end. The larva does not escape from the shell until the capsules are eaten by the intermediate host, an amphipod crustacean, in whose intestine the ciliated epidermis is lost. By the secretion of its frontal glands, the lycophore penetrates the intestinal wall of the host and enters the body cavity where it attaches by its hooks and undergoes a general dedifferentiation, losing its frontal glands and other larval structures. It then elongates and differentiates and forms a small round tail which, however, does not receive the hooks. The larva is therefore now a procercoid. The tail is soon shed and the larva becomes an elongated plerocercoid (Fig. 144*E*) in which the adult frontal glands and other parts differentiate. When an amphipod containing the plerocercoid is eaten by a sturgeon, the larva passes into the latter's coelom and grows to maturity. The larval hooks are retained throughout life buried in the posterior end in *Amphilina* and also in *Schizochoerus* and *Gigantolina*

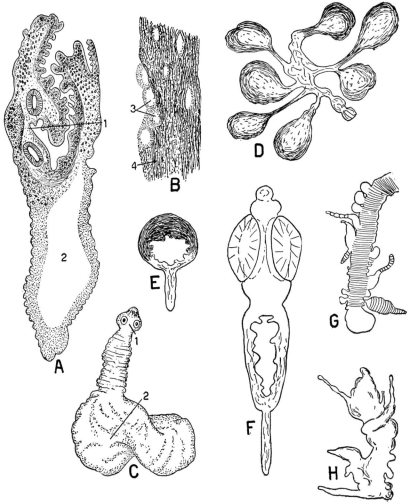

FIG. 142.—Cysticerci, asexual reproduction. *A*. Section of the cysticercus of *Taenia saginata* (*after Moniez*, 1880). *B*. Piece of measly pork with cysticerci of *Taenia solium*, natural size (*after Stiles*, 1898). *C*. Evaginated cysticercus of *Taenia solium* (*after Stiles*, 1898). *D*. Exogenous budding of *Urocystis* in a millipede. *E*. Later stage of *Urocystis* bud. *F*. Same developed into a cysticercoid. *G*. Rear end of *Urocystidium gemmiparum* (*after Beddard*, 1912) showing apparent budding. *H*. A specimen of *Sparganum prolifer* (*after Ijima*, 1905). 1, scolex; 2, vesicle; 3, cysticerci; 4, muscle fibers of pork.

(Fig. 144*B*). From this fact, also from their possession of frontal glands and coelomic habitat (the usual habitat of tapeworm larvae), the amphilinids are generally believed by students of the group to be neotenic plerocercoids (Pintner, 1906). The plerocercoid attains sexual maturity in what would be the second intermediate host in a normal life cycle and so no longer requires to enter the final host that presumably was included in the original cycle (Janicki, 1930). The Cestodaria cannot therefore be regarded as primitive tapeworms.

b. *Gyrocotylidea.*—This group is represented by the genus *Gyrocotyle*, found in the intestine of chimaeroid fishes and differing considerably from the amphilinids (accounts of the anatomy in Watson, 1911; Ward, 1912; and especially Lynch, 1945). *Gyrocotyle* is an elongate flattened worm (Fig. 145*A*) with a ruff, the *rosette*, at one end surrounding a funnel-shaped depression. Opposing views as to which end of *Gyrocotyle* is anterior (Watson, 1911; Dollfus, 1923) have been settled finally by Ruszkowski (1932), who showed that the lycophore hooks occur at the rosette end, which is therefore posterior. The worms are attached to the host by the rosette end but on being removed from the host move by peristaltic contractions with the opposite end forward (Watson 1911). The pointed anterior end bears a large opening that leads into a highly muscular, somewhat protrusible, oval mass, the proboscis, regarded by some as a sucker. Spines are present around the anterior end, also just anterior to the rosette, and elsewhere on the body varying with the species. The body margins are generally ruffled (Fig. 146). The surface is clothed with a thick cuticle beneath which is the subcuticular musculature followed by a layer of subcuticular cells, that, however, appear to have no connections with the cuticle. A powerful mesenchymal musculature is present, conferring on the worm a highly muscular build. A sphincter occurs in the distal part of the proboscis, and strong retractor muscles are attached to this organ (Fig. 145*B*). The nervous system comprises a strong commissure behind the proboscis, a pair of lateral nerves, and a commissure, pair of ganglia, and nerve ring in connection with the rosette (Fig. 146). The fact that the nervous system is better developed in the rosette than it is in relation to the proboscis was an added argument for those who in the past regarded the rosette end as anterior. However, augmentation of nerve supply in connection with adhesive organs is of common occurrence in flatworms. Two ridges and two pits believed from their rich innervation to be sensory were found by Watson (1911) on the distal part of the proboscis of *Gyrocotyle*. The excretory system takes the form of a network of partly ciliated vessels to which are attached numerous ordinary flame bulbs by way of capillaries. The system opens by a pair of nephridiopores in the anterior part of the body.

The reproductive system, except for the yolk glands, lies inside the main stratum of mesenchymal muscles. The numerous testes are strewn anteriorly (Fig. 146); the sperm duct forms a spermiducal vesicle and opens laterally near the anterior end on the ventral surface by way of a muscular terminal portion provided with a penis papilla, and supplied by prostatic glands. The ovary consists of numerous bilaterally arranged

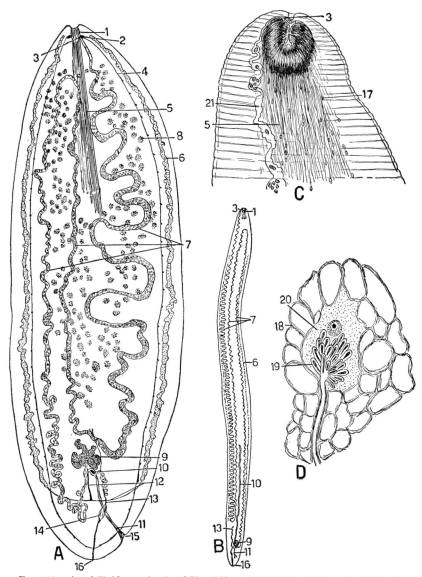

Fig. 143.—Amphilinidea. *A. Amphilina foliacea (after Hein, 1904). B. Schizochoerus liguloideus,* to 10 cm. long. *C.* Anterior end of *Schizochoerus* showing proboscis and frontal glands. (*B, C, after Poche,* 1925.) *D.* Flame cell of *Amphilina* with cluster of flame bulbs (*after Hein,* 1904). 1, proboscis; 2, brain; 3, uterine pore; 4, lateral nerve cords; 5, proboscis retractor; 6, yolk glands; 7, three parts of uterus; 8, testes; 9, ovary; 10, seminal receptacle; 11, vagina; 12, yolk ducts; 13, sperm duct; 14, propulsion vesicle; 15, female pore; 16, male pore; 17, frontal glands; 18, mesenchyme; 19, flame bulbs; 20, flame-cell; 21, terminal part of uterus.

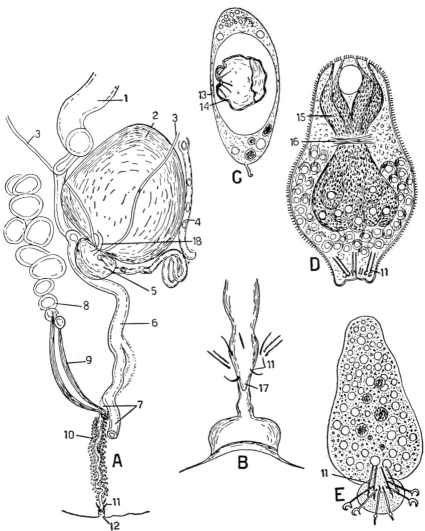

FIG. 144.—Amphilinidea (continued). *A.* Sex ducts of *Schizochoerus. B.* Termination of male duct of *Schizochoerus* to show embryonic hooks. (*A, B, after Poche,* 1925.) *C.* Capsule of *Amphilina,* containing the lycophore. *D.* Lycophore of *Amphilina* with large frontal glands. *E.* Procercoid of *Amphilina.* (*C–E, after Janicki,* 1928.) 1, seminal receptacle; 2, ovary; 3, yolk ducts; 4, beginning of uterus; 5, shell gland; 6, vagina; 7, dorsal and ventral terminations of vagina; 8, sperm duct; 9, propulsion vesicle; 10, prostatic glands; 11, embryonic hooks; 12, male pore; 13, capsule; 14, embryo; 15, frontal glands; 16, brain; 17, penis papilla; 18, oviduct.

follicles in the rear part of the body. Several oviductules from the ovarian follicles unite to form the oviduct which first presents an ovicapt, then receives the duct of the large seminal receptacle and the common yolk duct, and then becomes the uterus. After receiving the shell glands the uterus proceeds anteriorly in the central part of the body in closely appressed coils and opens in the middorsal line shortly behind the proboscis. The vagina extends from the seminal receptacle, which may be regarded as an expansion of it, to the anterior end, where it opens dorsally and laterally near the male pore. Thus the three sexual pores and the nephridiopores are near the anterior end, according to the orientation of *Gyrocotyle* here adopted. The yolk glands consist of follicles scattered throughout most of the body but especially in lateral regions. Numerous yolk ductules unite to form a pair of main transverse ducts that join to a common duct provided with a yolk reservoir.

Within the oval capsules provided or not with an operculum, the egg undergoes more or less development during its passage along the uterus. A typical lycophore larva results, closely resembling that of *Amphilina*, except that an epidermis is lacking; instead there is an embryonic membrane, presumably representing the epidermis, between the larva and the capsule. The capsules escape to the exterior through the abdominal pores of the host. Development of the lycophore, if incomplete, is completed after discharge into the water. According to the account of Ruszkowski (1932) for *G. urna*, there is no intermediate host but very young stages still retaining the larval hooks may be found in the host fish.

Besides several species of *Gyrocotyle*, the order contains only *Gyrocotyloides nybelini*, described by Fuhrmann (1930); this has a long slender neck-like posterior region with a slightly developed rosette. According to the opinion of Lynch (1945), *Gyrocotyloides* is merely an especially elongated immature specimen of *Gyrocotyle*.

12. Order Tetraphyllidea.—The tetraphyllid or phyllobothrioid tapeworms are polyzoic forms characterized by the scolex provided with four bothridia. The group as here limited parasitizes exclusively the intestine of elasmobranch fishes. The tetraphyllids are mostly of small size, not exceeding 10 cm. in length, with not more than a few hundred proglottids (Figs. 129C, 147C). The bothridia occur in a great variety of shapes, even in the same genus. They may be sessile or borne on short or long stalks (Fig. 147D). The simplest form is that of an elongated oval with incurved margins (Fig. 147D); a variant from this is a more or less extensive ruffling of the margins as in some species of *Phyllobothrium* (Fig. 128E). Very often the bothridium is divided by septa into areolae or loculi, as three in *Trilocularia* (Fig. 129C) and numerous small ones in *Echeneibothrium* (Fig. 128D). There may be one or more small accessory suckers in or above the upper end of the bothridia; they probably repre-

sent isolated areolae (Fig. 147A).   The bothridia may be armed at their
upper ends with one or more large, mostly bifid or trifid, hooks.   The
apex of the scolex may be provided with a single sucker or a conspicuous
cluster of glands or a myzorhynchus that may be armed with suckers

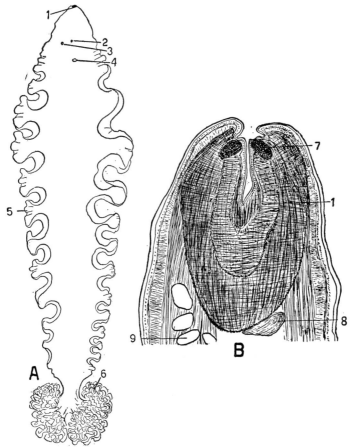

Fig. 145.—Gyrocotylidea.   A. *Gyrocotyle*, from life, Puget Sound.   B. Longitudinal
section through the proboscis of *Gyrocotyle* (*after Watson*, 1911).   1, proboscis; 2, male pore;
3, female pore; 4, uterine pore; 5, ruffle; 6, rosette; 7, sphincter; 8, brain; 9, testes.

(Fig. 128C).   A metascolex may be present as in *Thysanocephalum* (Fig.
129E).

    There may be a head stalk or a typical neck, or the proglottids may
begin directly behind the scolex.   The youngest proglottids are usually
much broader than long, but the older ones tend to be squarish or longer
than broad (Fig. 147C).   The proglottids may be craspedote, sometimes
with a scalloped velum.   An unusual method of proglottid formation was
reported by Curtis (1906) for *Phyllobothrium dohrnii* (= *Crossobothrium*

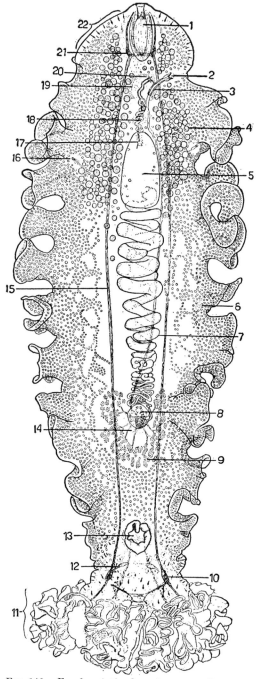

FIG. 146.—For descriptive legend see opposite page.

laciniatum) in which the strobila after proliferating in the usual manner
at the rear end of the neck begins to form proglottids immediately behind
the scolex from before backward, i.e., contrary to the usual method (Fig.
148*A*). The two areas of proliferation eventually meet so that the entire
strobila becomes segmented. In tetraphyllids the proglottids are often
shed while immature and develop to maturity while motile in the host
intestine. Such isolated proglottids often alter at their anterior end to a
rounded, scolex-like shape that is sometimes provided with spines (Fig.
147*B*).

The mesenchymal musculature shows varying degrees of development
but is usually sufficiently obvious to divide the mesenchyme into central
and cortical regions. There are usually fewer than 10 longitudinal nerve
trunks through the strobila. The excretory system generally retains its
primitive condition with a recurved tubule on each side that makes a loop
in each of two bothridia (Fig. 131*D*); transverse connections between the
two tubules may or may not be present. Both tubules enter the urinary
bladder at the rear end of the strobila.

Each proglottid contains a single reproductive system that opens at
the lateral margin by a genital antrum on either side, usually without
regularity. The numerous testis follicles extend throughout most of the
proglottid in the central mesenchyme either dorsally or in lateral fields
(Figs. 134*A*, 147*B*). The sinuous sperm duct proceeds anteriorly, makes
a coil, and enters the cirrus sac within which it is often extensively coiled.
The cirrus is usually armed with hairs, spines, or hooks. The ovary,
situated in the central mesenchyme in the rear part of the proglottid,
appears as a bilobed or butterfly-shaped mass of tubules but is generally
actually four-lobed so as to present an X-figure in cross sections (Fig.
134*C*). The oviduct begins with an ovicapt and after giving off the
vagina receives the shell glands at a slightly indicated ootype and then
the yolk ducts. The vagina presents a proximal seminal receptacle,
sometimes of very large size, and then runs forward to the antrum crossing the sperm duct so that its terminal part lies anterior to the latter
(Fig. 134*A*). The yolk glands typically occur in a lengthwise strand on
each side in the central mesenchyme lateral to the testes (Fig. 134*A*, *C*).
The uterus at first extends forward from the uterine tube as a median
tube through the length of the proglottid, but as the proglottid ripens the
uterus widens and may show lateral lobulations (Fig. 134*B*). The uterus
generally opens along the mid-ventral line of the proglottid by several

FIG. 146.—Gyrocotylidea (continued). *Gyrocotyle fimbriata*, showing details of structure
(*after Lynch*, 1945). 1, proboscis; 2, vaginal pore, 3, vagina; 4, testes; 5, uterine sac; 6, yolk
glands; 7, coils of uterus; 8, seminal receptacle; 9, ovary; 10, ganglion for rosette; 11, ruffles
of rosette; 12, nerve ring for rosette; 13, dorsal opening of funnel; 14, shell gland; 15, lateral
nerve cord; 16, nephridiopore; 17, uterine pore; 18, sperm duct; 19, prostatic glands; 20,
male pore; 21, brain ganglion; 22, spines on anterior margin.

openings, but these are usually regarded as ruptures. The thin-walled fusiform capsules lack an operculum but may be provided with a filament.

Very little is known of the life cycle of the tetraphyllids. A typical oncosphere larva occurs in the capsules either before or after they have been laid in seawater. Plerocercoids believed to belong to tetraphyllids have been found in copepods (Wundsch, 1912), marine fish (Monticelli, 1888), ctenophores (Van Cleave, 1927), mollusks, and various other marine animals. These plerocercoids, known for over 150 years under the name *Scolex pleuronectis* or *polymorphus*, have four cup-like suckers around the scolex and an apical sucker (Fig. 148E). Those from marine fishes have been observed to develop into young tetraphyllids of the genus *Calliobothrium* (Zschokke, 1886; Monticelli, 1888), but obviously larvae of many different species of tetraphyllids have been confused under one name. Cysticerci also occur in tetraphyllids, for Baylis (1919) found many such that were evidently young stages of *Phyllobothrium* encysted in the peritoneum of a dolphin. As dolphins are subject to attack by large sharks there would be opportunity for the completion of such a cycle. These fragmentary data indicate the same type of cycle for tetraphyllids as occurs in other eucestodes, involving two intermediate hosts.

The systematics of this order appears to be very confused, and generic distinctions have proved difficult of definition so that numerous generic names have been created in the past that have been reduced to synonyms by later authors. Some of the more extensive articles on the group are those of Shipley and Hornell (1906), Linton (1924), Southwell (1925, 1930), Woodland (1927), and Hart (1936). Two families are usually recognized: Phyllobothriidae without, and Onchobothriidae with, hooks on the scolex, but this character seems hardly adequate for familial distinctions. Some genera of the Phyllobothriidae are: *Anthobothrium* (Fig. 147D) with simple bothridia; *Phyllobothrium* (includes *Monorygma*, *Crossobothrium*, *Anthocephalum*) with simple, often ruffled bothridia provided with an accessory sucker at the upper end (Figs. 128E, 147A); *Dinobothrium* (Linton, 1922a) with a hook-like projection above each bothridium (Fig. 147E); *Orygmatobothrium* with an additional accessory sucker in the center of each bothridium (Fig. 148B); *Trilocularia* with three areolae (Fig. 129C); *Echeneibothrium* (= *Rhinebothrium*) with numerous small areolae and with a myzorhynchus at least in young stages (Figs. 128D, 131D); *Myzophyllobothrium* with a myzorhynchus topped with four suckers (Fig. 128C); and *Carpobothrium* with peculiar rounded bothridia bearing two flaps (Fig. 148D).

Of the Onchobothriidae may be mentioned: *Onchobothrium* with three loculi and two simple hooks to each bothridium; *Acanthobothrium* with three loculi, one to three accessory suckers and two bifid hooks to each

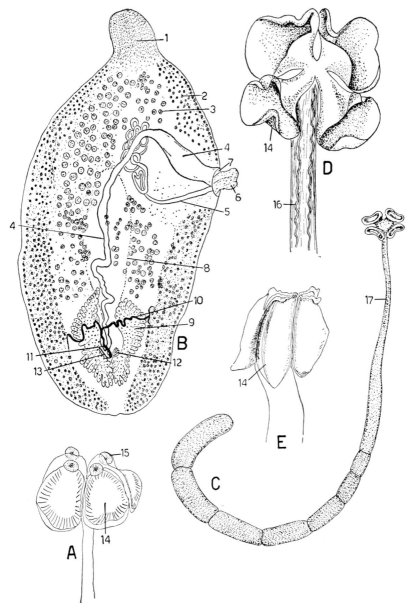

FIG. 147.—Tetraphyllidea. *A.* Scolex of *Phyllobothrium*, from life, Cape Cod. *B.* Free sexually mature proglottid of *Phyllobothrium* (*after Linton*, 1922b). *C. Anthobothrium*, entire worm (*after Southwell*, 1912). *D.* Scolex of *Anthobothrium* (*after Southwell*, 1925). *E.* Scolex of *Dinobothrium*, from life, Cape Cod. 1, modified anterior end of proglottid; 2, yolk glands; 3, testes; 4, vagina; 5, sperm duct; 6, cirrus; 7, gonopore; 8, early stage of uterus; 9, ovary; 10, yolk ducts; 11, common yolk duct; 12 shell gland; 13, oviduct; 14, bothridium; 15, accessory sucker; 16, excretory vessels; 17, head stalk.

bothridium (Fig. 128G); *Calliobothrium*, similar, but with two pairs of simple hooks above each bothridium (Fig. 148C); and *Thysanocephalum* with two loculi and two simple hooks to each bothridium and a very large ruff-like metascolex (usually erroneously called pseudoscolex, Fig. 129E). *Thysanocephalum* has been the subject of special articles by Linton (1892) and Causey (1926).

13. Order Lecanicephaloidea.—The systematic position of the forms included here has been very uncertain. Because of the tetraphyllid character of their reproductive system the cestodes in question are often placed in the order Tetraphyllidea but their scolex departs widely from that typical of this order. How they are classified therefore depends on whether the scolex or the reproductive system is regarded as of the more importance as a taxonomic character. They are here considered a separate order following Southwell (1930) and divided into three families as indicated by Pintner's study (1928). Many of the members of this order were originally described from Massachusetts by Linton (1890).

The lecanicephaloids are distinguished by the peculiar scolex divided into two portions, a lower mostly globose or collar-like part bearing four acetabula like those of taenioids, and an upper part that may be disk-like or globular or divided up into tentacles or petals, or provided with a powerful myzorhynchus or a gland cluster. Like the tetraphyllids, the lecanicephaloids inhabit exclusively the intestine of elasmobranch fishes with the rounded scolex buried in the intestinal wall. They are relatively small tapeworms mostly with a short slender strobila. The reproductive system is practically identical with that of the tetraphyllids, having the gonopore in the lateral margin and the yolk glands as lateral strands of follicles; however, the vagina may be anterior or posterior to the cirrus sac.

The principal family, Lecanicephalidae, forms acraspedote apolytic strobilae in which the ripe proglottids are long and slender. The rear part of the scolex is rounded or quadratic with four acetabula and the anterior part varies with the genus, but in any case is nonglandular. In *Lecanicephalum* (Fig. 149A), it is a myzorhynchus that is globular or disk-like when protruded. In *Polypocephalus* (= *Paraiaenia, Thysanobothrium*), the upper part of the scolex consists of a mass of tentacles (Fig. 149B) and in *Anthemobothrium* (Fig. 149C) of a circle of petal-like ruffled processes. *Adelobothrium* (Fig. 149D) also has a large conical myzorhynchus but differs from *Lecanicephalum* in the thin collar-like form of the rear part of the scolex.

The family Cephalobothriidae forms markedly craspedote strobilae and differs from the Lecanicephalidae also in that the anterior part of the scolex consists of a protrusible glandular mass as in *Cephalobothrium* (Fig. 149E, F), *Discobothrium*, and *Tylocephalum*.

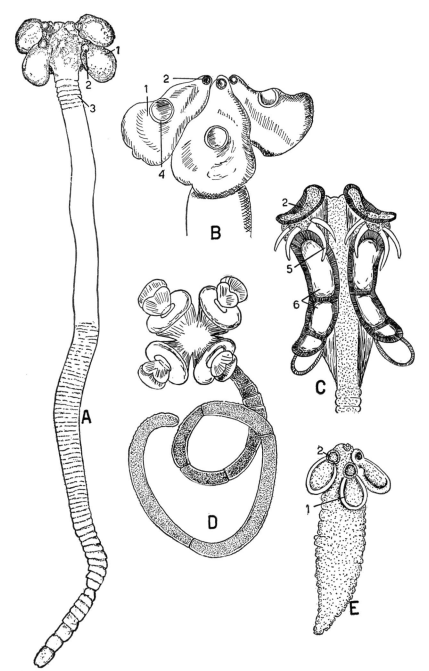

Fig. 148.—Tetraphyllidea (continued). *A. Phyllobothrium dohrnii*, entire worm, showing unusual method of proglottid formation (*after Curtis*, 1906). *B.* Scolex of *Orygmatobothrium* (*after Joyeaux and Baer*, 1936). *C.* Scolex of *Calliobothrium* (*after Southwell*, 1925). *D. Carpobothrium*, entire worm (*after Shipley and Hornell*, 1906). *E.* Plerocercoid of *Calliobothrium* from the swordfish (*after Linton*, 1922a). 1, bothridia; 2, accessory sucker; 3, secondary zone of proglottid formation; 4, sucker on bothridium; 5, hooks; 6, areolae.

The third family, Discocephalidae, comprises the single species *Disco-cephalum pileatum* from the spiral valve of the shark *Carcharias* (Linton, 1890). It has a globular scolex devoid of any organs of attachment but with a velum over the neck, and an acraspedote anapolytic strobila with ripe segments of quadratic shape (Fig. 150*A*, *B*). The reproductive system resembles that of tetraphyllids with the vagina anterior to the cirrus sac but the distribution of the follicles of the yolk gland is trypanorhynchid. The anatomy and histology of *Discocephalum* have been thoroughly described by Pintner (1928).

Little is known of the life cycle of the lecanicephaloids. Globular larvae (Fig. 149*G*) believed to be those of *Tylocephalum* are common in the digestive gland of the pearl oyster and other bivalves of the Orient; the best account of these has been given by Jameson (1912). Feeding of these larvae to sharks failed to yield adult *Tylocephalum* but possibly the proper host was not among those tried. A theory was put forth by Herdman in 1902 that the *Tylocephalum* larvae are one of the causes of pearl formation and remains of them are to be found in the center of the pearls. Although Southwell (1924) supported this theory, Jameson (1912), in whose article a complete history of the controversy is given, was unable to find any support for the idea and could identify nothing remotely resembling tapeworm larvae in the center of pearls. The theory appears unlikely since the tapeworm larvae occur encysted in the interior tissues of the oyster whereas pearls are produced by the epidermis.

14. Order Proteocephaloidea.—The members of this order are also of uncertain position because as in lecanocephaloids they combine a taenioid type of scolex with a tetraphyllid type of reproductive system. They are often considered families of the order Tetraphyllidea. Some principal articles on the group are those of Benedict (1900), La Rue (1909, 1914), Rudin (1917), Fuhrmann and Baer (1925), Woodland (1925, 1933), Meggitt (1927), and Harwood (1933). The proteocephaloid tapeworms are parasites of the intestine of fresh-water cold-blooded vertebrates, except *Lintoniella*, found in elasmobranchs.

The globular scolex bears four more or less mobile acetabula and often presents loose folds, wrinkles, etc., indicative of much lability of form. The apex of the scolex frequently bears an apical organ in the form of a sucker (chiefly in *Proteocephalus*, Fig. 150*C*, *D*) or a muscular or glandular mass or a structure of unrecognizable nature believed by La Rue (1914) to be a rudimentary or degenerate sucker. A rostellum encircled by hooks occurs in the genus *Gangesia* (Fig. 151*F*). A more or less ruffled fold or collar resembling a metascolex encircles the base of the scolex in some genera as *Corallobothrium* (Fig. 151*B*) and *Goezeella* (Fig. 150*F*). The strobila, varying from a few millimeters to over 60 cm. in length, is acraspedote with evident or obscure segmentation. The ripe proglottids

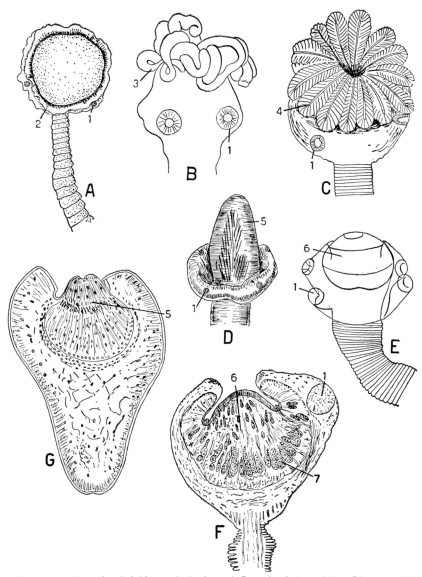

FIG. 149.—Lecanicephaloidea. *A*. Scolex of *Lecanicephalum* (*after Linton*, 1891). *B. Polypocephalus* (*after Linton*, 1891). *C. Anthemobothrium* (*after Shipley and Hornell*, 1906). *D. Adelobothrium* (*after Southwell*, 1925). *E. Cephalobothrium* (*after Pintner*, 1928). *F*. Section through the scolex of *Cephalobothrium*, showing protrusible glandular mass (*after Pintner*, 1928). *G. Tylocephalum* larva from the pearl oyster (*after Jameson*, 1912). 1, sucker; 2, upper part of scolex; 3, tentacles; 4, petals; 5, myzorhynchus; 6, glandular mass; 7, gland cells.

range from quadratic to elongated in shape with the gonopore in the lateral margin (Fig. 150E). Longitudinal mesenchymal muscle bundles, often very strongly developed, divide the mesenchyme into central and cortical regions in many species but may be weak or absent in others. There appears to be but one pair of longitudinal nerves, the lateral ones. The reproductive system is tetraphyllid in character. The numerous testes occur dorsally in an even distribution or disposed in more or less definite lateral fields, the bilobed ovary is at the posterior end of the proglottid, the follicular yolk glands form lateral bands, and the cirrus sac may be anterior or posterior to the vagina (Fig. 150E). The uterus is a slender median tube at first but as it ripens puts out a few to many broad to narrow lateral diverticula and may form one or more median ventral openings (Fig. 151C, E).

The classification within the order is confused, and the usual arguments exist about generic synonymy. Following certain authors, there are here recognized two families: the Proteocephalidae in which the main reproductive organs lie entirely within the central mesenchyme and the Monticelliidae in which some or all of them are in the cortical mesenchyme; but other workers unite all the genera under the first-named family. The sweeping elimination of genera proposed by Woodland (1925) has not met with general approval, although it must be admitted that many genera of the order rest on slight distinctions.

In the Proteocephalidae, the principal genus Proteocephalus (= Ichthyotaenia and includes Teleostotaenia and Choanoscolex), with numerous species in fresh-water fish, amphibians, and reptiles, is characterized by the simple scolex with four acetabula and an apical sucker, and the evenly distributed testes (Figs. 150C–E). Some other genera are Ophiotaenia (includes Ophidiotaenia, Solenotaenia, Batrachotaenia), in amphibians and reptiles, similar to Proteocephalus but with testes in lateral fields (Fig. 151A, C–E); Corallobothrium, in catfish, with a scolex collar (Fig. 151B); Crepidobothrium, with notched suckers, in reptiles; Acanthotaenia, with well-developed apical organ and fine spination on the scolex and anterior part of the strobila, found in lizards of the family Varanidae; Gangesia, from catfish, with armed rostellum (Fig. 151F); and Lintoniella with yolk glands encircling the other reproductive organs, from a shark.

The Monticelliidae parasitize the intestine of catfishes; they have various parts of the reproductive system in the cortical mesenchyme. Some genera are: Marsypocephalus (= Loennbergia) with only the testes cortical: Zygobothrium with only the yolk glands cortical; Ephedrocephalus (= Rudolphiella) with cortical testes and yolk glands; Monticellia with cortical testes, yolk glands, uterus, and ovary in part; and Goezeella with scolex collar and all four reproductive organs in the cortical mesenchyme.

Several studies have been made on the life cycle of the Proteoceph-

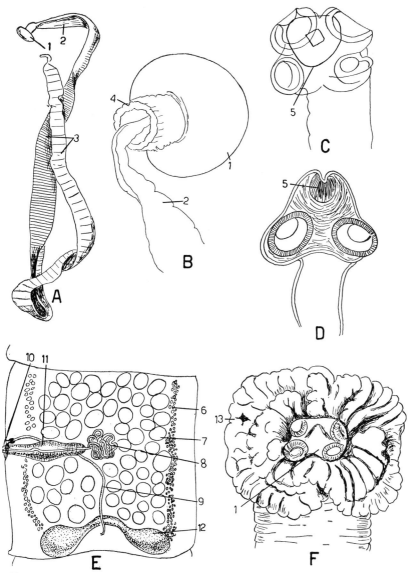

Fig. 150.—Lecanicephaloidea, Proteocephaloidea. *A. Discocephalum pileatum* entire
worm. *B.* Scolex of *Discocephalum.* (*A, B, after Pintner,* 1928.)   *C, D.* Scolex of *Proteocephalus,* entire and section (*after Woodland,* 1925), showing terminal sucker. *E.* Mature
proglottid of *Proteocephalus* (*after La Rue,* 1914). *F.* Scolex of *Goezeella* (*after Fuhrmann,*
1916). 1, scolex; 2, neck; 3, strobila; 4, velum; 5, apical sucker; 6, yolk glands; **7**, testes;
8, sperm duct; 9, vagina; 10, gonopore; 11, cirrus sac; 12, ovary; 13, ruff.

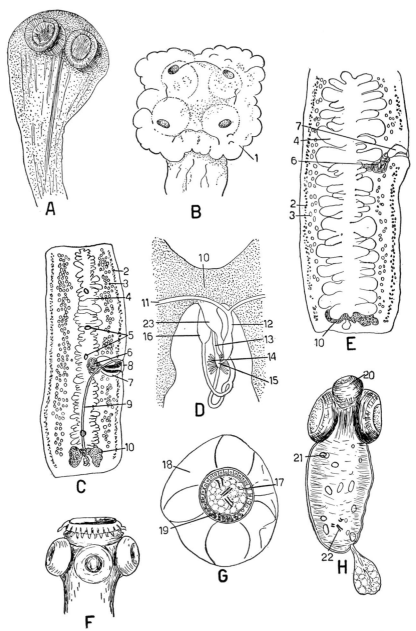

Fig. 151.—Proteocephaloidea (continued). A. Scolex of *Ophiotaenia* (*after Nybelin*, 1917). B. Scolex of *Corallobothrium* (*after Van Cleave and Mueller*, 1934). C. Mature proglottid of *Ophiotaenia*. D. Female ducts of same. E. Ripe proglottid of *Ophiotaenia*. (*C–E, after La Rue*, 1914). F. Scolex of *Gangesia* (*after Southwell*, 1913). G. Membranated hexacanth of *Ophiotaenia*. H. Procercoid of *Ophiotaenia*. (*G, H, after Thomas*, 1931.) 1, ruff; 2, yolk glands; 3, testes; 4, uterus; 5, uterine pores; 6, sperm duct; 7, cirrus sac; 8,

alidae: on *Proteocephalus* (Kuczkowski, 1925; Hunter, 1928); on *Ophiotaenia* (Magath, 1929; Thomas, 1931, 1934, 1941; Herde, 1938); and on *Corallobothrium* (Essex, 1927; Larsh, 1941). The cycle is similar to that of bothriocephaloids. The oncosphere surrounded by membranes (Fig. 151*G*) is ingested by copepods of the genus *Cyclops* in which it penetrates the intestine into the body cavity and there develops to a procercoid and then to a plerocercoid stage with suckers (Fig. 151*H*). The definitive host can be infected directly by eating parasitized *Cyclops* or by eating small fish or tadpoles that have fed on such *Cyclops*.

15. Order Diphyllidea.—This order contains the single genus *Echinobothrium*, small tapeworms of less than 20 proglottids that inhabit the intestine of elasmobranch fishes. The anatomy of *Echinobothrium* was thoroughly elucidated by Pintner (1889). The relatively large scolex has a powerful muscular rostellum armed with dorsal and ventral groups of large hooks and several rows of small hooks and bears four bothria of slight muscularity that are fused in pairs (Fig. 152*A*). This part of the scolex is followed by a long head stalk bearing eight longitudinal rows of T-shaped hooks. This is followed by the cylindroid acraspedote weakly muscular strobila. In the mature proglottids (Fig. 152*B*) the gonopore lies in the mid-ventral line in the posterior part. The anterior half of the proglottid is occupied by the few, relatively large, testes from which the sperm duct leads to the cirrus sac. In the rear part of the proglottid lies the bilobed ovary and the follicular yolk glands occur as lateral strands. The young uterus is a median tube that later expands to a sac, without external opening.

As regards the life cycle, it is known that larval stages of *Echinobothrium* inhabit marine mollusks and crustaceans. The best account is that of Ruszowski (1927), who found the cysticercoid larva of *E. benedeni* in the decapod crustacean *Hippolyte*.

16. Order Trypanorhyncha or Tetrarhynchoidea.—The members of this order are distinguished from all other cestodes by the four spiny proboscides that can be everted from the scolex (Fig. 152*C, D*). They are tapeworms of small to moderate size, ranging from a few to about 100 mm. in length, that parasitize the digestive tract, chiefly the spiral valve, of elasmobranch fishes. The genus *Haplobothrium* occurs in the ganoid fish *Amia calva*. Some of the principal studies on the group are those of Pintner (1880, 1893, 1896, 1903, 1925, 1929), Vaullegeard (1899), Johnstone (1912), Southwell (1929, 1930), and Hart (1936).

The elongated scolex is divisible into a bothrial part and a long head

gonopore; 9, vagina; 10, ovary; 11, yolk duct; 12, common yolk duct; 13, beginning of uterus; 14, shell gland; 15, ootype; 16, seminal receptacle; 17, hexacanth; 18, outer gelatinous membrane; 19, inner membrane; 20, apical sucker (degenerates later); 21, calcareous bodies; 22, hooks: 23, oviduct.

stalk that houses the proboscis apparatus (Fig. 152*D*). The bothrial
part bears two or four shallow sucking organs, usually considered to be
bothridia, but their weak muscularity more accurately classifies them as
bothria. When four are present they are often more or less fused in
pairs, and undoubtedly the presence of four distinct bothridia was the
original condition for the order. In consequence of the development of
the proboscides, the bothridia underwent degeneration into weak bothria.
The apertures of the four proboscides occur at or in the upper part of the
bothria. Each proboscis is contained in a long, often sinuous tube, the
proboscis sheath, that terminates at the proximal end of the long head
stalk in an oval muscular mass, the *proboscis bulb* (Fig. 152*D*). The
proboscis itself is situated inside the distal part of the proboscis sheath; it
is a blind tube lined with a variety of hooks, thorns, etc., and is eversible
to the exterior so that the thorny side is then the outer surface (Fig.
152*C, D*). The thorns may be alike or nearly so along the length of the
proboscides or of varying shapes and sizes, and their form and pattern
constitute important taxonomic characters for distinguishing species
(Fig. 152*E, F*). From the inner blind end of the proboscis a retractor
muscle runs down the center of the proboscis sheath and terminates on or
in the proboscis bulb. Proboscis and sheath are composed chiefly of
cuticle with some retention of subcuticular structures; the sheath is lined
with a flattened epithelium. The proboscis bulb consists of layers of
muscle fibers usually arranged in a concentric manner around the central
cavity that is a continuation of the sheath (Fig. 153*B*). The retractor
muscle usually proceeds along this cavity to terminate at the rear end of
the bulb. In some tetrarhynchids clusters of gland cells open into the
proboscis apparatus. The whole apparatus is filled with fluid, and
presumably contraction of the muscle bulbs forces the fluid against the
inner ends of the proboscides, causing them to evert to the exterior. The
retractor muscles draw them back in again. Both the proboscides and
the bothria are said to serve chiefly in locomotion rather than for attachment to the host. According to the generally accepted theory of Pintner
(1896) and Poche (1924), the proboscis apparatus has evolved from accessory suckers such as occur in tetraphyllids; these have sunk into the
interior, their cuticular lining has become the proboscis and sheath, and
their muscular wall develops into the bulb (Fig. 154*C–E*).

   In many tetrarhynchids, especially in the larval stages, one or more
clusters of frontal glands open on the apex of the scolex (Fig. 153*D*).

   The rear end of the head stalk may be separated from the neck by a
constriction (Fig. 152*D*) or may form a velum, but often the neck is not
evidently demarcated. The strobila is usually acraspedote but may be
craspedote with scalloped margin and is mostly anapolytic, sometimes
apolytic. The ripe proglottids vary from quadratic to elongated in shape

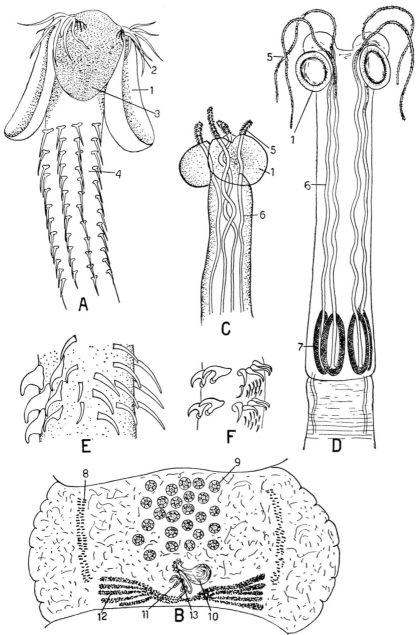

Fig. 152.—Diphyllidea, Trypanorhyncha. *A. Echinobothrium. B.* Mature proglottid of *Echinobothrium.* (*A, B, after Southwell,* 1930.) *C. Grillotia (after Hart,* 1936). *D. Gilquinia anteroporus,* from life, Puget Sound. *E.* Spine arrangement on proboscis of *Gilquinia (after Hart,* 1936). *F.* Spine arrangement on proboscis of *Grillotia (after Johnstone,* 1911). 1, bothria; 2, rostellar spines; 3, rostellum; 4, head stalk with spines; 5, proboscides; 6, proboscis sheath; 7, proboscis bulb; 8, yolk glands; 9, testes; 10, cirrus sac; 11, vagina; 12, ovary; 13, gonopore.

and bear the gonopore in the lateral margin; except in *Haplobothrium* in which the gonopore is in the mid-ventral line. The usual longitudinal muscle bundles divide the mesenchyme into central and cortical regions. The nervous system of the scolex (Pintner, 1880; Johnstone, 1912) consists of four ganglionic masses on each side connected by a median broad commissure and two slender more anterior commissures that form a ring (Fig. 154*A*). From each ganglion springs a large bothrial nerve so that each bothrium is supplied by an anterior and a posterior nerve. The main lateral nerve springs from the ganglionic masses of each side and extends backward throughout the strobila, forming at the rear end of the bothrial part of the scolex a ganglionic enlargement from which arises a proboscidial nerve forking to supply the two proboscis apparatuses of that side. *Aporhynchus* (Rees, 1941, Fig. 154*B*) differs in that the posterior ganglionic mass is single on each side, proboscidial nerves are absent as this genus lacks proboscides, and the four longitudinal bothrial nerves spring from the brain and lateral nerves by six roots and give off six nerves into the adjacent bothrium. Rees (1941) also described the nervous system of the plerocercoid larva of *Dibothriorhynchus;* this is characterized chiefly by the numerous regularly spaced branches arising from the lateral and proboscidial nerves. In most tetrarhynchids the lateral nerves appear to constitute the only longitudinal trunks of the strobila, but Subramanian (1940) reported in *Tentacularia* some sixty longitudinal nerves lying outside the yolk glands. From these fibers are distributed to the surface tissues and internal organs and a nerve plexus occupies the central mesenchyme.

The reproductive system (Fig. 155*A*) is single in each proglottid except in the genus *Dibothriorhynchus* (= *Coenomorphus*) in which it is double. It resembles that of tetraphyllids except that the vagina and sperm duct do not cross and the yolk glands, although sometimes in lateral strands, usually encircle the other reproductive organs, lying outside, intermingled with, or inside the longitudinal muscle bundles of the mesenchyme. The numerous testes occupy most of the proglottid during the immature phase, extending even behind the ovary. The cirrus sac often contains one or two seminal vesicles, or there may be one or two very muscular external seminal vesicles that seem to function as propulsion organs. The uterus, at first a median tube, becomes sacciform as it ripens and in some genera has a true opening in the mid-ventral line but usually discharges by ruptures.

The classification within the order has been much discussed (Pintner, 1913, 1927; Southwell, 1929, 1930; Dollfus, 1929, 1930; Guiart, 1931) and is characterized by confusion and multiplication of generic names. The attempt of Guiart (1931) adopted by Fuhrmann (1931) to classify the trypanorhynchids on the basis of the larval type was shown by Joyeaux and Baer (1934) to be mistaken. The following generic definitions and synonymy are taken from Joyeaux and Baer (1936). The principal genera with four bothria are *Tentacularia* (= *Tetrarhynchus*, *Stenobothrium*), *Nybelinia*, *Gymnorhynchus* (= *Floriceps*), and *Gilquinia* (Fig.

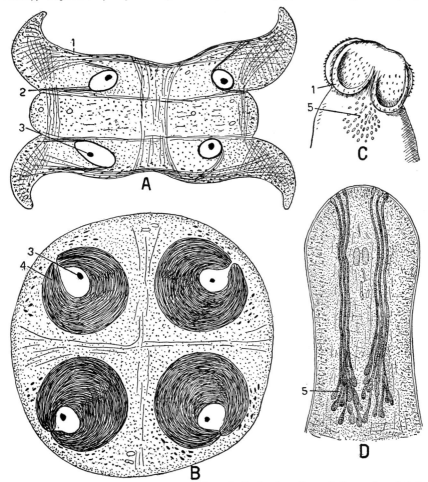

Fig. 153.—Trypanorhyncha (continued). *A, B.* Sections through the scolex of *Griliotia erinacea* (after Johnstone, 1911). *C.* Scolex of *Aporhynchus* (after Joyeaux and Baer, 1936). *D.* Longitudinal section of scolex of *Aporhynchus* (after Rees, 1941) to show frontal glands. 1, bothria; 2, proboscis sheath; 3, retractor muscle; 4, proboscis bulb; 5, frontal glands.

152D, E). In *Tentacularia* and *Nybelinia* (Fig. 155D, E) the bothria are elongated or foliaceous and the proboscis spines are equally sized throughout. *Gymnorhynchus* and *Gilquinia* (Fig. 152D) have circular or oval bothria and in the former the basal part of the proboscides lacks spines. The other genera (except the two aberrant ones, below) have two bothria, often with indications of an original doubleness.   In *Dibothriorhynchus*, with double reproductive system, and *Sphyriocephalus* the bothria are rounded with a thickened rim and are subdivided by a longitudinal septum.   More foliaceous bothria with a posterior notch occur in *Eutetra-rhynchus* with similar proboscis spines, *Grillotia* (Fig. 152*C*, *F*) with very dissimilar spines along the proboscides, and *Otobothrium* (Fig. 155*F*) with four eversible spiny pits on the bothria.   A definite uterine pore occurs in *Dibothriorhynchus, Sphyriocephalus,* and *Tentacularia.*

Two aberrant genera, *Aporhynchus* and *Haplobothrium*, are generally considered to be trypanorhynchids.   *Aporhynchus*, described by Nybelin (1918), nervous system by Rees (1941), has four bothria and conspicuous clusters of frontal glands (Fig. 153*C*, *D*) but altogether lacks the proboscis apparatus.   However, as it shows many trypanorhynchid characters (encircling of the other reproductive organs by the yolk glands, cirrus with large propulsion vesicle, vagina behind the cirrus with no crossing, testes strewn through the proglottid), *Aporhynchus* is generally regarded as a trypanorhynchid in which the proboscis apparatuses have been lost by degeneration, leaving only some traces in the scolex musculature.

A number of peculiarities are presented by *Haplobothrium globuliforme*, from the intestine of the fresh-water fish *Amia calva* (Cooper, 1914, 1915, 1919).   This tapeworm lacks bothria but has four proboscis apparatuses, atypical in that the proboscides are unarmed, the muscle bulbs are attached directly to them without the intervention of a sheath, and the sheaths seem to be represented by permanently protruded spiny tubes (Fig. 155*B*).   The strobila consists of long proglottids that undergo secondary segmentation anteriorly into a number of proglottids, some very craspedote (Fig. 155*C*).   These segmented proglottids break loose and exist free in the fish intestine as secondary strobila of which the first proglottid alters to imitate a scolex with indications of two bothria. These secondary strobilae are further peculiar in that the most anterior proglottid is the largest and oldest and the size decreases posteriorly in the chain.   Other peculiarities of *Haplobothrium* are the presence of a median dorsal excretory vessel in addition to the usual two lateral ones and the location of the gonopore in the mid-ventral line of the anterior part of the proglottid.   Other features of the reproductive system are trypanorhynchid.

The complete life cycle is not known for any marine trypanorhynchid, but numerous advanced larval stages of trypanorhynchids have been found encysted in the coelom or tissues of a great variety of marine animals as medusae, holothurians, snails, bivalves, cephalopods, crusta-ceans, and especially teleost fish.   These larvae are mostly plerocercoids, with fully developed scolex, tailless or with a tail, sometimes very long, or with a vesicular appendage (Fig. 155*D*, *F*).   Sometimes the larvae are

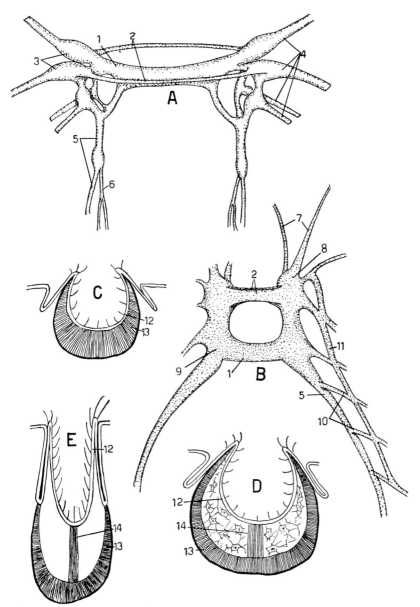

Fig. 154.—Trypanorhyncha (continued). *A.* Brain of *Grillotia* (*after Johnstone*, 1911). *B.* Brain of *Aporhynchus* (*after Rees*, 1941). *C, D, E.* Scheme of the origin of the proboscis apparatus from an accessory sucker (*after Pintner*, 1896). 1, transverse commissure; 2, anterior commissures to form ring; 3, ganglia; 4, four bothrial nerves; 5, main lateral nerve; 6, nerves to proboscis apparatus; 7, anterior nerves; 8, anterior ganglia (double); 9, posterior ganglion (single); 10, roots of bothrial nerve; 11, main bothrial nerve (two on each side); 12, lining, becomes proboscis sheath; 13, muscle layer, becomes proboscis bulb; 14, retractor muscle.

cysticercoids with the scolex enclosed in a tail or vesicle. All these forms represent the final larval stage that will develop into an adult trypanorhynchid when their host is eaten by a shark or ray. Presumably a procercoid stage in a first intermediate host exists, but none recognizable as such has been discovered.

The life cycle of *Haplobothrium globuliforme* has been completely elucidated (Essex, 1928, 1929; Thomas, 1930; Meinkoth, 1947). The eggs hatch into coracidia that develop into procercoids in *Cyclops*. Teleost fish, especially the bullhead (*Ameiurus nebulosus*), constitute the second intermediate host in which the fully developed plerocercoid with completed proboscides occurs encysted in the liver. The life cycle is therefore typically pseudophyllidean, and *Haplobothrium* should therefore possibly be transferred to the Pseudophyllidea; but a similar cycle may obtain for typical trypanorhynchids, and no decision can be reached until more is known about the latter.

17. Order Pseudophyllidea.—The pseudophyllid or bothriocephaloid tapeworms are polyzoic or monozoic forms that parasitize the intestine of all classes of vertebrates, chiefly nonelasmobranch fishes. Principal studies of this group are those of Lühe (1899, 1900), Cooper (1918), and Nybelin (1922).

The scolex, often not well differentiated, is in typical forms characterized by two shallow elongated bothria, one dorsal and one ventral (Fig. 156*A*), as in *Eubothrium, Dibothriocephalus, Bothriocephalus*, etc. Fusion processes result in various modifications of this condition. The edges of each bothrium may fuse together producing a tubular structure open at both ends as in *Bothridium* (Fig. 128*B*) or a flask-like sucking organ open only at the top (*Diplocotyle*, Fig. 156*H*). The two cups thus left on the anterior end of the scolex may fuse further to form a single sucking organ, partially divided by a septum as in *Bothrimonus* or undivided as in *Cyathocephalus* (Fig. 156*C, D*). An apical organ may also be present in the form of an additional depression or group of gland cells. A cap-like shape of the apex of the scolex is seen in a number of genera (Fig. 156*A, B*). In the family Triaenophoridae, the scolex is armed with hooks located either above the bothria or in a circle around the apex (*Ancistrocephalus*, Fig. 156*L*). In some pseudophyllids the bothrial edges widen posteriorly with or without partial fusion so as to give a fan-like shape to the scolex (Fig. 156*G*) and may be more or less ruffled. In the Caryophyllaeidae the flattened scolex may lack adhesive organs altogether or the scolex may be six-sided with six pit-like bothria (Figs. 127*A*, 157*E*). Finally, the scolex may degenerate or disappear and the anterior part of the strobila may become a pseudoscolex.

The scolex is not well delimited from the strobila, and a definite neck region is often lacking. The strobila is of small size in many genera but

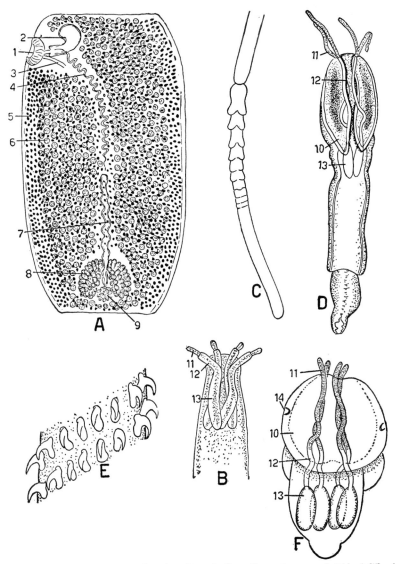

Fig. 155.—Trypanorhyncha (continued). *A.* Sexually mature proglottid of *Gilquinia anteroporus*, original. *B.* Scolex of *Haplobothrium*. *C.* Proglottid of *Haplobothrium*, developing a chain of proglottids. (*B, C, after Cooper, 1919.*) *D.* Larva of *Nybelinia*, from a ray. *E.* Spine arrangement of proboscis of *Nybelinia*. (*D, E, after Hart, 1936.*) *F.* Larva of *Otobothrium*, in bony fish (*after Southwell, 1929*). 1, antrum; 2, propulsion vesicle; 3, vagina; 4, sperm duct; 5, yolk glands; 6, testes; 7, young uterus; 8, ovary; 9, shell glands; 10, bothria; 11, proboscides; 12, sheath; 13, bulbs; 14, spiny pits.

reaches great length (to 10 m.) in the Diphyllobothriidae. The strobila is monozoic in the Caryophyllaeidae; in polyzoic genera it may be craspedote or acraspedote and is generally anapolytic, mostly with short broad proglottids. Growth is diffuse, and segmentation and proglottid formation are often irregular and obscure. Usually the external segmentation does not correspond to the internal anatomy in that an apparent proglottid may contain several to many sets of reproductive organs or one reproductive complex may show several often incomplete external constrictions. In the former case, secondary subdivisions of the proglottid may occur later, separating off the reproductive complexes. The pseudophyllids are mostly highly muscular. The longitudinal fibers of the subcuticular layer may be strengthened and the longitudinal mesenchymal muscles often form a thick zone that may be divisible into two layers permeated by the numerous dorsoventral and transverse fibers, and may be continuous with the subcuticular musculature.

The available accounts of the nervous system are not very satisfactory. Data have been furnished by Cohn (1898) for *Bothriocephalus*, *Bothridium*, *Schistocephalus*, and *Ligula* and Zernecke (1895) and Lühe (1896) have also reported on *Ligula* (Fig. 156J, K). In general, the two main lateral nerves form in the anterior part of the scolex two ganglionic thickenings (Fig. 156J) united by a commissure rich in nerve cells. In *Bothriocephalus* nerves proceeding anteriorly from this pair of ganglia are connected to form an apical nerve ring, but this appears to be absent in other genera. The two powerful tubular bothria of *Bothridium* (Fig. 128B) receive a complex innervation from nerves anterior to the brain ganglia whereas in *Bothriocephalus* the bothria are supplied from eight accessory longitudinal nerves that proceed posteriorly from the brain region; these accessory nerves are connected with the main lateral nerves (making 10 in all) by commissures in the scolex. The forms investigated have at least 10 longitudinal nerves in the strobila and *Ligula* (Fig. 156K) and *Schistocephalus* have up to 50 or 60. These are connected by a network and there also appears to be in *Ligula* a subcuticular nerve plexus with which the numerous neurosensory cells communicate (Fig. 131C).

In the excretory system there may be two, four, or many longitudinal vessels generally connected by a network in the central mesenchyme; and in addition there is generally present in pseudophyllids a subcuticular excretory network in the peripheral mesenchyme. This may open to the exterior by secondary openings, often numerous (Fig. 132G).

The pseudophyllid proglottid usually has but one set of reproductive organs (Figs. 135A, B, 158B) but two are present in certain genera (e.g., *Diplogonoporus*). The gonopore or pores may lie in or near the lateral margin but may also be situated ventrally or dorsally. From the numerous testes the coiled sperm duct, usually functioning as a spermiducal vesicle, proceeds to the cirrus sac before which it may enter a muscular seminal (propulsion) vesicle as in trypanorhynchids (Fig. 158*B*). The ovary is a lobulated body of varied shape situated in the central posterior part of the proglottid. The oviduct as usual presents an ovicapt, gives off the vagina, receives the common yolk duct, and enters a weak ootype provided with gland cells beyond which it becomes the uterus. The yolk glands are follicular and although sometimes in broad to narrow lateral fields usually are spread throughout the proglottid encircling the other reproductive organs (Fig. 135*B*) and are continuous throughout the strobila. The vagina frequently begins with a seminal receptacle. Its distal end may open in common with the cirrus sac or after junction with the cirrus into the genital antrum, or it may have a separate aperture near the male pore. The relative positions of vagina and cirrus sac are varied. The pseudophyllid uterus is usually a coiled tube (Fig. 158*B*) but may form a simple or lobulated sac in whole or in part. The sacciform condition appears to be the primitive one. The uterus usually opens on the ventral surface by a true uterine pore or by a rupture. In the families Cyathocephalidae and Caryophyllaeidae the uterus enters the vagina, and the resulting common uterovaginal canal (Fig. 159*D*) may or may not join the cirrus sac; the genital pores are median in these families. The capsules are thick-walled and operculate in the families Triaenophoridae, Ptychobothriidae, Cyathocephalidae, and Diphyllobothriidae, thin and nonoperculate in the others, except Caryophyllaeidae where varied conditions obtain. As a rule, the thick capsules develop only after laying whereas the thin ones are embryonated while in the uterus. The larva is a ciliated or unciliated coracidium.

The classification appears to have reached some stability, and seven families (some regarded as subfamilies by some authors) are generally recognized. Unless otherwise stated, all parasitize the intestine of ganoid and teleost fish. The Amphicotylidae are characterized by the lateral gonopore, sacciform uterus with no or a rudimentary pore, and small or absent seminal receptacle. Some genera are *Amphicotyle* with lower part of the bothria separated as an areola; *Eubothrium* (Fig. 156*A*) with cap-like apex and two ordinary rounded or oval bothria; *Marsipometra* (Fig. 156*B*) (Beaver and Simer, 1940) from the spoonbill *Polyodon* with lateral pouches to the uterus and distinct seminal receptacle; and *Abothrium*, in which the scolex, embedded in the mucosa of the pyloric caecae of fishes of the cod tribe, undergoes degeneration and deformation with loss of the bothria (Fig. 156*E, F*). The Triaenophoridae have also lateral gonopores but the uterus is tubular with a slightly enlarged terminal portion. The chief genera are *Triaenophorus*, a common cestode of fresh-water fishes, with monozoic strobila, and four trifid hooks above the bothria just beneath the cap-like summit of the scolex (Fig. 157*A*); *Ancistrocephalus*

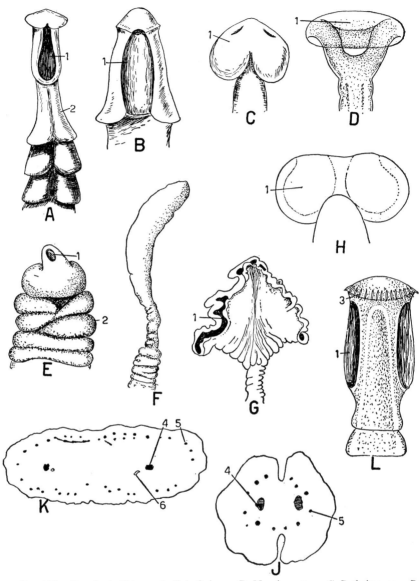

FIG. 156.—Pseudophyllidea. *A. Eubothrium. B. Marsipometra. C. Bothrimonus. D. Cyathocephalus. E. Abothrium gadi*, with scolex. *F. Abothrium*, later, with degenerated scolex. (*A–F*, after Cooper, 1919). *G. Duthiersia* (*after Southwell*, 1930). *H. Diplocotyle* (*after Nybelin*, 1922). *J.* Section through the scolex of *Ligula*, showing nerve trunks. *K.* Section through the strobila of *Ligula*, showing nerve trunks. (*J, K, after Cohn*, 1898.) *L. Ancistrocephalus* (after Southwell, 1930). 1, bothrium; 2, proglottids; 3, circle of spines; 4, main lateral nerve cords; 5, other longitudinal cords; 6, excretory vessels.

with a circle of spines on the scolex (Fig. 156*L*); and *Fistulicola* (Fig. 157*H, J*) without spines and with degenerate and deformed scolex buried in or piercing the rectal wall of swordfish. The Ptychobothriidae show the following characters: two bothria with edges often more or less fused, middorsal gonopore, more or less tubular uterus with sacciform end portion, and mid-ventral uterine pore. Of the several genera of this family may be mentioned *Bothriocephalus*, with many species in fishes, having an elongated scolex with two weak bothria; *Ptychobothrium* with flattened cordiform scolex (Fig. 157*B*); and *Clestobothrium* with deep spherical bothria. The Echinophallidae are known by the long spines on the cirrus; the gonopore is dorsal, the uterine pore ventral, and the uterus is tubular proximally, sacciform distally. The main genera are *Echinophallus* with double and *Bothriocotyle* with single reproductive system per proglottid.

The next two families are mostly monozoic tapeworms with dorsal or ventral genital openings. In most members the uterus and vagina join terminally to form a uterovaginal canal, that usually opens separately from the male pore (Fig. 159*D*). The tubular uterus receives many conspicuous gland cells. The Cyathocephalidae lack definite segmentation but have a number of sets of reproductive organs; there are usually one or two large rounded anteriorly directed bothria and the cirrus is supplied with prostatic glands. Principal genera are *Cyathocephalus* (Fig. 156*D*) with one terminal bothrium; *Bothrimonus* with two more or less fused bothria (Fig. 156*C*); *Diplocotyle* (Fig. 156*H*) with two similar but separate bothria; and *Spathebothrium* (Fig. 129*A*) without differentiated scolex. Hart and Guberlet (1936) created a special cestode group, Spathebothrioidea, for *Spathebothrium*, on inadequate grounds. There is a single species, *S. simplex*, discovered by Linton (1922) in the intestine of the teleost *Liparis*. It is a slender monzoic cestode to 33 mm. long, with a simple rounded anterior end lacking all adhesive organs and with up to 36 sets of reproductive organs. The reproductive system differs from that of other Cyathocephalidae chiefly in that the uterus, vagina, and cirrus all have separate pores, situated close together without regularity medially on either flat surface of the worm (Fig. 157*C*).

The Caryophyllaeidae are an interesting family of small monozoic cestodes with poorly differentiated scolex and one set of reproductive organs, opening ventrally. Because of its monozoic structure, this family has repeatedly been placed in the Cestodaria, but its pseudophyllid affinities are unquestionable. An excellent consideration of the family was published by Hunter (1930); other articles on the family with descriptions of new genera are those of Fuhrmann and Baer (1925), Woodland (1923, 1926, 1936), and Szidat (1937a).

The scolex lacks bothria or has one to six shallow bothrial depressions

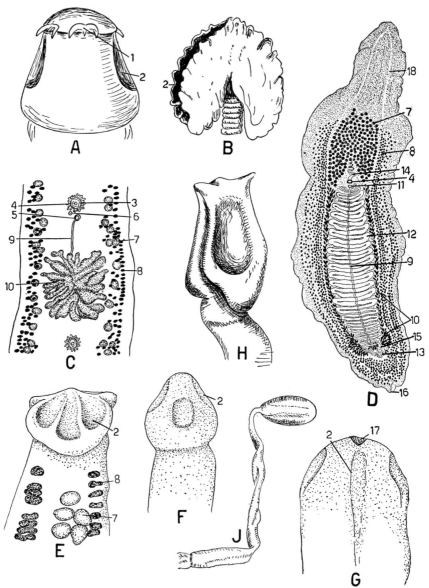

Fig. 157.—Pseudophyllidea (continued). *A. Triaenophorus*, original. *B. Ptycho-bothrium (after Lönneberg,* 1889). *C.* Reproductive system of *Spathebothrium (after Yama-guti,* 1934). *D. Wenyonia (after Woodland,* 1923). *E. Glaridacris. F. Biacetabulum,* adult of some *Archigetes. G. Monobothrium. (E–G, after Hunter,* 1927.) *H. Fistulicola,* normal condition of the scolex. *J. Fistulicola,* later phase, scolex degenerated. *(H, J, after Rudin,* 1914). 1, trifid hooks; 2, bothria; 3, cirrus sac; 4, male pore; 5, vaginal pore; 6, uterine pore; 7, testes; 8, yolk glands; 9, vagina; 10, ovary; 11, common uterovaginal pore; 12, uterus; 13, shell glands; 14, sperm duct; 15, ootype; 16, excretory pore; 17, apical sucker; 18, nerve cord.

and is often not well delimited from the body. It is followed by a short region free from reproductive organs, and then the remainder of the fluke-like body is occupied by this system. Typically the numerous testes occur centrally and the yolk glands laterally as elongated fields of follicles (Fig. 127*A*); the latter not infrequently extend behind the ovary. The sperm duct runs posteriorly and enters the rounded or oval highly muscular cirrus sac devoid of prostatic glands. The H-shaped ovary is generally situated near the posterior end. The coiled tubular uterus proceeds anteriorly and after junction with the vagina opens near the cirrus in the mid-ventral line independently or in a common antrum.

The Caryophyllaeidae parasitize fresh-water fishes mainly of the families Cyprinidae, Siluridae, and Catastomidae. Some of the better known genera are *Caryophyllaeus* with flattened ruffled scolex devoid of adhesive organs (Figs. 127*A*, 159*D*); *Monobothrium* with prismatic mobile scolex bearing two or six slight longitudinal grooves and an eversible apical sucker (Fig. 157*G*); *Glaridacris* (Cooper, 1920) with three pairs of rounded bothria (Fig. 157*E*); *Caryophyllaeides* without definite scolex and with uterine coils extending anterior to the cirrus sac; *Biacetabulum* (Hunter, 1927), with two deep rounded suckers resembling acetabula accompanied or not by four shallow bothria (Fig. 157*F*); and *Wenyonia* (Woodland, 1923), without bothria but with the genital pores anteriorly located (Fig. 157*D*) instead of in the posterior position usual in the family.

The last family, the Diphyllobothriidae, comprises polyzoic craspedote tapeworms, small to large, that parasitize chiefly birds and mammals, sometimes amphibians and reptiles. The tubular uterus, often arranged in a rosette, opens ventrally, the vagina is provided with a large seminal receptacle, and the cirrus sac is preceded by a muscular external seminal vesicle or propulsion vesicle (this also occurs in some Caryophyllaeidae). In the liguline group the scolex is poorly differentiated with slight bothrial indentations; here belong *Ligula* (Fig. 159*B*) with strobila segmented only anteriorly; *Schistocephalus*, segmented throughout; and *Digramma*, with double reproductive system per proglottid, all cestodes of fish-eating birds. The diphyllobothriine forms have a definite scolex with two long shallow bothria, whose edges may be more or less fused, and are completely segmented externally in correspondence with the internal anatomy. Fusion of bothria is illustrated in *Duthiersia* with fan-like scolex and partial fusion of the bothrial edges (Fig. 156*G*) and *Bothridium* with bothrial edges fused to form tubes open at both ends (Fig. 128*B*). The main genus *Diphyllobothrium* was long considered to supersede *Dibothriocephalus*, but the work of Mueller (1937), Wardle and associates (1947), and Stunkard (1948) indicates that both genera may be valid. The necessity of splitting *Diphyllobothrium* into several genera is clearly indicated by the work of these authors, but at the present writing no agreement has been reached as to the grounds on which the genus is to be split or what generic names are valid.   The name *Diphyllobothrium latum* in common use for the broad tapeworm of man is here retained, although it is quite likely that *Dibothriocephalus* is valid for this species.

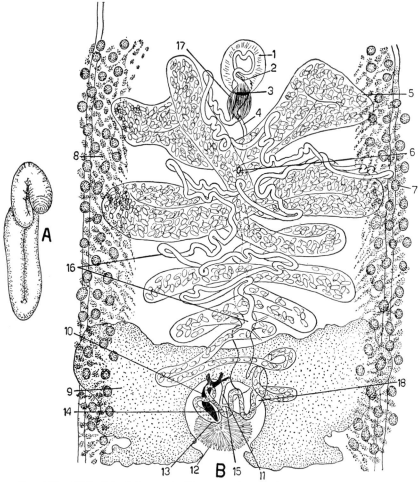

Fig. 158.—Diphyllobothrium. *A*. Plerocercoid of *D. latum*, from a fish (*after Vergeer*, 1929). *B*. Central part of mature proglottid of *D. latum*, showing sex organs (*after Sommer and Landois*, 1872). 1, cirrus sac; 2, male pore; 3, vaginal pore; 4, vagina; 5, uterus; 6, uterine pore; 7, testes; 8, yolk glands; 9, ovary; 10, yolk ducts; 11, oviduct; 12, shell gland; 13, ootype; 14, beginning of uterus; 15, beginning of vagina; 16, sperm duct; 17, seminal vesicle; 18, seminal receptacle.

Diphyllobothrium latum, the broad or fish tapeworm, is the largest and most injurious human cestode, reaching a length of 60 feet with a strobila of 3000 to 4000 proglottids.   The fusiform scolex provided with two slit-like bothria is followed by the long slender neck (Fig. 127*E*) and the strobila of which the ripe proglottids show prominently a central rosette-shaped uterus (Fig. 159*A*). The thick-walled oval operculate capsules (Fig. 136*J*) are shed from the ventral uterine pores of the strobila and later the spent proglottids detach. *D. latum* is a common cestode of Eurasian fish-eating countries and has been imported into the central United States, especially the Great Lakes region, with immigrants from Scandinavia. Several studies on the distribution and dissemination of *D. latum* in the United States have been published by Vergeer (1928, 1929, 1930). Infection results from eating or preparing raw or insufficiently cooked infected fish. Bears, cats, and other carnivores are also hosts to *D. latum* and to related forms that may rarely infect man. *Diplogonoporus grandis*, normally a parasite of whales and seals, has been found in Japanese.

The life cycle of the pseudophyllids was first elucidated (for *D. latum*) by Rosen (Janicki and Rosen, 1917), who later extended his researches (Rosen, 1917–1919) to other pseudophyllids (*Triaenophorus*, *Ligula*, *Eubothrium*). The life cycle was already described in detail above (page 336). Briefly the capsules either at laying or after development outside hatch into a ciliated or unciliated coracidium that must be eaten by the first intermediate host, usually a copepod of the genera *Cyclops* or *Diaptomus*. For each species of pseudophyllid, specific copepods are generally required; in the wrong species the coracidium is killed and digested. Arrived in the stomach of the proper species the coracidium perforates the stomach wall by bringing the six hooks together to form a point and then enlarging the opening by spreading the hooks apart. After reaching the body cavity of the copepod, the coracidium develops into the procercoid stage in which it remains until the host is ingested by the second intermediate host, usually a fish; but frogs, toads, snakes, and mammals serve in particular cases. The procercoid penetrates the intestinal wall of the second host by peristaltic movements probably assisted by the secretion of its frontal glands and wanders to various sites (liver, coelom, muscles, etc.) where it develops into a plerocercoid, usually encysting sooner or later. So many plerocercoids may occur in the muscles of food fishes as to render these unmarketable. The life cycle is completed when the host bearing the plerocercoids is devoured by the definitive host.

In *Diphyllobothrium latum* the successive hosts are *Cyclops* or *Diaptomus* (usually the latter in North America), various fresh-water fishes, and man and various carnivorous mammals (Janicki and Rosen, 1917; Vogel, 1929; Vergeer, 1929–1930, 1935). For other related species, frogs, toads, snakes, mice and other small mammals, and even man (see below) serve as the second intermediate host with dogs, cats, and other carnivorous mammals as final hosts (Okumura, 1919; Li, 1929; Iwata, 1934; Mueller, 1938). The cycle of *Triaenophorus* (Rosen, 1917–1918; Hjort-

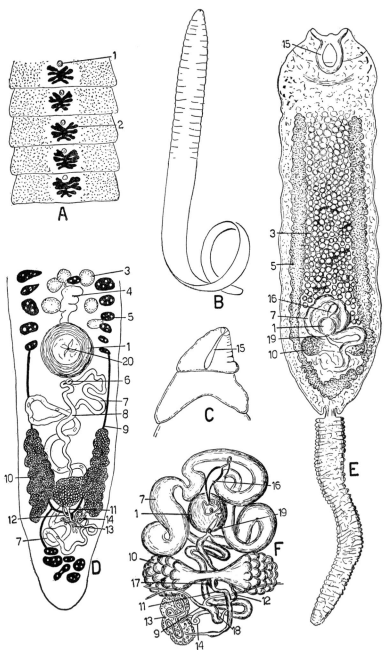

Fig. 159.—Pseudophyllidea (continued). A. Appearance of ripe proglottids of *Diphyl-lobothrium latum;* coils of uterus resemble a rosette, original. B. *Ligula*, mature, from a water bird, original. C. Scolex of mature *Ligula* (*after Rosen*, 1918–1919). D. Rear part of *Caryophyllaeus*, showing sex organs (*after Hunter*, 1927). E. *Archigetes*, from oligochaete

land, 1929; Miller, 1943–1945) is similar with a ciliated coracidium, procercoid stage in *Cyclops*, plerocercoid stage in the liver of various small fishes, and adult worm in the intestine of the pike. In *Eubothrium* (Rosen, 1917–1918) the nonciliated coracidium is ingested by *Cyclops*, the plerocercoid stage occurs in the intestine of small fish, and the adult worm inhabits the pyloric caeca of trout. *Ligula* and *Schistocephalus* differ from the foregoing genera in that the plerocercoid stage, found in the coelom of numerous fresh-water fishes, is a juvenile tapeworm reaching a length of 40 cm., with beginning development of the reproductive system. The *Schistocephalus* plerocercoid is segmented, that of *Ligula* not. Both after ingestion of the intermediate fish host by aquatic birds attain maturity in a few days and live as adults only a short time. The complete cycle is known for *Ligula* (Rosen, 1918–1919); the ciliated coracidium becomes a procercoid in *Cyclops* and a plerocercoid in fish.

Some other bothriocephaloids present variants of the typical diphyllobothriine cycle. In *Bothriocephalus* (Essex, 1928; Thomas, 1937), the ciliated coracidium develops to an advanced procercoid, or what might be called an early plerocercoid stage with bothria in *Cyclops*, and this is directly infective to the final host (fish, newt). The oncosphere of *Cyathocephalus* (Wisniewski, 1932, 1933) lacks hooks and has no free existence; the capsules are directly eaten by the first intermediate host, the amphipod *Gammarus*, in which the procercoid develops to an advanced stage so that it is infective to the definitive fish host.

The life cycle of the Caryophyllaeidae is not fully known and evidently differs from that of the Diphyllobothriidae, for in the genera *Caryophyllaeus*, *Biacetabulum*, and *Brachyurus*, the advanced procercoid with a long tail and with almost completely developed reproductive system inhabits the coelom of fresh-water oligochaetes, chiefly Tubificidae. These procercoids are directly infective to the definitive fish host. The procercoid of *Caryophyllaeus* (Fig. 160C) has long been recognized as such (Mrazek, 1901), but the larval form of the two other genera was known as *Archigetes* and was believed to be a neotenic plerocercoid until Szidat (1937b, 1938) showed that *Archigetes* develops to an adult caryophyllaeid in fishes. The anatomy of *Archigetes* (Fig. 159E, F) was exhaustively described by Wisniewski (1930). *Archigetes*, to 5 mm. long, consists of a broad flat body, and a slender tail bearing the six larval hooks at its rear end. The mobile anterior end has two shallow bothria and an apical eversible area on which open frontal glands. The body contains a

worm *Tubifex*. F. Sex organs of *Archigetes*. (E, F, after *Wisniewski*, 1930.) 1, cirrus sac; 2, coils of uterus; 3, testes; 4, spermiducal vesicle; 5, yolk glands; 6, common uterovaginal pore; 7, uterus; 8, vagina; 9, yolk ducts; 10, ovary; 11, oviduct; 12, beginning of vagina; 13, shell gland; 14, beginning of uterus; 15, bothrium; 16, seminal vesicle; 17, ovicapt; 18, yolk reservoir; 19, common gonopore; 20, male pore.

mature set of reproductive organs of caryophyllaeid type (Fig. 159*F*). According to Wisniewski, the mature *Archigetes* escapes by rupture from the annelid host and disintegrates, freeing its capsules. The latter contain an unciliated coracidium that has no free existence and hatches after ingestion by the annelid. The hexacanth larva penetrates the intestinal wall of the annelid and lodges in the coelom, usually near the reproductive organs.

From the fact that various pseudophyllids as *Caryophyllaeus, Archigetes, Ligula, Schistocephalus* become sexually mature or nearly so while in procercoid or plerocercoid stages it would seem that this group of tapeworms is tending toward neoteny with eventual deletion of the final host from the cycle.

Advanced plerocercoids in the form of slender white wrinkled but unsegmented worms to 30 cm. in length have long been known in man, especially in the Orient, by the name *Sparganum*, and the condition is termed *sparganosis*. These larvae occur in the muscles, beneath the skin, and around the eye. They are now recognized to be diphyllobothriine plerocercoids; and, according to the work of Mueller (1937) and Wardle and associates (1947), they fall into the genus *Spirometra*. The spargana found in man belong to *Spirometra* species in which the plerocercoids normally occur in amphibians, reptiles, chickens, and small mammals with cats, dogs, and other carnivores as the definitive hosts. A number of species furnishing human spargana have been named; but, according to Iwata (1934) and Joyeaux, Houdemer, and Baer (1934), all oriental spargana are referable to *S. erinacei* (= *mansoni*). Human infection results from eating any of the second intermediate hosts or from the Oriental practice of applying split frogs as poultices for wounds. Sparganosis in the United States has been attributed to *S. mansonoides* (Mueller, 1938). The curious *Sparganum prolifer* occasionally found in man was considered above (page 340).

18. Order Nippotaeniidea.—This order was erected by Yamaguti (1939) for the single genus *Nippotaenia*, small tapeworms to 13 mm. long found in the intestine of Japanese fresh-water fishes. Later Achmerov (1941) added another genus, *Amurotaenia*, from Russia. The anterior end of these cestodes is not set off as a scolex but bears a single apical acetabulum (Fig. 160*A*). There are a few proglottids each with a single sex system opening laterally (Fig. 160*A, B*). The excretory system comprises numerous longitudinal canals with cross connections in the cortical mesenchyme and a few canals in the central mesenchyme, but the usual main lateral canals are lacking. The reproductive system (Fig. 160*B*) is characterized by the small bilobed yolk gland placed anterior to the bilobed ovary. The uterus when mature presents lateral sacculations but lacks an external pore.

The general anatomy of members of this order is taenioid, especially as regards the yolk gland, but the excretory system is pseudophyllidean. The order therefore seems to fit between the Pseudophyllidea and the Taenioidea.

19. Order Taenioidea or Cyclophyllidea.—This order comprises the common tapeworms of birds and mammals, seldom occurring in reptiles and amphibians. The taenioid cestodes are mostly of small to moderate length, from 1 to 3 mm. up to 10 to 30 cm., but some species reach a length of 10 m. with a strobila of 1000 or more proglottids. The small rounded, pyriform, or clavate scolex is characterized by the four deep hemispherical acetabula symmetrically placed around its circumference (Fig. 127*D*). In the family Tetrabothriidae, an ear-like appendage occurs at the upper border of each sucker (Fig. 161*A*). The suckers are sometimes reduced or wanting (*Priapocephalus*, Fig. 161*B*, some species of *Dioecocestus*). The apex of the scolex typically and apparently primitively forms a mobile muscular rostellum armed with thorns of diagnostic value, usually arranged in one or more circlets, but sometimes in groups or festoons. The rostellum is often withdrawable into a cavity, the *rostellar receptacle* (Fig. 168*A*). The absence of a rostellum as in the Anoplocephalidae and in *Taenia saginata* is presumably a derived condition. The scolex may be covered with fine bristles or spines and the margins, less often the concavities, of the suckers are also sometimes spiny (Fig. 163*C*). In *Priapocephalus*, the scolex, deeply embedded in the host intestinal wall, is altered to a swollen acorn-shaped body with reduced suckers (Fig. 161*B*), and in *Fimbriaria* (Fig. 130*A*) and *Idiogenes* the broadened crest-like anterior part of the strobila acts as a pseudoscolex. The taenioid scolex is rarely provided with a velum.

The short or long neck, often not well delimited from the scolex, is followed by a strobila of definite proglottids corresponding to the internal anatomy. The strobila is generally strongly flattened but is cyiindroid in the Nematotaeniidae (Fig. 168*F*). It is usually craspedote, sometimes with markedly lobed or lappeted proglottidal margins (Fig. 165*A*), and is nearly always apolytic, dropping off the terminal ripe proglottids filled with hexacanths to be discharged with the feces. Glands at the interproglottidal margins are peculiar to the genus *Moniezia* (Fig. 133*A*). The mesenchymal musculature is well developed with one or two layers of longitudinal fibers or bundles of fibers coursing throughout the strobila. The excretory system is typical, consisting of two longitudinal vessels in the central mesenchyme on each side, forming a plexus in the scolex (Fig. 132*A*). The ventral vessels are connected in each proglottid by a transverse channel, less often by a plexus. There are sometimes additional vessels, up to 20. Valves commonly occur in the ventral vessels just anterior to the transverse connection. The main features of the taenioid nervous system, best known for *Moniezia* and *Anoplocephala*, were considered above (page 321).

The Taenioidea are hermaphroditic, except the genus *Dioecocestus* (Fuhrmann, 1900), in which the sexes are separate and the male and female strobilae differ in shape (Fig. 161C). The reproductive system shows a graded series of stages from anterior to posterior in the strobila and displays the usual marked protandry. There are one or two sets of sex organs in each proglottid, and in some genera the male system is double, the female single. The common gonopore and antrum lie in the lateral margin except in *Mesocestoides*, in which they are mid-ventral. In the anoplocephalid genus *Aporina* a gonopore is absent except in very young proglottids. In the family Acoleidae a vagina is lacking or fails to reach the antrum, and in the Amabiliidae there is a pseudovagina that either opens on the flat surfaces or communicates with the excretory system.

The testes are usually small and numerous, larger and one to three or a few in number in the Hymenolepididae (Fig. 135C). They occupy a dorsal position in the central mesenchyme, situated usually behind the level of the ovary, but they may surround the main female organs or occur in lateral fields. The coils of the sperm duct act as a spermiducal vesicle prior to entrance into the rounded, pyriform, or tubular cirrus sac within which the sinuous ejaculatory duct sometimes forms a true seminal vesicle. The cirrus may be unarmed or lined with bristles, spines, fine thorns, or large hooks (Acoleidae); or in certain species of *Hymenolepis* the cirrus is replaced by a protrusible long slender stylet.

The ovary is usually a small compact or radially lobulated body, seldom bilobed, and occupies a median position in the proglottid when single, lateral when double. The oviduct generally lacks a well-marked ovicapt (present in Acoleidae and Tetrabothriidae); it soon receives the vagina and enters a poorly defined ootype embraced by the small shell gland. The yolk duct also enters the ootype, coming from the small compact yolk gland. The Taenioidea are distinguished from most other cestodes by the lack of follicular yolk glands. The vagina is usually provided with a seminal receptacle, sometimes two, sometimes of enormous size, and may degenerate distally after the seminal receptacle has become filled with sperm. When the vagina is lacking, hypodermic impregnation obtains. The vagina generally lies behind the cirrus sac.

After leaving the ootype the oviduct becomes the uterus, an organ of great variability among the Taenioidea. It may consist of a central tube with lateral outpouchings as in the genus *Taenia* (Fig. 162D, E) or form a partial or complete ring with side branches as in *Gyrocoelia* (Fig. 162B) or constitute a reticulum filling the entire proglottid (*Moniezia*, Fig. 162C) or take the form of a large sac or a transverse sacculated tube (*Hymeno-*

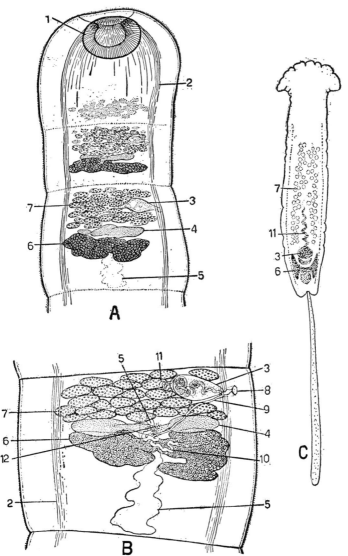

FIG. 160.—Caryophyllaeus, Nippotaeniidea. *A*. Anterior part of *Nippotaenia*. *B*. Mature proglottid of *Nippotaenia*. (*A, B, after Yamaguti*, 1939.) *C*. Larva of *Caryophyllaeus*, from oligochaete worms (*after Fuhrmann*, 1931). 1, apical sucker; 2, longitudinal muscles; 3, cirrus sac; 4, yolk gland; 5, uterus; 6, ovary; 7, testes; 8, gonopore; 9, vagina; 10, oviduct; 11, sperm duct; 12, shell gland.

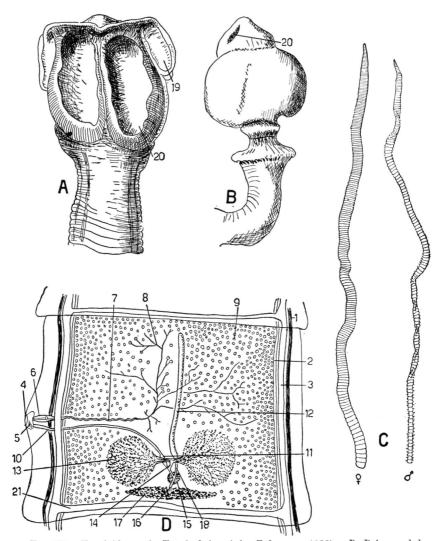

FIG. 161.—Taenioidea. *A. Tetrabothrium (after Fuhrmann, 1932).   B. Priapocephalus
(after Joyeaux and Baer, 1936).   C.* Male and female strobilae of *Dioecocestus (after Fuhrmann,* 1932).   *D.* Mature proglottid of a member of the genus *Taenia (after Stiles,* 1898).
1, nerve cord; 2, dorsal nephridial canal; 3, ventral nephridial canal; 4, gonopore; 5, antrum;
6, cirrus sac; 7, sperm duct; 8, sperm ductules; 9, testes; 10, vagina; 11, seminal receptacle;
12, early stage of uterus; 13, ovary; 14, oviduct; 15, shell gland; 16, yolk duct; 17, yolk
gland; 18, beginning of uterus; 19, ear-like appendage; 20, bothrium; 21, transverse excretory canal.

lepis, Fig. 162*A*). Its shape is frequently related to the proglottidal shape. In a number of taenioids the originally branching or reticulate uterus may divide up into a number of small sacs each of which contains one to several hexacanths (Fig. 163*G*). These sacs are known as *uterine capsules*. Another variant seen in *Idiogenes, Paruterina, Thysanosoma, Mesocestoides*, and other genera consists in the formation of parauterine organs. These are mesenchymal areas that take over the hexacanths from the true uterus and form a dense fibrous coat around them (Figs. 163*D*, 165*C*). There may be one, two, or many such parauterine organs in each proglottid. These parauterine organs filled with hexacanths are the infective agents swallowed by the intermediate host. The taenioid uterus usually lacks an external aperture but sometimes has a surficial opening. The hexacanths are generally freed by the disintegration of the proglottids after reaching the exterior.

The eggs of the Taenioidea are enclosed with a single yolk cell in a thin, usually evanescent capsule (Fig. 137*B*). While still in the uterus the eggs develop to typical hexacanths enclosed in two or three embryonic membranes of which the outer may be lost later. The ripe or gravid proglottids when shed thus contain chiefly the uterus or its variants filled with hexacanth embryos. All other organs have generally degenerated by this time. The further history of the embryos was detailed above; they must be passively ingested by either aquatic or terrestrial intermediate hosts before they can develop further. In the Taenioidea there is usually but one intermediate host, which may be omitted in certain species. After being ingested by the proper host, the hexacanth escapes from its membranes; passes through the intestinal wall, into the coelom in case of invertebrates, into the coelom, liver, or other organs or tissues in the case of vertebrates; and develops into an advanced larva, sometimes a tetrathyridium, usually various types of cysticercoids or cysticerci. Invertebrate hosts include crustaceans, leeches, oligochaetes, mollusks, fleas, lice, flies, beetles, butterflies, dragonflies, centipedes, millipedes, ants; the vertebrate intermediate host is usually a mammal, such as dogs, cats, mice, rats, rabbits, hares, squirrels, horses, sheep, cattle, goats, pigs, etc.; but lizards and snakes, rarely birds, may also be utilized. Further details of the life cycle are given below in the account of the families.

An extensive literature exists on this order of cestodes; among the larger articles may be mentioned those of Stiles and Hassall (1893), Stiles (1896a, 1896b), Fuhrmann (1907, 1908, 1931, 1932), Ransom (1909), Hall (1919), Meggitt (1924), Southwell (1930), and Yamaguti (1935). General agreement appears to have been reached regarding the familial arrangement, which here follows Fuhrmann (1931).

The Tetrabothriidae (Nybelin, 1922), without rostellum, with a more

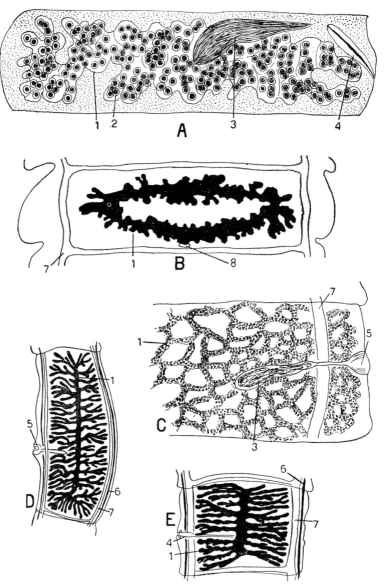

Fig. 162.—Taenioidea, types of uterus. A. *Hymenolepis*, with transverse sacculated uterus (*after Southwell*, 1930). B. *Gyrocoelia* with ring uterus (*after Fuhrmann*, 1899). C. Part of ripe proglottid of *Moniezia*, showing reticulate uterus, original. D. Gravid proglottid of *Taenia saginata*. E. Gravid proglottid of *Taenia solium*. (*D, E, after Stiles*, 1898.) 1, uterus; 2, membranated hexacanths; 3, seminal receptacle; 4, cirrus sac; 5, antrum; 6, nerve cord; 7, excretory canal; 8, uterine pore.

or less functional dorsal uterine pore (or pores), with yolk gland anterior to the ovary, and gonopores all on one side of the strobila, are a small family parasitic in whales, seals, and dolphins, and in oceanic birds of the albatross-petrel group. In *Tetrabothrium* (Fig. 161*A*) and *Chaetophallus* characteristic ear-like flaps occur above the acetabula; *Anophryocephalus* (Baylis, 1922) lacks these; and in *Priapocephalus* (Fig. 161*B*), the scolex is deformed into a bulbous mass. This family is generally considered to show pseudophyllid affinities. The life cycle is unknown.

The Davaineidae, characterized by the simple rostellum encircled with numerous small hammer-shaped hooks (Fig. 163*A*, *B*), are common cestodes of birds, some genera also occurring in mammals. The suckers are often spiny, at least in young stages (Fig. 163*C*). In the principal genera *Davainea* and *Raillietina*, the uterus breaks up into uterine "capsules" (Fig. 163*G*), each containing one to several membranated embryos; *Cotugnia* has a double reproductive system in each proglottid. The genus *Davainea* (Fuhrmann, 1896, 1920; Jones, 1936) comprises small tapeworms of less than 20 proglottids that parasitize ratite (ostriches, emus, cassowaries) and gallinaceous (fowl-like) birds. *Davainea proglottina* with mostly four to six proglottids (Fig. 163*A*) is a common cestode of chickens with a cysticercoid stage in slugs and other terrestrial snails (Wetzel, 1936; Levine, 1938). The very similar but larger *Raillietina* (Hughes and Schultz, 1942) with over 200 species in various kinds of birds and in small mammals also includes some common poultry cestodes. Those usually found in the domestic fowl are *R. cesticillus* with the cysticercoid stage (Fig. 163*E*) in beetles, usually ground beetles (Carabidae, Ackert and Reid, 1936; Reid, Ackert, and Case, 1938; Wisseman, 1945), and *R. echinobothrida* (Fig. 163*C*) and *tetragona* with cysticercoids in ants (Jones and Horsfall, 1934; Horsfall, 1938; Joyeaux and Baer, 1938). Several species of *Raillietina*, probably some of them synonyms, have been infrequently found in man in tropical countries (Dollfus, 1940); infection probably ensues from eating the intermediate host or infected small mammals. In *Idiogenes* and related genera, there is an anterior parauterine organ into which the embryos eventually pass from the sacciform uterus (Fig. 163*D*). Most species of *Idiogenes* lose the scolex and develop a pseudoscolex; and in *I. otidis* (Fuhrmann, 1925) secondary strobilae are given off and undergo segmentation after the manner described for *Haplobothrium* (page 368).

The Anoplocephalidae have a simple unarmed scolex devoid of a rostellum and a broad, often neckless, strobila (Fig. 164*A*) composed usually of short broad segments containing one or two sets of sex organs; the testes are usually numerous and the oncosphere is enclosed in three membranes of which the inner often bears a pyriform apparatus (Fig. 164*E*). Because of the short broad form of the proglottids the sex organs when

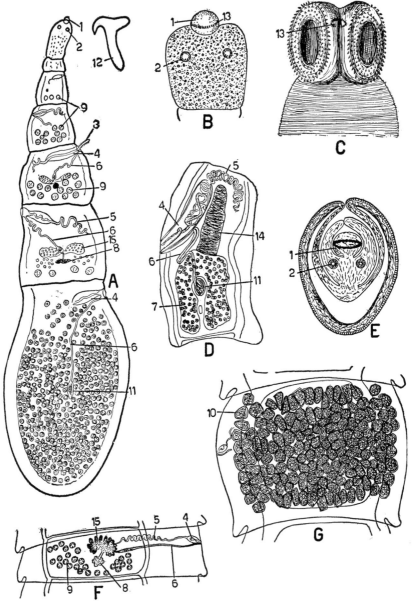

Fig. 163.—Family Davaineidae. *A. Davainea proglottina*, from the fowl, entire worm (*after Joyeaux and Baer*, 1936). *B.* Scolex of *D. proglottina*. *C.* Scolex of *Raillietina echinobothrida* with spiny suckers. (*B, C, after Blanchard*, 1891.) *D.* Ripe proglottid of *Idiogenes* with parauterine organ (*after Clausen*, 1915). *E.* Cysticercoid of *Raillietina cesticillus* from a beetle (*after Joyeaux and Baer*, 1938). *F.* Mature proglottid of *Raillietina*. *G.* Ripe proglottid of *Raillietina* with uterine capsules. (*F, G, after Yamaguti*, 1935.) 1, rostellum; 2, sucker; 3, cirrus protruded; 4, cirrus sac; 5, sperm duct; 6, vagina; 7, uterus; 8, yolk gland; 9, testes; 10, uterine capsules; 11, seminal receptacle; 12, hook of rostellum enlarged; 13, rostellar hooks; 14, parauterine organ; 15, ovary.

only one set is present are often asymmetrically arranged with the female organs nearer the margin bearing the gonopore, the testes displaced toward the opposite side (Fig. 164B). The family parasitizes mostly mammals, especially marsupials, rodents, and ungulates, but also occurs in birds and reptiles. Principal studies of the family are those of Fuhrmann (1902), Douthitt (1915), and Baer (1927). The family falls into three subfamilies: the anoplocephaline forms in which the uterus is a transverse sacculated tube or reticulate; the linstowiine group in which the uterus becomes divided up into capsules; and the thysanosomine anoplocephalids with one to many parauterine organs.

The anoplocephaline taenioids include many cestodes of economic importance. Some of the principal genera are: *Anoplocephala* (Fig. 164A) with unilateral gonopores and transverse sacculated uterus, in horses, zebras, rhinoceroses, and elephants (Becker, 1921; Yorke and Southwell, 1921; Stunkard, 1926); the similar *Bertiella* with irregularly alternating gonopores and glandular vagina, in man, monkeys, and apes (Blanchard 1891; Baylis, 1934; Stunkard, 1940); *Andrya*, with prostatic vesicle (Fig. 164B) attached to the cirrus sac, in rabbits, hares, and other rodents (Stiles, 1896a; Arnold, 1938); *Cittotaenia*, with double set of sex organs (Fig. 164C, D) per proglottid, in hares, rabbits, and other rodents (Stiles, 1896a; Rees, 1933; Arnold, 1938); *Moniezia*, also with double sex organs (Figs. 133A, 164G) but with interproglottidal glands and reticulate uterus, in sheep, cattle, and other ruminants and large mammals (Stiles and Hassall, 1893; Theiler, 1924; Taylor, 1928); *Aporina*, with small cirrus, often abortive gonopore, and no pyriform apparatus, in birds (Fuhrmann, 1902, 1932); *Paronia*, with double sex organs and initially double, horseshoe-shaped uterus (Fig. 164F), in birds (Fuhrmann, 1902, 1932); *Schizotaenia* with spiny cirrus, testes on the gonopore side of the proglottid, and vagina anterior to the cirrus, in rodents (Douthitt, 1915); and *Paranoplocephala*, differing from *Anoplocephala* in the asymmetrical arrangement of the gonads, in rodents and horses. The genus *Prototaenia* (Baer, 1927) in marsupials and insectivores appears to be identical with *Bertiella*. Many attempts over a period of fifty years (history in Stunkard, 1934) were made by parasitologists to elucidate the life cycle of the anoplocephaline cestodes, because of the economic importance of their hosts, but the cycle remained unknown until 1937 when it was brilliantly solved by Stunkard, first for *Moniezia* (Stunkard, 1937, 1939a), then for *Cittotaenia* (Stunkard, 1939b, 1941) and *Bertiella* (Stunkard, 1940). The cysticercoids develop in minute free-living mites. Mites also serve as intermediate hosts for *Anoplocephala* from horses (Bashkirova, 1941) and for *Catenotaenia* from rodents (Joyeaux and Baer, 1945) and may be assumed to carry the cysticercoids throughout the Anoplocephalinae. Cysticercoids may remain infective in mites for nearly a year (Soldatova,

1945) and this longevity probably accounts for the great prevalence of anoplocephaline cestodes.

In the linstowiine group, the strobila is generally more slender with elongated proglottids. The most common genera are *Oochoristica*, with a single embryo in each uterine capsule, found chiefly in lizards and snakes but also in various mammals (Zschokke, 1905; Meggitt, 1934; Loewen, 1940; Hughes, 1940a) and *Inermicapsifer* with several embryos per capsule, in the coney and rodents (Zschokke, 1898; Janicki, 1910; Bischoff, 1913). The genus *Linstowia* parasitizes the most primitive mammals, the monotremes.

The thysanosomine anoplocephalids inhabit the intestine, also the bile ducts, of cattle, sheep, and other ruminants (Stiles and Hassall, 1893; Gough, 1911; Southwell, 1929). The proglottids are wider than long, and the genera here mentioned lack yolk and shell glands. The chief genera are *Thysanosoma* with transverse uterus connecting with numerous parauterine organs (Fig. 165*B*, *C*); *Stilesia* with double uterus and parauterine organs (Fig. 165*D*, *E*); and *Avitellina* with single uterus and parauterine organ (Fig. 165*F*). *Thysanosoma actinioides*, common in the sheep, is notable for the fimbriated proglottidal margins (Fig. 165*A*). The life cycle of the linstowiine and thysanosomine anoplocephalids was unknown until recently when Rendtorff (1948) showed that dermestid and tenebrionid beetle larvae, but not mites, serve as intermediate hosts for *Oochoristica ratti* in rats.

Members of this family rarely occur in man. *Bertiella studeri* has been found about ten times in children in the Indo-Malay and West Indian regions (Africa and Garcia, 1935), and a species of *Inermicapsifer* occurs in children in Cuba (Kouri, 1940).

The family Mesocestoididae comprises the single genus *Mesocestoides*, parasitic in birds and in dogs, cats, and other carnivores, distinguished from all other taenioids by the mid-ventral position of the gonopore (Fig. 166*A*). The genus is discussed by Cameron (1925), Mueller (1928), Witenberg (1934), and Chandler (1946). The scolex lacks rostellum and armature; the median tubular uterus connects at its posterior end with a parauterine organ into which all the embryos in the proglottid pass (Fig. 166*B*, Chandler, 1946). Something is known of the life cycle. A taenioid larval type termed tetrathyridium (or less correctly, dithyridium), long unsegmented worms with introverted scolex (Fig. 166*C*, *D*), occurs commonly in the coelom or coelomic membranes of dogs, cats, mice, snakes, and other vertebrates. The resemblance of these larvae to *Mesocestoides* has been noticed by a number of helminthologists, first by Neumann (1896), and feeding them to dogs and cats results in infection with adult *Mesocestoides* (Neumann, 1896; Schwartz, 1927a; Joyeaux and Baer, 1932; Witenberg, 1934). However, the hexacanths of *Mesocestoides*

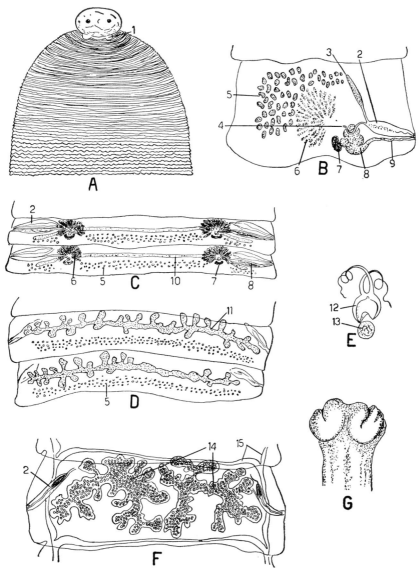

Fig. 164.—Family Anoplocephalidae. A. Anterior end of *Anoplocephala perfoliata*, from the horse, original. B. Mature proglottid of *Andrya* with prostatic vesicle. C. Mature proglottid of *Cittotaenia*. D. *Cittotaenia*, ripe proglottid with uterus. (C, D, after Stiles, 1896a.) E. Pyriform apparatus of *Cittotaenia*, releasing the hexacanth (after Blanchard, 1891). F. Ripe proglottid of *Paronia*, with double uterus (after Yamaguti, 1935). G. Scolex of *Moniezia expansa*, common tapeworm of sheep (after Stiles, 1898). 1, lappets of scolex; 2, cirrus sac; 3, prostatic vesicle; 4, sperm duct; 5, testes; 6, ovary; 7, yolk gland; 8, seminal receptacle; 9, vagina; 10, early stage of uterus; 11, later stage of uterus; 12, pyriform apparatus; 13, hexacanth; 14, horseshoe-shaped uterus; 15, excretory canals.

are not directly infective to the hosts that harbor the tetrathyridia, and therefore a prior stage in some other intermediate host must be involved in the life cycle. *Mesocestoides* has been reported from man (Chandler, 1942).

The Dilepididae are a large and important family, chiefly in birds, but also in mammals, characterized by a retractile rostellum armed with one or more circlets of rose-thorn-like hooks; there are more or less numerous testes. The family is divisible into three groups: the Dilepidinae with a persistent sacciform or lobulated uterus, the Dipylidiinae in which the uterus breaks up into uterine capsules, and the Parauterininae with a parauterine organ. The Dilepidinae comprise a large number of genera, most of them confined to bird hosts, of which the more common ones are *Dilepis*, with a double circle of rostellar hooks and unilateral gonopores (Figs. 166*E*, 167*A*); *Anomotaenia*, with similar scolex but irregularly alternating gonopores; and *Amoebotaenia* and *Paricterotaenia* with a single circle of hooks. In the Dipylidiinae the principal genus is *Dipylidium*, a common cestode of dogs and cats, which has been the subject of many studies (Millzner, 1926; Lopez-Neyra, 1929; Witenberg, 1932; Venard, 1938). Numerous species of *Dipylidium* have been described, but it is certain that nearly all of them are the same species, *D. caninum*, a common parasite of dogs throughout the world, infecting over 50 per cent of individuals (Fig. 167*B*). *D. caninum* reaches a length of 25 cm. with up to 150 proglottids; the mature segments are long and slender with double sex organs (Fig. 167*C*) opening at the center of the lateral margins and numerous testes before and behind the female organs. The ripe proglottids contain numerous oval uterine capsules each enclosing 3 to 30 ovic embryos (Fig. 167*D*, *E*). The life cycle involves dog fleas (see below). Children sometimes become infected with *D. caninum* through playing with dogs, and thereby ingesting infected fleas. Some other dipylidiine genera, all with only one embryo in the uterine capsules, are *Choanotaenia* (Fig. 168*A*) with one or two rows of rostellar hooks and single sex organs, found in chickens, sparrows and other birds; *Diplopylidium*, with double sex organs and two to five rows of unequal hooks; and *Joyeauxiella*, with 14 to 25 rows of small rostellar hooks (Fig. 168*D*) and double sex organs. The parauterine Dilepididae comprise several genera of somewhat unfamiliar cestodes of birds.

The life cycle is known for several Dilepididae. Melnikov in 1869 found cysticercoids (Fig. 167*F*) of the dog tapeworm *Dipylidium* in the dog louse *Trichodectes canis*. Later investigators, however, showed that the dog fleas, *Ctenocephalus canis* and *Pulex irritans*, are the common intermediate hosts of *D. caninum;* and the work of Zimmermann (1937) indicates that the cysticercoids carried by the dog louse belong to a different species, *D. sexcoronatum*. Joyeaux (1920) proved that adult

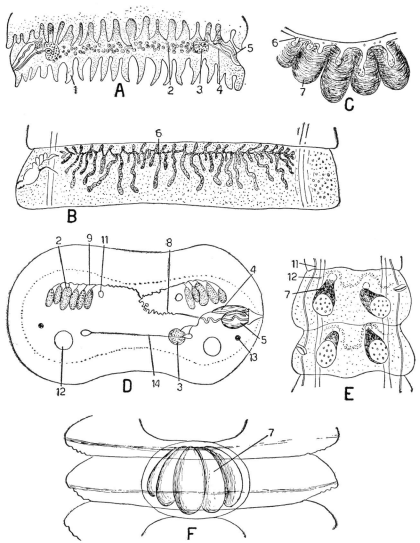

FIG. 165.—Thysanosomine Anoplocephalidae. *A. Thysanosoma actinioides*, from the
sheep, with fringed velum *(after Baer*, 1927). *B.* Early stage of uterus of *T. actinioides*.
C. Parauterine organs forming around uterine branches of *T. actinioides.* (*B, C, after
Stiles and Hassall*, 1893.) *D.* Scheme of the sex organs of *Stilesia (after Gough,* 1911).
E. Ripe proglottids of *Stilesia*, showing two parauterine organs. *F.* Ripe proglottid of
Avitellina with pouched parauterine organs *(after Gough,* 1911). 1, fringes; 2, testes; 3,
ovary; 4, vagina; 5, cirrus sac; 6, uterus; 7, parauterine organ; 8, sperm duct; 9, sperm
ductules; 10, muscle layer; 11, dorsal excretory canal; 12, ventral excretory canal; 13, nerve
cord; 14, early stage of uterus.

dog fleas cannot be directly infected by the hexacanths of *D. caninum*, but infection occurs in the larval stages. The flea larvae live in the debris and litter of dog kennels where they come in contact with *D. caninum* proglottids in dog feces. The cysticercoid of *Choanotaenia infundibulum* (Fig. 168*B*), a common cestode of poultry, occurs in beetles and houseflies (Gutberlet, 1916; Joyeaux, 1920; Reid and Ackert, 1937) and probably houseflies also serve as intermediate hosts for *C. passerina* in the English sparrow (Stunkard and Milford, 1937). Cysticercoids of some species of *Amoebotaenia* (Meggitt, 1926) and *Paricterotaenia* (see page 342) occur in earthworms. Cysticercoids of *Joyeauxiella* and *Diplopylidium* (Fig. 168*C*) form rounded white cysts in the coelomic wall of lizards, snakes, amphibians, and small mammals; but as the hexacanths of these tapeworms are not directly infective to such hosts, a primary host, probably a coprophagous insect, must be involved in the cycle (Witenberg, 1932).

The Nematotaeniidae comprise a few small cestodes of amphibians, characterized by the unarmed scolex (Fig. 168*E*) without rostellum, the cylindroid strobila segmented only posteriorly, the few testes, and the formation of parauterine organs (Fig. 168*F*). The chief genera are *Nematotaenia* (Fuhrmann, 1895) with two testes and *Cylindrotaenia* (Jewell, 1916) with one testis. According to Joyeaux (1924) the life cycle of *Cylindrotaenia* is direct, involving no intermediate host. After the ripe proglottids have been ingested by frogs, the oncospheres develop into tetrathyridia in cysts in the intestinal mucosa, and then escape from the cysts into the intestine where they drop their tails and mature.

The important family Hymenolepididae has a rostellum armed with one circlet of hooks, usually one to three testes, sacciform uterus, and both external and internal seminal vesicles. It occurs primarily in birds (Mayhew, 1925; Fuhrmann, 1932), especially passerine, anseriform, gallinaceous, and wading birds but is also found in mammals, as insectivores and rodents. The chief genus *Hymenolepis* with three testes (Fig. 135*C*) has over 300 species (Hughes, 1940b, 1941), mostly in birds, also in rodents. *H. nana*, the smallest human tapeworm, hence called the dwarf tapeworm of man, occurs throughout the world and is fairly common in some localities, reaching an incidence of 10 per cent in the southeastern United States (Otto, 1936); it particularly infects children, and large numbers may be present in one individual. *H. nana* ranges to 10 cm. in length and has 20 to 30 hooks in the rostellar circlet. The inner embryonic membrane bears long wavy filaments (Fig. 169*D*). Other well-known species of *Hymenolepis* are *H. fraterna* and *diminuta* in rats and mice. Some other genera are *Diorchis* with ten rostellar hooks and two testes (Fig. 169*A*, *B*, Mayhew, 1929; Schultz, 1940b); *Diploposthe* with two gonopores, cirrus sacs, and vaginae but single group of testes and

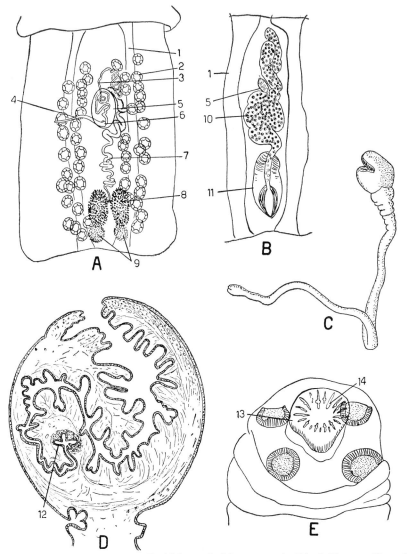

Fig. 166.—Mesocestoides, Dilepididae. *A.* Mature proglottid of *Mesocestoides*. *B.* Ripe proglottid of *Mesocestoides*; distal end of uterus becomes parauterine organ. (*A, B, after Southwell*, 1930.) *C.* Tetrathyridium larva of *Mesocestoides* from a lizard. *D.* Section through the anterior end of same, showing cysticercus structure. (*C, D, after Penrose*, 1882.) *E.* Scolex of *Dilepis* (*after Burt*, 1936). 1, nephridial canals; 2, testes; 3, sperm duct; 4, cirrus; 5, cirrus sac; 6, gonopore; 7, vagina; 8, ovary; 9, yolk gland; 10, uterus; 11, parauterine organ; 12, scolex; 13, rostellum; 14, rostellar hooks.

female complex per proglottid (Fig. 169C); *Drepanidotaenia* with eight rostellar hooks and three testes; *Echinocotyle* with spiny acetabula; and *Fimbriaria* with large ruffled pseudoscolex (Fig. 130A), unsegmented strobila, and reticular ovary and uterus continuous throughout the strobila (Webster, 1943). *Drepanidotaenia* is frequently included in *Hymenolepis*.

Many studies have been made on the life cycle of *Hymenolepis*, especially of *H. nana* and *fraterna*. Whether these two forms are identical or distinct has been much disputed; according to an extensive study by Joyeaux (1920), they are morphologically distinct and the human form will usually not infect rats and mice. The rodent form is now often referred to as *H. nana fraterna*. This cestode differs from most other eucestodes in that an intermediate host is not required. The hexacanths develop to cysticercoids in the intestinal villi in about 4 days, and then pass into the intestinal lumen where they attach and grow to maturity in 2 or 3 weeks (cycle discovered by Grassi, 1887; verified by Joyeaux, 1920, 1925; Woodland, 1924; Brumpt, 1933; Hunninen, 1935). However, an intermediate invertebrate host (beetles, fleas) may also be employed (Bacigalupo, 1931; Brumpt, 1933). A similar cycle without an intermediate host also occurs in *H. erinacei* in the intestine of the hedgehog (Joyeaux, 1927). Other species of *Hymenolepis* investigated require an intermediate insect host, beetles and fleas in *H. diminuta* (Fig. 170D) from rats, mice, and other rodents (Joyeaux, 1920), and *H. microstoma* from mice (Joyeaux and Kobozieff, 1928); and dung beetles in *H. cantaniana* from poultry (Jones and Alicata, 1935). In the last species, the early larvae in beetles reproduce asexually, putting forth buds that develop into cysticercoids (Fig. 169E). A more complicated cycle obtains in *Hymenolepis* (or *Drepanidotaenia*) *lanceolata* (Ruszowski, 1932), found in ducks and related birds; here *Cyclops* and *Diaptomus* constitute the intermediate hosts in which the larvae pass through a procercoid-like stage to a cysticercoid type with a very long slender tail (Fig. 170E). Other crustaceans may also serve as hosts to hymenolepid cysticercoids as the amphipod *Orchestia* for *Hymenolepis exigua*, an Hawaiian chicken tapeworm (Alicata, 1936; Alicata and Chang, 1939).

The Acoleidae and Amabiliidae are two small families of bird cestodes with mostly armed rostellum and without the usual vaginal opening into the genital antrum. In the Acoleidae the vagina simply fails to reach the antrum and as hypodermic impregnation is practiced the cirrus is correspondingly heavily armed with large hooks. Some of the genera are: *Acoleus* with single sex organs per proglottid, *Diplophallus* with double male organs but single ovary and yolk gland (Fig. 170C), *Gyrocoelia* with single sex organs and ring uterus opening by pores (Fig. 162B), and *Dioecocestus* with male and female strobilae (Fig. 161C) and double male

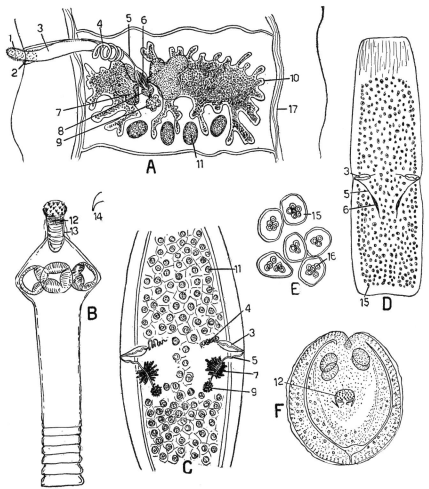

Fig. 167.—Dilepididae (continued). *A.* Mature proglottid of *Dilepis* (*after Burt*, 1936). *B.* Scolex of *Dipylidium caninum*, original. *C.* Mature proglottid of *D. caninum*. *D.* Ripe proglottid of *D. caninum*, full of uterine capsules. *E.* Uterine capsules enlarged. (*C–E, after Southwell*, 1930.) *F.* Cysticercoid of *D. caninum*, from dog flea (*after Venard*, 1938). 1, cirrus; 2, gonopore; 3, cirrus sac; 4, sperm duct; 5, vagina; 6, seminal receptacle; 7, ovary; 8, shell gland; 9, yolk gland; 10, uterus; 11, testes; 12, rostellum; 13, rostellar sac; 14, hook of rostellum enlarged; 15, uterine capsules; 16, hexacanths; 17, excretory canals.

and single female organs. In the Amabiliidae there are various types of female openings; in *Amabilia* with double male and single female organs the vagina enters the excretory system; in *Schistotaenia*, the vagina is replaced by a canal with surficial pores; and in *Tatria* (Fig. 170*A*) the tubular seminal receptacle winds back and forth throughout the whole strobila and opens at the posterior lateral edge of each proglottid (Fig. 170*B*).

The Taeniidae are distinguished primarily by the uterus, which in the elongate ripe proglottids forms a median tube with slender lateral branches (Fig. 162D, E). The scolex usually has a rostellum provided with an inner circlet of large hooks and an outer circlet of smaller ones (Fig. 170F, G). There is a single set of reproductive organs per proglottid opening irregularly on either side in the body margin. There are numerous testes and the bilobed ovary and yolk gland lie in the posterior part of the segment (Fig. 161D). The Taeniidae occur chiefly in mammals, especially carnivores and man, but a few species parasitize birds of prey. The gravid proglottids longer than wide contain the branched uterus loaded with hexacanths enclosed in a thick striated shell (Fig. 138D) formed of the outer membrane. The larval stage is a cysticercus or bladder worm, a fluid-filled vesicle bearing at one point the inverted scolex (Fig. 142A). These cysticerci, often of considerable size, occur in the muscles, connective tissue, liver, heart, nervous system, and other parts of various mammals, as rodents, pigs, cattle, sheep, etc.

The principal genus *Taenia* comprises a considerable number of species, distinguished mostly by the number and shape of the uterine branches, and includes the two common tapeworms of man, *T. saginata* and *T. solium*. The beef tapeworm, *T. saginata*, without hooks or rostellum (Fig. 127B–D), is the commonest large human tapeworm, reaching a length of 5 to 10 or more meters. The gravid proglottids, with 15 to 20 branches on each side of the uterus (Fig. 162D), must be eaten by cattle or other ungulates in which the liberated oncospheres penetrate the intestinal wall, enter the blood or lymph vessels, and finally lodge in the heart or muscles, especially the jaw muscles, where they develop to cysticerci, known as *Cysticercus bovis*. The pork tapeworm, *T. solium*, has the typical taeniid hook-bearing rostellum (Fig. 128F) and 7 to 10 uterine branches (Fig. 162E) on each side; the life cycle is similar except that the cysticerci, known as *C. cellulosae*, occur in the muscles of pigs.

Some other common Taenias are: *T. taeniaeformis* (= *crassicollis*) in the cat and other carnivores with *Cysticercus fasciolaris* as a strobilocercus (page 340, Fig. 171) in the liver and peritoneum of rats, mice, and other rodents; *T. pisiformis* (= *serrata*) in the dog and other carnivores with its cysticercus in the liver of rabbits; *T. hydatigena* (= *marginata*) in the dog and other carnivores with *C. tenuicollis* in the liver of pigs and ruminants; *T. crassiceps* in the dog and other canines with *C. longicollis*, multiplying by external budding, in rodents; and *T. ovis* in the dog with its cysticercus in the sheep and goat. Cysticerci often bear different names from the mature cestode because they were known and described before their relation to the adult was discovered.

Certain taeniid cysticerci have extensive powers of asexual multiplication and hence constitute dangerous parasites of economic importance.

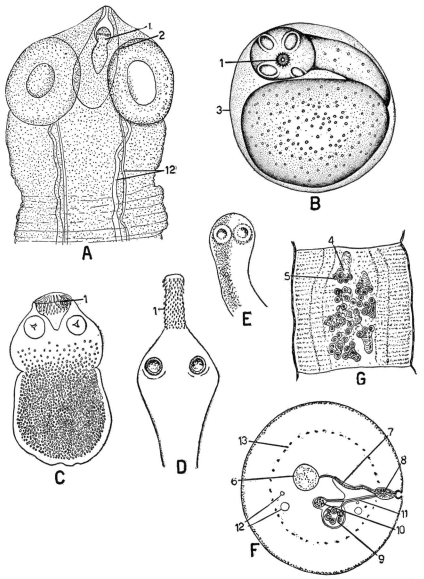

Fig. 168.—Dilepididae (continued). Nematotaeniidae. A. Scolex of fowl cestode, *Choanotaenia infundibulum* (*after Gutberlet*, 1916). B. Cysticercoid of *Ch. infundibulum* (*after Reid and Ackert*, 1937). C. Cysticercoid of *Diplopylidium* from a lizard (*after Witenberg*, 1932). D. Scolex of *Joyeauxiella* (*after Witenberg*, 1932). E. Scolex of *Cylindrotaenia*. F. Section through *Cylindrotaenia*, showing sex organs. G. Ripe proglottid of *Nematotaenia*, showing parauterine organs. (E–G, after Jewell, 1916.) 1, rostellum; 2, rostellar sac; 3, cyst wall; 4, parauterine organs; 5, hexacanths; 6, testis; 7, sperm duct; 8, cirrus sac; 9, ovary; 10, yolk gland; 11, vagina; 12, excretory vessels; 13, longitudinal muscle layer.

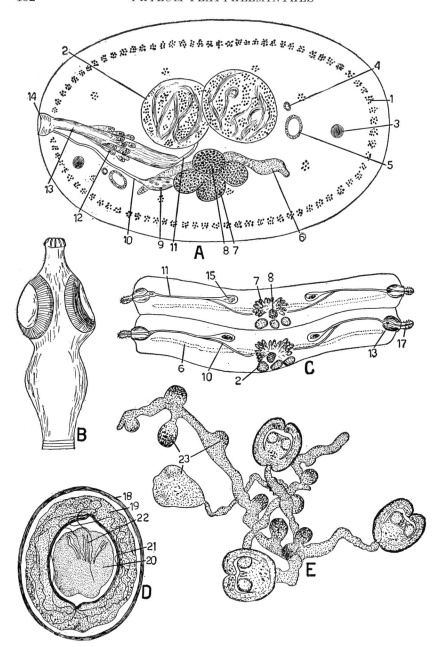

FIG. 169.—Hymenolepididae. *A.* Section through *Diorchis*, showing reproductive system. *B.* Scolex of *Diorchis.* (*A, B, after Jacobi,* 1898.) *C.* Mature proglottids of *Diploposthe* (*after Yamaguti,* 1935). *D.* Membranated hexacanth of *Hymenolepis nana fraterna* (*after Joyeaux,* 1920). *E.* Branching larva of *Hymenolepis cantaniana,* with budding cysticercoids (*after Jones and Alicata,* 1935). 1, layer of longitudinal muscles; 2,

In the coenurus type, sometimes made the basis of a separate genus *Multiceps*, the inner wall of the bladder proliferates groups of cysticerci (Fig. 172*C*, *D*) that usually do not detach and that may bud other cysticerci from their stalks of attachment. The principal species with coenurus bladder is *Taenia multiceps* (= *Multiceps multiceps*, *Taenia coenurus*, *Coenurus cerebralis*), a relatively harmless tapeworm of the dog. When the proglottids are eaten in grazing by sheep and other herbivores, the oncospheres wander throughout the body, but only those that reach the brain or spinal cord continue their development. Here they develop into coenurus bladders 3 to 5 cm. across containing up to 100 scolex buds. The presence of coenurus bladder in the brain causes the sheep disease termed the gid or the staggers in which the animal shows vertigo and abnormal movements and eventually dies (Ransom, 1905). Other dog tapeworms with coenurus larvae are *Taenia serialis*, of which the coenurus bladders occur in the subcutaneous tissue and muscles of rabbits and hares, *T. gaigeri* with the coenurus stage in the brain and other organs and tissues of Indian goats (Hall, 1919), and *T. glomeratus* with coenuri in mice, rabbits, and other rodents (Clapham, 1940). Coenuri, especially of *T. serialis*, have been reported several times from man and apes (Schwartz, 1927b; Elek and Finkelstein, 1939; Clapham, 1941).

The highest powers of asexual multiplication among tapeworms are exhibited by a minute tapeworm of the dog, *Echinococcus granulosus* (= *Taenia echinococcus*). This tapeworm is only a few millimeters long with a hook-bearing rostellum and strobila of four proglottids (Fig. 172*A*). The cysticercus, termed a *hydatid* cyst, occurs in a large variety of mammals—man, monkeys, cattle and other herbivores, cats, dogs, and other felines and canines, horses, pigs, etc.—generally in the liver which the oncosphere reaches by way of the portal system but also elsewhere. The growth of the bladder is very slow, and months or even years may elapse before the bladder wall begins to proliferate on its inner surface vesicles termed *brood capsules* each of which buds internally up to 30 scolices (Fig. 172*B*). These brood capsules and scolices may break loose into the interior of the bladder. Daughter bladders that repeat the process may be produced either internally or externally. Sometimes instead of forming the usual proliferating bladder the hydatid turns into a spongy mass of small vesicles that spreads and grows like a tumor; these cysts termed alveolar or multilocular cysts usually do not proliferate brood capsules or scolices and seem to be abnormal growths limited chiefly to the human host. The regular hydatid cysts may reach the size of an orange,

testes; 3, lateral nerve cord; 4, dorsal excretory vessel; 5, ventral excretory vessel; 6, beginning uterus; 7, ovary; 8, yolk gland; 9, seminal receptacle; 10, vagina; 11, sperm duct; 12, prostatic glands; 13, cirrus sac; 14, antrum; 15, spermiducal vesicle; 16, seminal vesicle; 17, cirrus; 18, outer membrane; 19, inner membrane; 20, hexacanth; 21, filaments; 22, hooks; 23, cysticercoid buds.

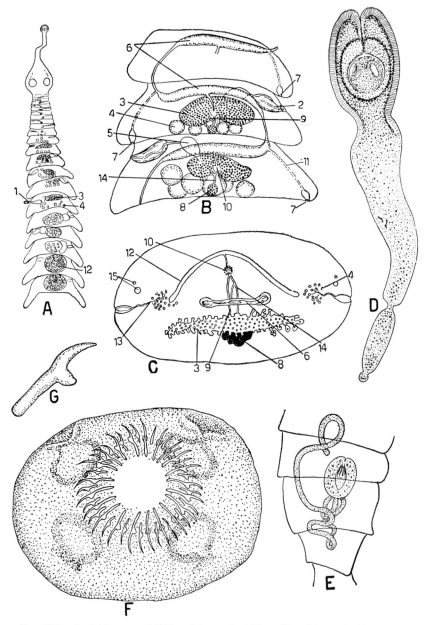

FIG. 170.—Acoleidae, Amabiliidae, Hymenolepididae, Taeniidae. *A. Tatria,* entire worm from a grebe (*after Olsen*, 1939). *B.* Mature proglottids of *Tatria* with continuous winding seminal receptacle (*combined from Olsen*, 1939, *and Schultz*, 1940). *C.* Mature proglottid of *Diplophallus* (*after Joyeaux and Baer*, 1936). *D.* Cysticercoid of *Hymenolepis dimunuta* (*after Joyeaux*, 1920). *E.* Cysticercoid of *Hymeno epis lanceolata* in *Cyclops* (*after Ruszkowski*, 1932). *F.* Scolex of *Taenia pisiformis* from the dog, showing typical

sometimes much larger. Through pressure on or disturbance of vital organs they frequently produce grave symptoms terminating in death. The infection of humans results from too great familiarity with dogs and is common in certain parts of the world, particularly Iceland, Australia, parts of Africa, and southern South America. For further details of hydatid disease the work of Dew (1927), Magath (1937), and Cameron (1927) may be consulted.

20. Order Aporidea.—This order was created by Fuhrmann (1934) for the remarkable genus *Nematoparataenia*, a cestode of swans, first described by Maplestone and Southwell (1922). This is a monozoic tapeworm to 9 mm. in length with a relatively large scolex and a cylindroid body (Fig. 173*A*). The scolex is provided with four acetabula and a large bulging rostellum armed with tiny hooks arranged in eight festoons (Fig. 173*B*). The summit of the rostellum has the muscular structure of an acetabulum and the interior contains muscle fibers and a glandular mass. A longitudinal groove runs along one side of the body. The excretory system has the usual two vessels on each side opening by a posterior nephridiopore. The sex organs are peculiar. A testicular mass runs most of the body length on the side toward the groove and is encircled on its other side by ovarian follicles (Fig. 173*C*), which seem to be of the nature of germovitellaria. There appear to be no sex ducts or gonopores. The eggs develop in the follicles, after fertilization by the sperm from the testis mass, and the follicles apparently expand to become uterine capsules, containing the ovic embryos. These uterine capsules occur in the rear part of the body (Fig. 173*A*). Later Wolffhügel (1939) described another member of this order, *Gastrotaenia cygni*, that has some traces of segmentation, a yolk gland, and an hymenolepid type of scolex.

21. Ecology and Physiology.—Little information is available concerning the environmental relations of tapeworms, as free-living stages are mostly lacking and the parasitic stages are difficult to maintain in artificial media. The shed proglottids are capable of considerable motility and in some tapeworms, especially tetraphyllids, may remain in the host intestine for some time and even alter at the anterior end into a scolex-like form. Some tapeworms, e.g., *Haplobothrium* and *Idiogenes*, give rise to secondary strobilae that lead an independent existence in the host intestine and may also alter anteriorly to imitate a scolex (Fig. 155*C*). The discharge of proglottids to the exterior is sometimes related to time of day. Thus the poultry cestodes *Davainea proglottina* (Levine, 1938) and *Raillietina cesticillus* (Reid, Ackert, and Case, 1938) discharge their proglot-

Taenia rostellum with alternating circles of inner large and outer smaller hooks. *G.* One of the hooks enlarged. (*F, G, after Hall,* 1919.) 1, cirrus; 2, cirrus sac; 3, ovary; 4, testes; 5, spermiducal vesicle; 6, seminal receptacle; 7, vaginal pore; 8, yolk gland; 9, oviduct; 10, shell gland; 11, vagina; 12, uterus; 13, sperm duct; 14, yolk duct; 15, excretory canals.

tids late in the afternoon apparently in relation to the nocturnal habits of the intermediate hosts (slugs, beetles). The proglottids of *R. cesticillus* are extremely motile and rapidly move to the periphery of the fecal masses, without regard to light, moisture, or gravity; this behavior appears related to the fact that the intermediate hosts are not coprophagous. Proglottid production was observed to occur in cycles in *R. cesticillus* (Harwood, 1938) and *Moniezia expansa* (Stoll, 1936); after sexual maturity was attained, proglottid production was abundant for some time, then declined or else proglottids without hexacanths were passed, and then there was a renewed increase in proglottid production. Starvation or a deficient diet causes a decline or cessation of proglottid shedding (Levine, 1938) or of hexacanth production (Hager, 1941), or the ejection of the worms (Reid, 1942).

There appear to be few data on the number of hexacanths per proglottid. Reid, Ackert, and Case (1938) reported 300 hexacanths in the proglottids of *Raillietina cesticillus*. Stoll (1936) made observations on sheep infected with one *Moniezia expansa;* the worm discharged a total of 4000 proglottids, equalling a length of 6 m., and containing a total of 40 to 80 million hexacanths or 10,000 to 20,000 per proglottid. The proglottids of *Taenia saginata* contain an average of 80,000 embryos (Penfold, Penfold, and Phillips, 1937). One *Hymenolepis diminuta* passes 1149 hexacanths daily (Hager, 1941).

The ovic oncospheres are generally freed by the disintegration or rupture of the shed proglottids and appear to be without power of movement, although in *Thysanosoma actinioides* they somehow leave the proglottids in a short time and escape from the fecal mass (Hall, 1934); this behavior indicates that the intermediate host (unknown) is not coprophagous. The ovic oncospheres of taenioids seem to be of poor viability so far as tested, whence no doubt the frequent occurrence of additional protective devices as the uterine capsules and parauterine organs. Observations have been made chiefly on the hexacanths of anoplocephalids (Scott, 1931; Scott and Honess, 1931; Stunkard, 1940). These are susceptible to drying and high temperature and remain viable only from one to a few weeks. The pyriform apparatus seems to undergo some changes after the proglottids reach the exterior. The outer membrane or shell is freely permeable to water but the pyriform apparatus is not. Apparently the anoplocephalid ovic embryo must be wetted before discharge occurs; the pyriform apparatus then swells and ruptures and the hexacanth emerges. Freed oncospheres of taenioids do not of course survive in nature; they survive and develop only if freed in the digestive tract of the proper host. The striated shells of *Taenia* oncospheres are more or less resistant to the acidity of mammalian gastric juice. As gastric juice is fatal to the naked oncospheres it is important that hatching be delayed until the intestine is reached. The shell fragments in the alkaline intestinal juices, releasing the oncosphere (de Waele, 1933a).

Very little has been done on the environmental relations of later larval stages. The plerocercoids of *Diphyllobothrium latum*, easily obtained from fish muscles, have been studied by a few workers. They can resist acid and alkali and temperatures ranging from −8 to 55°C. They can be kept alive in balanced salt solutions (see further below) for considerable periods at low temperatures.

The evagination of the scolex of taenioid cysticerci can be artificially induced by imitation of conditions in the host digestive tract as exposure first to gastric juice and then to pancreatic juice or to acid followed by alkali (Scott, 1913) or by placing them in bile salts (de Waele, 1933b, 1934; Edgar, 1941). The scolices of *Echinococcus* are resistant to gastric juice but are digested by the intestinal juice of various mammals except their natural hosts (dogs and cats, Berberian, 1936).

Wardle and Green (1941) attempted to study the growth rate of *Diphyllobothrium latum* by infecting dogs with the plerocercoid and killing the dogs and measuring the tapeworms at various intervals. There was little growth for 6 days after ingestion of the plerocercoids, then rapid growth for about 10 days when sexual maturity was attained; thereafter discharge of parts of the strobilae about compensated for growth in length. *Taenia saginata* grows eight to nine proglottids daily (Penfold, Penfold, and Phillips, 1937).

The duration of life of tapeworms is subject to wide variation. The time that elapses between ingestion of plerocercoids, cysticercoids, or cysticerci by the final host and the shedding of ripe proglottids or embryos by the resulting tapeworms usually varies from a few days to several

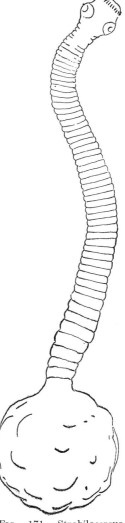

Fig. 171.—Strobilocercus of *Taenia taeniaeformis*.

weeks. Some tapeworms appear to survive in the adult state only a few days as *Hymenolepis fraterna* in the rat and mouse (Shorb, 1933) and *Ligula* and *Schistocephalus* in birds, but generally tapeworms live at least several months. A definite seasonal cycle probably obtains for cestodes

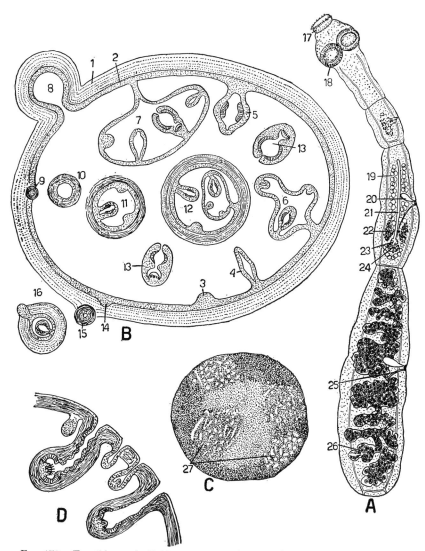

Fig. 172.—Taeniidae. *A. Echinococcus granulosus*, entire worm, from the dog (*after Southwell*, 1930). *B.* Scheme of a hydatid cyst, original. *C.* A coenurus cyst (*after Stiles*, 1898), showing four groups of scolices. *D.* Scheme of a section through a scolex group of a coenurus cyst. 1, lamellated cyst wall; 2, germinative layer; 3–7, stages in development of scolices from germinative layer; 8, constriction to form daughter cyst; 9–12, stages in budding of endogenous daughter cyst; 13, isolated scolices free in cyst fluid; 14–16, stages in budding of an exogenous daughter cyst; 17, rostellum; 18, suckers; 19, testes; 20, cirrus sac; 21, young uterus; 22, ovary; 23, shell gland; 24, yolk gland; 25, vagina; 26, ripe uterus with hexacanths; 27, group of scolices.

inhabiting fresh-water hosts. Thus *Triaenophorus* and other pseudo-phyllids parasitizing fresh-water fish reach sexual maturity in spring and early summer, shed the ripe capsules, and then die and are expelled. Plerocercoids from this generation infect new hosts late in the year and reach maturity the following spring (Scheuring, 1928; Miller, 1943, 1945). Annual cycles also seem to obtain for such pseudophyllids as *Caryophyl-laeus* and *Archigetes* that have their plerocercoid stages in tubificid oligochaetes (Wisniewski, 1930; Wunder, 1939). The cestodes of wild birds probably also have seasonal cycles. Poultry tapeworms live 4 to 14 months in the mature state (Ackert, 1921). Sheep tapeworms of the genus *Moniezia* survive up to 350 days (Gordon, 1932). The larger human cestodes as *Diphyllobothrium latum* and *Taenia saginata* may live 5 to 35 years in the human intestine (Riley, 1919; Leiper, 1936), and the latter appears to live as long as the host survives (up to 60 years, Penfold, Penfold, and Phillips, 1937).

For adequate study of the physiology of larval and adult tapeworms methods of cultivation outside the host body must be discovered. Some progress has been made along these lines. The plerocercoids of *Dibothrio-cephalus* and *Triaenophorus* survive poorly in solutions of single salts but can be kept alive in a balanced salt solution as Ringer-Locke 1 or 2 days at 38°C., a week at 20°C., and longer periods (up to 47 days) at cold temperatures (Le Bas, 1924; Wardle, 1932; Markov, 1938); somewhat longer survival at cold temperatures was obtained by addition of fish broth, glucose, and vitamins (Markov, 1938). No growth resulted in these experiments, but Green and Wardle (1941) noted growth of *D. latum* plerocercoids in nutrient agar plus hog serum. Wardle (1934) experimented extensively with the larva of the tetrarhynchid *Nybelinia* from the stomach mucosa of bony fish. This also survived poorly in solutions of single salts but lived without growth up to 19 days in Ringer-Locke. Addition of antiseptics was not helpful, and such nutrients as fish bouillon, glucose, dextrin, gelatin, egg albumin, soluble starch, and peptones failed to lengthen the survival time although some gave better maintenance of the appearance and movements of the larvae. Dévé (1926) and Coutelen (1926, 1929) note vesicle formation by hydatid and coenurus scolices in media containing serum. Green and Wardle (1941) attempted to cultivate several adult tapeworms in artificial media and again obtained the best results with balanced salt solution; addition of peptones, hormones, vitamins, and serum favored the survival of *Hymeno-lepis fraterna*. Smyth (1946) obtained excellent survival of the advanced plerocercoids of *Schistocephalus* from fish in ¾ Locke's solution and especially in peptone broth; some larvae in the latter medium survived 300 days. When peptone-broth cultures of this plerocercoid were raised to the temperature of the definitive bird host (40°C.), the larvae at once

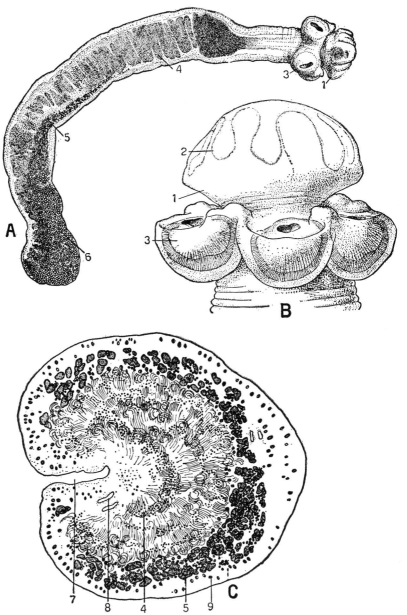

Fig. 173.—Nematoparataenia. *A*. Enitire worm. *B*. Scolex enlarged. *C*. Section through the body. (*All after Fuhrmann, 1933.*) 1, rostellum; 2, festoons of hooks; 3, suckers; 4, testis; 5. ovary; 6, uterine capsules; 7, lateral groove; 8, excretory canals; 9, longitudinal muscles.

became sexually mature and discharged eggs and sperm into the medium, but fertilization failed. Similar results were later obtained with *Ligula* (Smyth, 1947b).

Tapeworms become flaccid and expanded in hypotonic media, flaccid and contracted in hypertonic ones. Smyth (1946) found the osmotic pressure of *Schistocephalus* plerocercoids to equal a 0.75 per cent sodium chloride solution with a freezing-point depression of $-0.44°C$.

Many larval and adult cestodes exhibit rhythmic peristaltic contractions while normally attached and these are usually accelerated at first in artificial media, declining later and terminating in a tetanic contraction followed by death (Wardle, 1934). The peristaltic contractions begin at any anterior level and proceed posteriorly. They are not interrupted by various transverse cuts in the strobila but are blocked by compression of a proglottid (Rietschel, 1935). These facts seem to indicate diffuse nervous transmission.

Tapeworms obtain their nutrition by direct absorption through the surface, but scarcely anything is known of the process. Langer (1905) kept *Taenia saginata* and *Dipylidium caninum* 8 to 24 hours in media containing horse serum and egg albumin but observed no passage of these proteins into the cestodes. Glucose and similar carbohydrates are absorbed, however. If tapeworms are able to absorb only the split products of host digestion, they would not seem to require any digestive enzymes. The available scanty evidence indicates that they do not emit enzymes into their surroundings but are provided with proteolytic enzymes (Kobert, 1903; Abderhalden, 1911; Smorodinzev and Bebeshin, 1936). The wall of hydatid cysts contains diastase, lipase, and protease (G. Cameron, 1926), especially the former, an indication of the use of the glycogen of the host liver as nutrition.

While the gut contents of the host are the main source of nutrition of tapeworms, the fact that in many forms the scolex is deeply embedded in the intestinal wall indicates some absorption of host tissue fluids by the scolex. Studies on the nutritive requirements of the rat cestode *Hymenolepis diminuta* have been made by Hager (1941), Chandler (1943), and Addis and Chandler (1944) by feeding cysticercoids to rats and after the resulting tapeworms had attained maturity noting hexacanth or proglottid production during various dietary regimes of the host. Elimination of protein from the host diet was without effect, an indication that protein can be obtained from host tissue fluids. Omission of carbohydrates was very deleterious, resulting in stunting of the worms and failure to establish themselves in the gut. Of various vitamin-deficiencies tested, only lack of G affected adversely growth, maintenance, and hexacanth production; except in female rats where lack of B complex was also deleterious to the tapeworms. Thus carbohydrates and certain vitamins are the most important elements absorbed by tapeworms from the host gut.

The food reserves of tapeworms consist chiefly of glycogen, to a less extent of various lipoid substances. As in the case of other parasites, glycogen is an important constituent of tapeworms and may constitute as much as 60 per cent of the dry weight. Some data on the glycogen content by wet weight are: 4 to 5 per cent for *Raillietina cesticillus* (Reid, 1942); 1 to 5 per cent for *Moniezia expansa* and 5 to 8 per cent for *Taenia marginata* (Brand, 1933); 1.9 per cent for *Diphyllobothrium latum*, 2.17 per cent for *Taenia solium*, and 7.37 per cent for *Taenia saginata* (Smorodinzev and Bebeshin, 1935). The glycogen content by dry weight was determined for several pseudophyllids by Markov (1939) who found 33.7 per cent in *Ligula*, 29.8 per cent in *Eubothrium rugosum*, 13.8 per cent in *Triaenophorus*, and 17.9 per cent in the plerocercoids of *D. latum*. The strobilocercus of *Taenia taeniaeformis* from the liver of rats has 28 per cent glycogen by dry weight (Salisbury and Anderson, 1939). Glycogen also occurs in the fluid of hydatid cysts. According to the investigations of Ortner-Schönbach (1913), the glycogen of tapeworms is localized in the mesenchyme and in the membranes of the hexacanths. Glycogen is undoubtedly the chief energy source of tapeworms and is used in anoxybiotic respiration (see below). During starvation of the host or when worms are kept in nonnutrient media the glycogen content rapidly diminishes.

The lipoid substances found in tapeworms include phospholipids related to lecithin, cholesterol, cerebrosides, and a variety of fatty acids (Brand, 1933; Salisbury and Anderson, 1939; Smorodinzev and Bebeshin, 1939; Lesuk and Anderson, 1941); some of the fatty acids, however, are the product of anoxybiotic respiration (see below). The lipoid content of taenioid tapeworms varies from 1 to 9 per cent by wet weight (Brand, 1929, 1933; Smorodinzev and Bebeshin, 1935; Lesuk and Anderson, 1941; Reid, 1942), or up to 30 per cent of the dry weight (Oesterlin and Brand, 1933, for *Moniezia expansa*). The lipoid content of adult *D. latum* was 1.54 per cent by wet weight (Smorodinzev and Bebeshin, 1935), of the embryos, 4.95 per cent (Smorodinzev and Pavlova, 1936). The latter authors reported a lipoid content of 6.88 per cent by wet weight for the ovic embryos of *Taenia saginata* as compared with 1.36 per cent for the adult worm. A high lipoid content, 5.35 per cent by wet weight, was also found for the strobilicercus of *Taenia taeniaeformis* (Lesuk and Anderson, 1941). Apparently embryonic and larval stages are well provided with lipoids. According to Brand (1933) the fatty substances occur in droplets of various sizes in the mesenchyme, in the membranes of the hexacanths, and in the bladder wall of cysticerci. As the membranes of hexacanths are well supplied with glycogen and lipoids, they must be of considerable importance in the maintenance of the larvae.

Chemical analyses of tapeworms, mostly taenioids, have been made by Brand (1929, 1933), Smorodinzev and Bebeshin (1935), Salisbury and Anderson (1939), Lesuk and Anderson (1941), and Reid (1942). The general figures per wet weight are: 70 to 90 per cent water, 4 per cent protein, 1 to 9 per cent lipoids, 1 to 8 per cent glycogen, 1 to 7 per cent ash. The ash contains sodium, potassium, calcium, magnesium, sulphur, and phosphorus. Analysis of hydatid cysts (Flöszner, 1924, 1925) showed that the wall consists of protein and a chitin-like substance and the fluid has a salt content and osmotic pressure similar to those of mammalian blood. The fluid contains potassium, calcium, sodium, ammonium, and magnesium as chlorides, sulphates, carbonates, and phosphates, glycogen, various organic acids (acetic, oxalic, valerianic, tartaric, lactic), creatinin and purine bases but no protein or sugars. The calcareous bodies of *Moniezia expansa* consist of calcium and magnesium carbonate and phosphate (Brand, 1933).

The respiratory metabolism of tapeworms has been studied by several investigators (Alt and Tischer, 1931; and Brand, 1933, using *Moniezia expansa;* and Friedheim and Baer, 1933, using *D. latum* and *Triaenophorus*). During the experiments the worms were kept in salt solutions with or without glucose; the inadequacy of the medium probably accounts for the rapid decline in respiratory activity. The worms consume oxygen when this is available in the medium and from the facts that the oxygen consumption is affected by temperature and cyanide and that the presence of cytochrome C was demonstrated this oxygen consumption appears to be a true oxidative metabolism. It is generally higher in the anterior part of the worm, less in mature, and still less in ripe proglottids. The figures obtained by Alt and Tischer were: 1.1 cu. mm. oxygen consumed per hour per gram of dry weight for the scolex and anterior part of the strobila, 0.9 for mature, and 0.6 for gravid proglottids. The R. Q. was 0.9 to 1.2, an indication of carbohydrate metabolism. However, the main respiratory metabolism of tapeworms is anoxybiotic and operates regardless of the presence or absence of oxygen in the medium. In this anoxybiotic metabolism glycogen is utilized as the energy source and the end products are carbon dioxide and organic acids. The chief nonfatty organic acids produced are lactic and tartaric; oxalic was found for *Taenia* by Loeper and Tonnet (1931). The fatty acids formed are various acids high in the series. Brand (1933) reported that 100 g. fresh weight of *Moniezia expansa* would produce in 6 hours an organic acid acidity equal to 5 to 18 cc. of $N/10$ acid. The larval stages of tapeworms also appear to be facultative anoxybionts, but the coracidia of pseudophyllids are obligate oxybionts.

Little attention has been paid to the question of the excretory products of cestodes.   The organic acids mentioned above are normal end products of metabolism of these parasites.   As to the end products of protein breakdown, nothing seems to be known.   The creatinine and purine bases found in analyses of tapeworms by some investigators probably come from the host, and similarly the nitrogenous substances in the fluid of hydatid cysts and the bladders of cysticerci appear to have been absorbed from the host.   Westblad (1922) was unable to find any solid or visible material in the nephridial system of tapeworms, and this system also usually failed to take up vital dyes; the calcareous bodies stained deeply in several vital dyes, an indication that they may be excretion products.

An excellent summary of our knowledge of tapeworm physiology has been published by Smyth (1947a).

22. Host-Parasite Relations; Immune Reactions.—The relations of tapeworms to their hosts are similar to those of flukes.   Specificity varies within wide limits; some species are very strictly limited to a particular species of host, others infect a number of related hosts, and still others are capable of inhabiting many different, not closely related hosts belonging to the same vertebrate class.   Whereas tapeworm species of the same genus may utilize as hosts members of different vertebrate classes as *Hymenolepis* in birds and mammals, a given species of cestode is limited to hosts from the same class of vertebrates.   Larval stages frequently tolerate a much wider range of hosts than do adults.

Usually infection with one or a few tapeworms evokes no symptoms whereas the presence of numerous worms is generally injurious although not necessarily so.   Contrary to popular belief the deleterious effects of tapeworms do not result from their robbing the host of food but rather from damage to the intestinal wall by hooks and suckers and also from the release of toxic substances (further below).   The number of tapeworms of one species infesting the intestine of a vertebrate may be prodigious.   Numerous observers report that the tapeworm population may be so dense as seemingly to block the lumen of the intestine.   Venard (1938) states that one dog may harbor over a thousand *Dipylidium caninum*.   As many as 7000 *Hymenolepis nana* may occur in a child (Hunninen, 1936).   Joyeaux (1927) records 782 *Hymenolepis erinacei* from the hedgehog.   Coatney (1936) found 120 *Taenia pisiformis* and 12 *D. caninum* in a bulldog.   The maximum number of *Diphyllobothrium latum* obtained in dogs by artificial infection was 27 (Wardle and Green, 1941) despite feeding of numerous plerocercoids; but as many as 143 have been recorded from man (Tarassov, 1934).   In her experiments with *Hymenolepis diminuta* in rats Hager (1941) found a maximum of 42 worms.   The taenias of man usually occur singly, or occasionally 2 worms are present, but 10 *T. saginata* are recorded from a Syrian, a race that seems peculiarly susceptible to this worm (Meserve and Coatney, 1937). In infection experiments in which larval stages are fed to experimental animals, the number of resulting adult worms is generally far less than the number of larvae fed. For instance, in mice fed with 7000 hexacanths of *Hymenolepis nana fraterna,* one to 383 adult worms resulted (Hunninen, 1936), and cattle fed 400,000 hexacanths of *Taenia saginata* developed 11,000 to 30,000 cysticerci each (the Penfolds, 1936).

When a number of tapeworms of one species is present in one host, the worms are usually stunted and of low reproductive capacity (Hunninen, 1935; Chandler, 1939; Wardle and Green, 1941; Hager, 1941; Reid, 1942). In Hager's experiments the total number of hexacanths passed daily by infected rats was about the same regardless of the number of worms present up to about 15 worms per rat, i.e., the more worms present, the fewer larvae produced per worm. With greater number of worms, the larvae per worm daily fell to a very small figure. This stunting effect seems to result not from insufficient food supply but from some action of the tapeworms on each other, and this also seems to be the factor involved in the failure of take of many larvae when large numbers are fed.

As in the case of flukes, resistance to tapeworm infection is evidenced in certain host-parasite combinations. The best cases of this resistance concern *Hymenolepis nana fraterna* in the mouse and the strobilocercus of *Taenia taeniaeformis* in the rat liver. In the former, one infection conveys immunity to a succeeding infection for a long period, probably for life, whether or not the adult worms remain in the mouse intestine. The immunity appears as little as 12 hours after the ingestion of hexacanths and results from the invasion of the intestinal villi by the cysticerci (Hearin, 1941). The resistance is passed on to the young of infected mothers, *in utero* and with the milk (Larsh, 1942). The strobilocercus of *T. taeniaeformis* occurs in cysts in the liver of rats; as many as 600 cysts may be present in one rat, although the number is usually less than 100. Rats so infected cannot again be infected, and this immunity persists even if the cysts are operatively removed (Miller, 1932, 1935). Calves that have cysticerci of *T. saginata* are immune to further infection and hexacanths fed to them die (Larsh, 1945).

The foregoing cases are cases of true immunity, i.e., the invasion of tissues by the larval stages evokes the formation of antibodies that destroy further larvae. The serum of the host will give the usual immune reactions, precipitation test, etc., with extracts of the cestode involved. In general adult tapeworms in the intestine do not evoke immune reactions, but their presence seems to have an antagonistic effect on superinfection with further specimens of the same species in certain cases. The nature of this antagonism is unknown. In man the presence of adult *D. latum*, *T. solium*, and *T. saginata* seems to prevent or limit further infection with these species (Tarassov, 1937; Larsh, 1945). In *Hymenolepis diminuta*, the per cent of take of a second feeding of larvae depends on the number of worms present from the first feeding (Chandler, 1939). Birds are resistant to reinfection with *Ligula* for 20 to 30 days after expulsion of a preceding infection (Joyeaux and Baer, 1939). On the other hand, no resistance to superinfection was found for *Diphyllobothrium erinacei* (= *mansoni*) in mammals (Joyeaux and Baer, 1939) or for the fowl cestode *Raillietina cesticillus* (Luttermoser, 1938).

Other factors involved in resistance to tapeworm infection are age and sex, and these also do not depend on immune reactions. Age resistance is seen in the fact that some human tapeworms as *Hymenolepis nana* and *Inermicapsifer* occur mainly in children. Mice become resistant to *H. nana fraterna* after reaching five months of age (Hunninen, 1935); very young mice are also resistant to this worm apparently because the intestine and its villi are at that age too small or too short to accommodate the cysticercoids (Larsh, 1943a). Rats of one or two months are most susceptible to *Cysticercus fasciolaris*, the larval stage of *Taenia taeniaeformis;* newly born rats and those past four months of age rarely become infected (Greenfield, 1942). An influence of sex is evidenced in the development of this cysticercus in rats. This cysticercus is more frequent in male than in female rats as a consequence of the action of sex hormones; gonadectomy lowers the resistance of females and increases that of males to infection, and injection of female hormones into males also increases the resistance of the latter whereas injection of females with male hormones lowers their resistance to the cysticercus (Campbell, 1939; Campbell and Melcher, 1940).

Resistance to tapeworm infection can be conferred on animals by the injection of immune bodies. As noted above, the presence of larval cestodes in the tissues and organs of intermediate hosts evokes the formation of antibodies, and these can be transferred to other individuals, or extracts of adult and larval tapeworms or the larvae themselves may be injected to act as antigens invoking the formation of immune bodies. Thus the serum of mice that have become immune to cysticercoids of *H. nana fraterna* will confer immunity when injected into other mice (Hearin, 1941); or repeated injection of mice with extracts of adult tapeworms will greatly reduce the ability of cysticercoids to develop (Larsh, 1944). Antigens prepared from larval or adult worms or from cysticercus fluid will when injected confer some resistance to infection by the worms involved (strobilocercus of *T. taeniaeformis* in the rat, Miller, 1932, 1935; Campbell, 1936; *Echinococcus* in dogs and sheep, Turner, Berberian, and Dennis, 1936, 1937). In rabbits artificially immunized against *Cysticercus pisiformis*, the seat of protection against the oncospheres was found to be the intestinal mucosa. Of 2000 oncospheres injected directly into the portal circulation 1339 established themselves and became cysticercoids in the liver, whereas when ingested only 39 cysticerci resulted (Leonard, 1940, 1941); the larvae were killed in attempting to pass the intestinal wall.

Immune sera from animals infected with larval tapeworms give the usual immune reactions (precipitation test, complement fixation) when tested against extracts of tapeworms or their larvae, and animals harboring larval tapeworms show skin reactions to cestode antigens. Skin reactions may also be employed to determine whether or not a given animal is infected with larval tapeworms. Such reactions have been particularly employed to diagnose the presence in man of hydatid cysts, a very dangerous condition, and a large literature exists on the technique of such tests. It has been found that antigens for such skin tests need not be prepared from hydatid cysts (the scolices are the most potent part), but a wide variety of taenioid and pseudophyllid tapeworms can be used in making the antigenic extracts (Rose and Culbertson, 1939, 1940; Culbertson and Rose, 1941). The immune tests for the presence of tapeworms are, however, neither very specific nor entirely reliable.

Tapeworms may emit deleterious substances. The severe symptoms sometimes caused by *D. latum*, especially the pernicious anemia, are believed to result from substances released from the worm (Schwartz, 1921). The fluid of hydatid cysts and of other taenioid cysticerci is toxic and may kill or shock small mammals on intravenous injection. The hydatid cyst wall is impervious to the contained fluid, which therefore escapes into the host only on rupture of the cyst wall.

The most remarkable of the effects of larval tapeworms on the host is the stimulation of tumor tissue by the presence of *Cysticercus fasciolaris* in the rat liver. The liver tissue around the cysticercus undergoes inflammation and necrosis, and the eventual result is a malignant growth (sarcoma) composed of host connective tissue and endothelial linings of liver capillaries (Bullock and Curtis, 1924). Tumorous stomach lesions may also accompany heavy infections with this cysticercus (Blumberg and Gardner, 1940). A tumor caused by a coenurus cyst has been reported from a baboon (Schwartz, 1927).

VII. GENERAL AND PHYLOGENETIC CONSIDERATIONS

1. Effects of Parasitism on Parasites.—As the majority of the Platyhelminthes lead a parasitic life, it is pertinent here to consider the consequences of parasitism. Perusal of the foregoing pages will have made these consequences more or less obvious, but a summary here may be convenient. The greater the degree of parasitism the more pronounced become the departures from normal morphology, and all gradations of morphological change exist from slightly altered ectocommensals to highly modified endoparasites.

In the first place, the loss of the surface epidermis and its replacement by a resistant cuticle is a notable feature of parasites. The value of this alteration is obviously greater protection of the parasite against the defenses of the host. This cuticle is composed as already noted of highly insoluble types of protein. A second conspicuous external characteristic of parasites is the presence of organs of adhesion. These take the form of hooks and various types of suckers, and to a lesser extent of adhesive secretions. In the discussion of the Turbellaria, it was shown that organs of this type, especially areas of adhesive secretion, are of common occurrence, employed in locomotion and capture of prey and in the case of ectocommensals for clinging to some other animal. It is evidently but a short step from such structures in free-living forms to parasitic adaptations. The presence of adhesive organs often greatly alters the external appearance of the animal as in the case of the enormous ventral sucker of the Aspidobothria.

Although adhesive organs are in themselves usually highly muscular or operated by special muscle bands, their presence usually is correlated with a general loss of motility of the parasite. External parasites are often capable of lively movements as exemplified by the dactylogyroid Monogenea, but endoparasitic flatworms have little power of locomotion and are helpless when detached from the host. Their bodies, however, are provided with the usual flatworm muscle strata and are capable of maintaining peristaltic contractions, transmitted along the strobila (Rietschel, 1935).

Progressive parasitism is accompanied by progressive loss of sense organs. Whereas ectoparasites often possess ocelli and other types of sense organs, these are lacking in endoparasites, which appear to be provided only with tangoreceptors. There is also a concomitant degradation of the nervous system which, however, remains well-developed in relation to adhesive organs; the latter in fact frequently show an augmented innervation.

Simplification and eventual loss of the digestive tract accompany increasing dependence on the host for food. A mouth and digestive tract are retained by even the endoparasitic flukes but are lost in tapeworms which obtain their nutrition wholly by absorption from the surrounding medium. This mode of life would seem to call for a very exact adjustment to that medium; hence the difficulty of culturing endoparasitic flatworms outside their hosts and the fatality to the parasite of removal from the host.

Of course, the most notable feature of flatworm parasites is their complicated reproductive system and excessive capacity for egg production. However, this system in flukes and tapeworms is scarcely more complicated than it is in the free-living flatworms.   The principal change consists in the great elongation or widening of the ovovitelline duct to act as uterus in which a tremendous accumulation of ripe eggs or embryos is possible. Still further augmentation of egg production is secured in tapeworms by the multiplication of sex organs along the strobila.   This enormous production of offspring is necessary to ensure perpetuation of the species; for the chances of the offspring reaching the proper host are small in many cases.

Perhaps the most remarkable feature of the parasitic flatworms is the complexity of the life cycle.   This cycle involves one to three intermediate hosts in flukes and cestodes and as many larval stages.   It is difficult to understand what advantage accrues to the parasite from such complexity; in fact the chances of offspring reaching the definitive host and maturing to the reproductive stage would seem to be greatly reduced by this round-about way of reaching adulthood.   While the difficulty of completing the life cycle explains the excessive egg production of flukes and tapeworms, the strange and devious cycles themselves appear explicable only from the point of view of evolution.   These cycles seem to repeat the phylo-genetic history of the parasite; in short, what are now intermediate hosts were presumably at one time definitive hosts, and new hosts were added as higher groups of animals evolved.

2. Relationships of the Classes and Orders of Flatworms.—As the origin of flatworms from a planuloid type of ancestor by way of a form resembling the Acoela was fully considered in Chap. IX, it remains here to discuss the interrelationships within the phylum.   Obviously the entire phylum stems from the Acoela or forms closely resembling them. The other orders of Turbellaria similarly derive from the Acoela.   Among them the Alloeocoela are most obviously related to the Acoela; in fact the only difference between the more primitive Alloeocoela and the Acoela lies in the possession of a digestive lumen by the former.   Such forms as *Nemertoderma* can fit into either order or possibly require the creation of an intermediate group.   The Alloeocoela lead directly to the triclads by way of such forms as *Bothrioplana* in which the trifid intestine is in process of development.   Some recent authorities in fact seek to make the triclads a subgroup under Alloeocoela.   The Polycladida probably stem directly from the Acoela, although transitional forms have not been found.   The lack of yolk glands, the net-like nervous system, and the presence of frontal glands during larval stages all serve to link the poly-clads with the acoels.   The most difficult problem among the Turbellaria is to determine the affinities of the Rhabdocoela.   It is usually supposed that they also derive from the Acoela, and as evidence is cited the occur-rence of the pharynx simplex and statocysts, and the absence of sex ducts among the lowest groups of rhabdocoels, the Catenulida and Macrostomida. However, the gap is rather wide between the two orders.

In regard to the parasitic classes of flatworms it appears to be a safe assumption that parasitic animals in all cases stem from free-living ones. The most likely ancestors for the parasitic flatworms are the dalyellioid rhabdocoels, a group in which it will be recalled there are several families that lead entocommensal lives and are tending toward parasitism. It is noteworthy that these entocommensal rhabdocoels occur primarily in mollusks and echinoderms. Mollusks are the chief intermediate hosts of flukes, and echinoderms are now believed to lie along the line of evolution of vertebrates. Among the dalyellioid characters of flukes are the single ovary, single or paired testis, doliiform pharynx, and paired protonephridial system with separate pores in larval stages. There is also to be noted the general resemblance of the redial stage to a rhabdocoel. It seems probable that the monogenetic and digenetic trematodes have originated separately from parasitic rhabdocoels. Among the former may be recalled the marked resemblance of the copulatory apparatus of certain genera to that of the genus *Dalyellia*. Other rhabdocoel characters of the Monogenea are the sacciform intestine in many genera, the separate protonephridia, and the short uterus. In the Monogenea, the Monopisthocotylea with their posterior simple adhesive disk are evidently the more primitive and the Polyopisthocotylea with this disk divided into a number of suckers clearly derive from them, as shown by the fact that the latter pass through gyrodactyloid larval stages. Among the Digenea, the forms with a posterior sucker, as the Paramphistomidae, are apparently the most primitive type from which other families have been derived by the anterior shifting or loss of the acetabulum. As regards the affinities of the Aspidobothria, nothing can be said at present.

Concerning the significance and origin of the complicated life cycle of the Digenea, it is difficult to offer any positive suggestions. As stated above, this group presumably began in rhabdocoel ancestors that parasitized invertebrates, especially mollusks and echinoderms. The redial generation is apparently a reminiscence of such an ancestor; among its rhabdocoel characteristics are the doliiform pharynx, sac intestine, paired protonephridia with separate pores, surface muscle sheath. Presumably the flukes originally had their adult stage in mollusks. When the vertebrates evolved, the flukes, while retaining their connection with the original molluscan hosts, became adapted to vertebrate hosts, chiefly by the elaboration of adhesive organs already existing in rhabdocoels and by modification of the reproductive system in the direction of greater egg production. In the case of those rhabdocoels parasitizing echinoderms, the passage to a vertebrate host would be more direct in view of the presumed phylogenetic relationship of echinoderms and vertebrates.

In the past it has been customary to derive the cestodes from the trematodes by way of monozoic tapeworms such as *Amphilina* and *Caryophyllaeus*. But, as already indicated, the Cestodaria are no longer regarded as primitive forms but rather as neotenic types, and *Caryophyllaeus* and other similar monozoic cestodes belong to the Pseudophyllidea. In general, no phylogenetic importance can be attributed to the monozoic condition. The derivation of the cestodes from the trematodes lacks plausibility on two grounds: first, the difference in types, arrangement, and location of the organs of attachment; and, second, the differences in the reproductive system, particularly as regards the uterus. Whereas in the trematodes the uterus always opens with the male duct into the common antrum, this is typically not the case in cestodes where primitively the uterus appears to have opened mid-ventrally independent of the genital antrum. The course followed by the vagina (copulation or Laurer's canal) also differs in the two groups. It seems reasonable to conclude that the trematodes and cestodes have stemmed independently from parasitic rhabdocoel ancestors.

Concerning the Cestodaria, all that can be said is that they do not seem to be closely related to other tapeworms and that the amphilinoids and gyrocotyloids are not closely allied to each other. Among the Cestoda proper, the Tetraphyllidea are probably to be recognized as the most primitive group. From a tetraphyllid type with four bothridia, other types of adhesive apparatus can be easily derived by reduction; but the reverse process, the derivation of bothridia from bothria, for instance, is scarcely plausible. Among generalized characters of the Tetraphyllidea are the tubular uterus, the mid-ventral uterine openings, the arrangement of the vitellaria in paired lateral fields, and the simple rhabdocoel type of protonephridial canals. Further the Tetraphyllidea are limited to more primitive vertebrate hosts, the elasmobranch fishes, than are other cestode orders except the Trypanorhyncha.

The close resemblance of their reproductive systems indicates that the trypanorhynchids are derived from the tetraphyllids by the evolution of the accessory suckers of the latter into the proboscides of the former. The tetrarhynchids further parasitize the same kind of host as do the tetraphyllids. In the trypanorhynchids stages occur in the reduction of bothridia to bothria and in the fusion of four adhesive organs into two. Such changes suggest an easy transition from the trypanorhynchids to the pseudophyllids by the loss of the proboscides—a change that has already occurred in *Aporhynchus*—and the reduction of the bothridia to two simple bothria. The family Amphicotylidae is considered to be the most primitive pseudophyllid family, having the greatest resemblance to the tetrarhynchids, and parasitizing lower fishes. From them the pseudophyllids have diverged to parasitize all classes of vertebrates, but especially higher fishes. The numerous monozoic forms found among the pseudophyllids are probably simply neotenic plerocercoids in process of dropping the present definitive host.

Such groups as the Proteocephaloidea with a tetraphyllid type of reproductive system combined with a taenioid type of scolex indicate the origin of taenioid tapeworms from tetraphyllids by the conversion of bothridia into acetabula. As shown in the text and figures, bothridia and acetabula have the same histological construction. The taenioids are undoubtedly the latest and most specialized offshot of the cestode line. This is shown not only by peculiarities of structure, as the single yolk gland, absence of uterine openings, varied forms of the original tubular uterus, reduction of the bilobed ovary to a single body, nephridial plexus in the scolex, and modified types of larval forms, but also by the fact that the taenioids parasitize exclusively the highest vertebrates, the birds and mammals.

Janicki (1921), in his "cercomer" theory, has called attention to the resemblance between the cercaria and the procercoid larva and has postulated that the tail (cercomer) of these larvae is an ancestral reminiscence of the hooked posterior disk of the monogenetic trematodes and that, indeed, the hooks of the oncosphere are similarly derivable. This theory proposes the origin of both the digenetic trematodes and the cestodes from the Monogenea. Reasons opposed to such a view have already been given. Apart from the tail there is certainly very little resemblance between a cercaria and a procercoid. The occurrence of frontal glands in various trematode and cestode larval stages cannot be taken as indicative of relationship in particular cases as these glands are a feature of the entire phylum and derive from a common acoeloid ancestor. It is probable that the tail of the cercaria and of the procercoid is without phylogenetic significance and is a larval adaptation for swimming. Its occurrence in tapeworm larvae may indicate that such larvae were originally free-swimming. Further, the tail originates differently in the two larval types; in cercariae it is an outgrowth while in procercoids it is the constricted posterior portion of the body.

Serological tests also indicate a lack of close relationship between trematodes and cestodes (Eisenbrandt, 1938; Wilhelmi, 1940). Unfortunately, as already indicated (page 5), no great confidence can be placed in such tests until technical inadequacies have been eliminated.

Bibliography

Historical

Cuvier, Georges. 1817. *Le Regne animal distribué d'après son organisation.* **Ehlers, E.** 1864. Die Borstenwürmer, Annelida Chaetopoda. **Ehrenberg, C. G.** 1831. Animalia evertebrata. In **Hemprich** and **Ehrenberg,** Symbolae physicae.

I. Entozoa. 1835. Die Akalephen des rothen Meeres und der Organismus der Medusen der Ostsee erläutert und auf Systematik angewendet. Abhandl. Akad. Wiss. Berlin. **Gegenbaur, C.** 1859. *Grundzüge der vergleichenden Anatomie.* **Goeze, J. A. E.** 1787. *Versuche einer Naturgeschichte der Eingeweidewürmer thierischer Körper.* **Haeckel, Ernst.** 1896. Systematische Phylogenie. Teil II. Systematische Phylogenie der wirbellosen Tiere (Invertebrata). **Lamarck, J. B. P. A.** 1809. *Philosophie zoologique,* ou exposition des considérations relatives à l'histoire naturelles des animaux. **Leuckart, R.** 1848. Ueber die Morphologie und die Verwandtschaftsverhältnisse der wirbellosen Tiere. 1854. Bericht über die Leistungen in der Naturgeschichte der niederen Tiere während der Jahre 1848–1953. Arch. Naturgesch. 20, Pt. 2. **Minot, C. S.** 1876. On the classification of some of the lower worms. Proc. Boston Soc. Natur. Hist. 19. 1877. Studien an Turbellarien. Beiträge zur Kenntnis der Plathelminthen. Arb. Zool. Zootom. Inst. Würzburg 3. **Pagenstecher, H.,** and **M. Braun.** 1879–1893. Vermes. In **H. G. Bronn** (ed.), *Klassen und Ordnungen des Tier-Reichs,* Bd. IV, Abt. 1a. **Pallas, P. S.** 1766. *Elenchus zoophytorum.* **Rudolphi, K. A.** 1808–1810. *Entozoorum sive vermium intestinalium historia naturalis.* 1819. *Entozoorum synopsis.* **Van Beneden, P. J.** 1861. Mémoire sur les vers intestinaux. C. R. Acad. Sci. Paris, Suppl. 2. **Zeder, J. G. H.** 1800. Erster Nachtrag zur Naturgeschichte der Eingeweidewürmer von J. A. E. Goeze.

TURBELLARIA

General

Allee, W. C. 1931. *Animal aggregations.* **Bresslau, E.** 1904. Die Entwicklung der Rhabdocölen und Alloiocölen. Ztschr. Wiss. Zool. 76. 1933. Turbellaria. In **W. Kukenthal and T. Krumbach** (eds.), *Handbuch der Zoologie,* vol. II, Pt. 1. **Cernosvitov, L.** 1931, 1932. Studien über Spermaresorption. Zool. Jahrb. Abt. Anat. 54, 55. **Graff, L. von.** 1882. Monographie der Turbellarien. I. Rhabdocoelida. 1903. Die Turbellarien als Parasiten und Wirte. Festschrift Univ. Graz. 1904. Marine Turbellarien Orotavas und der Küsten Europas. Ztschr. Wiss. Zool. 78. 1904–1908. Acoela und Rhabdocoelida. In **H. G. Bronn** (ed.), *Klassen und Ordnungen des Tier-Reichs,* Bd., IV, Abt. 1c, Pt. 1. 1911. Acoela, Rhabdocoela, und Alloeocoela des Ostens der Vereinigten Staaten von Amerika. Ztschr. Wiss. Zool. 99. 1912–1917. Tricladida. In **H. G. Bronn** (ed.), *Klassen und Ordnungen des Tier-Reichs,* Bd. IV, Abt. 1c, Pt. 2. **Martin, C. H.** 1908. The nematocysts in Turbellaria. Quart. Jour. Micro. Sci. 52. 1914. A note on the occurrence of nematocysts and similar structures in the various groups of the animal kingdom. Biol. Centralbl. 34. **Meixner, J.** 1938. Turbellaria (Strudelwürmer). In **G. Grimpe** and **E. Wagler** (eds.), *Die Tierwelt der Nord- und Ostsee,* Teil IVb, Lief. 33. **Prenant, M.** 1919. Recherches sur les rhabdites des Turbellariés. Arch. Zool. Exp. Gén. 58. 1922. Recherches sur le parenchyme des Platelhelminthes. Arch. Morph. Exp. Gén., Fasc. 5. **Reisinger, E.** 1923. Turbellaria Strudelwürmer. In **P. Schulze** (ed.), *Biologie der Tiere Deutschlands,* Lief. 6, Teil 4. 1930. Zum Ductus genito-intestinalis Problem. Ztschr. Morphol. Ökol. Tiere 16. 1933. Turbellaria der deutschen limnologischen Sunda-Expedition. Arch. Hydrobiol. Suppl. 12 (Tropische Binnengewässer 4). **Sekera, E.** 1926. Beiträge zur kenntnis der Lebensdauer bei einigen Turbellarien. Zool. Anz. 66. **Steinböck, O.** 1924. Untersuchungen über die Geschlechtstrakt-Darmverbindung bei Turbellarien. Ztschr. Morphol. Ökol. Tiere 2. **Steinmann, P.,** and **E. Bresslau.** 1913. Die Strudelwürmer. Monographien einheimischer Tiere 5. **Westblad, E.** 1922. Zur Physiologie der Turbellarien. I. Die Verdauung. II. Die Exkretion. Lunds Univ. Arsskrift, n. F., Avd. 2, 18. **Young, R. T.** 1912. The epithelium of Turbellaria. Jour. Morphol. 23.

Acoela

An der Lan, H. 1936. Acoela I. Vidensk. Meddel. Dansk Naturh. Foren. 99. **Beklemischev, M.** 1914. Über einige acoele Turbellarien des Kaspischen Meeres. Zool. Anz. 45. 1915. Sur les Turbellariés parasites de la côte Mourmanne. I. Acoela. Trav. Soc. Natural. Pétrograd 43, Livr. 4. **Böhmig, L.** 1895. Die Turbellaria Acoela der Plankton-Expedition. Ergebn. Plankton-Exped., vol. II, H, g. **Bohn, G.,** and **A. Drzewina.** 1920. Variations de la sensibilité a l'eau douce des Convoluta suivant les etats physiologiques et le nombre des animaux en expérience. C. R. Acad. Sci. Paris 171. 1928. Les "Convoluta." Ann. Sci. Natur., Zool., ser. 10, 11. **Brauner, K.** 1926. Die Turbellaria Acoela der deutschen Tiefsee-Expedition. Wiss. Ergebn. Dtsch. Tiefsee-Exped. 22. **Bresslau, E.** 1909. Die Entwicklung der Acoelen. Verhandl. Dtsch. Zool. Gesell. 19. **Child, C. M.** 1907. The localization of different methods of form regulation in Polychoerus caudatus. Arch. Entw'mech. Org. 23. **Costello, H. M.,** and **D. P. Costello.** 1938a. Copulation in the acoelous turbellarian Polychoerus carmelensis. Biol. Bull. 75. 1938b. A new species of Polychoerus from the Pacific Coast. Ann. Mag. Natur. Hist., ser. 11, 1. 1939. Egg laying in the acoelous turbellarian Polychoerus carmelensis. Biol. Bull. 76. **Fraenkel, G.** 1929. Über die Geotaxis von Convoluta roscoffensis. Ztschr. Vergl. Physiol. 10. **Fühner, H.** 1906. Notizen zur Biologie von Convoluta roscoffensis. Biol. Centralbl. 26. **Gamble, F.,** and **F. Keeble.** 1903. The bionomics of Convoluta roscoffensis with special reference to its green cells. Quart. Jour. Micro. Sci. 47. **Gardiner, E. G.** 1895. Early development of Polychoerus caudatus. Jour. Morphol. 11. **Graff, L. von.** 1891. *Die Organization der Turbellaria Acoela.* 1905. Acoela. Tierreich 23. **Hyman, L. H.** 1937. Reproductive system and copulation in Amphiscolops langerhansi. Biol. Bull. 72. 1939. Acoel and polyclad Turbellaria from Bermuda and the Sargassum. Bull. Bingham Oceanogr. Collect. 7. 1944. Marine Turbellaria from the Atlantic coast of N. A. (Afronta, Ectocotyla). Amer. Mus. Novitates, No. 1266. **Keeble, F.,** and **F. Gamble.** 1907. Nature and origin of the green cells of Convoluta roscoffensis. Quart. Jour. Micro. Sci. 51. **Keil, E.** 1929. Regeneration in Polychoerus. Biol. Bull. 57. **Leiper, R. T.** 1904. Avagina incola. Proc. Zool. Soc. London, Pt. 1. **Löhner, L.** 1910. Über Polychoerus caudatus. Ztschr. Wiss. Zool. 95. 1911. Zum Exkretionsprobleme der Acölen. Ztschr. Allg. Physiol. 12. **Löhner, H.,** and **H. Micoletzky.** 1911. Über zwei neue pelagische Acölen des Golfes von Triest. Ztschr. Wiss. Zool. 98; Zool. Anz. 37. **Luther, A.** 1912. Studien über acoele Turbellarien. Acta Soc. Fauna Flora Fennica 36, No. 5. **Mark, E. L.** 1892. Polychoerus caudatus. Festschrift 70 Geburtstag Leuckarts. **Martin, L.** 1907. La mémoire chez Convoluta roscoffensis. C. R. Acad. Sci. Paris 145. **Peebles, F.** 1913. Regeneration acöler Plattwürmer. Bull. Inst. Océanogr. Monaco, No. 263. **Steinböck, O.** 1931. Nemertoderma bathycola. Vidensk. Meddel. Dansk Naturh. Foren. 90. 1938. Über die Stellung der Gattung Nemertoderma in System der Turbellarien. Acta Soc. Fuana Flora Fennica 62. **Stevens, N. M.,** and **A. M. Boring.** 1905. Regeneration in Polychoerus caudatus. Jour. Exp. Zool. 2. **Welsh, M. F.** 1936. Oxygen production by zooxanthellae in a Bermudan turbellarian. Biol. Bull. 70. **Weldon, W. F. R.** 1889. Haplodiscus piger: a new pelagic organism from the Bahamas. Quart. Jour. Micro. Sci. 29. **Westblad, E.** 1937. Die Turbellarien-Gattung Nemertoderma Steinböck. Acta Soc. Fauna Flora Fennica 60. 1940. Studien über skandinavische Turbellaria Acoela I (Diopisthoporus). Arkiv Zool. 32A, No. 20.

Rhabdocoela

Baer, J. G. 1938. Anatomy and systematic position of Cleistogamia. Records Indian Mus. 40. **Ball, S. J.** 1916. Development of Paravortex gemellipara. Jour. Morphol. 27. **Beauchamp, P. de.** 1911. Astasia captiva parasite de Catenula. Arch. Zool. Exp. Gén., ser. 5, 6, Notes et Revues No. 2. 1926. 23 generations d'oeufs immédiats chez Mesostoma. C. R. Soc. Biol. Paris 95. 1927. Rhabdocoeles des sables a diatomées d'Arcachon. Bull. Soc. Zool. France 52. **Beklemischev, W.** 1916. Sur la turbellariés parasites de la côte Mourmanne. II. Rhabdocoela. Trav. Soc. Natural. Pétrograd 45. 1927. Über die Turbellarienfauna des Aralsees. Zool. Jahrb. Abt. System. 54. **Bock, S.** 1925. Anoplodium stichopi. Zool. Bidrag 10. **Böhmig, L.** 1886. Das Genus Graffilla. Ztschr. Wiss. Zool. 43. **Bresslau, E.** 1903. Die Sommer- und Wintereier der Rhabdocölen des süssen Wassers. Verhandl. Dtsch. Zool. Gesell. 13. 1906. Ein neue Art der marinen Turbellariengattung Polycystis aus dem Süsswasser. Zool. Anz. 30. **Bresslau, E.,** and **H. von Voss.** 1913. Das Nervensystem von Mesostoma. Zool. Anz. 43. **Brinkmann, A.** 1906. Studier over Danmarks Rhabdocöle og Acöle Turbellarier. Vidensk. Meddel. Dansk Naturh. Foren. 58. 1909. Alaurina composita. Meddel. Havundersog. Ser. Plankton 1, No. 7. **Busch, W.** 1851. Beobachtungen über Anatomie und Entwicklung einiger wirbellosen Seethiere. **Caullery, M.,** and **F. Mesnil.** 1903. Recherches sur les Fecampia. Ann. Fac. Sci. Marseille 13, Fasc. 4. **Child, C. M.** 1902. Fission and regulation in Stenostoma. Arch. Entw'mech. Org. 15. 1903a. Experimental control of form-regulation in zooids and pieces of Stenostoma. Arch. Entw'mech. Org. 15. 1903b. Regulative destruction of zooids and parts of zooids of Stenostoma. Arch. Entw'mech. Org. 17. **Ferguson, F. F.** 1939–1940. Monograph of the genus Macrostomum. 8 pts. Zool. Anz. 126–129. **Ferguson, F. F.,** and **W. J. Hayes.** 1941. A synopsis of the genus Mesostoma. Jour. Elisha Mitchell Scient. Soc. 57. **Findenegg, Ingo.** 1930. Untersuchungen an einigen Arten der Familie Typhloplanidae. Zool. Jahrb. Abt. System. 59. **Flory, W. S.,** and **H. M. Showalter.** 1930. The histology of the bursa copulatrix of Gyratrix. Trans. Amer. Micro. Soc. 49. **Fulinski, B.** 1922. Über das Restitutionsvermögen der Rhabdocölen. Arch. Entw'mech. Org. 51. **Gelei, J. von.** 1930. Echte freie Nervenendigungen. Ztschr. Morphol. Ökol. Tiere 18. **Gieysztor, M.** 1938. Untersuchungen an Turbellarien Polens. Zoologica Poloniae, Lwow, 2. **Gilbert, G. M.** 1935. Comparative study of species of the genus Phaenocora. Acta Zool. 16. 1937. A remarkable North American species of the genus Phaenocora. Ztschr. Morphol. Ökol. Tiere 33. 1938. Two new North American rhabdocoels. Zool Anz. 122. **Graff, L. von.** 1905. Marine Turbellarien Orotavas und der Kusten Europas. II. Rhabdocoela. Ztschr. Wiss. Zool. 83. 1913. Rhabdocoelida. Das Tierreich 35. **Haffner, K. von.** 1925. Untersuchungen über die Symbiose von Dalyellia viridis mit Chlorellen. Ztschr. Wiss. Zool. 126. **Hall, S. R.** 1931. Observations on Euglena leucops, parasite of Stenostomum. Biol. Bull. 60. **Hallez, P.** 1909. Paravortex cardii. Arch. Zool. Exp. Gén. 39. **Hein, Charlotte.** 1928. Zur Kenntnis der Regenerationsvorgänge bei den Rhabdocoelen. Ztschr. Wiss Zool. 130. **Hess, Margaret.** 1937. Edema and general atrophy in Stenostomum associated with atrophy of the protonephridium. Jour. Exp. Zool. 76. **Hofker, J.** 1930. Die Turbellaria der Zuidersee. Ztschr. Morphol. Ökol. Tiere 18. **Hofsten, N. von.** 1911–1912. Rhabdocölen und Allöocölen der Schweiz. Zool. Bidrag 1. **Husted, L.,** and **T. K. Ruebush.** 1940. Mesostoma ehrenbergii wardii. Jour. Morphol. 67. **Hyman, L. H.** 1938. Mesostoma arctica. Amer. Mus. Novitates No. 1005. 1943. Macrostomum gigas. Amer. Midland Natural. 30. **Ihering, H. von.** 1880. Graffila muricicola. Ztschr. Wiss. Zool. 34. **Jacek, S.** 1916. Untersuchungen über den Stoffwechsel bei rhabdocoelen Turbellarien (Stenostomum). Bull. Internat. Acad. Sci. Cracovie, Cl. Sci. Math. Natur., ser. B. **Jägersten, Gosta.** 1941. Glanduderma myzostomatis. Arkiv. Zool. 33A, No. 3. **Karling, T. G.** 1931. Kalyptorhynchia aus dem Brackwasser der Finnischen Meerbusen. Acta Zool. Fennica 11. **Kepner, W. A.** 1911. Nematocysts of Microstomum. Biol. Bull. 20. **Kepner, W. A.,** and **J. F. Barker.** 1924. Nematocysts of Microstomum. Biol. Bull. 47. **Kepner, W. A.,** and **R. P. Carroll.** 1923. Ciliate endoparasitic in Stenostoma. Jour. Parasitol. 10. **Kepner, W. A., J. S. Carter,** and **M. Hess.** 1933. Observations upon Stenostomum. Biol. Bull. 64. **Kepner, W. A.,** and **J. R. Cash.** 1915. Ciliated pits of Stenostomum. Jour. Morphol. 26. **Kepner, W. A., W. C. Gregory,** and **R. J. Porter.** 1938. The manipulation of the nematocysts of Chlorohydra by Microstomum. Zool. Anz. 121. **Kepner, W. A.,** and **F. Helvestine.** 1920. Pharynx of Microstoma. Jour. Morphol. 33. **Kepner, W. A.,** and **J. W. Nuttycombe.** 1929. Nematocysts of Microstomum. Biol. Bull. 57. **Kepner, W. A.,** and **W. H. Taliaferro.** 1912. Sensory epithelium of pharynx and ciliated pits of Microstoma. Biol. Bull. 23. **Kromhout, G.** 1943. Protonephridia of fresh-water, brackish water and marine specimens of Gyratrix. Jour. Morphol. 72. **Laidlaw, F.** 1902. Typhlorhynchus nanus. Quart. Jour. Micro. Sci. 45. **Lehman, H.** 1946. Syndisyrinx franciscanus, an endoparasitic rhabdocoel of Strongylocentrotus. Biol. Bull. 91. **Linton, E.** 1910. New rhabdocoel commensal with Modiolus. Jour. Exp. Zool. 9. **Luther, A.** 1904. Die Eumestominen. Ztschr. Wiss. Zool. 77. 1905. Gattung Macrostoma. Festschrift für Palmen. **Marcus, E.** 1945. Sobre Microturbelarios do Brasil. Communicac. Zool. Mus. Hist. Natur. Montevideo 1, No. 25. Sobre Catenulida Brasileiros. Zoologica, São Paulo, Brasil, No. 10. **Meixner, J.** 1923. Über den Bau des Geschlechtsapparates bei Kalyptorhynchien. Zool. Anz. 57. 1924a. Über das Ovarium von Microstomum und die Abscheidungsfolge des Schalen- und Dottermaterials bei rhabdocölen Turbellarien. Zool. Anz. 58. 1924b. Studien zu einer Monographie der Kalyptorhynchia. Zool. Anz. 60. 1925. Die Kalyptorhynchia. Ztschr. Morphol. Ökol. Tiere 3. 1926. Typhlorhynchus nanus und die parasitischen Rhabdocölen nebst Nachtragen zu den Kalyptorhynchia. Ztschr. Morphol. Ökol. Tiere 5. 1928. Aberrante Kalyptorhynchia aus dem Sande der Kieler Bucht. Zool. Anz. 77. 1929. Morphologisch-ökologische Studien an neuen Turbellarien aus dem Meeressande der Kieler Bucht. Ztschr. Morphol. Ökol. Tiere 14. **Müller, H. G.** 1936. Untersuchungen über spezifische Organe niedere Sinne bei rhabdocoelen Turbellarien. Ztschr. Vergl. Physiol. 23. **Nasonov, N.** 1930. Vertreter der Familie Graffillidae des Baikalsees. Bull. Acad. Sci. U.R.S.S., Cl. Sci. Phys. Math. 1935. Über den Heliotropismus der Turbellaria Rhabdocoela des Baikalsees. Trav. Lab. Zool. Exp. Morphol. Animaux 4. **Nuttycombe, J. W.** 1932. Observations on Stenostomum. Zool. Anz. 97. **Nuttycombe, J. W.,** and **A. J. Waters.** 1935. Feeding habits and pharyngeal structure in Stenostomum. Biol. Bull. 69. 1938. The American species of Stenostomum. Proc. Amer. Philos. Soc. 79. **Ott, H. N.** 1892. A study of Stenostoma leucops. Jour. Morphol. 7. **Ozaki, Y.** 1932. On a new genus of parasitic Turbellaria Xenometra and a new species of Anoplodium. Jour. Sci. Hiroshima Univ., ser. B, (Zool.), Div, 1, vol. 1. **Packard, A. S.** 1883. A cave-inhabiting flatworm. Amer. Natural. 17. **Reisinger, E.** 1922, 1923. Untersuchungen über Bau und Funktion des Exkretionsapparates bei rhabdocölen Turbellarien. Zool. Anz. 54, 56. 1924a. Die Gattung Rhynchoscolex. Ztschr. Morphol. Ökol. Tiere 1. 1924b. Die terricolen Rhabdocoelen Steiermarks. Zool. Anz. 59. 1924c. Zur Turbellarienfauna der Ostalpen. Zool. Jahrb. Abt. System. 49. 1930. Bresslauilla. Oekiocolax. Ztschr. Morphol. Okol. Tiere 16.

Riedel, G. 1932. Macrostomida. Dalyellidae (Greenland). Vidensk. Meddel. Naturh. Foren. Copenhagen 94. **Ruebush, T. K.** 1935a. The occurrence of Provortex in the United States. Zool. Anz. 111. 1935b. The genus Olisthanella in the United States. Zool. Anz. 112. 1937. The genus Dalyellia in America. Zool. Anz. 119. 1939. Report on the rhabdocoele Turbellaria collected by the Yale North India Expedition. Zool. Anz. 126. 1941. A key to the American freshwater turbellarian genera exclusive of the Tricladida. Trans. Amer. Micro. Soc. 60. **Ruebush, T. K.,** and **J. W. Hayes.** 1939. The genus Dalyellia in America. II. Zool. Anz. 128. **Ruhl, L.** 1927. Regenerationserscheinungen an Rhabdocoelen. Zool. Anz. 72. **Sabussow, H.** 1897. Über den Bau der männlichen Geschlechtsorgane von Stenostomum. Zool. Jahrb. Abt. Anat. 10. **Sekera, E.** 1888. (Sex organs Microstomum.) Sitzungsber. Böhm. Gesell. Wiss., Math. Naturwiss. Kl. 1903. Erneute Untersuchungen über die Geschlechtsverhältnisse der Stenostomiden. Zool. Anz. 26. 1906. Über die Verbreitung der Selbstbefruchtung bei den Rhabdocoeliden. Zool. Anz. 30. 1912. Über die grünen Dalyelliden. Zool. Anz. 40. **Soest, H.** 1937. Dressurversuche mit rhabdocoelen Turbellarien. Ztschr. Vergl. Physiol. 24. **Van Cleave, C. D.** 1929. An experimental study of fission and reconstitution in Stenostomum. Physiol. Zool. 2. **Wahl, B.** 1906, 1909, 1910. Bau der parasitischen Turbellarien aus der Familie der Dalyelliiden. I. Die Genera Anoplodium, Graffilla und Paravortex. II. Die Genera Umagilla und Syndesmis. III. Das Genus Collastoma. Sitzungsber. Akad. Wiss. Wien, Math. Naturwiss. Cl. 115, Abt. 1; 118, Abt. 1, Pt. 2; 119, Abt. 1. **Westblad, E.** 1922. Protonephridium der parasitischen Turbellarien. Zool. Anz. 67. 1926. Parasitische Turbellarien von der Westküste Skandinaviens. Zool. Anz. 68. 1930. Anoplodiera und Wahlia. Ztschr. Morphol. Ökol. Tiere 19.

Temnocephalida

Annandale, N. 1912. Caridinicola, a new type of Temnocephaloidea. Records Indian Mus. 7. **Baer, J. G.** 1929. Dactylocephala. Bull. Biol. France Belg. 63. 1931. Etude monographique du groupe des Temnocephales. Bull. Biol. France Belg. 65. **Fernando, W.** 1934. The female reproductive apparatus in Caridinicola and Monodiscus. The embryology of Caridinicola. Proc. Zool. Soc. London. 1945. Storage of glycogen in the Temnocephaloidea. Jour. Parasitol. 31. **Fyfe, Marian.** 1942. The anatomy and systematic position of Temnocephala novae-zealandiae. Trans. Roy. Soc. New Zealand 72. **Goetsch, W.** 1930. Die Temnocephalen und das Regenerationsproblem. Phoenix, Buenos Aires. 1932. Regeneration bei Chilenischen Temnocephalen. Sitzungsber. Gesell. Morphol. Physiol. München 41. 1935. Biologie und Regeneration von Temnocephala chilensis. Zool. Jahrb. Abt. System. 67. **Haswell, W. A.** 1887. On Temnocephala. Quart. Jour. Micro. Sci. 28. 1893. A monograph of the Temnocephaleae. An apparently new type of the Platyhelminthes [Actinocephalus]. Macleay Memorial Vol., Linn. Soc. New South Wales. 1900. On Didymorchis. Proc. Linn. Soc. New South Wales 25. 1909. The development of the Temnocephaleae. Quart. Jour. Micro. Sci. 54. 1924. Critical notes on the Temnocephaloidea. Proc. Linn. Soc. New South Wales 49. **Honjo, I.** 1937. Physiological studies on the neuromuscular systems of lower worms. 1. Caridinicola. Mem. Coll. Sci. Kyoto Univ., ser. B, vol. 12. **Merton, H.** 1913. Beiträge zur Anatomie und Histologie von Temnocephala. Abhandl. Senckenberg Naturforsch. Gesell. 35. 1922. Neue Beiträge zur Anatomie von Temnocephala. Zool. Jahrb. Abt. Anat. 43. **Monticelli, F. S.** 1899. Sulla Temnocephala brevicornis e sulle Temnocefale in generale. Boll. Soc. Natural. Napoli 12. **Mrazek, A.** 1906. Ein Europäischer Vertreter der Gruppe Temnocephaloidea. Sitzungsber.

428 PHYLUM PLATYHELMINTHES

Kongl. Böhm. Gesell. Wiss. 11, No. 36. **Pereira, C.,** and **R. Cuocola.** 1940. Contribucao para Temnocephala brevicornis. Arquivos Inst. Biol. São Paulo, Brasil, 11. 1941. Studies on Temnocephalidae. Arquivos Inst. Biol. São Paulo, Brasil, 12. **Plate, L.** 1914. Über zwei Ceylonische Temnocephaliden. Jena. Ztschr. Naturwiss. 51. **Vayssière, A.** 1892. Etude sur le Temnocephale [Dactylocephala]. Ann. Fac. Sci. Marseille 2. **Wacke, R.** 1905. Beiträge zur Kenntnis der Temnocephalen. Zool. Jahrb., Suppl. 6.

Alloeocoela

Bock, S. 1923. Eine neue marine Turbellariengattung aus Japan [Hofstenia]. Uppsala Univ. Arsskrift, Mat. Naturvet. 1. **Friedmann, G. M.** 1926. Baicalarctia gulo, eine allöocöle des Baikalsees. Bull. Inst. Recherches Biol. Univ. Perm 5. **Hofsten, N.** 1907. Zur Kenntnis des Plagiostomum lemani. Zool. Studien tillögnade Prof. T. Tullberg. 1918. Die Anatomie, Histologie und systematische Stellung von Otoplana intermedia. Zool. Bidrag 7. **Hyman, L. H.** 1938. Rediscovery of Hydrolimax grisea. American Mus. Novitates, No. 1004. 1941. Terrestrial flatworms from the Canal Zone [Geocentrophora]. Amer. Mus. Novitates, No. 1105. **Jones, E. Ruffin.** 1941. Morphology of Enterostomula. Jour. Morphol. 68. **Kepner, W. A.,** and **W. H. Taliaferro.** 1916. Sense organs of Prorhynchus. Jour. Morphol. 27. **Maristo, L.** 1938. Beiträge zur Kenntnis der Monocelidinen. Ann. Zool. Soc. Zool. Bot. Fennica 6. **Midelburg, A.** 1908. Zur Kenntnis der Monocelididae. Ztschr. Wiss. Zool. 89. **Nasonov, N.** 1927. Über eine neue Familie Multipeniatidae. Bull. Acad. Sci. U.R.S.S., ser. 6, vol. 21, Pt. 1. **Rees, Gwendolen.** 1941. The resistance of the flatworm Monocelis fusca to change in temperature and salinity. Jour. Animal Ecol. 10. **Reisinger, E.** 1923. Promonotresis. Zool. Anz. 58. 1925. Untersuchung am Nervensystem der Bothrioplana. Ztschr. Morphol. Ökol. Tiere 5. 1926. Zur Turbellarien Fauna der Antarktis [Gnosonesima]. Dtsch. Südpolar Expedition 1901–1903, 18 (Zool. 10). 1935. Proporoplana. Vidensk. Meddel. Dansk Naturh. Foren. 98. **Schmidt, O.** 1852. Neue Rhabdocoelen aus dem Nordischen und dem Adriatischen Meere. Sitzungsber. Akad. Wiss. Wien Math. Naturwiss. Kl. 9. **Steinböck, O.** 1923. Eine neue Gruppe allöocöler Turbellarien: Alloeocoela typhlocoela. Zool. Anz. 58. 1924. Die Bedeutung von Hofstenia für die Stellung der Alloeocoela im System der Turbellarien. Zool. Anz. 59. 1927. Monographie der Prorhynchidae. Ztschr. Morphol. Ökol. Tiere 8. **Steinböck, O.,** and **E. Reisinger.** 1924. On Prorhynchus putealis. Quart. Jour. Micro. Sci. 68. **Stirewalt, M., W. K. Kepner,** and **F. F. Ferguson.** 1940. A new turbellarian worm, Archiloa. Jour. Elisha Mitchell Scient. Soc. 56. **Wilhelmi, J.** 1908. Über einige Alloiocoelen des Mittelmeeres. Mitt. Zool. Sta. Neapel 18.

Tricladida

Adolph, E. F. 1925. The regulation of body volume in fresh-water organisms. Jour. Exp. Zool. 43. **Allen, G. D.** 1915. Reversibility of the reactions of Planaria to a current of water. Biol. Bull. 29. **Alverdes, F.** 1922. Über Galvanotaxis und Flimmerbewegung. Biol. Centralbl. 43. **Anderson, Louise.** 1927. The effects of alkalies on the oxygen consumption and susceptibility of Planaria dorotocephala. Biol. Bull. 53. **Arndt, W.** 1925. Über die Gifte der Plattwürmer. Zool. Anz., Suppl. Bd. 1. 1934. Die Landplanarienfunde in Deutschland und Europa. Zoogeographica 2. 1935. Die bisher in der Mark Brandenberg und in Schlesien gefundenen Landplanarien. Märkische Tierwelt 1, Heft 2. **Arndt, W.,** and **P. Manteufel.** 1925. Die Turbellarien als Träger von Giften. Ztschr. Morphol. Ökol. Tiere 3. **Averinzev, S.** 1925. Neue Art von parasitaren Tricladen (Micropharynx). Zool. Anz. 64.

Bahrs, Alice. 1929. The effect of refrigeration upon the growth-promoting power of rabbit tissues for planarian worms. Physiol. Zool. 2. 1931. The modification of the normal growth-promoting power for planarian worms of the digestive mucosa of the rabbit under variations in diet, fasting, and age. Physiol. Zool. 4. **Bahrs, Alice,** and **Rosalind Wulzen.** 1936. Nutritional value for planarian worms of vitamin depleted mammalian tissues. Proc. Soc. Exp. Biol. Med. 33. **Bandier, J.** 1936. Histologische Untersuchungen über die Regeneration von Landplanarien. Arch. Entw'mech. Org. 135. **Bardeen, C. R.** 1901a. The function of the brain in Planaria maculata. Amer. Jour. Physiol. 5. 1901b. On the physiology of Planaria maculata with especial reference to the phenomena of regeneration. Amer. Jour. Physiol. 5. **Bardeen, C. R.,** and **F. H. Baetjer.** 1904. The inhibitive action of the Roentgen rays on regeneration in planarians. Jour. Exp. Zool. 1. **Bartsch, O.** 1923. Zur Histogenese der Planarienregenerate. Arch. Mikro. Anat. 99. **Beadle, L. C.** 1931. The effect of salinity changes on the water content and respiration of marine invertebrates. Jour. Exp. Biol. 8. 1934. Osmotic regulation in Gunda ulvae. Jour. Exp. Biol. 11. **Beauchamp, P. de.** 1931. Campagne spéologique dans l'Amerique du Nord. 2. Turbellariés Triclades. (Sphalloplana percoeca.) Arch. Zool. Exp. Gén. 71. 1931. Races et modes de reproduction chez la plannaire Fonticola vitta. C. R. Soc. Biol. Paris 107. 1935a. Observationes sur la planarie Fonticola vitta en élevages. C. R. Soc. Biol. Paris 120. 1935b. Observations sur les Dendrocoelum obscuricoles en élevages. C. R. Soc. Biol. Paris 120. **Beauchamp, R. S. A.** 1933. Rheotaxis in Planaria alpina. Jour. Exp. Biol. 10. **Behre, Ellinor.** 1918. An experimental study of acclimation to temperature in Planaria dorotocephala. Biol. Bull. 35. **Beissenhirtz, H.** 1928. Experimentelle Erzeugung von Mehrfachbildungen bei Planarien. Ztschr. Wiss. Zool. 132. **Benazzi, M.** 1936. Razzi fisiologiche di Euplanaria gonocephala. Accad. Naz. Lincei, Rend. Cl. Sci. Fis. Mat. Natur., ser. 6, vol. 23. 1937. Comportamento ereditario della moltiplicazione agamica in una razza di Euplanaria gonocephala. Boll. Soc. Ital. Biol. Sperim. 12. 1938. Ricerche sulla reproduzione delle planarie tricladi paludicole con particolare reguardo all moltiplicazione asessuale. Mem. Accad. Naz. Lincei, Cl. Sci. Fis. Mat. Natur., ser. 6, vol. 7. 1940. Nuove osservazioni sul determinismo e sulla ereditarieta della reproduzione asessuale in una razza di Dugesia gonocephala. Boll. Zool. 11. **Bergendal, D.** 1890. Studien über nordische Turbellarien [Uteriporus]. Ofersigt Vetensk. Akad. Forhandl. Stockholm, Arg 47. **Berninger, J.** 1911. Über die Einwirkung des Hungers auf Planarien. Zool. Jahrb. Abt. Allg. Zool. 30. **Beyer, Kathe,** and **C. M. Child.** 1930. Reconstitution of lateral pieces of Planaria. Physiol. Zool. 3. **Bishop, Ann.** 1926. Notes upon Sieboldiellina planariarum, a ciliate parasite of Planaria torva. Parasitology 18. **Bock, H.** 1936. Lichtrückeneinstellung und andere lokomotorische Lichtreaktionen bei Planaria. Zool. Jahrb. Abt. Allg. Zool. 46. **Bock, S.** 1925. Planaria affinis wiederentdeckt. Zool. Anz. 64. **Böhmig, L.** 1906. Tricladida maricola. Ztschr. Wiss. Zool. 81. **Bolen, H. M.** 1938. Planarians of the Reelfoot Lake region. Jour. Tennessee Acad. Sci. 13. **Botezat, E.,** and **W. Bendl.** 1909. Über Nervenendigungen in der Haut von Süsswassertricladen. Zool. Anz. 34. **Brand, T. von.** 1936. Studies on the carbohydrate metabolism in planarians. Physiol. Zool. 9. **Buchanan, J. W.** 1931. Modification of the rate of oxygen consumption by changes in oxygen concentration in solutions of different osmotic pressure. Biol. Bull. 60. 1933. Regeneration in Phagocata gracilis. Physiol. Zool. 6. 1936. Notes on an American cave flatworm, Sphalloplana percoeca. Ecology 17. **Burr, A.** 1912. Zur Fortpflanzungsgeschichte der Süsswassertricladen. Zool. Jahrb. Abt. System. 33. **Carlé, R.** 1935. Beiträge zur Embryologie der Landplanarien. Ztschr. Morphol. Ökol.

Tiere 29. **Carpenter, Kathleen.** 1928. On the tropisms of some freshwater planarians. Brit. Jour. Exp. Biol. 5. **Castle, W. A.** 1927. The life history of Planaria velata. Biol. Bull. 53. 1928. An experimental and histological study of the life-cycle of Planaria velata. Jour. Exp. Zool. 51. **Castle, W. A., and L. H. Hyman.** 1934. Observations on Fonticola velata including a description of the anatomy of the reproductive system. Trans. Amer. Micro. Soc. 53. **Cernosvitov, L.** 1931. Die Sameresorption bei den Tricladen. Zool. Jahrb. Abt. Anat. 54. **Child, C. M.** 1904a, b, c, 1905a. Studies on regulation [in Leptoplana] IV–VII. Jour. Exp. Zool. 1, 2. 1905b, c, d. Studies on regulation [in Cestoplana] VIII–X. Arch. Entw'mech. Org. 19, 20. 1906. The relation between regulation and fission in Planaria. Biol. Bull. 11. 1910a. The central nervous system as a factor in the regeneration of polyclad Turbellaria. Biol. Bull. 16. 1910b. Physiological isolation of parts and fission in Planaria. Arch. Entw'mech. Org. 30. 1911a. The axial gradient in Planaria dorotocephala as a limiting factor in regulation. Jour. Exp. Zool. 10. 1911b. Physiological dominance of anterior over posterior regions in the regulation of Planaria. Jour. Exp. Zool. 11. 1911c. Experimental control of morphogenesis in the regulation of Planaria. Biol. Bull. 20. 1911d. The formation of new zooids in Planaria and other forms. Jour. Exp. Zool. 11. 1913a. The asexual cycle of Planaria velata in relation to senescence and rejuvenescence. Biol. Bull. 25. 1913b. The nature of the axial gradients in Planaria and their relation to antero-posterior dominance, polarity, and symmetry. Arch. Entw'mech. Org. 37. 1914. Asexual breeding and prevention of senescence in Planaria velata. Biol. Bull. 26. 1929. Physiological dominance and physiological isolation in development and reconstitution. Arch. Entw'mech. Org. 117. 1941. *Patterns and problems of development.* **Commoner, Barry.** 1940. Cyanide inhibition as means of elucidating the mechanism of cellular respiration. Biol. Rev. Cambridge 15. **Crozier, W. J.** 1918. On the method of progression in polyclads. Proc. Nation. Acad. Sci. U.S.A. 4. **Curtis, W. C.** 1902. The life history, the normal fission and the reproductive organs of Planaria maculata. Proc. Boston Soc. Natur. Hist. 30. 1936. Effects of x-rays and radium upon regeneration. Chap. XII in **B. M. Duggar** (ed.), *Biological effects of radiation.* **Curtis, W. C., and L. M. Schulze.** 1934. The contrasting powers of regeneration in Planaria and Procotyla. Jour. Morph. 55. **Dilk, F.** 1937. Ausbildung von Assoziationen bei Planaria gonocephala. Ztschr. Vergl. Physiol. 25. **Doflein, I.** 1925. Chemotaxis und Rheotaxis bei den Planarien. Ztschr. Vergl. Physiol. 3. **Eddy, M. W., and D. L. Gleim.** 1932. A thermotropic gradient apparatus with some preliminary studies on Phagocata gracilis. Proc. Pennsylvania Acad. Sci. 6. **Erhardt, A.** 1932. Ein Beitrag zu den Helligkeitsreaktionen von Planaria. Biol. Centralbl. 52. **Fuhrmann, O.** 1914. Turbellariés d'eau douce de Colombie. Mém. Soc. Neuchat. Sci. Natur. 5. **Fulinski, B.** 1914. Die Entwicklungsgeschichte von Dendrocoelum lacteum. Bull. Internat. Acad. Sci. Cracovie, Cl. Sci. Math. Natur., ser. B. 1916. Die Keimblätterbildung bei Dendrocoelum lacteum. Zool. Anz. 47. **Gelei, J. von.** 1913. Bau, Teilung, und Infektionsverhältnisse von Trypanoplasma dendrocoeli. Arch. Protistenk. 32. 1924. Existiert ein Selbstbefruchtung bei den Planarien? Biol. Centralbl. 44. 1927. Der Bau der Tricladenmuskulatur. Zool. Anz. 73. **Gianferrari, Luisa.** 1929. Raggi X e condrioma in Polycelis nigra. Raggi X, regenerazione, e mortalia nelle planarie. Boll. Soc. Ital. Biol. Sperim. 4. **Goetsch, W.** 1925. Versuche über Selbstbefruchtung bei Planarien. Biol. Centralbl. 44. 1933. Verbreitung und Biologie der Landplanarien Chiles. Zool. Jahrb. Abt. System. 64. **Graff, L. von.** 1899. Monographie der Turbellarien. II. Tricladida Terricola. 1912–1917. Tricladida. In **H. G. Bronn** (ed.), *Klassen und Ordnungen des Tier-Reichs,* Bd. IV, Abt. 1c, Pt. 2. **Greenberg, L. D., and C. L.**

Schmidt. 1936. Studies on the properties of a growth-promoting factor for Planaria. Jour. Exp. Zool. 73. **Gresens, J.** 1928. Versuche über die Widerstandsfähigkeit einiger Süsswassertiere gegenüber Salzlösungen. Ztschr. Morphol. Ökol. Tiere 12. **Hallez, P.** 1913. Vers polyclades et triclades maricoles. (Synsiphonium.) 2d Exped. Antarctique Française (1908–1910) 4. **Hammerschmidt, J.** 1908. Über den feineren Bau und die Entwicklung der Spermien von Planaria lactea. Ztschr. Wiss. Zool. 91. **Hanström, B.** 1926. Über den feineren Bau des Nervensystems der Tricladen Turbellarien auf Grund von Untersuchungen an Bdelloura candida. Acta Zoologica 7. **Hess, Olga.** 1930. The effects of pure solutions of sodium, potassium, and calcium chlorides on the oxygen consumption of Planaria dorotocephala. Physiol. Zool. 3. **Hesse, R.** 1897. Die Augen der Plathelminthen, inbesonderheit der tricladen Turbellarien. Ztschr. Wiss. Zool. 62. 1902. Untersuchungen über die Organe der Lichtempfindung bei niederen Tieren. VIII. Ztschr. Wiss. Zool. 72. **Hull, F. M.** 1940. Regeneration and regulation of multiple-headed forms in planarians. Trans. Amer. Micro. Soc. 59. **Hyman, L. H.** 1918. Suggestions regarding the causes of bioelectric phenomena. Science 48. 1919a. Oxygen consumption in relation to feeding and starvation. Amer. Jour. Physiol. 49. 1919b. Oxygen consumption in relation to regeneration. Amer. Jour. Physiol. 50. 1919c. Oxygen consumption in relation to age (size) differences. Biol. Bull. 37. 1919d. Action of potassium cyanide on the oxygen consumption of Planaria. Amer. Jour. Physiol. 48. 1920. A further study of oxygen consumption during starvation. Amer. Jour. Physiol. 53. 1923. Oxygen consumption of pieces with respect to length, level, and time after section. Jour. Exp. Zool. 37. 1925a. Action of acids on oxygen consumption. Biol. Bull. 49. 1925b. The reproductive system and other characters of Planaria dorotocephala. Trans. Amer. Micro. Soc. 44. 1928. Procotyla fluviatilis. Trans. Amer. Micro. Soc. 47. 1929. Effect of oxygen tension on oxygen consumption in Planaria. Physiol. Zool. 2. 1931. On Polycelis coronata. Trans. Amer. Micro. Soc. 50. 1932. Studies on the correlation between metabolic gradients, electrical gradients, and galvanotaxis. II. Galvanotaxis of some non-fissioning planarians. Physiol. Zool. 5. 1937. Some cave planarians of the United States. Trans. Amer. Micro. Soc. 56. 1938. Land planarians from Yucatan. In **A. S. Pearse** (ed.), *Fauna of the caves of Yucatan*, Carnegie Inst. Washington Publ. No. 491. 1939a. New species of flatworms from North, Central, and South America [Sorocelis]. Proc. U.S. Nation. Mus. 86. 1939b. Priority of Dugesia over Euplanaria with notes on American species of Dugesia. Trans. Amer. Micro. Soc. 58. 1939c. Addition species of cave planarians. Trans. Amer. Micro. Soc. 58. 1941a. Terrestrial flatworms from the Canal Zone, Panama. Amer. Mus. Novitates, No. 1105. 1941b. Environmental control of sexual reproduction in a flatworm. Anat. Rec. 81, Suppl. 1943. Endemic and exotic land planarians in the United States. Amer. Mus. Novitates, No. 1241. **Hyman, L. H.,** and **A. W. Bellamy.** 1922. Studies on the correlation between metabolic gradients, electrical gradients, and galvanotaxis. I. Biol. Bull. 43. **Hyman, L. H., B. H. Willier,** and **S. A. Rifenburgh.** 1924. Respiratory and histochemical study of the source of the increased metabolism after feeding. Jour. Exp. Zool. 40. **Ijima, I.** 1884. Untersuchungen über den Bau und die Entwicklungsgeschichte der süsswasser Dendrocoelen. Ztschr. Wiss. Zool. 40. **Jägerskiöld, L. A.** 1896. Micropharynx parasitica. Ofversigt Vetensk. Akad. Förhandl. Stockholm 53. **Kawaguti, S.** 1932. Physiology of land planarians. Mem. Fac. Sci. Agric. Taihoku Univ. 7. **Keil, E.** 1924. Studien über Regenerationserscheinungen an Polycelis nigra. Arch. Entw'mech. Org. 102. **Kenk, R.** 1930. Beiträge zum System der Probursalier (Tricladida paludicola). I–III. Zool. Anz. 89. 1935. Studies on Virginia triclads. Jour. Elisha

Mitchell Scient. Soc. 51. 1937. Sexual and asexual reproduction in Euplanaria tigrina. Biol. Bull. 73. 1940. Reproduction of Dugesia tigrina. Amer. Natural. 74. 1941. Induction of sexuality in the asexual form of Dugesia tigrina. Jour. Exp. Zool. 87. 1944. The fresh-water triclads of Michigan. Miscell. Publ. Mus. Zool. Univ. Michigan No. 60. **Kennel, J.** 1889. Planaria fissipara. Zool. Jahrb. Abt. Anat. 3. **Kepner, W. A.,** and **A. Rich.** 1918. Reactions of the proboscis of Planaria. Jour. Exp. Zool. 26. **Kew, H. W.** 1900. On the slime threads of planarian worms. The Naturalist. **Koehler, O.** 1932. Beiträge zur Sinnesphysiologie der Süsswasserplanarien. Ztschr. Vergl. Physiol. 16. **Korotneff, A. A.** 1912. Die Planarien des Baikalsees. Wiss. Ergebn. Zool. Exped. Baikalsee, Lief. 5. **Lang, P.** 1912. Über Regeneration bei Planarien. Arch. Micro. Anat. 79. **Lehnert, G. H.** 1891. Beobachtungen an Landplanarien. Arch. Naturgesch. 57, Pt. 1. **Lemke, Gerda.** 1935. Beiträge zur Lichtorientierung und zur Frage des Farbensehens der Planarien. Ztschr. Vergl. Physiol. 22. **Li, Y.** 1928. Regulative Erscheinungen bei den Planarienregeneration. Arch. Entw'mech. Org. 114. **Lillie, F. R.** 1901. A comparison of the power of regeneration in three genera of planarians. Science 13. **Lloyd, Dorothy.** 1914a. The influence of the position of the cut upon regeneration in Procerodes. Proc. Roy. Soc. London, ser. B, 87. 1914b. The influence of osmotic pressure upon the regeneration of Gunda. Proc. Roy. Soc. London, ser. B, 88. **Lund, E. J.** 1921. Oxygen concentration as a limiting factor in the respiratory metabolism of Planaria. Biol. Bull. 41. **Lus, J.** 1924. Some consideration on polarity and heteromorphosis in fresh-water planarians. [Russ., Eng. summ.]. Bull. Soc. Natural. Moscow, Sect. Exp. Biol. 1. 1926. Regenerationsversuch an mariner Tricladen. Arch. Entw'mech. Org. 108. **Mast, S. O.** 1903. Reactions to temperature changes in fresh-water planarians. Amer. Jour. Physiol. 10. **Mattes, O.** 1932. Über die Wirkungsweise und die Bedeutung der Turbellarien-Hautdrüsen. Ztschr. Morphol. Ökol. Tiere 24. **Mattiesen, E.** 1904. Ein Beitrag zur Embryologie der Süsswasserdendrocölen. Ztschr. Wiss. Zool. 77. **Meixner, J.** 1928. Der Genitalapparat der Tricladen und seine Beziehungen zu ihre allgemeinen Morphologie, Phylogenie, Ökologie und Verbreitung. Ztschr. Morphol. Ökol. Tiere 11. **Merker, E.,** and **H. Gilbert.** 1932. Die Widerstandsfähigkeit von Süsswasserplanarien in Ultraviolettreichem Licht. Zool. Jahrb. Abt. Allg. Zool. 50. **Meserve, F. G.,** and **M. Kenney.** 1934. The effects of crowding on head frequency and length of life of Planaria exposed to Roentgen rays. Amer. Jour. Roentgenol. 32. **Metschnikoff, E.** 1878. Ueber die Verdauungsorgane einiger Süsswasserturbellarien. Zool. Anz. 1. 1883. Die Embryologie von Planaria polychroa. Ztschr. Wiss. Zool. 38. **Micoletzky, H.** 1906. Beiträge zur Morphologie des Nervensystems und Exkretions-apparates der Süsswassertricladen. Zool. Anz. 30. 1907. Zur Kenntnis des Nerven- und Exkretionssystems einiger Süsswassertricladen. Ztschr. Wiss. Zool. 87. **Miller, J. A.** 1938. Studies on heteroplastic transplantation in triclads. Physiol. Zool. 11. **Morgan, T. H.** 1898. Experimental studies of the regeneration of Planaria maculata. Arch. Entw'mech. Org. 7. 1900a. Regeneration in Bipalium. Arch. Entw'mech. Org. 9. 1900b. Regeneration in planarians. Arch. Entw'mech. Org. 10. **Murray, Margaret.** 1927. The cultivation of planarian tissues in vitro. Jour. Exp. Zool. 47. 1928. The calcium-potassium ratio in culture media for Planaria. Physiol. Zool. 1. **Okada, Y. K.,** and **H. Sugino.** 1937. Transplantation experiments in Planaria. Jap. Jour. Zool. 7. **Olmsted, J. M. D.** 1917. Geotropism in Planaria. Jour. Animal Behavior 7. 1918. The regeneration of triangular pieces of Planaria. Jour. Exp. Zool. 25. **Pantin, C. F. A.** 1931. The adaptation of Gunda to salinity. Jour. Exp. Biol. 8. **Parker, G. H.** 1929. The metabolic gradient and its applications. Brit. Jour.

Exp. Biol. 6. **Parker, G. H.,** and **F. L. Burnett.** 1900. The reactions of planarians with and without eyes to light. Amer. Jour. Physiol. 4. **Pearl, R.** 1903. The movements and reactions of fresh-water planarians. Quart. Jour. Micro. Sci. 46. **Pettibone, M.,** and **R. Wulzen.** 1934. Variations in growth-promoting power for planarian worms of adult and embryonic tissues. Physiol. Zool. 7. **Redfield, Elizabeth.** 1915. The grasping organ of Dendrocoelum lacteum. Jour. Animal Behavior 5. **Robertson, J.** 1927. Galvanotropic reactions of Polycelis in relation to inherent electrical polarity. Jour. Exp. Biol. 5. **Santos, F. V.** 1931. Studies in transplantation in Planaria. Physiol. Zool. 4. **Schaper, A.** 1904. Einfluss der Radiumstrahlen und der Radiumemanation auf embryonale und regenerative Entwickelungsvorgänge. Anat. Anz. 25. **Schultz, E.** 1904. Über Hungererscheinungen bei Planaria. Arch. Eentw'mech. Org. 18. **Silber, R. H.,** and **V. Hamburger.** 1939. The production of duplicitas cruciata and multiple heads by regeneration in Euplanaria. Physiol. Zool. 12. **Steinböck, O.** 1925. Zur Systematik der Turbellaria metamerata, zugleich ein Beitrag zur Morphologie des Tricladen-Nervensystems. Zool. Anz. 64. **Steinmann, P.** 1908. Untersuchungen über das Verhalten des Verdauungssystems bei der Regeneration der Tricladen. Arch. Entw'mech. Org. 25. 1926. Die Vorgänge in den Zellen, Geweben, und Organen während der Restitution von Planarienfragmenten. Arch. Entw'mech. Org. 108. 1929. Zur Orientierungssinn der Tricladen. Ztschr. Vergl. Physiol. 11. 1930. Eine neue getrenntgeschlechtliche marine Triclade. Zool. Anz. 92. **Stoppenbrink, F.** 1905. Der Einfluss herabgesetzter Ernährung auf den histologischen Bau der Süsswassertricladen. Ztschr. Wiss. Zool. 79. **Strandskov, H. H.** 1937. Certain physiological effects of X-rays on Euplanaria. II. Regeneration. Physiol. Zool. 10. **Stringer, Caroline.** 1917. The means of locomotion of planarians. Proc. Nation. Acad. Sci. U.S.A. 3. **Taliaferro, W. H.** 1920. Reactions to light in Planaria. Jour. Exp. Zool. 31. **Toedtmann, W.** 1913. Die Schalenbildung der Eicocons bei Turbellarien. Arch. Hydrobiol. 8. **Ullyott, P.** 1936. The behavior of Dendrocoelum lacteum. I. Response to light and dark boundaries. II. Responses to non-directional gradients. Jour. Exp. Zool. 13. **Vandel, A.** 1920. Le développement de l'appareil copulateur des planaires est sous la dépendance des glandes genitales. C. R. Acad. Sci. Paris 170. 1921. Lankesteria planariae. C. R. Soc. Biol. Paris 84. 1922. Recherches expérimentales sur les modes de reproduction des planaires. Bull. Biol. France Belg. 55. **Waïter, H. E.** 1907. The reactions of planarians to light. Jour. Exp. Zool. 5. **Weigand, K.** 1930. Regeneration bei Planarien unter den Einfluss von Radiumstrahlen. Ztschr. Wiss. Zool. 136. **Weiss, A.** 1910. Beiträge zur Kenntnis der Australischen Turbellarien. Ztschr. Wiss. Zool. 94. **Werner, O.** 1926. Reizphysiologische Untersuchungen an Planarien in ultravioletten Lichte. Zool. Jahrb. Abt. Allg. Zool. 43. **Wheeler, W. M.** 1894. Syncoelidium. Jour. Morphol. 9. **Wilhelmi, J.** 1904. Über die Exkretionsorgane der Süsswassertricladen. Zool. Anz. 28. 1906. Untersuchungen über die Excretionsorgane der Süsswassertricladen. Ztschr. Wiss. Zool. 80. 1908a. Sinnesorgane der Auriculargegend bei Süsswassertricladen. Zool. Anz. 33. 1908b. On the North American marine triclads. Biol. Bull. 15. 1909. Tricladen. Fauna und Flora des Golfes von Neapel, Monogr. 32. **Willier, B. H., L. H. Hyman,** and **S. A. Rifenburgh.** 1925. A histochemical study of intracellular digestion in triclad flatworms. Jour. Morphol. 40. **Wulzen, Rosalind.** 1917. Some chemotropic and feeding reactions of Planaria. Biol. Bull. 33. 1923. A study on the nutrition of Planaria. Univ. Calif. Publ. Physiol. 5. 1926. Study. II. The effect of heating on certain foods. Univ. Calif. Publ. Physiol. 7. 1929. The growth promoting power of egg for planarian worms. Proc. Soc. Exp. Biol. Med. 27. **Wulzen, R.,** and **A. M. Bahrs.** 1931. Unbalance in planarian nutrition.

Physiol. Zool. 4. 1935. A dietary factor which imparts to certain mammalian tissues a quality necessary for the correct nutrition of planarian worms. Physiol. Zool. 8.

Polycladida

Bock, S. 1913. Studien über Polycladen. Zool. Bidrag 2. 1923. Boninia. Nova Acta Reg. Soc. Scient. Upsaliensis, ser. 4, vol. 6. 1925. Planarians. Dr. Mortensen's Pacific Expedition. Parts I–IV. Vidensk. Meddel. Dansk Naturh. Foren. 79. 1926. Apidioplana. Zool. Anz. 66; Göteborgs Kungl. Vetensk. Samh. Handl. 30. 1927. Ductus genito-intestinalis in the polyclads. Arkiv Zool. 19A, No. 14. **Boone, Eleanor.** 1929. Five new polyclads from the Pacific coast. Ann. Mag. Natur. Hist., ser. 10, 3. **Crozier, W. J.** 1917. On the pigmentation of a polyclad. Proc. Amer. Acad. Sci. 52. 1918. On the method of progression in polyclads. Proc. Nation. Acad. Sci. U.S.A. 4. **Freeman, D.** 1930. Three polyclads from San Pedro, California. Trans. Amer. Micro. Soc. 49. 1933. The polyclads of the San Juan region, Puget Sound. Trans. Amer. Micro. Soc. 52. **Graff, L. von.** 1889. Enantia spinifera. Mitt. Naturwiss. Ver. Steuermark. 26. 1892. Pelagische Polycladen. Ztschr. Wiss. Zool. 55. **Hadenfeldt, D.** 1929. Das Nervensystem von Stylochoplana und Notoplana. Ztschr. Wiss. Zool. 133. **Heath, H.** 1928. A sexually mature turbellarian resembling Müller's larva. Jour. Morphol. 45. **Heath, H.,** and **E. A. McGregor.** 1912. New polyclads from Monterey Bay, California. Proc. Acad. Natur. Sci. Philadelphia 64. **Hovey, H. B.** 1929. Associative hysteresis in marine flatworms. Physiol. Zool. 2. **Hyman, L. H.** 1939a. Some polyclads of the New England coast. Biol. Bull. 76. 1939b. Acoel and polyclad Turbellaria from Bermuda and the Sargassum. Bull. Bingham Oceanogr. Collect. 7. 1940. The polyclad flatworms of the Atlantic coast of the United States and Canada. Proc. U.S. Nation. Mus. 89. **Kato, K.** 1935a. Stylochoplana parasitica, a polyclad parasitic in the pallial groove of chiton. Annot. Zool. Japon. 15. 1935b. Discoplana takewakii, a polyclad parasitic in the genital bursa of the ophiuran. Annot. Zool. Japon. 15. 1936–1939. Series of papers on Japanese polyclads. Jap. Jour. Zool. 7; Annot. Zool. Japon. 16; Sci. Repts. Tohoku Univ., ser. 4, Biol. 14. 1940. On the development of some Japanese polyclads. Jap. Jour. Zool. 8. **Levetzow, K.** 1936. Beiträge zur Reizphysiologie der Polycladen. Ztschr. Vergl. Physiol. 23. 1939. Regeneration der polycladen Turbellarien. Arch. Entw'mech. Org. 139. **Moore, A. R.** 1923. The function of the brain in the locomotion of Yungia. Jour. Gen. Physiol. 6. **Olmsted, J. M. D.** 1922a. The role of the nervous system in the locomotion of certain marine polyclads. Jour. Exp. Zool. 36. 1922b. The role of the nervous system in the regeneration of polyclad Turbellaria. Jour. Exp. Zool. 36. **Palombi, A.** 1924. Policladi pelagici. Raccolte planctoniche Nave Liguria 3, fasc. 1. 1929. Gli apparecchi copulatori della famiglia Polyposthiidae. Boll. Soc. Natural. Napoli 40. **Pearse, A. S.,** and **G. W. Wharton.** 1938. The oyster "leech" associated with oysters on the coasts of Florida. Ecol. Monogr. 8. **Plehn, Marianne.** 1896a. Neue Polyclade. Jena. Ztschr. Naturwiss. 30. 1896b. Die Polycladen der Planktonexpedition. Ergebn. Planktonexped. 2, H1. 1897. Drei neue Polycladen. Jena. Ztschr. Naturwiss. 31. **Stummer-Traunfels, R.** 1902. Eine Süsswasser-Polyclade aus Borneo. Zool. Anz. 26. 1933. Polycladida. In **H. G. Bronn** (ed.), *Klassen und Ordnungen des Tier-Reichs*, Bd. IV, Abt. 1c [incomplete]. **Surface, F. M.** 1907. The early development of a polyclad Planocera inquilina. Proc. Acad. Natur. Sci. Philadelphia 59. **Watanabe, Y.,** and **C. M. Child.** 1933. The longitudinal gradient in Stylochus ijimai. Physiol. Zool. 6. **Yeri, M.,** and **T. Kaburaki.** 1918. Description of some Japanese polyclad Turbellaria. Jour. Coll. Sci. Tokyo Univ. 39.

Helminthology, General

Bangham, R. V. 1941. Parasites from fish of Buckeye Lake, Ohio. Ohio Jour. Sci. 41. **Belding, D. L.** 1942. *Textbook of clinical parasitology.* **Braun, M.,** and **O. Seifert.** 1925–1926. *Die tierischen Parasiten des Menschen.* 2 vols. **Busch, P. W. C.** 1905. Sur la localization du glycogene chex quelques parasites intestinaux. Arch. Internat. Physiol. 3. **Byrd, E. E.** 1936a. Intestinal parasites in 257 college freshman. Jour. Parasitol. 22. 1936b. Incidence of intestinal parasites in 537 individuals. Amer. Jour. Trop. Med. 16. **Cameron, T. W. M.** 1934. *The internal parasites of domestic animals.* **Campbell, D. H.** 1937. The immunological specificity of a polysaccharide fraction from some common parasitic helminths. Jour. Parasitol. 23. **Chandler, A. C.** 1937. Studies on the nature of immunity to intestinal helminths. Amer. Jour. Hygiene 26. 1949. *Introduction to parasitology.* 8 ed. **Craig, C. F.,** and **E. C. Faust.** 1945. *Clinical parasitology.* 4 ed. **Culbertson, J. T.** 1941. *Immunity against animal parasites.* **Eisenbrandt, L. L.** 1936. Precipitin reactions of helminth extracts. Proc. Soc. Exp. Biol. Med. 35. 1938. On the serological relationship of some helminths. Amer. Jour. Hygiene 27. **Faust, E. C.** 1933. Parasitic infections in New Orleans. Jour. Pediatrics 2. 1939. *Human helminthology.* **Faust, E. C.,** and **W. H. Headlee.** 1936. Intestinal parasite infections of the white clinic population of New Orleans. Amer. Jour. Trop. Med. 16. **Gower, W. C.** 1939. Host-parasite catalogue of the helminths of ducks. Amer. Midland Natural. 22. **Hall, M., E. W. Price,** and **W. H. Wright.** 1934. Parasites and parasitic diseases of dogs. U.S. Dept. Agricult. Circ. 338. **Harwood, P. D.** 1932. Helminths parasitic in the Amphibia and reptiles of Texas. Proc. U.S. Nation. Mus. 81. **Hassall, A.,** *et al.* 1932. Index-catalogue of medical and veterinary zoology (by authors, reprint and revision of Stiles and Hassall, 1902–1912). U.S. Dept. Agricult. **Hegner, R. W., F. M. Root, D. L. Augustine,** and **C. G. Huff.** 1938. *Parasitology with special reference to man and domesticated animals.* **Hsu, H. F.,** and **C. Y. Chow.** 1938. Studies on human intestinal helminths in 809 cases. Bull. Fan Memorial Inst. Biol., Zool. ser. 8, No. 3. **Lu, C.** 1941. A survey of the parasites of dogs, rats, and cats in China. Chin. Med. Jour. 59. **McCoy, O. R.** 1935. The physiology of the helminth parasites. Physiol. Reviews 15. **MacLulich, D. A.** 1943. Parasites of trout in Ontario. Canad. Jour. Research 21, Sect. D. **Manter, H. W.** 1938. *Laboratory manual in clinical parasitology.* **Mönnig, H. O.** 1934. *Veterinary helminthology and entomology.* **Moss, Emma.** 1941. Criteria for the identification of the more common intestinal parasites. Amer. Jour. Med. Tech. 7. **Neveu-Lemaire, M.** 1936. *Traité d'helminthologie médicale et vétérinaire.* **Poche, F.** 1926. Das System der Platoderia. Arch. Naturgesch. 91, Abt. A. **Pratt, H. S.** 1909. The cuticula and subcuticula of trematodes and cestodes. Amer. Natural. 43. **Riley, W. A.,** and **R. O. Christenson.** 1930. *Guide to the study of animal parasites.* **Sandground, J. H.** 1929. Relation of host-specificity of helminths to age-resistance and acquired immunity. Parasitology 21. 1936. Potential longevity of various species of helminths. Jour. Parasitol. 22. **Schwartz, B.** 1938. Animal parasites transmissible to man. Scient. Monthly 47. **Sprehn, C. E. W.** 1932. *Lehrbuch der Helminthologie.* **Stempell, W.** 1938. *Die tierischen Parasiten des Mensches.* **Stiles, C. W.,** and **A. Hassall.** 1902–1912. Index-catalogue of medical and veterinary zoology. Pts. 1–36. (by authors). U.S. Dept. Agricult., Bur. Animal Industry, Bull. 39. 1926. Key-catalogue of the worms reported for man. Hygienic Lab. Bull. 142. 1929. Key-catalogue of parasites reported for primates (monkeys and lemurs). Hygienic Lab. Bull. 152. 1931. Key-catalogue of parasites reported for Chiroptera (bats). Nation. Inst. Health,

Bull. 155. 1932. Key-catalogue of parasites reported for Insectivora (moles, shrews, etc.). Nation. Inst. Health, Bull. 159. 1935. Key-catalogue of parasites reported for Carnivora (cats, dogs, bears, etc.). Nation. Inst. Health, Bull. 163. **Stoll, N. R.** 1943. Changed viewpoints on helminthic disease: World War I vs. World War II. Ann. New York Acad. Sci. 44. **Swales, W. E.** 1940. The helminth parasites and parasitic diseases of sheep in Canada. Canad. Jour. Research 18. **Taliaferro, W. H.** 1929. *The immunology of parasitic infections.* 1940a. Mechanism of acquired immunity in infections with parasitic worms. Physiol. Reviews 20. 1940b. Mechanism of immunity to metazoan parasites. Amer. Jour. Trop. Med. 20. **Threlkeld, W. L.** 1941. Helminth parasites in sheep. Virginia Agricult. Exp. Sta., Tech. Bull. 68. **Van Cleave, H. J., and J. Mueller.** 1932–1934. Parasites of Oneida Lake (N.Y.) fishes. Pts. 1–4. Roosevelt Wild Life Annals (Bull. New York State Coll. Forestry) 3, Nos. 1–4. **Wilhelmi, R. W.** 1940. Serological reactions and species specificity in some helminths. Biol. Bull. 79. **Yamaguti, S.** 1933–1940. Studies on the helminth fauna of Japan. Jap. Jour. Zool. 5–9.

TREMATODA

General

Axmann, M. 1947. Morphological studies on glycogen deposition in schistosomes and other flukes. Jour. Morphol. 80. **Brand, T. v.** 1944. Occurrence of anaerobiosis among invertebrates. Biodynamica 4. **Brandes, G.** 1892. Zum feiner Bau der Trematoden. Ztschr. Wiss. Zool. 53. **Dawes, Ben.** 1946. *The Trematoda.* 1947. *The Trematoda of British fishes,* Ray Society. **Fuhrmann, O.** 1928. Trematoda. In **W. Kükenthal** and **T. Krumbach** (eds.), *Handbuch der Zoologie,* Bd. II, 2d half. **Goldschmidt, R.** 1909. Eischale, Schalendrüse, und Dotterzellen der Trematoden. Zool. Anz. 34. **Hein, W.** 1904. Zur Epithelfrage der Trematoden. Ztschr. Wiss. Zool. 77. **Linton, E.** 1940. Trematodes from fishes from the Woods Hole region. Proc. U.S. Nation. Mus. 88. **Lühe, M.** 1909. *Die Süsswasserfauna Deutschlands.* Heft 17. Trematoda. **Prenant, M.** 1928. Quelques remarques sur le tégument des trématodes digénétiques. Bull. Soc. Zool. France 53. **Stiles, C. W., and A. Hassall.** 1908. Index-catalogue of medical and veterinary zoology. Subjects: Trematodes. U.S. Publich Health Serv., Hygienic Lab. Bull. 37. **Stunkard, H. W.** 1917. Studies on North American Polystomidae, Aspidogastridae, and Paramphistomidae. Illinois Biol. Monogr. 3.

Monogenea

Alvey, C. H. 1936. Morphology and development of Sphyranura. Parasitology 28. **Alvey, C. H., and W. E. Martin.** 1934. Lymph system of Sphyranura. Jour. Parasitol. 20. **André, J.** 1910. Zur Morphologie des Nervensystems von Polystomum. Die Augen von Polystomum. Ztschr. Wiss. Zool. 95. **Bonham, K., and J. E. Guberlet.** 1938. Acanthocotyle. Amer. Midland Natural. 20. **Dawes, B.** 1940. Formation of egg capsules in Hexacotyle. Parasitology 32. **Fischthal, J. H., and L. N. Allison.** 1941. Acolpenteron from the ureters of the black basses. Jour. Parasitol. 27. 1942. Acolpenteron from the ureters of suckers. Trans. Amer. Micro. Soc. 61. **Gallien, L.** 1932. Sur la reproduction néoténique chez Polystomum C. R. Acad. Sci. Paris 194. 1934. Le dimorphisme évolutif et la biologie du Polystomum. Trav. Sta. Zool. Wimereux 12. **Goldschmidt, R.** 1902. Die Eireifung, Befruchtung und Zellteilung bei Polystomum. Ztschr. Wiss. Zool. 71. **Goto, S.** 1890. On Diplozoon nipponicum. Jour. College Sci. Univ. Tokyo 4. 1894. Studies on the ectoparasitic trematodes of Japan. Jour. College Sci. Tokyo Univ. 8.

Goto, S., and H. Kikuchi. 1917. Two new trematodes of the family Gyrodactylidae. Jour. College Sci. Tokyo Univ. 39. Gröben, G. 1940. Entwicklung verschiedener Arten aus der Gattung Dactylogyrus. Ztschr. Parasitenk. 11. Guberlet, J. E. 1936. Ectoparasitic trematodes from the sting ray. Amer. Midland Natural. 17. Halkin, H. 1901. Recherches sur le développement du Polystomum. Arch. Biol. 18. Hesse, R. 1897. Die Augen der Trematoden. Ztschr. Wiss. Zool. 62. Jahn, T. L., and L. Kuhn. 1932. Life history of Epibdella. Biol. Bull. 62. Johnston, T. H., and O. W. Teigs. 1922. New gyrodactyloid trematodes from Australian fishes with a reclassification of the Gyrodactyloidea. Proc. Linn. Soc. New South Wales 47. Kathariner, L. 1893. Die Gattung Gyrodactylus. Arbeit. Zool. Inst. Würzburg 10. 1904. Entwicklung von Gyrodactylus. Zool. Jahrb. Suppl. 7. MacCallum, G. A. 1913. Fertilization and egg-laying in Microcotyle. Science 37. MacCallum, G. A., and W. G. MacCallum. 1913. Microcotyle. Zool. Jahrb. Abt. System. 34. Mizelle, J. D. 1938. Comparative studies on Gyrodactyloidea from the gills of North American fresh-water fishes. Illinois Biol. Monogr. 17. Mizelle, J. D. et al. 1939–1943. Studies on monogenetic trematodes. I–X. Jour. Parasitol. 25, 26, 27; Amer. Midland Natural. 26, 27, 30. Mueller, J. F. 1936a. Studies on North American Gyrodactyloidea. Trans. Amer. Micro. Soc. 55. 1936b. New Gyrodactyloid trematodes from North American fishes. Trans. Amer. Micro. Soc. 55. 1937. Further studies on North American Gyrodactyloidea. Amer. Midland Natural. 18. 1938. Additional Gyrodactyloidea. Amer. Midland Natural. 19. Mueller, J. F., and H. J. Van Cleave. 1932. Parasites of Oneida Lake fishes. Pt. II. Roosevelt Wild Life Annals 3, No. 2. Nigrelli, R. F. 1935. Effect of fish mucus on Epibdella melleni. Jour. Parasitol. 21. 1937. Susceptibility and acquired immunity of marine fishes to Epibdella melleni. Zoologica, New York, 22. Nigrelli, R. F., and C. M. Breder. 1934. Susceptibility and immunity of certain marine fishes to Epibdella. Jour. Parasitol. 20. Nybelin, O. 1941. Dictyocotyle, ein Leibeshöhle bewohnender monogenetischer Trematode. Göteborgs Kungl. Vetensk. Vitterh. Samh. Handl. ser. B, 1, No. 3. Paul, A. A. 1938. Life history studies of North American fresh-water polystomes. Jour. Parasitol. 24. Price, E. W. 1934. A new term for the adhesive organs of trematodes. Proc. Helminthol. Soc. Washington 1. 1937–1943. North American monogenetic trematodes. I–VI. Jour. Washington Acad. Sci. 27, 28, 29, 33; Proc. Helminthol. Soc. Washington 6, 9. Remley, L. W. 1942. Morphology and life history studies on Microcotyle. Trans. Amer. Micro. Soc. 61. Siwak, J. 1931. Ancyrocephalus. Bull. Acad. Polonaise Sci. Lettr. BII. Stunkard, H. W. 1917. North American Polystomidae. Illinois Biol. Monogr. 3. 1924. Some trematodes from Florida turtles. Trans. Amer. Micro. Soc. 43. Wilde, Johanna. 1936. Dactylogyrus. Ztschr. Parasitenk. 9. Wright, R. R., and G. B. MacCallum. 1887. Sphyranura. Jour. Morphol. 1. Zeller, E. 1872a. Untersuchungen über die Entwicklung des Diplozoon. Ztschr. Wiss. Zool. 22. 1872b. Entwicklung und Bau des Polystomum. Ztschr. Wiss. Zool. 22. 1876. Weiterer Beitrag zur Kenntnis der Polystomen. Ztschr. Wiss. Zool. 27. 1888. Über den Geschlechtsapparat des Diplozoon paradoxum. Ztschr. Wiss. Zool. 46.

Aspidobothria

Barker, F. D., and S. Parsons. 1914. A new aspidobothrid trematode (Cotylaspis). Trans. Amer. Micro. Soc. 33. Burmeister, H. 1856. Systematische Übersicht der Saugwürmer, Trematodes. Zoonomische Briefe, Theil 2: 250–252. Bychowsky, I., and B. Bychowsky. 1934. Aspidogaster limacoides. Ztschr. Parasitenk, 7. Cunningham, J. T. 1887. On Stichocotyle nephropsis. Trans. Roy. Soc. Edinburgh 32. Eckmann, F. 1932. Über zwei neue Trematoden der Gattung

Aspidogaster. Ztschr. Parasitenk. 4. **Faust, E. C.** 1922. Excretory system in Aspidogaster conchicola. Trans. Amer. Micro. Soc. 41. **Faust, E. C.,** and **C. Tang.** 1936. Notes on a new aspidogastrid species with a consideration of the phylogeny of the group. Parasitology 28. **Jägerskiöld, L. A.** 1899. Über den bau von Macraspis. Ofvers. Svenska Vetensk. Akad. Förhandl. 56. **Manter, H. W.** 1932. [Larva of Lophotaspis]. Carnegie Inst. Washington Yearb. 31. **Monticelli, F. S.** 1892. Cotylogaster e revisione degli Aspidobothridae. Festschrift 70 Geburtstag R. Leuckart. **Nickerson, W. S.** 1894. On Stichocotyle nephropis. Zool. Jahrb. Abt. Anat. 8. 1902. Cotylogaster and a revision of the Aspidobothridae. Zool. Jahrb. Abt. System. 15. **Odhner, T.** 1910. Stichocotyle nephropis. Kungl. Svenska Vetensk. Akad. Handl. 45. **Osborn, H. L.** 1903. Habits and structure of Cotylaspis insignis. Jour. Morphol. 18. **Rumbold, D. W.** 1927. A new trematode from the snapping turtle (Cotylaspis). Jour. Elisha Mitchell Scient. Soc. 43. **Stafford, J.** 1896. Structure of Aspidogaster conchicola. Zool. Jahrb. Abt. Anat. 9. **Steinberg, D.** 1931. Die Geschlechtsorgane von Aspidogaster conchicola. Zool. Anz. 94. **Stunkard, H. W.** 1917. Studies on North American Aspidogastridae. Illinois Biol. Monogr. 13. **Van Cleave, H. J.,** and **C. O. Williams.** 1945. Maintenance of Aspidogaster conchicola outside its host. Jour. Parasitol. 29. **Voeltzow, A.** 1888. Aspidogaster conchicola. Arbeit. Zool. Inst. Würzburg 8. **Ward, H. B.,** and **S. H. Hopkins.** 1931. Lophotaspis. Jour. Parasitol. 18. **Wharton, G. W.** 1939. Studies on Lophotaspis. Jour. Parasitol. 25. **Williams, C. O.** 1942. Life history and taxonomic relationships of Aspidogaster conchicola. Jour. Parasitol. 28.

Digenea

Africa, C. M., and **E. Y. Garcia.** 1935. Heterophyid trematodes of man and dog in the Philippines. Philipp. Jour. Sci. 57. 1937. Plagiorchis in the human intestine. Papers Helminthol. 30 yr. Jub Skriabin. **Allison, L. N.** 1943. Leucochloridiomorpha (Brachylaimidae), its life cycle and taxonomic relationships among digenetic trematodes. Trans. Amer. Micro. Soc. 62. **Ameel, D. J.** 1934. Paragonimus, its life history and distribution in North America. Amer. Jour. Hygiene 19. 1937. Life history of Crepidostomm cornutum. Jour. Parasitol. 23. 1938. Morphology and life cycle of Euryhelmis. Jour. Parasitol. 24. **Andrews, Mary.** 1935. The complement-fixation reaction in Schistosoma japonicum. Jour. Helminthol. 13. **Azim, M. A.** 1935. Entwicklungsgeschichte von Apharyngostrigea. Ztschr. Parasitenk. 7. **Baker, J. R.** 1943. Macrocercous cercaria. Trans. Amer. Micro. Soc. 62. **Barlow, C. H.** 1925. Life cycle of Fasciolopsis buski. Amer. Jour. Hygiene, Monogr. Ser. 4. **Baylis, H. A.** 1938. Didymozoon from the mackerel. Jour. Marine Biol. Assoc. 22. **Beaver, P. C.** 1929. Development of Allassostoma. Jour. Parasitol. 16. 1937. Echinostoma revolutum. Illinois Biol. Monogr. 15. 1939. Morphology and life history of Petasiger. Jour. Parasitol. 25. **Bennett, H. J.** 1936. Life history of Cotylophoron cotylophorum. Illinois Biol. Monogr. 14. 1942. Life cycle of Leucochloridium. Proc. Louisiana Acad. Sci. 6. **Bennett, H. L.,** and **A. G. Humes.** 1939. Pre-cercarial development of Stichorchis. Jour. Parasitol. 25. **Bettendorf, H.** 1897. Über Musculatur und Sinneszellen der Trematoden. Zool. Jahrb. Abt. Anat. 10. **Bevelander, G.** 1933. Response to light in the cercariae of Bucephalus. Physiol. Zool. 6. **Bosma, Nelly.** 1931. Alaria mustelae, a trematode requiring four hosts. Science 74. 1934. Life history of Alaria mustelae. Trans. Amer. Micro. Soc. 53. **Brackett, S.** 1940. Notes on the behavior of schistosome cercariae. Amer. Jour. Hygiene 31, Sect. D. 1941. Schistosome dermatitis. Symposium Hydrobiol. Univ. Wisconsin Press. 1942. Avian schistosomes and the life cycle of Gigantobilharzia. Jour. Parasitol. 28. **Brand, T. v.** 1928. Zusammensetzung des Fettes von Fasciola hepatica. Ztschr. Vergl. Physiol. 8. 1938. Nature of the metabolic activities of intestinal helminths. Biodynamica 2, No. 41. **Brandes, G.** 1890. Die Familie der Holostomiden. Zool. Jahrb. Abt. System. 5. **Brooks, F. G.** 1928. Germ cell cycle of digenetic trematodes. Science 68. 1930. Studies on the germ cell cycle of trematodes. Amer. Jour. Hygiene 12. 1943. Larval trematodes of northwest Iowa. Jour. Parasitol. 29. **Buckley, J. J. C.** 1939. Gastrodiscoides hominis and Fasciolopsis in Assam. Jour. Helminthol. 17. **Byrd, E. E.** 1935. Life history studies of Reniferinae. Trans. Amer. Micro. Soc. 54. 1939. Studies on Spirorchidae. Jour. Tennessee Acad. Sci. 14. **Byrd, E. E., and J. F. Denton.** 1938. New trematodes of the subfamily Reniferinae. Jour. Parasitol. 24. **Byrd, E. E., M. V. Parker, and R. J. Reiber.** 1940. Styphlodora. Trans. Amer. Micro. Soc. 59. **Caballero y C, E.** 1940. Heronimus. Anal. Inst. Biol. Univ. Mexico 11. **Cable, R. M.** 1937. Resistance of the herring gull to infections with Parorchis. Jour. Parasitol. 23. 1939. Cotylomicrocercous cercariae from Indiana. Trans. Amer. Micro. Soc. 58. **Cable, R. M., and A. V. Hunninen.** 1940. Life history of Spelotrema. Biol. Bull. 78. 1942a. Life history of Siphodera (pleurolophocercous cercariae). Jour. Parasitol. 28. 1942b. Studies on Deropristis (trichocerous cercariae). Biol. Bull. 82. **Chen, H. T.** 1940. Studies of Paragonimus. Lignan Sci. Jour. 19. **Chen, P. D.** 1937. Germ cell cycle of Paragonimus. Trans. Amer. Micro. Soc. 56. **Coe, W. R.** 1896. [Miracidium of liver fluke.] Zool. Jahrb. Abt. 9. **Cole, L.** 1911. Trematode parasite of English sparrow [Collyriclum]. Bull. Wisconsin Natur. Hist. Soc. 9. **Cort, W. W.** 1912. North American frog bladder flukes. Trans. Amer. Micro. Soc. 31. 1913. Notes on Clinostomum. Trans. Amer. Micro. Soc. 32. 1914. Larval trematodes from North American freshwater snails. Jour. Parasitol. 1. 1915a. North American frog lung flukes. Trans. Amer. Micro. Soc. 34. 1915b. Some North American larval trematodes. Illinois Biol. Monogr. 1. 1919. Cercaria of Schistosoma japonicum. Notes on the eggs and miracidia of human schistosomes. Univ. Calif. Publ. Zool. 18. 1921a. Sex in the trematode family Schistosomidae. Science 53. 1921b. Development of Schistosoma japonicum in its final host. Amer. Jour. Hygiene 1. 1922. Study of the escape of cercariae from their snail hosts. Jour. Parasitol. 8. 1928. Schistosome dermatitis in the United States. Jour. Amer. Med. Assoc. 90; Science 68. 1936. Schistosome dermatitis. Amer. Jour. Hygiene 23, 24. 1944. Germ cell cycle in digenetic trematodes. Quart. Rev. Biol. 19. **Cort, W. W., and D. J. Ameel.** 1944. Development of sporocyst stages of plagiorchid trematodes. Jour. Parasitol. 30. **Cort, W. W., D. J. Ameel, and L. Olivier.** 1944. Development of Schistosomatium. Jour. Parasitol. 30. **Cort, W. W., S. Brackett, and L. Olivier.** 1944. Lymnaeid snails as second intermediate hosts of Cotylurus. Jour. Parasitol. 30. 1945. Influence of larval trematode infections in snails on the second intermediate host relations of Cotylurus. Jour. Parasitol. 31. **Cort, W. W., and S. T. Brooks.** 1928. Studies on holostome cercariae. Trans. Amer. Micro. Soc. 47. **Cort, W. W., D. B. McMullen, and S. Brackett.** 1937. Ecological studies on the cercariae in Stagnicola. Jour. Parasitol. 23. **Cort, W. W., and E. Nichols.** 1920. New cystophorous cercaria. Jour. Parasitol. 7. **Cort, W. W., and L. Olivier.** 1941. Early developmental stages of strigeid trematodes. Jour. Parasitol. 27. 1943a. Larval stages of Plagiorchis muris. Jour. Parasitol. 29. 1943b. Development of the sporocysts of a schistosome. Jour. Parasitol. 29. **Crawford, W. W.** 1940. Life history of a gorgoderid trematode. Jour. Parasitol. 26, suppl. to No. 6. 1943. Life history of Crepidostomum. Jour. Parasitol. 29. **Culbertson, J. T.** 1938. Recent contributions to the immunology of helminth infections. Arch. Pathol. 25. **Culbertson, J. T., and H. M. Rose.** 1942. Skin tests in schistosomiasis with antigen from Pneumoneces.

Amer. Jour. Hygiene 36. **Davis, D. J.** 1936. Histolytic ferment in bodies of cercariae. Jour. Parasitol. 22. **Denton, J. F.** 1944. Life history of Eurytrema. Jour. Parasitol. 30. 1945. Life history of Brachylecithum. Jour. Parasitol. 31. **Dickerman, E. E.** 1934. Morphology and life cycle of Proterometra. Trans. Amer. Micro. Soc. 53. 1945. Parthenitae and cercariae of Proterometra. Trans. Amer. Micro. Soc. 64. **Dietz, E.** 1910. Die Echinostomiden der Vögel. Zool. Jahrb. suppl. 12. **Dobrovolny, C. G.** 1939. Life history of Plagioporus and embryology of new cotylocercous cercariae. Trans. Amer. Micro. Soc. 58. **Dollfus, R. Ph.** 1925. Cercaries marines a queue sétigère. Trav. Sta. Zool. Wimereux 9. **Dubois, G.** 1937. Diplostomes d'oiseaux. Bull. Soc. Neuchateloise Sci. Natur. 62. 1938. Monographie des Strigeida. Mém. Soc. Neuchateloise Sci. Natur. 6. **Eckmann, F.** 1932. Familie Bucephalidae. Ztschr. Parasitenk. 5. **Ejsmont, L.** 1925. Untersuchungen an Arten des Genus Sanguinicola. Bull. Internat. Acad. Polonaise Sci. Lettr., ser. B. **Fairley, N. H.** 1919. The discovery of a specific complement-fixation test for bilharziasis. Jour. Roy. Army Med. Corps 32. 1933. Bilharzia complement-fixation reaction in goats. Jour. Helminthol. 11. **Fairley, N. H., and F. Jasudasan.** 1930. Studies in Schistosoma spindale. Pts. I–VI. Indian Med. Research Mem. No. 17. **Faust, E. C.** 1918a. Eye spots in Digenea. Biol. Bull. 35. 1918b. Life history studies on Montana trematodes. Illinois Biol. Monogr. 4. 1918c. Cystocercous cercariae. Jour. Parasitol. 4. 1918d. Studies on Illinois cercariae. Jour. Parasitol. 4. 1918e. Tetracotyliform larvae. Jour. Parasitol. 5. 1919, 1921. Excretory system in Digenea. I–IV. Parasitology 13; Biol. Bull. 36. 1932. Excretory system as a method of classification of digenetic trematodes. Quart. Rev. Biol. 7. **Faust, E. C., and W. A. Hoffman.** 1933–1934. Studies on schistosomiasis mansoni in Puerto Rico. I–III. Puerto Rico Jour. Public Health Trop. Med. 9, 10; Proc. Soc. Exp. Biol. Med. 31. **Faust, E. C., and O. K. Khaw.** 1927. Studies on Clonorchis sinensis. Amer. Jour. Hygiene, Monogr. Ser. No. 8. **Faust, E. C., and H. E. Meleney.** 1924. Studies on Schistosomiasis japonica. Amer. Jour. Hygiene, Monogr. Ser. No. 3. **Ferguson, M. S.** 1936. Experimental studies on Neascus. Jour. Parasitol. 22. 1940. Encystment and sterilization of Posthodiplostomum and development in sterile cultures. Jour. Parasitol. 26. 1943a. Migration and localization of an animal parasite within the host. Jour. Exp. Zool. 93. 1943b. Development of eye flukes of fishes in the lenses of frogs, turtles, birds, and mammals. Jour. Parasitol. 29. 1943c. In vitro cultivation of trematode metacercariae free from microorganisms. Jour. Parasitol. 29. **Fischoeder, F.** 1903. Die Paramphistomidae der Säugetiere. Zool. Jahrb. Abt. System. 17. **Folger, H. T., and L. E. Alexander.** 1938. Response to mechanical shock by Bucephalus cercariae. Physiol. Zool. 11. **Flury, F., and F. Leeb.** 1926. Zur Chemie und Toxikologie der Distomen. Klin. Wochenschr. 5. **Fukui, T.** 1929. Studies on Japanese amphistomatous parasites. Jap. Jour. Zool. 2. **Goldschmidt, R.** 1905. Embryonalentwicklung bei Zoogonus. Zool. Jahrb. Abt. Anat. 21. **Goodchild, C. G.** 1943. Life history of Phyllodistomum. Biol. Bull. 84. **Griffiths, H. J.** 1939. Bionomics of ova and miracidia of Fasciola hepatica in eastern Canada. Canad. Jour. Research 17, Sect. D. **Harnisch, O.** 1932. Untersuchungen über das Gaswechsel von Fasciola hepatica. Ztschr. Vergl. Physiol. 17. **Harper, W. F.** 1929. Structure and life histories of British fresh-water larval trematodes. Parasitology 21. **Harrah, E. C.** 1922. North American monostomes. Illinois Biol. Monogr. 7. **Harwood, P. D.** 1939. North American trematodes of the subfamily Notocotylinae. Jour. Tennessee Acad. Sci. 14. **Heckert, G. A.** 1889. Leucochloridium. Zoologica, Cassel, 1, Heft 4. **Herber, E. C.** 1942. Life history studies of Notocotylinae. Jour. Parasitol. 28. **Hopkins, S. H.** 1934. The papillose Allocreadiidae. Illinois

Biol. Monogr. 13. 1937. New type of allocreadiid cercaria. Jour. Parasitol. 23. **Horsfall, Margery.** 1934. Cystocercous cercariae. Trans. Amer. Micro. Soc. 53. **Hsu, H. F.** 1939. Food of liver flukes. Chinese Med. Jour. 56. **Hsu, H. F.,** and **E. Y. Li.** 1940. Food of certain helminths living in the digestive tract of vertebrates. Chinese Med. Jour. 57. **Hughes, R. C.** 1927–1929. Studies on the Strigeidae (Neascus, Tetracotyle, Diplostomulum larvae). Trans. Amer. Micro. Soc. 46, 47, 48; Jour. Parasitol. 15; Parasitology 20; Occas. Papers Mus. Zool. Univ. Michigan, No. 202; Papers Michigan Acad. Sci. Arts Lett. 10. **Hughes, R. C.,** and **P. G. Berkhout.** 1928. Studies on the Strigeidae. XI. Papers Michigan Acad. Sci. Arts Lett. 10. **Hughes, R. C.,** and **F. J. Holl.** 1928. Studies on the Strigeidae. XVI. Papers Michigan Acad. Sci. Arts Lett. 10. **Hughes, R. C., J. W. Higginbotham,** and **J. W. Clary.** 1942. Trematodes of reptiles. Amer. Midland Natural. 27. **Hunninen, A. V.,** and **R. M. Cable.** 1941. Life history of Anisoporus (Allocreadiidae). Jour. Parasitol. 29. 1943a. Life history of Podocotyle (Opecoelidae, cotylomicrocercous larva). Trans. Amer. Micro. Soc. 62. 1943b. Life history of Lecithaster (Hemiuridae). Jour. Parasitol. 29. **Hunter, G. W.** 1936. Penetration of the common sunfish by holostome cercaria. Jour. Parasitol. 22. **Hunter, G. W.,** and **H. C. Dalton.** 1939. Cyst of Clinostomum. Proc. Helminthol. Soc. Washington 6. **Hunter, G. W.,** and **J. M. Hamilton.** 1941. Cyst of Uvulifer. Trans. Amer. Micro. Soc. 60. **Hunter, G. W.,** and **W. S. Hunter.** 1933, 1934. Studies on fish and bird parasites [Clinostomum, Uvulifer]. Ann. Rept. N. Y. State Conserv. Dept., Suppl. to 23, 24, Biol. Surveys VIII, IX. 1934. The life cycle of the yellow grub of fish [Clinostomum]. Jour. Parasitol. 20. 1935a. Penetration and growth of the cercaria of Clinostomum. 1935b. Miracidium of Clinostomum. Jour. Parasitol. 21. 1940. Metacercaria and cyst of Posthodiplostomum. Trans. Amer. Micro. Soc. 59. 1942. Integumentary type of strigeid cyst. Trans. Amer. Micro. Soc. 61. **Hussey, Katharine.** 1941. Comparative embryological development of the excretory system in digenetic trematodes. Trans. Amer. Micro. Soc. 60. **Ingles, L. G.** 1933. Structure and life-history of Zeugorchis from snake Thamnophis. Univ. Calif. Publ. Zool. 39. **Ishii, Y.** 1934. Development of Fasciolopsis buski. Jour. Med. Assoc. Formosa 33. 1935. Studies on the Didymozoonidae. Jap. Jour. Zool. 6. **Jegen, G.** 1917. Collyriclum. Ztschr. Wiss. Zool. 117. **Johnson, J. C.** 1920. Life cycle of Echinostoma revolutum. Univ. Calif. Publ. Zool. 19. **Johnston, S. J.** 1916. Trematodes of Australian birds (schistosomes). Jour. Proc. Roy. Soc. New South Wales 50. **Johnston, T. H.,** and **L. M. Angel.** 1941. Life cycle of Echinostoma revolutum. Trans. Roy. Soc. S. Australia 65. **Jordan, H. E.,** and **B. D. Reynolds.** 1933. Blood cells of Diplodiscus. Jour. Morphol. 55. **Joyeaux, C.,** and **J. G. Baer.** 1927. Note sur les Cyclocoelidae. Bull. Soc. Zool. France 52. **Komiya, Y.** 1938. Die Entwicklung des Exkretionsystems einiger Trematodenlarven. Ztschr. Parasitenk. 10. **Komiya, Y.,** and **T. Tajimi.** 1940. Cercaria and metacercaria of Clonorchis sinensis. Jour. Shanghai Sci. Inst. sect. 4, 5. **Kopczynski, P.** 1907. Über den Bau von Codonocephalus. Zool. Jahrb. Abt. System. 24. **Kossak, W.** 1911. Über Monostomiden. (Cyclocoelidae.) Zool. Jahrb. Abt. System. 31. **Kouri, P.,** and **R. W. Nauss.** 1938. Formation of the egg shell in Fasciola hepatica. Jour. Parasitol. 24. **Krause, R.** 1915. Zur Kenntnis der Hemistominen. Ztschr. Wiss. Zool. 112. **Krull, W. H.** 1930. Life history of North American frog lung flukes. Jour. Parasitol. 16. 1931. Life history studies on frog lung flukes. Trans. Amer. Micro. Soc. 50. 1934a. Life history of frog bladder fluke Gorgodera. Papers Michigan Acad. Sci. Arts Lett. 20. 1934b. Additional notes on life history of frog lung fluke. Trans. Amer. Micro. Soc. 53. 1934c. Hatchability and infectivity of refrigerated eggs of Fasciola hepatica.

Proc. Iowa Acad. Sci. 41. 1935. Life history of Halipegus. Amer. Midland Natural. 16. **Krull, W. H., and R. S. Jackson.** 1943. Route of migration of the liver fluke in the definitive host. Jour. Washington Acad. Sci. 33. **Krull, W. H., and Helen Price.** 1932. Life history of Diplodiscus. Occas. Papers Mus. Zool. Univ. Michigan, No. 237. **Lander, C. H.** 1904. Anatomy of Hemiurus. Bull. Mus. Comp. Zool. Harvard 45. **La Rue, G. R.** 1926. Trematode with two ani. Jour. Parasitol. 12. 1926–1927. Studies on the Strigeidae. I–V. [No. IV concerns strigeid larvae in fish eyes.] Trans. Amer. Micro. Soc. 45, 46. 1932. Morphology of Cotylurus. Trans. Amer. Micro. Soc. 51. **Lebour, Marie.** 1916. Medusae as hosts for larval trematodes. Jour. Marine Biol. Assoc. 11. **Leiper, J. W. G.** 1938. Longevity of Fasciola hepatica. Jour. Helminthol. 16. **Leiper, R. T.** 1915–1918. Results of the Bilharzia mission in Egypt. Pts. I–VI. Jour. Roy. Army Medical Corps 25, 26, 27, 30. **Leon, N.** 1927. Accouplement et fécondation du Fasciola hepatica. Ann. Parasitol. Hum. Comp. 5. **Lewis, F. J.** 1935. Trematode genus Phyllodistomum. Trans. Amer. Micro. Soc. 54. **Linton, E.** 1915. Sporocysts in an annelid. Biol. Bull. 18. **Looss, A.** 1892. Über Amphistomum und seine Entwicklung. Festschrift 70 Geburtstag R. Leuckarts. 1894. Die Distomen unserer Fische und Frosche. Bibliotheca Zoologica 6, Heft 16. 1895. Zur Anatomie und Histologie der Bilharzia haematobia. Arch. Mikro. Anat. 46. 1900. Recherches sur le faune parasitaire de l'Egypte. Mem. Inst. Egyptien 3. 1902. Trematoden aus Seeschildkröten. Zool. Jahrb. Abt. System. 16. 1907a. Parasites in the school of tropical medicine, Liverpool [Clonorchis]. Ann. Trop. Med. Parasitol. 1. 1907b, 1908. Zur Kenntnis der Distomenfamilie Hemiuriden. Zool. Anz. 31; Zool. Jahrb. Abt. System. 26. **Lühe, M.** 1901. Über Hemiuriden. Zool. Anz. 24. **Lundahl, W. S.** 1941. Life history of Caecincola. Trans. Amer. Micro. Soc. 60. **Lutz, A.** 1920. Entwicklungszyklus der Holostomiden. Centralbl. Bakteriol. Parasitenk., Abt. 1, Orig. 86. **Lynch, J.** 1933. Miracidium of Heronimus. Quart. Jour. Micro. Sci. 76. **MacCallum, G. A.** 1926. Revue du genus Spirorchis. Ann. Parasitol. Hum. Comp. 4. **MacCallum, G. A., and W. G. MacCallum.** 1916. Family Didymozoidae. Zool. Jahrb. Abt. System. 39. **MacCallum, W. G.** 1899. Clinostomum. Jour. Morphol. 15. 1902. Heronimus chelydrae. Centralbl. Bakteriol. Parasitenk. 32. **Macy, R. W.** 1934. Prosthogonimus macrorchis, oviduct fluke of domestic fowls. Univ. Minnesota Agricult. Exp. Sta., Tech. Bull. 98. 1942. Life cycle of Echinostomum. Jour. Parasitol. 28. **Magath, T. B.** 1920. Leucochloridium. Jour. Parasitol. 6. **Magath, T. B., and D. Mathieson.** 1945. Factors affecting the hatching of ova of Schistozoma japonicum. Jour. Parasitol. 32. **Manson-Bahr, P., and N. H. Fairley.** 1920. Bilharziasis. Parasitology 12. **Manter, H. W.** 1926. Some North American fish trematodes. Illinois Biol. Monogr. 10. 1938. Trematodes from Florida Amphibia. Trans. Amer. Micro. Soc. 57. **Maplestone, P. A.** 1923. Revision of the Amphistomata of mammals. Ann. Trop. Med. Parasitol. 17. **Martin, W. E.** 1938. Life cycle of Lepocreadium. Biol. Bull. 75. 1944. Observations upon cercaria developing in an annelid. Trans. Amer. Micro. Soc. 63. **Mathias, P.** 1925. Recherches expérimentales sur le cycle évolutif de quelques trématodes. Bull. Biol. France Belg. 59. **Mattes, O.** 1926. Zur Biologie der Larvenentwicklung von Fasciola hepatica. Zool. Anz. 69. 1936. Der Entwicklungsgang der Lanzettegels Dicrocoelium lanceolatum. Ztschr. Parasitenk. 8. 1936. Zur Frage der Wirtsauffindung der Parasiten. Verhandl. Dtsch. Zool. Gesell. 38; in Zool. Anz. Suppl. Bd. 9. **McCoy, O. R.** 1928. Life history studies on trematodes from Missouri. Jour. Parasitol. 14. 1929a. Life history of Hamacreadium. Parasitology 21. 1929b. Seasonal fluctuations in the infestation of Planorbis with larval trematodes. Jour. Parasitol. 15.

1930. Fish trematodes of the genus Hamacreadium. Jour. Parasitol. 17. **McIntosh, A.** 1932. New species of Leucochloridium. Jour. Parasitol. 19. **McLeod, J. A.** 1936. Further notes on cercarial dermatitis. Trans. Roy. Soc. Canada, ser. 3, 30, sect. 5. 1940. Studies on cercarial dermatitis and the family Schistosomatidae. Canad. Jour. Research 18, sect. D. **McLeod, J. A.,** and **G. E. Little.** 1942. Continued studies on cercarial dermatitis and Schistosomatidae. Canad. Jour. Research 20, sect. D. **McMullen, D. B.** 1937a. Family Plagiorchiidae. Jour. Parasitol. 23. 1937b. Life history of three trematodes, genus Plagiorchis. Jour. Parasitol. 23. 1937c. Infection of Plagiorchis muris in man. Jour. Parasitol. 23. **McMullen, D. B.,** and **S. Brackett.** 1941. Distribution and control of schistosome dermatitis. Amer. Jour. Trop Med. 21. **Miller, E. L.** 1936. Studies on North American cercariae. Illinois Biol. Monogr. 14. **Miller, H. M., Jr.** 1925–1926. Behavior studies on Tortugas larval trematodes. Carnegie Inst. Washington Yearb. 25, 26. 1928. Variety of behavior of larval trematodes. Science 68. **Miller, H. M.,** and **Elsie Mahaffy.** 1930. Reactions of cercaria to light and to mechanical stimuli. Biol. Bull. 59. **Miller, H. M.,** and **O. R. McCoy.** 1928–1930. Behavior of cercariae in relation to fish intermediate host. Carnegie Inst. Washington Yearb. 28; Jour. Parasitol. 16. **Miller, H. M.,** and **Flora Northrup.** 1926. Seasonal infestation of Nassa with larval trematodes. Biol. Bull. 50. **Mueller, J. F.** 1935. Harmostome from Campeloma. Jour. Parasitol. 21. **Mueller, J. F.,** and **H. J. Van Cleave.** 1932. Parasites of Oneida Lake fishes. Pt. II. Roosevelt Wild Life Annals 3, No. 2. **Mühlschlag, G.** 1914. Otodistomum veliporum. Zool. Jahrb. Abt. System. 37. **Müller, W.** 1923. Die Nahrung von Fasciola hepatica. Zool. Anz. 57. **Nakagawa, K.** 1922. Development of Fasciolopsis buski. Jour. Parasitol. 8. **Näsmark, K. E,** 1937. Revision of the Paramphistomidae. Zool. Bidrag 16. **Neuhaus, W.** 1936. Bau und Entwicklung der Lanzettegelcercaria. Ztschr. Parasitenk. 8. 1938. Invasionsweg der Lanzettegelcercarie und ihre Entwicklung zum Dicrocoelium lanceolatum. Ztschr. Parasitenk. 10. 1940. Entwicklung und Biologie von Pleurogenes. Zool. Jahrb. Abt. System. 74. **Nicoll, W.** 1909. Structure and classification of digenetic trematodes. Quart. Jour. Micro. Sci. 53. 1914. Trematode parasites of fishes from the English channel. Jour. Marine Biol. Assoc. 10. **Nigrelli, R. F.** 1936. Some tropical fishes as hosts for the metacercariae of Clinostomum. Zoologica, New York, 21. 1939. Didymocystis. Trans. Amer. Micro. Soc. 58. **Niyamasena, S. G.** 1940. Chromosomen und Geschlecht bei Bilharzia. Ztschr. Parasitenk. 11. **Odhner, T.** 1907. Zur Anatomie der Didymozoen. Zool. Stud. til. Prof. T. Tullberg. 1910. Gigantobilharzia. Zool. Anz. 35. 1911a. Azygiidae. Zool. Anz. 38. 1911b. Sanguinicola. Zool. Jahrb. Abt. System. 31. 1911–1912. Zum natürlichen System der digenen Trematoden. Zool. Anz. 37, 38, 41, 42. 1924. Sanguinicola. Quart. Jour. Micro. Sci. 68. 1928. Weitere Trematoden mit Anus. Arkiv Zool. 20B. **Odlaug, T. O.** 1937. Development of Gorgodera. Biol. Bull. 72. 1940. Morphology and life history of Alaria. Trans. Amer. Micro. Soc. 59. **Olivier, L.,** and **W. W. Cort.** 1942. Life cycle of Cotylurus communis. Jour. Parasitol. 28. **Olsen, W. W.** 1937. Trematode subfamily Plagiorchiinae. Trans. Amer. Micro. Soc. 56. **Onorato, A. R.,** and **H. W. Stunkard.** 1931. Development and hatching of blood flukes [Spirorchis]. Biol. Bull. 61. **O'Roke, E. C.** 1917. Larval trematodes from Kansas fresh-water snails. Kansas Univ. Sci. Bull. 10, No. 7. **Ortmann, W.** 1908. Zur Embryonalentwicklung der Leberegels. Zool. Jahrb. Abt. Anat. 26. **Ortner-Schönbach, Pauline.** 1913. Glycogen bei Trematoden und Cestoden. Arch. Zellforsch. 11. **Osborn, H. L.** 1911. Clinostomum. Biol. Bull. 20. 1912. Structure of Clinostomum. Jour. Morphol. 13. **Ozaki, Y.** 1928a. On some trematodes with anus. 1928b. Some gasterostomatous trematodes of Japan. Jap. Jour.

Zool. 2. **Ozawa, M.** 1930. Acquired immunity to schistosomiasis. Jap. Jour. Exp. Med. 8. **Palombi, A.** 1929. Ciclo evolutivo di Helicometra (Allocreadiidae). Pubbl. Staz. Zool. Napoli 9. 1930. Ciclo biologico di Diphterostomum. Pubbl. Staz. Zool. Napoli 10. 1931. Rapporti genetici tra Lepocreadium e Cercaria setifera. Boll. Zool. 2. 1932a. La copulazione nei Trematodi. Arch. Zool. Ital. 17. 1932b. Rapporti genetici tra Cercaria setifera e Allocreadiidae. Boll. Soc. Natural. Napoli 45. 1937a. Cercaria di Mesometra e la sua trasformazione in metacercaria. Riv. Parassitol. 1. 1937b. Ciclo biologico di Lepocreadium. Riv. Parassitol. 1. 1934, 1938, 1940. Gli stadi larvali dei trematodi del Golfo di Napoli. I–III. Pubbl. Staz. Zool. Napoli 14; Riv. Parassitol. 2, 4. **Porter, Annie.** 1938. Larval Trematoda found in certain South Africa Mollusca. Publ. South African Inst. Med. Research No. 42. **Pratt, H. S.** 1898. Appendiculate distomes. Zool. Jahrb. Abt. Anat. 11. **Price, E.** 1929. Synopsis of the Schistosomatidae. Proc. U.S. Nation. Mus. 75. 1932. Trematode parasites of marine mammals. Proc. U.S. Nation. Mus. 81. 1940. Review of the Opisthorchioidea. Proc. Helminthol. Soc. Washington 7. **Price, Helen.** 1931. Life history of Schistosomatium. Amer. Jour. Hygiene 13. **Rankin, J. S., Jr.** 1937. Ecological study of parasites of some North Carolina salamanders. Ecol. Monogr. 7. 1939a. Levinseniella (Microphallidae). Trans. Amer. Micro. Soc. 58. 1939b. Life cycle of Gorgoderina. Amer. Midland Natural. 21. 1939c. Ecological studies on larval trematodes. Jour. Parasitol. 25. 1940a. Spelotrema (Microphallidae). Trans. Amer. Micro. Soc. 59. 1940b. Life cycle of Gynaecotyla (Microphallidae). Biol. Bull. 79. 1944a. Review of Halipegus. Trans. Amer. Micro. Soc. 63. 1944b. Glypthelmins (Plagiorchidae). Trans. Amer. Micro. Soc. 63. **Ransom, B. H.** 1920. Synopsis of Heterophyidae. Proc. U.S. Nation. Mus. 57. **Rasin, K.** 1933. Echinoparyphium und seine Entwicklung. Biol. Spisy Vysoké Skoly Zveral. Brno 12. **Rees, Gwendolin.** 1940. Germ cell cycle of the digenetic trematode Parorchis. Parasitology 32. **Reisinger, E.** 1923. Bau und Funktion des Exkretionsapparatus digenetischer Trematoden. Zool. Anz. 57. **Roewer, C. P.** 1906. Histogenese von Cercariaeum. Jena. Ztschr. Naturwiss. 41. **Ross, I. C., and A. C. McKay.** 1929. Bionomics of Fasciola hepatica. Bull. Council Scient. Indust. Research Commonwealth Australia 43. **Rothschild, Miriam.** 1936. Gigantism and variation caused by infection with larval trematodes. Jour. Marine Biol. Assoc. 20. 1942. Seven-year old infection of Cryptocotyle. Jour. Parasitol. 28. **Sandground, J. H.** 1940. Plagiorchis in man. Rev. Med. Trop. Parasitol. 6. **Sandground, J. H., and C. Bonne.** 1940. Echinostoma lindoensis of man in the Celebes. Amer. Jour. Trop. Med. 20. **Schauinsland, H.** 1883. Die embryonale Entwicklung der Trematoden. Jena. Ztschr. Naturwiss. 16. **Scheuring, L.** 1922. Der Lebenscyklus von Sanguinicola. Zool. Jahrb. Abt. Anat. 44. **Scheuring, L., and E. Everbusch.** 1926. Entwicklungsgeschichte von Strigea. Zool. Anz. 66. **Schubmann, W.** 1905. Über die Eibildung und Embryonal entwicklung von Fasciola hepatica. Zool. Jahrb. Abt. Anat. 21. **Schumacher, W.** 1938. Wanderungsweg von Fasciola hepatica im Endwirt. Ztschr. Parasitenk. 10. **Schuurmans-Stekhoven, J. H.** 1931. Der zweite Zwischenwirt von Pseudamphistomum. Ztschr. Parasitenk. 3. **Severinghaus, A. E.** 1928. Sex studies on Schistosoma. Quart. Jour. Micro. Sci. 71. **Sewell, R. B. S.** 1922. Cercariae Indicae. Indian Jour. Med. Research, suppl. to 10. 1930. Evaluation of the excretory system in certain groups of furcocercous cercariae. Records Indian Mus. 32. **Shaw, J. M., and B. T. Simms.** 1930. Studies on fascioliasis. Bull. Oregon Agric. Exp. Sta. 266. **Sievers, H. K., and R. Oyarzun.** 1932. Diagnostie de la distomatose hépatique par la réaction allergique. C. R. Soc. Biol. Paris 110. **Simms, B. T., C. R. Donham, and J. N. Shaw.** 1931. Salmon poisoning. Amer. Jour.

Hygiene 13. **Sinitsin, D.** 1907. Observations sur les métamorphoses des trématodes (gorgoderids). Arch. Zool. Exp. Gén. ser. 4, vol. 7, Notes et Revues. 1931a. Life histories of Plagioporus. Ztschr. Wiss. Zool. 138. 1931b. Revision of Harmostominae. Ztschr. Parasitenk. 3. **Smith, Septima.** 1932. New cystocercous cercariae. Jour. Parasitol. 19. 1934. Cystocercous cercaria of Proterometra. Jour. Alabama Acad. Sci. 6. 1936. Life-cycle studies of (cystocercous) cercariae. Jour. Alabama Acad. Sci. 8. **Sommer, F.** 1880. Die Anatomie des Leberegels Distomum hepaticum. Ztschr. Wiss. Zool. 34. **Stafford, J.** 1902. Haematoloechus. Zool. Jahrb. Abt. System. 16. **Steelman, G. M.** 1939. Macrocercous cercaria. Trans. Amer. Micro. Soc. 58. **Steenstrup, J. J. S.** 1842. Ueber den Generationswechsel oder die Fortpflanzung und Entwicklung, etc. **Stephenson, W.** 1945. Survival of Fasciola hepatic in vitro. Nature (London) 155. 1947. Physiological and histochemical observations on Fasciola hepatica. Parasitology 38. **Stiles, C. W.** 1894, 1895. Anatomy of Fasciola magna. Jour. Comp. Med. Veter. Arch. 15, 16. **Stiles, C. W., and J. Goldberger.** 1910. Anatomy of Watsonius watsoni. U.S. Treas. Dept. Public Health, Marine Hosp. Service Bull. 60. **Stunkard, H. W.** 1919. Heronimus chelydrae. Jour. Parasitol. 6. 1923. Studies on North American blood flukes. Bull. Amer. Mus. Natur. Hist. 48. 1929. Excretory system of Cryptocotyle. Jour. Parasitol. 15. 1930. Life history of Cryptocotyle. Jour. Morphol. 50. 1931. Occurrence of anal openings in digenetic trematodes. Ztschr. Parasitenk. 3. 1934. Life history of Typhlocoelum. Bull. Soc. Zool. France 59. 1938a. Larval stage of Zoogonus. Biol. Bull. 75. 1938b. Morphology and life cycle of Himasthla. Biol. Bull. 75. 1943. Morphology and life cycle of Zoogonoides. Biol. Bull. 85. **Stunkard, H. W., and R. M. Cable.** 1932. Life history of Parorchis. Biol. Bull. 62. **Stunkard, H. W., C. H. Willey, and Y. Rabinowitz.** 1941. Apatemon. Trans. Amer. Micro. Soc. 60. **Swales, W. E.** 1935. Life cycle of Fascioloides magna. Canad. Jour. Research 12. **Szidat, L.** 1924. Entwicklungsgeschichte der Holostomiden. Zool. Anz. 58. 1929. Strigea. Ztschr. Parasitenk. 1. 1932a. Über cysticerke Riesencercarien der Gattung Azygia. Ztschr. Parasitenk. 4. 1932b. Zum Entwicklungsgeschichte der Cyclocoeliden. Zool. Anz. 100. 1936. Entwicklungsgeschichte von Paramphistomum cervi. Ztschr. Parasitenk. 9. **Talbot, S. B.** 1933. Life history studies on trematodes of the subfamily Reniferinae. Parasitology 25. 1934. New trematodes of the subfamily Reniferinae with a discussion of the systematics of the family. Trans. Amer. Micro. Soc. 53. 1936. Studies on schistosome dermatitis. Amer. Jour. Hygiene 23. **Taliaferro, W. H., W. A. Hoffman, and D. H. Cook.** 1928. A precipitin test in intestinal schistosomiasis. Jour. Preventive Med. 2. **Taliaferro, W. H., and L. G. Taliaferro.** 1931. Skin reactions in persons infected with Schistosoma mansoni. Puerto Rico Jour. Public Health Trop. Med. 7. **Tanabe, B.** 1923. Life cycle of Schistosomatium. Jour. Parasitenk. 9. **Tennent, D.** 1906. Life history of Bucephalus. Quart. Jour. Micro. Sci. 49. **Thomas, A. P.** 1883. Life history of the liver fluke. Quart. Jour. Micro. Sci. 23. **Thomas, L. G.** 1939. Life cycle of Halipegus. Jour. Parasitol. 25. **Travassos, L.** 1928. Fauna helminthologica de Mateo Grosso (Plagiorchidae). Mem. Inst. Oswaldo Cruz 21. 1934. Synopse dos Paramphistomoidea. Mem. Inst. Oswaldo Cruz 29. **Tubanqui, M. A., and A. M. Pasco.** 1933. Life history of human intestinal fluke Euparyphium ilocanum. Philipp. Jour. Sci. 51. **Ujiie, J.** 1936. Process of egg shell formation in Clonorchis. Structure and function of Mehlis glands in the formation of the egg shell. Jour. Med. Assoc. Formosa 35. **Van Haitsma, J. P.** 1930, 1931. Studies on the trematode family Strigeidae. 20–23 [Cotylurus, Diplostomum]. Trans. Amer. Micro. Soc. 49; Jour. Parasitol. 16; Papers Michigan Acad. Sci. Arts Lett. 13. **Vazquez-Colet, A., and C. M. Africa.** 1940.

Philippine heterophyid metacercariae. Philipp. Jour. Sci. 72. **Vialli, M.** 1933. Ricerche istochemiche sui vitellogenie dei platelminti. Boll. Zool. 4. **Vogel, H.** 1933. Himasthla. Centralbl. Bakteriol. Parasitenk., Abt. 1, Orig. 127. 1934. Entwicklungszyklus von Opisthorchis felineus. Zoologica, Stuttgart, 33, Heft 86. **Vogel, H., and T. v. Brand.** 1933. Verhalten des Fettes in den einzelnen Entwicklungsstadien von Fasciola hepatica. Ztschr. Parasitenk. 5. **Walker, J. H.** 1939. Studies on subfamily Reniferinae. Trans. Amer. Micro. Soc. 58. **Wall, L. D.** 1941a. Spirorchis, life history and development of excretory system. Trans. Amer. Micro. Soc. 60. 1941b. Life history of Spirorchis. Amer. Midland Natural. 25. **Wallace, F. G.** 1939. Life cycle of Pharyngostomum. Trans. Amer. Micro. Soc. 58. **Ward, H. B.** 1916. Notes on two larval trematodes. Jour. Parasitol. 3. **Ward, H. B., and E. F. Hirsch.** 1915. Species of Paragonimus and their differentiation. Ann. Trop. Med. Parasitol. 9. **Weinland, E., and T. v. Brand.** 1926. Beobachtungen an Fasciola hepatica (Stoffwechsel und Lebensweise). Ztschr. Vergl. Physiol. 4. **Wesenberg-Lund, C.** 1931. Biology of Leucochloridium. Kongl. Danske Vidensk. Selsk. Skr. Nat. Math. Afd., ser. 9, vol. 4. 1934. Biology of cercariae in Danish fresh waters. Kongl. Danske Vidensk. Selsk. Skr. Nat. Math. Afd., ser. 9, vol. 5. **Westblad, E.** 1924. Zur Kenntnis der vitalen Alizarinfärbung. Zool. Anz. 61. **Wheeler, N. C.** 1939. Behavior of four pleurolophocercous cercariae. Jour. Parasitol. 25. **Willey, C. H.** 1930. Lymph system of digenetic trematodes. Jour. Morphol. 50. 1935. Excretory system of Typhlocoelum. Jour. Morphol. 57. 1941. Life history of Zygocotyle (Paramphistomidae). Zoologica, New York, 26. **Willey, C. H., and H. W. Stunkard.** 1942. Pathology and resistance in terns and dogs infected with Cryptocotyle. Trans. Amer. Micro. Soc. 61. **Wilmoth, J. H., and R. Goldfisher.** 1945. Distribution of glycogen in Ostiolum. Jour. Parasitol. 31, suppl. **Winfield, G. F.** 1932. Immunity of snails infested with the sporocysts of Cotylurus to the penetration of its cercaria. Jour. Parasitol. 19. **Witenberg, G.** 1925. Versuche einer Monographie der Trematodenunterfamilie Harmostominae. Zool. Jahrb. Abt. System. 51. 1926. Die Trematoden der Familie Cyclocoelidae. Zool. Jahrb. Abt. System. 52. 1929. Studies on the trematode family Heterophyidae. Ann. Trop. Med. Parasitol. 23. 1932. Anatomy and systematic position of the causative agent of so-called salmon poisoning. Jour. Parasitol. 18. 1944. Transversotrema, a new fish trematode. Jour. Parasitol. 30. **Woodhead, A. E.** 1929, 1930. Life history studies on Bucephalidae. Trans. Amer. Micro. Soc. 48, 49. 1935. Mother sporocysts of Leucochloridium. Jour. Parasitol. 21. 1936. Gasterostome cercariae of the Huron River. Trans. Amer. Micro. Soc. 55. **Wright, Sewall.** 1912. Anatomy of Microphallus. Trans. Amer. Micro. Soc. 31. **Wunder, W.** 1924. Die Schwimmbewegungen von Bucephalus. Ztschr. Vergl. Physiol. 1. **Yamaguti, S.** 1935. Cercarie von Clonorchis sinensis. Ztschr. Parasitenk. 8. 1938. Entwicklungsgeschichte von Notocotylus. Ztschr. Parasitenk. 10. 1940a. Vergleichend-anatomische Studien der Miracidien. Ztschr. Parasitenk. 11. 1940b. Entwicklungsgeschichte von Cyathocotyle. Ztschr. Parasitenk. 12. **Yokogawa, S.** 1913. Metagonimus yokogawai. Centralbl. Bakteriol. Parasitenk., Abt. I, Orig. 72. **Young, R. T.** 1938. Life history of Levinseniella. Biol. Bull. 74. **Zailer, O.** 1914. Anatomie der Muskulatur und des Nervensystems der Trematoden. Zool. Anz. 44. **Zeller, E.** 1874. Leucochloridium. Ztschr. Wiss. Zool. 24.

CESTODA

General

Balss, H. H. 1908. Entwicklung der Geschlechtsgänge bei Cestoden. Ztschr. Wiss. Zool. 91. **Beddard, F. E.** 1912. On an asexual tapeworm showing a new form of propagation. Proc. Zool. Soc. London. **Benham, W. B.** 1901. The Platyhelmia. In **E. R. Lankester** (ed.), *A treatise on zoology*, Pt. IV. **Brand, T. von.** 1945. The anaerobic metabolism of invertebrates. Biodynamica 5. **Brand, T. von, and W. Weise.** 1932. Beobachtungen über den Sauerstoffgehalt der Umwelt einiger Entoparasiten. Ztschr. Vergl. Physiol. 18. **Bugge, G.** 1902. Zur Kenntnis des Exkretionsgefäss-Systems der Cestoden. Zool. Jahrb. Abt. Anat. 16. **Child, C. M.** 1900, 1902. Abnormalities in the cestode Moniezia. Biol. Bull. 1, 3. **Cohn, L.** 1898. Untersuchungen über das centrale Nervensystem der Cestoden. Zool. Jahrb. Abt. Anat. 12. 1907. Die Orientierung der Cestoden. Zool. Anz. 32. 1911. Zur Frage wie die Cestoden zu orientieren sind. Zool. Anz. 38. **De Waele, A.** 1933a. Comportement des oeufs et des larvae oncospheres dans le système digestif et dans le sang de l'hote intermédiaire. Acad. Roy. Belgique, Bull. Cl. Sci. ser. 5, 19. 1933b. Sur le méchanism de l'infection de l'hote definitiv par la larve. Expériences sur le type cysticerque. Acad. Roy. Belgique, Bull. Cl. Sci. ser. 5, 19. 1934. Etude de la fonction biliare dans le phénomène de l'évagination chez les cysticerques des cestodes. Ann. Parasitol. Hum. Comp. 12. **Dollfus, R.** 1923, 1924, 1931. Enumérations des cestodes du plancton et des invertébrés marins. Ann. Parasitol. Hum. Comp. 1, 2, 9. **Fuhrmann, O.** 1931. Cestoidea. In **W. Kükenthal,** and **T. Krumbach** (eds.), *Handbuch der Zoologie*, Band 2, 1st half. **Green, N. K.,** and **R. A. Wardle.** 1941. The cultivation of tapeworms in artificial media. Canad. Jour. Research 19, sect. D. **Guiart, J.** 1935. Cestodes parasites. Result. Campagnes Scient. Monaco, Fasc. 91. **Hall, M. C.** 1929. Arthropods as intermediate hosts for helminths. Smithson. Miscell. Collect. 81. **Haswell, W. A.,** and **J. P. Hill.** 1894. On Polycercus, a proliferating cystic parasite of the earthworm. Proc. Linn. Soc. New South Wales, ser. 2, 8. **Hsu, H. F.** 1935. Contributions a l'etude des cestodes de Chine. Rev. Suisse Zool. 42. **Hughes, R. C., J. R. Baker,** and **C. B. Dawson.** 1942. The tapeworms of reptiles. Pt. I. Amer. Midland Natural. 25. **Iwata, S.** 1934. Experimental studies on the regeneration of the plerocercoid of Manson's tapeworm. Jap. Jour. Zool. 6. **Janicki, C.** 1921. Grundlinien einer "cercomer" Theorie zur Morphologie der Trematoden und Cestoden. Festschrift für Zschokke. **Joyeaux, C.** 1922. Recherches sur l'Urocystis prolifer. Bull. Soc. Zool. France 47. **Joyeaux, C.,** and **J. G. Baer.** 1936. Cestodes. Faune de France 30. **Kofoid, C. A.,** and **Edna Watson.** 1907. On the orientation of Gyrocotyle and of the cestode strobila. Proc. 7 Internat. Congr. Zool. **Linton, E.** 1941. Cestode parasites of teleost fishes of the Woods Hole region. Proc. U.S. Nation. Mus. 90. **Lönnberg, E.** 1891–1892. Anatomische Studien über skandinavische Cestoden I, II. Kungl. Svenska Vetensk. Akad. Handl. 24, Nos. 6, 16. **Lühe, M.** 1910. Die Cestoden. *Die Süsswasserfauna Deutschlands*, Heft 18. **Markov, G. S.** 1939. Nutrition of tapeworms in artificial media. C. R. Acad. Sci. U.R.S.S. 25. **Ortner-Schönbach, P.** 1913. Zur Morphologie des Glycogens bei Trematoden und Cestoden. Arch. Zellforsch. 11. **Pratt, H. S.** 1909. The cuticula and subcuticula of trematodes and cestodes. Amer. Natural. 43. **Rietschel, P.** 1935. Zur Bewegungsphysiologie der Cestoden. Zool. Anz. 111. **Schaefer, R.** 1913. Die Entwicklung der Geschlechtsausführwege bei einigen Cestoden. Zool. Jahrb. Abt. Anat. 35. **Smorodinzev, I. A.,** and **K. W. Bebeshin.** 1935. Glycogen content in tapeworms. C. R. Acad. Sci. U.R.S.S. 8. 1936a. Die chemische Zusammensetzung des T. solium. Jour. Biochem., Tokyo, 23. 1936b. Die chemische Zusammensetzung des D. latum. Jour. Biochem., Tokyo, 23. 1936c. Les protéinases des ténias. Bull. Soc. Chim. Biol. 18. **Smorodinzev, I. A., K. W. Bebeshin,** and **P. I. Pavlova.** 1933. Die chemische Zusammensetzung von Taenia saginata. Biochem. Ztschr. 261. **Smyth, J. D.** 1946. Cultivation of Schistocephalus in vitro. Jour. Exp. Biol. 23. 1947a. The physiology of tapeworms. Biol. Rev. Cambridge Philos. Soc. 22. 1947b.

Cultivation and development of Ligula intestinalis in vitro. Parasitology 38. **Southwell, T.** 1929. Classification of the cestodes. Spolia Zeylanica 15. 1930. Fauna of British India. Cestoda, 2 vols. **Southwell, T., and B. Prashad.** 1918. Methods of sexual and parthenogenetic reproduction in cestodes. Jour. Parasitol. 4. **Stiles, C. A., and A. Hassall.** 1912. Index catalogue of medical and veterinary zoology. Cestoda. U.S. Public Health Service, Hygienic Lab. Bull. 85. **Villot, A.** 1883. Mémoire sur les cystiques des ténias. Ann. Sci. Natur. Zool., ser. 6, 15. **Wardle, R. A.** 1932. The Cestoda of Canadian fishes, I–III. Contribs. Canad. Biol. 7, Nos. 18, 30; 8, No. 5. 1934. The viability of tapeworms in artificial media. Physiol. Zool. 7. **Watson, Edna.** 1911. The genus Gyrocotyle and its significance for problems of cestode structure and phylogeny. Univ. Calif. Publ. Zool. 6. **Wilmoth, J.** 1945. Studies on the metabolism of Taenia taeniaeformis. Physiol. Zool. 18. **Yamaguti, S.** 1934. Studies on the helminth fauna of Japan. Pt. 4. Cestodes of fishes. Pt. 6. Cestodes of birds. Pt. 7. Cestodes of mammals and snakes. Jap. Jour. Zool. 6. **Young, R. T.** 1908. The histogenesis of Cysticercus pisiformis. Zool. Jahrb. Abt. Anat. 26. 1913. The histogenesis of the reproductive organs of Taenia pisiformis. Zool. Jahrb. Abt. Anat. 35. 1935. Some unsolved problems of cestode structure and development. Trans. Amer. Micro. Soc. 54. **Zernecke, E.** 1895. Untersuchungen über den feinern Bau der Cestoden. Zool. Jahrb. Abt. Anat. 9. **Zschokke, F.** 1888. Recherches sur la structure anatomique et histologique des cestodes. Mem. Inst. Nation. Genevois 17.

Cestodaria

Cohn, L. 1904. Zur Anatomie der Amphilina foliacea. Ztschr. Wiss. Zool. 76. **Dollfus, R.** 1923. L'orientation morphologique des Gyrocotyle et les cestodes en général. Bull. Soc. Zool. France 48. **Goto, S., and N. Ishii.** 1936. On a new Amphilina. Jap. Jour. Exp. Med. 14. **Hein, W.** 1904. Beiträge zur Kenntnis von Amphilina foliacea. Ztschr. Wiss. Zool. 76. **Janicki, C.** 1908. Über den Bau von [Nesolecithus]. Ztschr. Wiss. Zool. 89. 1928. Die Lebensgeschichte von Amphilina. Arbeit. Biol. Volga-Station 10; Naturwissenschaften 16. 1930. Über die jüngsten Zustande von Amphilina. Zool. Anz. 90. **Johnston, T. H.** 1931. An amphilinid cestode from an Australian tortoise. Austral. Jour. Exp. Biol. Med. 8. **Lynch, J. E.** 1945. Redescription of the species of Gyrocotyle. Jour. Parasitol. 31. **Pintner, T.** 1903. Studien über Tetrahynchen nebst histologische Notizen über Amphilina. Sitzungsber. Akad. Wiss. Wien, Math. Naturwiss. Kl. 122, Abt. 1. 1906. Über Amphilina. Verhandl. Gesell. Dtsch. Naturforscher und Ärtze 77, Pt. 2, 1st half. **Poche, F.** 1922. Zur Kenntnis der Amphilinidea. Zool. Anz. 54. 1925a. Das System der Platodaria. Arch. Naturgesch. 91, Abt. A. 1925b. Zur Kenntnis von Amphilina foliacea. Ztschr. Wiss. Zool. 125. 1926. On the morphology and systematic position of Gigantolina. Records Indian Mus. 28. **Ruszkowski, J. S.** 1932. Sur les larves de Gyrocotyle. Bull. Internat. Acad. Polonaise B II. **Salensky, W.** 1874. Bau und Entwickelungsgeschichte der Amphilina. Ztschr. Wiss. Zool. 24. **Southwell, T.** 1915. On some Indian parasites of fishes [Gigantolina]. Records Indian Mus. 11. 1928. Cestodaria from India and Ceylon. Ann. Trop. Med. Parasitol. 22. **Ward, H. B.** 1912. Anatomy of Gyrocotyle. Zool. Jahrb. suppl. 15. **Watson, Edna.** 1911. The genus Gyrocotyle. Univ. Calif. Publ. Zool. 6. **Woodland, W.** 1923. On Amphilina paragonopora [Schizochoerus]. Quart. Jour. Micro. Sci. 67.

Tetraphyllidea

Baylis, H. A. 1919. A remarkable cysticercus from a rare dolphin. Ann. Mag. Natur. Hist. ser. 9, 3. **Causey, D.** 1926. Morphology of Thysanocephalum.

Trans. Amer. Micro. Soc. 45. **Curtis, W. C.** 1903. Crossobothrium. Biol. Bull.
5. 1906. Formation of proglottids in Crossobothrium. Biol. Bull. 11. **Hart, J. E.**
1936. Cestoda from fishes of Puget Sound. III. Phyllobothrioidea. Trans. Amer.
Micro. Soc. 55. **Haswell, W. A.** 1903. On a cestode Phyllobothrium from Cestra-
cion. Quart. Jour. Micro. Sci. 46. **Linton, E.** 1889, 1890. Notes on Entozoa from
marine fishes of New England. Rept. U.S. Fish Comm. for 1886, 1887. 1892.
Anatomy of Thysanocephalum. Rept. U.S. Fish. Comm. for 1888. 1922a. Anatomy of Dinobothrium. Proc. U.S. Nation. Mus. 60, art. 6. 1922b. New shark
cestode. Proc. U.S. Nation. Mus. 61, art. 12. 1924. Cestode parasites of sharks
and skates. Proc. U.S. Nation. Mus. 64, art. 21. **Monticelli, F. S.** 1888. Ricerche
sullo Scolex polymorphus. Mitt. Staz. Zool. Napoli 8. **Shipley, A. E.**, and **J.
Hornell.** 1906. Cestode and nematode parasites. In **W. A. Herdman**, Rept. to
Ceylon Govern. on Pearl Oyster Fisheries, Pt. V. **Southwell, T.** 1912. New
species of cestode parasites from marine fishes of Ceylon. Ceylon Marine Biol.
Repts. Pt. VI, No. 22. 1921. Larval cestode from the umbrella of a jelly-fish.
Mem. Indian Mus. 5. 1925. Monograph of the Tetraphyllidea. Liverpool School
Trop. Med. Mem. No. 2 (new ser.). **Van Cleave, H. J.** 1927. Ctenophores as host
of a cestode. Trans. Amer. Micro. Soc. 46. **Woodland, W. N. F.** 1927. A revised
classification of the tetraphyllidean Cestoda. Proc. Zool. Soc. London. **Wundsch,
H. H.** 1912. Neue plerocercoide aus marinen Copepoden. Arch. Naturgesch. 78,
Abt. A, Heft 9. **Yoshida, S.** 1917. Some cestodes from Japanese selachians.
Parasitology 9. **Zschokke, F.** 1886. Le développement du Scolex polymorphus.
Arch. Sci. Phys. Natur. ser. 3, 16.

Lecanicephaloidea

Jameson, H. L. 1912. Shell and pearls of the pearl oyster with an examination
of the cestode theory of pearl formation. Proc. Zool. Soc. London. **Linton, E.** 1890.
Entozoa of marine fishes of New England. Pt. II. Rept. U.S. Fish Comm. for 1887.
1916. Notes on the cestodes from the spotted sting ray. Jour. Parasitol. 3. **Pint-
mer, T.** 1928. Die sogenannte Gamobothriidae. Zool. Jahrb. Abt. Anat. 50.
Southwell, T. 1924. The pearl inducing worm in the Ceylon pearl oyster. Ann.
Trop. Med. Parasitol. 18. **Subramanian, M. K.** 1941. The nervous system of
Tylocephalum. Records Indian Mus. 43.

Proteocephaloidea

Beddard, F. E. 1913. On six species of the genus Ichthyotaenia. Proc. Zool.
Soc. London. **Benedict, H. M.** 1900. Structure of two Proteocephalus. Jour.
Morphol. 16. **Essex, H. E.** 1927. The structure and development of Coral-
lobothrium. Illincis Biol. Monogr. 11. **Fuhrmann, O.**, and **J. G. Baer.** 1925.
Third Tanganyika Expedition. Report on the Cestoda. Proc. Zool. Soc. London.
Harwood, P. D. 1933. Helminths parasitic in a water moccasin with a discussion
of the characters of the Proteocephalidae. Parasitology 25. **Herde, H. E.** 1938.
Early development of Ophiotaenia. Trans. Amer. Micro. Soc. 57. **Hunter, G.
W., III.** 1928. Life history of Proteocephalus ambloplitis. Jour. Parasitol. 14.
Hunter, G. W., III, and **W. S. Hunter.** 1928. Further studies on the bass tapeworm,
Proteocephalus ambloplitis. Biol. Survey Erie-Mogina System, suppl. to 18th Ann.
Rept. New York State Conserv. Dept. **Kuczkowski, S.** 1925. Die Entwicklung
im Genus Ichthyotaenia. Bull. Acad. Polonaise Sci. Cracovie, Cl. Math. Natur.,
ser. B. **Larsh, J. E.** 1941. Corallobothrium from the bullhead. Jour. Parasitol.
27. **La Rue, G. R.** 1909. Proteocephalus. Trans. Amer. Micro. Soc. 29. 1914.
Revision of the Proteocephalidae. Illinois Biol. Monogr. 1. **Magath, B. M.** 1929.

Life history of Crepidobothrium. Ann. Trop. Med. Parasitol. 23. **Meggitt, F. J.** 1927. Remarks on the Monticellidae and Ichthyotaeniidae. Ann. Trop. Med. Parasitol. 21. **Nybelin, O.** 1917. Australischen Cestoden. Kungl. Svenska Vetensk. Akad. Handl. 52. **Osler, C. P.** 1931. New cestode from Rana. Jour. Parasitol. 17. **Rudin, E.** 1917. Die Ichthyotaenien der Reptilien. Rev. Suisse Zool. 25. **Thomas, L. G.** 1931. Life history of Ophiotaenia from Rana. Jour. Parasitol. 17. 1934. Further studies on the life cycle of a frog tapeworm. Jour. Parasitol. 20. 1941. Life cycle of Ophiotaenia cestode of snakes. Rev. Med. Trop. Parasitol. Bact. Clin. Lab. (Havana) 7. **Woodland, W.** 1924. New genus of Proteocephalidae from Indian fishes [Gangesia]. Parasitology 16. 1925. New proteocephalids and a revision of the genera of the family. Parasitology 17. 1933. New subfamily of proteocephalid cestodes. Parasitology 25. Anatomy of some fish cestodes from the Amazon. Quart. Jour. Micro. Sci. 76.

Diphyllidea

Pintner, T. 1889. Zur Kenntnis der Gattung Echinobothrium. Arbeit. Zool. Inst. Wien 8. **Ruszowski, J. S.** 1927. Echinobothrium, ses larves et sur l'hôte intermédiaire. Bull. Acad. Polonaise Sci. Cracovie, Cl. Math. Natur., ser. B.

Trypanorhyncha

Cooper, A. R. 1914. Systematic position of Haplobothrium. Trans. Roy. Soc. Canada, ser. 3, 8, sect. 4. 1915. A new cestode from Amia calva. Univ. Toronto Stud., Biol. Ser. No. 15. 1919. North American pseudophyllidean cestodes from fishes. Illinois Biol. Monogr. 4. **Dollfus, R.** 1929, 1930. Sur les Tétrarhynques. Bull. Soc. Zool. France 54; Mem. Soc. Zool. France 29. 1935. Sur quelques tétrarhynches. Bull. Soc. Zool. France 60. **Essex, H.** 1928. Cestode larva from the liver of the bullhead. Jour. Parasitol. 15. 1929. Life cycle of Haplobothrium. Science 69. **Guiart, J.** 1931. Sur la nomenclature et sur la classification des Tétrarhynques. Bull. Inst. Océanogr. Monaco, No. 575. **Hart, J. E.** 1936. Cestoda from fishes of Puget Sound. II. Tetrarhynchoidea. Trans. Amer. Micro. Soc. 55. **Johnstone, J.** 1912. Tetrarhynchus erinaceus. Parasitology 4. **Joyeaux, C.,** and **J. G. Baer.** 1934. Sur quelques cestodes de France. Arch. Mus. Hist. Natur. Paris, ser. 6, 11. **Kuitunen-Ekbaum, E.** 1933. Possible intermediate host of Gilquinia. Contribs. Canad. Biol., new ser. 8, No. 7. **Meinkoth, N. A.** 1947. Life cycle and taxonomic position of Haplobothrium. Trans. Amer. Micro. Soc. 66. **Nybelin, O.** 1918. Zur Anatomie und systematische Stellung von Aporhynchus. Göteborgs Kungl. Vetensk. Handl., ser. 4, 20. **Pintner, T.** 1880. Bau der Tetrabothrien und Tetrarhynchen. Arbeit. Zool. Inst. Wien 3. 1896. Versuch einer morphologischen Erklärung des Tetrarhynchenrüssels. Biol. Centralbl. 16. 1893, 1896, 1903. Studien an Tetrarhynchen, I–III. Sitzungsber. Akad. Wiss. Wien, Math. Naturwiss. Kl. 102, Abt. 1; 105, Abt. 1; 112, Abt. 1. 1913. Vorarbeiten zu einer Monographie der Tetrarhynchoiden. Sitzungsber. Akad. Wiss. Wien, Math. Naturwiss. Kl. 122, Abt. 1. 1925. Bemerkenswerte Strukturen im Kopfe von Tetrarhynchoiden. Ztschr. Wiss. Zool. 125. 1927. Kritische Beiträge zum System der Tetrarhynchen. Zool. Jahrb. Abt. System. 53. 1929. Studien über Tetrarhynchen. Sitzungsber. Akad. Wiss. Wien, Math. Naturwiss. Kl. 138, Abt. 1. 1930. Wenig bekanntes und unbekanntes von Rüsselbandwürmern. Sitzungsber. Akad. Wiss. Wien, Math. Naturwiss. Kl. 139, Abt. 1. **Poche, F.** 1924. Die Entstehung der Rüssel der Tetrarhynchiden. Zool. Anz. 59. **Rees, Gwendolen.** 1941. The musculature and nervous system of the plerocercoid larva of Dibothriorhynchus. The scolex of Aporhynchus. Parasitology 33. **Ruszkowski, J. S.** 1922. Cycle

évolutif du tetrarhynque Grillotia erinaceus.   C. R. Acad. Polonaise Sci. Lett. No. 9.
Southwell, T. 1929. A monograph on cestodes of the order Trypanorhyncha from Ceylon and India. Spolia Zeylanica 15. **Subramanian, M. K.** 1940. Nervous system of a proglottid of Tentacularia. Current Science 9. **Thomas, L. J.** 1930. Life history of Haplobothrium. Jour. Parasitol. 16. **Vaullegeard, A.** 1899. Recherches sur les tetrarhynques. Mem. Soc. Linn. Normandie 19.

Pseudophyllidea

Beaver, P. C., and **P. H. Simer.** 1940. Study of the species of the genus Marsipometra from the spoonbill. Trans. Amer. Micro. Soc. 59. **Bonne, C.** 1942. Researches on sparganosis in the Netherlands East Indies. Amer. Jour. Trop. Med. 22. **Cooper, A. R.** 1918. Bothriocephalid cestodes from fish. Jour. Parasitol. 4. 1919. North America pseudophyllidean cestodes from fishes. Illinois Biol. Monogr. 4. 1920. Glaridacris. Trans. Amer. Micro. Soc. 39. **Essex, H. E.** 1927. Early development of Diphyllobothrium latum in northern Minnesota. Jour. Parasitol. 14. 1928. Life history of Bothriocephalus cuspidatus. Trans. Amer. Micro. Soc. 47. **Friedheim, E.,** and **J. G. Baer.** 1933. Untersuchungen über die Atmung von Diphyllobothrium latum. Biochem. Ztschr. 265. **Fuhrmann, O.,** and **J. G. Baer.** 1925. Third Tanganyika Expedition. Report on the Cestoda. Proc. Zool. Soc. London. **Harnisch, O.** 1933. Sauerstoffverbrauch von Triaenophorus. Ztschr. Vergl. Physiol. 19. **Hart, J. F.,** and **J. E. Guberlet.** 1936. Cestoda from fishes of Puget Sound. I. Spathebothrioidea. Trans. Amer. Mirco. Soc. 55. **Hjortland, A. L.** 1929. Structure and life history of Triaenophorus. Jour. Parasitol. 15. **Hunter, G. W. III.** 1927. Notes on the Caryophyllaeidae of North America. Jour. Parasitol. 14, 15. 1930. Studies on the Caryophyllaeidae of North America. Illinois Biol. Monogr. 11. **Ijima, I.** 1905. Cestode larva parasitic in man. Jour. College Sci. Tokyo Imper. Univ. 20. **Janicki, C.,** and **F. Rosen.** 1917. Le cycle évolutif du Dibothriocephalus latus. Bull. Soc. Neuchâteloise Sci. Natur. 42. **Joyeaux, C.,** and **J. G. Baer.** 1939. Recherches biologiques sur quelques cestodes Pseudophyllidae. Vol. Jub. Prof. Sadao Yoshida 2. **Joyeaux, C., E. Houdemer,** and **J. Baer.** 1934. Recherches sur la biologie de Sparganum. Bull. Soc. Pathol. Exot. 27. **Kiessling, F.** 1882. Bau von Schistocephalus und Ligula. Arch. Naturgesch. 48, Abt. 1. **Kuitunen-Ekbaum, E.** 1933. Study of the cestode genus Eubothrium. Contribs. Canad. Biol., new ser. 8. **Le Bas, G.** 1924. Experimental studies on Dibothriocephalus latus in man. Jour. Helminthol. 14. **Leiper, R. T.** 1936. Some experiments and observations on the longevity of Diphyllobothrium infections. Jour. Helminthol. 14. **Li, H. C.** 1929. The life histories of Diphyllobothrium decipiens and erinacei. Amer. Jour. Hygiene 10. **Linton, E.** 1922. A new cestode from Liparis [Spathebothrium]. Trans. Amer. Micro. Soc., 41. **Lönnberg, E.** 1889. Bidrag till kännedomen am i sverige förekommande cestoder. Bihang Svenska Vetensk. Akad. Handl. 14, Afd. 4, No. 9. 1982. Einige Experimente Cestoden künstlich lebend zu erhalten. Centralbl. Bakteriol. Parasitenk. 11. **Lühe, M.** 1896. Das Nervensystem von Ligula. Zool. Anz. 19. 1898. Die Gliederung von Ligula. Centralbl. Bakteriol. Parasitenk. 23. 1899. Zur Anatomie und Systematik der Bothriocephaliden. Verhandl. Dtsch. Zool. Gesell. 9. 1899–1900. Beiträge zur Kenntnis der Bothriocephaliden I–III. Centralbl. Bakteriol. Parasitenk. 26, 27. 1900. Untersuchungen über die Bothriocephaliden mit marginaler Genitalöffnungen. Ztschr. Wiss. Zool. 68. 1902. Revision meines Bothriocephalidsystems. Centralbl. Bakteriol. Parasitenk. Abt. 1, Orig. 31. **Markov, G.** 1938. The survival of a broad tepeworm's plerocercoids in artificial media. C. R. Acad. Sci. U.R.S.S. 19. 1939. Nutrition of tapeworms in artificial media. C. R. Acad. Sci.

U.R.S.S. 25. **McIntosh, A.** 1937. New host records for Diphyllobothrium man-sonoides. Jour. Parasitol. 23. **Miller, R. B.** 1943, 1945. Studies on Triaenophorus I–IV. Canad. Jour. Research 21, sect. D; 23, sect. D. 1945. Effect of Triaenophorus on growth of two fishes. Jour. Fisheries Research Bd. Canada 6. **Mrazek, A.** 1897. Archigetes. Sitzungsber. Böhm. Gesell. Wiss. Prag, No. 32. 1901. Über die Larve von Caryophyllaeus. Centralbl. Bakteriol. Parasitenk., Abt. 1, Orig. 29. **Mueller, J. F.** 1935. A Diphyllobothrium from cats and dogs in the Syracuse region. Jour. Parasitol. 21. 1937. A repartition of the genus Diphyllobothrium. Jour. Parasitol. 23. 1938. Life history of D. mansonoides and some considerations with regard to sparganosis in the United States. Amer. Jour. Trop. Med. 18. **Nybelin, O.** 1922. Anatomischsystematische Studien über Pseudophyllideen. Göteborg's Kungl. Vetensk. Vitterh. Samh. Handl. ser. 4, 26. **Okumura, T.** 1919. Life history of Sparganum mansoni. Jap. Med. World 1; Kitasaki Arch. Exp. Med. 3. **Riley, W. A.** 1919. Longevity of the fish tapeworm of man. Jour. Parasitol. 5. **Rosen, F.** 1917–1919. Recherches sur le developpement des cestodes I, II. Bull. Soc. Neuchâteloise Sci. Natur. 43, 44. **Rudin, E.** 1914. Studien an Fistulicola. Rev. Suisse Zool. 22. **Schauinsland, H.** 1886. Die embryonale Entwicklung der Bothriocephalen. Jena. Ztschr. Naturwiss. 19. **Scheuring, L.** 1923. Studien an Fischparasiten. Ztschr. Fischerei 22. 1928. Biologie des Genus Triaenophorus. Ztschr. Parasitenk. 2. **Schwartz, B.** 1921. Haemotoxins from parasitic worms. Jour. Agricult. Research 22. **Sommer, F., and L. Landois.** 1872. Bau der geschlechtreifen Glieder von Bothriocephalus latus. Ztschr. Wiss. Zool. 22. **Stiles, C. A.** 1908. Occurrence of a proliferating cestode larva (Sparganum proliferum) in man in Florida. Bull. U.S. Hydienic Lab. No. 40. **Stunkard, H.** 1948. Pseudophyllidean cestodes from Alaskan pinnipeds. Jour. Parasitol. 34. **Szidat, L.** 1937a. Über einige neue Caryophyllaeiden aus ostpreussischen Fischen. Ztschr. Parasitenk. 9. 1937b. Archigetes die progenetischen Larve einer Caryophyllaeiden Gattung Biacetabulum. Zool. Anz. 119. 1938. Brachyurus, ein neue Caryophyllaeiden-Art aus Gobio. Zool. Anz. 124. **Tarassov, V.** 1934. Beiträge zum Problem des Kampfes gegen Diphyllobothrium latum. Arch. Schiffs. Tropenhyg. 38. 1937. De l'immunité acquise envers le bothriocéphale Diphyllobothrium latum. Ann. Parasitol. Hum. Comp. 15. **Thomas, L. J.** 1937. Bothriocephalus rarus, from the newt. Jour. Parasitol. 23. **Vergeer, T.** 1928. Dissemination of the broad tapeworm by wild Carnivora. Canad. Med. Assoc. Jour. 19. Canadian fish, a source of the broad tapeworm of man. Jour. Amer. Med. Assoc. 90. An important source of broad tapeworm in America. Science 68. Diphyllobothrium latum, the broad tapeworm of man. Jour. Amer. Med. Assoc. 90. 1929. The broad tapeworm in America with suggestions for its control. Jour. Infect. Diseases 44. The dog a reservoir of the broad tapeworm. Jour. Amer. Med. Assoc. 92. 1930. Causes underlying increased incidence of broad tapeworm of man in North America. Jour. Amer. Med. Assoc. 95. 1935. Eggs and coracidia of Diphyllobothrium latum. Papers Michigan Acad. Sci. Arts Lett. 21. **Vogel, H.** 1929. Studien zur Entwicklung von Diphyllobothrium. Ztschr. Parasitenk. 2. **Ward, H. B.** 1911. Discovery of Archigetes in America. Science 33. **Wardle, R. A.** 1932. Significant factors in the plerocercoid environment of D. latum. Jour. Helminthol. 11. **Wardle, R. A., and N. K. Green.** 1941. The rate of growth of D. latum. Canad. Jour. Research 19, sect. D. **Wardle, R. A., J. McLeod, and E. Stewart.** 1947. Lühe's "Diphyllobothrium." Jour. Parasitol. 33. **Will, H.** 1893. Anatomie von Caryophyllaeus. Ztschr. Wiss. Zool. 56. **Wisniewski, L.** 1928. Archigetes. Zool. Anz. 77. 1930. Das Genus Archigetes. Mém. Acad. Polonaise Sci. Lettr. Cracovie, Cl. Sci. Math. Natur. ser. B. 1932. Zur postembryonale Entwicklung von Cyathocephalus. Zool. Anz. 98. 1933. Cyathocephalus. Bull. Internat. Acad. Polonaise Sci. B II. **Woodland, W.** 1923. Some remarkable new forms of Caryophyllaeidae and a revision of the families of the Cestodaria. Quart. Jour. Micro. Sci. 67. 1926. On the genera and possible affinities of the Caryophyllaeidae. Proc. Zool. Soc. London. 1936. Wenyonia. Proc. Zool. Soc. London. 1937. New caryophyllaeid. Proc. Zool. Soc. London 107B. 1941. Review of African and Asiatic forms of Duthiersia. Proc. Zool. Soc. London 110B. **Wunder, W.** 1939. Das Jahreszeitliche Auftreten des Caryophyllaeus im Darm des Karpfens. Ztschr. Parasitenk. 10. **Yoshida, S.** 1914. Second and third case of infection with Plerocercoides prolifer. Parasitology 7.

Nippotaeniidea

Achmerov, A. K. 1941. Amurotaenia. C. R. Acad. Sci. U.R.S.S. 30. **Yamaguti, S.** 1939. Studies on the helminth fauna of Japan. 28. Nippotaenia, a new cestode representing a new order. Jap. Jour. Zool. 8. **Yamaguti, S., and I. Miyata.** 1940. Nippotaenia mogurndae from a Japanese fresh-water fish. Jap. Jour. Med. Sci., ser. 6, 1.

Taenioidea

Abderhalden, E. 1911. Über den Gehalt von Eingeweidewürmern an peptolytischen Fermenten. Ztschr. Physiol. Chem. 74. **Ackert, J. E.** 1921. The longevity of fowl tapeworms. Jour. Parasitol. 7. **Ackert, J. E., and W. Reid.** 1936. The cysticercoid of the fowl tapeworm Raillietina cesticillus. Trans. Amer. Micro. Soc. 55. **Addis, C., and A. C. Chandler.** 1944. Studies on the vitamin requirements of tapeworms. Jour. Parasitol. 30. **Africa, C., and E. Garcia.** 1935. The occurrence of Bertiella in man, monkey, and dog in the Philippines. Philipp. Jour. Sci. 56. **Alicata, J. E.** 1936. The amphipod, Orchestia, an intermediate host of Hymenolepis exigua. Jour. Parasitol. 22. **Alicata, J. E., and E. Chang.** 1939. The life history of Hymenolepis exigua. Jour. Parasitol. 25. **Alt, H., and O. Tischer.** 1931. Metabolism of Moniezia expansa. Proc. Soc. Exp. Biol. Med. 29. **Arnold, J. G.** 1938. Anoplocephaline cestodes of North American rabbits. Zoologica, New York, 23. **Bacigalupo, J.** 1931. Evolution de l'Hymenolepis fraterna chez Pulex, Xenopsylla, et Ctenocephalus. Ann. Parasitol. Hum. Comp. 9. **Baer, J. G.** 1927. Monographie des cestodes de la famille des Anoplocephalidae. Bull. Biol. France Belg. Suppl. 10. **Bartels, E.** 1902. Cysticercus fasciolaris, Anatomie, Entwicklung und Umwandlung in Taenia crassicollis. Zool. Jahrb. Abt. Anat. 16. **Bashkirova, E.** 1941. Biology of the tapeworm Anoplocephala perfoliata in the horse. C. R. Acad. Sci. U.R.S.S. 30. **Baylis, H. A.** 1922. New cestode and other parasitic worms from Spitzbergen. Ann. Mag. Natur. Hist., ser. 9, 9. 1934. New species of Bertiella. Ann. Mag. Natur. Hist., ser. 10, 14. **Becker, R.** 1920. Über die Art der Begattung bei Pferdebandwürmern. Centralbl. Bakteriol. Parasitenk. 84, Abt. 1. 1921. Beiträge zur Kenntnis des Nervensystems der Pferdebandwürmer. Zool. Jahrb. Abt. Anat. 43. Die aussere Gestalt der Pferdebandwürmer. Der Genitalapparat der Pferdebandwürmer. Centralbl. Bakteriol. Parasitenk. 87, Abt. 1; 88, Abt. 1. **Berberian, D. A.** 1936. Some observations on the effect of digestive juices on scolices of Echinococcus. Jour. Helminthol. 14. **Bhalerao, G. D.** 1936. Cestode genus Avitellina from India. Jour. Helminthol. 14. **Bischoff, C. R.** 1913. Die Cestoden aus Hyrax. Rev. Suisse Zool. 21. **Blanchard, R.** 1891. Sur les helminthes des primates anthropoides Bertiella. Mem. Soc. Zool. France 4. **Blumberg, H., and R. E. Gardner.** 1940. Adenomatous stomach lesion of the rat associated with heavy Cysticercus fasciolaris infestation. Proc. Soc. Exp. Biol. Med. 45. **Brand, T. von.** 1929, 1933. Stoffbestand und Stoffwechsel von Moniezia expansa.

Zool. Anz. Suppl. Band 4; Ztschr. Vergl. Physiol. 18. **Brumpt, E.** 1933. Evolution de l'Hymenolepis nana var. fraterna. Arch. Zool. Exp. Gén. 75. **Bullock, F. D.**, and **M. R. Curtis.** 1920. The experimental production of sarcoma of the liver of rats. Proc. New York Pathol. Soc. 20. 1924. Reactions of the tissue of the rat's liver to the larvae of Taenia crassicollis. Jour. Cancer Research 8. **Bullock, F. D., W. F. Dunning,** and **M. R. Curtis.** 1934. Observations on the digestion of the shells of the eggs of Taenia taeniaeformis. Amer. Jour. Cancer 20. **Burt, D.** 1936. New species of Dilepis. Spolia Zeylanica 19. **Cameron, G. R.** 1926. Enzymes of the hydatid cyst. Austral. Jour. Exp. Biol. Med. Sci. 3. **Cameron, G. R.,** and **A. S. Fitzpatrick.** 1925. Microchemical reactions of the hydatid cyst wall. Amer. Jour. Pathol. 1. **Cameron, T. W. M.** 1925. Cestode genus Mesocestoides. Jour. Helminthol. 3. 1927. Some modern biological conceptions of hydatid. Proc. Roy. Soc. Med. 20. **Campbell, D. H.** 1936. Active immunization of albino rats with protein fractions from Taenia taeniaeformis and its larval form. Amer. Jour. Hygiene 23. 1939. Effect of sex hormones on the normal resistance of rats to Cysticercus crassicollis. Science 89. **Campbell, D. H.,** and **L. R. Melcher.** 1940. Relation of sex factors to resistance against Cysticercus crassicollis in rats. Jour. Infect. Diseases 66. **Case, A. A.,** and **J. E. Ackert.** 1940. Intermediate hosts of chicken tapeworms in Kansas. Trans. Kansas Acad. Sci. 42. **Chandler, A. C.** 1939. Effect of number and age of worms on development of primary and secondary infections with Hymenolepis diminuta. Amer. Jour. Hygiene 29, sect. D. 1942. First case of human infection with Mesocestoides. Science 94. 1943. Studies on the nutrition of tapeworms. Amer. Jour. Hygiene 37. 1946. Observations on the anatomy of Mesocestoides. Jour. Parasitol. 32. **Clapham, Phyllis.** 1940. Studies on Coenurus glomeratus. Jour. Helminthol. 18. 1941. Coenurus cerebralis in the human brain. Jour. Helminthol. 19. **Clausen, E.** 1915. Recherches anatomiques et histologiques sur quelques cestodes d'oiseaux. Thesis, Neuchâtel. **Coatney, G. R.** 1936. Some notes on cestodes from Nebraska. Jour. Parasitol. 22. **Cook, S. F.,** and **E. Shannan.** 1930. Effect of acids and bases on the respiration of tapeworms. Physiol. Zool. 3. **Coutelen, F.** 1926. Essai de culture in vitro de scolex et d'hydatides échinococciques. Ann. Parasitol. Hum. Comp. 5. 1929. Essai de culture in vitro du cénure serial. C. R. Soc. Biol. Paris 100. 1931. Présence chez les hydatides echinococciques de cellules libres a glycogène et a graisse. Ann. Parasitol. Hum. Comp. 9. **Culbertson, J. T.,** and **H. M. Rose.** 1941. Further observations on skin reactions to antigens from heterologous cestodes in echinococcus disease. Jour. Clinical Investigation 20. **Dévé, F.** 1926. Évolution vésiculaire du scolex echinococcique in vitro. La culture artificielle du kyst hydatique. C. R. Soc. Biol. Paris 94. **Dew, H. R.** 1927. *Hydatid disease.* **Dollfus, R.** 1940. Cestodes du genre Raillietina trouvés chez l'homme en Amérique tropicale. Ann. Parasitol. Hum. Comp. 17. **Douthitt, H.** 1915. Studies on the cestode family Anoplocephalidae. Illinois Biol. Monogr. 1. **Edgar, S. A.** 1941. Use of bile salts for the evagination of tapeworm cysts. Trans. Amer. Micro. Soc. 60. **Elek, S. R.,** and **L. Finkelstein.** 1939. Multiceps serialis infestation in a baboon. Zoologica, New York, 24. **Flöszner, O.** 1924, 1925. Neue Untersuchungen über die Echinococcus Flüssigkeit. Ztschr. Biol. 80, 82. **Fuhrmann, O.** 1895. Die Tänien der Amphibien. Zool. Jahrb. Abt. Anat. 9. 1896. Davainea. Rev. Suisse Zool. 4. 1899. Deux singuliers Tenias d'oiseaux. Rev. Suisse Zool. 7. 1900a. Zur Kenntnis der Acoleinae. Centralbl. Bakteriol. Parasitenk. 28, Abt. 1. 1900b. Ein getrenntgeschlechtlicher Cestode. Zool. Anz. 23. 1902. Die Anoplocephalidae der Vögel. Centralbl. Bakteriol. Parasitenk., Abt. 1, Orig. 32. 1906. Die Hymenolepis-Arten der Vögel. Centralbl. Bakteriol. Parasitenk., Abt. 1, Orig. 41, 42. 1907. Die Systematik der Ordnung der Cyclophyllidea. Zool. Anz. 32. 1908. Die Cestoden der Vögel. Zool. Jahrb. Suppl. 10. 1914. Sur l'origin du Fimbriaria. C. R. 9 Congr. Internation. Zool. 1920. Considerations générales sur les Davainea. Festschrift für Zschokke, No. 27. 1921. Die Cestoden der deutschen Südpolar-Expedition. Dtsch. Süd-polar-Expedition 16, Zool. VIII. 1925. Sur la développement et la reproduction asexuée de Idiogenes otidis. Ann. Parasitol. Hum. Comp. 3. 1932. Les tenias des oiseaux. Mém. Univ. Neuchâtel 8. **Gordon, H. M.** 1932. Longevity of Moniezia in sheep. Austral. Veterinary Jour. 8. **Gough, L.** 1911. Monograph of the Avitellininae. Quart. Jour. Micro. Sci. 56. **Grassi, P.** 1887. Entwick-lungscyclus der Taenia nana. Centralbl. Bakteriol. Parasitenk. 2. **Grassi, P.,** and **G. Rovelli.** 1892. Ricerche embriologiche sui cestodi. Atti Accad. Gioenia Sci. Natur. Catania ser. 4, 4. **Greenfield, Sylvia.** 1942. Age resistance of the albino rat to Cysticercus fasciolaris. Jour. Parasitol. 28. **Gutberlet, J. E.** 1916. Morphology of adult and larval cestodes from poultry. Trans. Amer. Micro. Soc. 35. **Hager, Anne.** 1941. Effects of dietary modifications of host rats on the tapeworm Hymenolepis diminuta. Iowa State College Jour. Sci. 15. **Hall, M. C.** 1919. Adult taenioid cestodes of dogs and cats and of related carnivores. Proc. U.S. Nation. Mus. 55, No. 2258. 1934. Discharge of eggs from segments of Thysanosoma acti-noides. Proc. Helminthol. Soc. Washington 1. **Hamann, O.** 1885. Mesocestoides. Ztschr. Wiss. Zool. 42. 1889, 1891. In Gammarus pulex lebende cysticercoiden mit Schwanzanhängen. Jena. Ztschr. Naturwiss. 24, 25. **Harper, W. F.** 1930. British larval cestodes from land and fresh-water invertebrate hosts. Parasitology 22. **Harwood, P. D.** 1938. Reproductive cycles of Raillietina cesticillus of the fowl. Livro Jub. Prof. Lauro Travassos. **Hearin, J.** 1941. Studies on the acquired immunity to the dwarf tapeworm in the mouse host. Amer. Jour. Hygiene 33. **Horsfall, Margery.** 1938. Observations on the life history of Raillietina echino-bothrida and of R. tetragona. Jour. Parasitol. 24. Meal beetles as intermediate hosts of poultry tapeworms. Poultry Science 17. **Hughes, R. C.** 1940a. The genus Oochoristica. Amer. Midland Natural. 23. 1940b. The genus Hymenolepis. Technic. Bull. Oklahoma Agricult. Exp. Sta. 8. 1941. Key to the species of Hymen-olepis. Trans. Amer. Micro. Soc. 60. **Hughes, R. C.,** and **R. L. Schultz.** 1942. The genus Raillietina. Bull. Oklahoma Agricult. Mechan. College 39. **Hunninen, A. V.** 1935. Studies on the life-history and host-parasite relations of Hymenolepis fraterna. Amer. Jour. Hygiene 22. 1936. Study of internal autoreinfection with Hymenolepis fraterna in white mice. Jour. Parasitol. 22. **Hussey, Kathleen.** 1941. Aporina from the pigeon. Amer. Midland Natural. 25. **Jacobi, A.** 1898. Über den Bau von [Diorchis]. Zool. Jahrb. Abt. System. 12. **Janicki, C.** 1907. Embry-onalentwicklung von Taenia serrata. Ztschr. Wiss. Zool. 87. 1910. Die Cestoden aus Procavia. Denkschr. Med. Naturwiss. Gesell. Jena 16. **Jewell, Minna.** 1916. Cylindrotaenia. Jour. Parasitol. 2. **Jones, Myrna.** 1936. Davainea meleagridis from the turkey. Proc. Helminthol. Soc. Washington 3. **Jones, M.,** and **J. Alicata.** 1935. Development and morphology of Hymenolepis cantaniana. Jour. Washington Acad. Sci. 25. **Jones, M.,** and **M. Horsfall.** 1934. Ants as intermediate hosts for two species of Raillietina in chickens. Jour. Parasitol. 21. **Joyeaux, C.** 1920. Cycle évolutif de quelques cestodes. Bull. Biol. France Belg. Suppl. 2. 1924. Recherches sur le cycle évolutif de Cylindrotaenia. Ann. Parasitol. Hum. Comp. 2. 1925. Hymenolepis nana et H. fraterna. Ann. Parasitol. Hum. Comp. 3. 1926. Sur quelques cysticercoides de Gammarus pulex. Arch. Schiffs. Tropenhyg. 30. 1927. Cycle évolutif d'Hymenolepis erinacei. Ann. Parasitol. Hum. Comp. 5. **Joyeaux, C.,** and **J. G. Baer.** 1932. Recherches sur les cestodes au genre Meso-cestoides. Bull. Soc. Pathol. Exot. 25. 1938. Sur quelques cestodes de Galliformes.

Trav. Sta. Zool. Wimereux 13. 1945. Morphologie, évolution et position systématique de Catenotaenia. Rev. Suisse Zool. 52. **Joyeaux, C.,** and **N. Kobozieff.** 1928. Recherches sur l'Hymenolepis microstoma. Ann. Parasitol. Hum. Comp. 6. **Kerr, W.** Immunity against Cysticercus pisiformis. Amer. Jour. Hygiene 22. **Kobert, R.** 1903. Ueber einige Enzyme wirbelloser Tiere. Arch. Ges. Physiol. 99. **Koehler, E.** 1894. Der Klappenapparat in den Exkretionsgefässen der Tänien. Ztschr. Wiss. Zool. 57. **Kouri, P.** 1940. A new human helminthic infection in Cuba [Inermicapsifer]. Jour. Parasitol. 26. **Langer, J.** 1905. Zur Frage der Bildung spezifischer Antikörper im Organismus von Bandwurmwirten. München. Med. Wochenschr. 52. **Larsh, J. E.** 1942. Transmission from mother to offspring of immunity against Hymenolepis nana fraterna. Amer. Jour. Hygiene 36. 1943a. Relationships between the intestinal size of young mice and their susceptibility to Hymenolepis nana fraterna. Jour. Parasitol. 29. 1943b. Serological studies on Hymenolepis nana fraterna. Amer. Jour. Hygiene 37. 1944. Artificial immunization of mice against Hymenolepis nana fraterna. Amer. Jour. Hygiene 39. 1945. Immunity relations in human cestode infections. Jour. Elisha Mitchell Scient. Soc. 61. **Leonard, A. B.** 1940. Accelerated tissue response to Cysticercus pisiformis in passively immunized rabbits. Amer. Jour. Hugiene 32, sect. D. **Leonard, A. B.,** and **A. E. Leonard.** 1941. Intestinal phase of the resistance of rabbits to the larvae of Taenia pisiformis. Jour. Parasitol. 27. **Lesuk, A.,** and **R. Anderson.** 1941. Chemical composition of Cysticercus fasciolaris II. Jour. Biol. Chem. 139. **Levine, P.** 1938. Biology of Davainea proglottina in the intestine of the host. Jour. Parasitol. 24. **Loeper, M.,** and **J. Tonnet.** 1931. Production d'acide oxalique par le Taenia. C. R. Soc. Biol. Paris 106. **Loewen, S.** 1940. On some reptilian Oochoristica. Trans. Amer. Micro. Soc. 59. **Lopez-Neyra, C.** 1927. Sur les cysticercoids de quelques Dipylidium. Ann. Parasitol. Hum. Comp. 5. 1929. Revision del genero Dipylidium. Mem. Acad. Cienc. Madrid, ser. 1, 32. **Luttermoser, G.** 1938. Susceptibility of chickens to reinfection with Raillietina cesticillus. Jour. Parasitol. 24. **Magath, T.** 1937. Hydatid disease in Canada and the United States. Amer. Jour. Hygiene 25. **Mayhew, R.** 1925. Studies on the avian genera of the Hymenolepididae. Illinois Biol. Monogr. 10. 1929. The genus Diorchis. Jour. Parasitol. 15. **Meggitt, F. J.** 1924. *The cestodes of mammals.* 1926. The tapeworms of domestic fowl. Jour. Burma Research Soc. 15. 1934. On some tapeworms from the bullsnake with remarks on the species of Oochoristica. Jour. Parasitol. 20. **Melnikov, N.** 1869. Ueber die Jugendzustände der Dipylidium caninum. Arch. Naturgesch. 35, Abt. 1. **Meserve, F.,** and **G. R. Coatney.** 1937. Taenia saginata—an unusual case. Jour. Parasitol. 23. **Metschnikoff, E.** 1868. Ueber eine Scolexcolonie. Trav. Soc. Natural. Pétersbourg, Zool. 1. **Miller, H. M.** 1932. Further studies on immunity of a metazoan parasite Cysticercus fasciolaris. Jour. Preventive Med. 6. 1935. Acquired immunity to a metazoan parasite by use of non-specific worm materials. Amer. Jour. Hygiene 21. **Miller, H. M.,** and **C. Dawley.** 1928. Effects of Cysticercus fasciolaris in the white rat. Jour. Parasitol. 15. **Millzner, Theresa.** 1926. On the genus Dipylidium. Univ. California Publ. Zool. 28. **Moniez, R.** 1880. Essai monographique sur les cysticerques. Trav. Inst. Zool. Lille et Wimereux 3. **Mueller, J. F.** 1928. The genus Mesocestoides in mammals. Zool. Jahrb. Abt. System. 55. **Neumann, L.** 1896. Sur le genre Mesocestoides. Mém. Soc. Zool. France 9. **Oesterlin, M.,** and **T. von Brand.** 1933. Chemische Eigenschaften des Polysaccharides einiger Würmer und der oxyfettsäuren von Moniezia expansa. Ztschr. Vergl. Physiol. 20. **Olsen, O. W.** 1939. Tatria duodecacantha from the pied-billed grebe. Jour. Parasitol. 25. **Otto, G.** 1936. Human infestation with the dwarf tapeworm in the southern United States. Amer.

Jour. Hygiene 23. **Penfold, W.,** and **H. Penfold.** 1936. Cysticercosis bovis and its prevention. Jour. Helminthol. 15. Acquired active immunity in the ox to Cysticercus bovis. Med. Jour. Australia 1. **Penfold, W., H. Penfold,** and **M. Phillips.** 1936. Ridding pasture of Taenia saginata ova. Jour. Helminthol. 14. 1937. Taenia saginata: its growth and propagation. Jour. Helminthol. 14. **Penrose, F. G.** 1882. Cysticercus from the peritoneal cavity of a dog. Ann. Mag. Natur. Hist., ser. 5, 10. **Ransom, B. H.** 1905. The gid parasite, its presence in American sheep. Bull. Bur. Animal Industry, U.S. Dept. Agricult. 66. 1909. The taenioid cestodes of North American birds. Bull. U.S. Nation. Mus. 69. **Rees, Gwendolen.** 1933. Studies on Cittotaenia pectinata. Proc. Zool. Soc. London. **Reid, W. M.** 1942. Certain nutritional requirements of the fowl cestode Raillietina cesticillus. Jour. Parasitol. 28. 1947. Penetration glands in cyclophyllidean oncospheres. Jour. Parasitol. 33. **Reid, W. M.,** and **J. E. Ackert.** 1937. Cysticercoids of Choanotaenia infundibulum. Trans. Amer. Micro. Soc. 56. **Reid, W. M., J. E. Ackert,** and **A. A. Case.** 1938. Life history and biology of Raillietina cesticillus. Trans. Amer. Micro. Soc. 57. **Rendtorff, R.** 1948. Life cycle of Oochoristica ratti. Jour. Parasitol. 34. **Riehm, G.** 1881. Studien an Cestoden. Ztschr. Gesamt. Naturwissensch. 54. **Rose, H.,** and **J. Culbertson.** 1939. Diagnosis of echinococcal disease by intradermal reaction. Proc. Soc. Exp. Biol. Med. 41. 1940. Diagnosis of Echinococcus disease by immunologic reactions with substitute Taenia antigens. Jour. Amer. Med. Assoc. 115. **Ruszowski, J. S.** 1932. Le cycle évolutif du cestode Drepanidotaenia lanceolata. Bull. Internat. Acad. Polonaise Sci. Lett. Cl. Sci. Math. Natur., ser. B II. **Salisbury, L. F.,** and **R. Anderson.** 1939. Chemical composition of Cysticercus fasciolaris. Jour. Biol. Chem. 129. **Schmidt, J. E.** 1894. Die Entwicklungsgeschichte und der anatomische Bau der Hymenolepis anatina. Arch. Naturgesch. 60, Abt. 1. **Schultz, R. L.** 1940a. On Tatria duodecacantha. Jour. Parasitol. 26. 1940b. The genus Diorchis. Amer. Midland Natural. 23. **Schwartz, B.** 1927a. Life-history of tapeworms of the genus Mesocestoides. Science 66; Jour. Parasitol. 15. 1927b. A subcutaneous tumor in a primate caused by tapeworm larvae. Jour. Agricult. Research 35. **Scott, J. W.** 1913. Some factors producing evagination of a cysticercus. Biol. Bull. 25. 1931. Experimental study of embryonated eggs of some Anoplocephalidae. Anat. Rec. 51, suppl. **Scott, J. W.,** and **R. F. Honess.** 1931. A study of the eggs of Moniezia expansa. Jour. Parasitol. 18. **Shorb, D.** 1933. Host-parasite relations of Hymenolepis fraterna. Amer. Jour. Hygiene 18. **Skrjabin, K. I.,** and **R. Schultz.** 1926. Affinité entre le Dithyridium des souris et le Mesocestoides des Carnivora. Ann. Parasitol. Hum. Comp. 4. **Smorodinzev, I. A.,** and **K. V. Bebeshin.** 1939. La teneur en lipoides dans Taenia saginata. Bull. Soc. Chim. Biol. 21. **Smorodinzev, I. A.,** and **P. I. Pavlova.** 1936. La composition chimique des oeufs de Taenia saginata et de Diphyllobothrium latum. C. R. Acad. Sci. U.R.S.S. 12. **Soldatova, A. P.** 1945. Biology of oribatei mites, intermediate hosts of cestodes of the family Anoplocephalidae. C. R. Acad. Sci. U.R.S.S. 46. **Southwell, T.** 1929. Anatomy of Stilesia and genera of the Thysanosominae. Ann. Trop. Med. Parasitol. 23. **Spätlich, W.** 1925. Die Furchung und Embryonalhüllenbildung des Eies von Diorchis. Zool. Jahrb. Abt. Anat. 47. **Stiles, C. W.** 1896a. Revision of the adult tapeworms of hares and rabbits. Proc. U.S. Nation. Mus. 19. 1896b. Report upon the present knowledge of the tapeworms of poultry. Bull. U.S. Bur. Animal Industry No. 12. 1898. Flukes and tapeworms of cattle, sheep, and swine. Bull. U.S. Bur. Animal Industry No. 19. **Stiles, C. W.,** and **A. Hassall.** 1893. Revision of the adult cestodes of cattle, sheep, and allied animals. Bull. U.S. Bur. Animal Industry No. 4. **Stoll, N. R.** 1936. Sheep parasitized with one Moniezia each. Jour. Parasitol. 22. **Stunkard, H. W.** 1926. The

458 PHYLUM PLATYHELMINTHES

tapeworms of rhinoceroses. Amer. Mus. Novitates No. 210. 1934. Studies on the
life-history of anoplocephaline cestodes. Ztschr. Parasitenk. 6. 1937. The life
cycle of Moniezia expansa. Biol. Bull. 73; Science 86. 1939a. Development of
Moniezia expansa in the intermediate host. Parasitology 30. 1939b. Life cycle of
the rabbit cestode, Cittotaenia. Ztschr. Parasitenk. 10. 1940. Bertiella studeri in
Macacus rhesus, morphology and life cycle. Amer. Jour. Trop. Med. 20. 1941.
Studies on the life history of the anoplocephaline cestodes of hares and rabbits. Jour.
Parasitol. 27. **Stunkard, H. W.,** and **J. J. Milford.** 1937. Cestodes of North
American sparrows. Zoologica, New York, 22. **Subramanian, M. K.** 1941. Sym-
pathetic innervation of proglottides in Avitellina. Current Science 10. **Swingle,
L. D.** 1914. Morphology of the sheep tapeworm, Thysanosoma actinioides. Univ.
Wyoming Agricult. Exp. Sta. Bull. No. 102. **Taylor, E.** 1928. Moniezia and the
proposed reduction of its species to three. Proc. U.S. Nation. Mus. 74, art. 9.
Theiler, G. 1924. Classification of the genus Moniezia. Ann. Trop. Med. Para-
sitol. 18. **Tower, W. L.** 1900. Nervous system of Moniezia expansa. Zool.
Jahrb. Abt. Anat. 13. **Turner, E., D. Berberian,** and **E. Dennis.** 1936. The produc-
tion of artificial immunity in dogs against Echinococcus. Jour. Parasitol. 22.
Turner, E., E. Dennis, and **D. Berberian.** 1937. Production of artificial immunity
against hydatid disease in sheep. Jour. Parasitol. 23. **Venard, C. E.** 1938. Mor-
phology, bionomics and taxonomy of Dipylidium caninum. Ann. New York Acad.
Sci. 37. **Wardle, R. A.** 1937. Physiology of Moniezia expansa. Canad. Jour.
Research 15, sect. D. **Webster, J.** 1943. Revision of the Fimbriariinae. Trans.
Amer. Micro. Soc. 62. **Wetzel, R.** 1936. Neue Ergebnisse über die Entwicklung
von Hühnerbandwürmern. Zool. Anz. Suppl. Bd. 9. **Wisseman, C.** 1945. Morphology of the cysticercoid of Raillietina cesticillus. Trans. Amer. Micro. Soc. 64.
Witenberg, G. 1932. On the subfamily Diphylidiinae. Ztschr. Parasitenk. 4.
1934. Studies on Mesocestoides. Arch. Zool. Ital. 20. **Wolffhügel, K.** 1898.
Anatomie von Taenia polymorpha. Zool. Anz. 21. 1900. Beiträge zur Kenntnis
der Vogelhelminthen. Thesis, Basel. **Woodland, W.** 1924. Life cycle of Hymenolepis fraterna. Parasitology 16. **Yamaguti, S.** 1935. Studies on the helminth
fauna of Japan. Pt. 6. Cestodes of birds I. Jap. Jour. Zool. 6. 1940. Cestodes
of birds II. Jap. Jour. Med. Sci., Pt. VI, Bacteriol. Parasitol. 1. **Yorke, W.,** and
T. Southwell. 1921. Lappeted Anoplocephala in horses. Ann. Trop. Med.
Parasitol. 15. **Zimmermann, H.** 1937. Life-history studies of Dipylidium from
the dog. Ztschr. Parasitenk. 9. **Zschokke, F.** 1898. Die Cestoden der Marsupia-
lia und Monotremata. Jena. Denkschrift Med. Naturwiss. Gesell. Jena 8. 1905.
Das Genus Oochoristica. Ztschr. Wiss. Zool. 83.

Aporidea

Fuhrmann, O. 1934. Un cestode aberrant. Bull. Soc. Neuchâteloise Sci.
Natur. 58. **Maplestone, P.,** and **T. Southwell.** 1922. Notes on Australian cestodes.
V. Three cestodes from the black swan. Ann. Trop. Med. Parasitol. 16. **Wolffhügel,
K.** 1939. Erbegnisse von Nematoparataeniidae. Vol. Jub. Prof. Sadao Yoshida II.

CHAPTER XI

THE ACOELOMATE BILATERIA—PHYLUM RHYNCHOCOELA

I. HISTORICAL

The nemertine worms were noticed by zoologists in the last half of the eighteenth century and were generally considered to be planarians or flukes. A distinction between planarians and nemertines was first drawn in 1817 by Cuvier who described a nemertine under the name *Nemertes* and remarked that it should be placed in a new order. Cuvier assembled the parasitic worms in a group Entozoa or Intestinaux and subdivided this into Intestinaux parenchymateux, including the flatworms and acanthocephalans, and the Intestinaux cavitaires, including the roundworms and *Nemertes*. Since this publication, the group of worms under consideration has been called nemertines or nemerteans after Cuvier's name *Nemertes* (Greek, a sea nynph). De Blainville (1828) considered the nemertines to be most closely allied to the planarians as worms without suckers, contrasted with the parasitic flatworms, possessing suckers, and distinguished them from planarians by the presence of an anus. He placed the nemertines in a family Teretularia but erred in including with them an echiuroid worm *Bonellia*. Ehrenberg (1828) included the nemertines under Turbellaria, order Rhabdocoela, by which he understood a general mixture of rhabdocoels, polyclads, roundworms, annelids, and nemertines. He employed the name Nemertina for some genera of nemertines, but other genera were grouped indiscriminately and Ehrenberg in fact had no real comprehension of nemertine structure. Delle Chiaje studied nemertines for a number of years and in 1841 used for them the name Annulosa Nemertea but erroneously included the chordate *Balanoglossus*. Oersted (1844) was the first to create a group Cestoidina that contained nothing but nemertines; this group he placed under Vermes Apoda, or worms without appendages, together with *Gordius*, sipunculids, leeches, and planarians. The Cestoidina were divided into two families for one of which Oersted employed the name Nemertina. Oersted had no correct conception of the nemertines, considering the proboscis to be a penis, but did separate them sharply from planarians through their possession of an anus. Von Siebold (1846) devised the name Nemertini for the nemertines and again placed them in the Vermes Apodes but considered them to be allied to leeches rather than to Turbellaria. He had a very inaccurate idea of their anatomy and denied the presence of an anus. Quatrefages (1846) gave a good account of the anatomy of the Nemertina and recognized the proboscis as at least in part a protrusible pharynx but failed to find any anus. He allied them to the Turbellaria under the name Nemertea but also suggested a new name, Miocoela. Johnston (1846) reverted to the name Nemertina but confused under this name *Gordius*, nemertines, and planarians. Deising (1850) placed the nemertines in a tribe Nemertinea under Turbellaria and included in this tribe only nemertines but erred in major points of their anatomy. It remained for Max Schultze to publish in 1850–1851 a correct account of the general anatomical features of the nemertines. Schultze knew the use of the proboscis, distinguished between the armed and unarmed types of proboscis, discovered the nephridia, and defined the nemertines, which he called Rhynchocoela or Nemertina, as turbellarians with an anus and an eversible proboscis.

459

The various names derived from Cuvier's *Nemertes*—Nemertina, Nemertea, Nemertinea, Nemertini—have all been employed for the phylum in recent times. It appears most just to adopt the name employed by that zoologist who first clearly understood the group. We therefore term the phylum Rhynchocoela or Nemertina after Schultze. Common names employed for the phylum are nemertines, nemerteans, and ribbon worms.

The nemertines are frequently regarded as a class of the phylum Platyhelminthes; but, while presenting many similarities to the flatworms, they are more highly organized in several respects, such as their possession of a circulatory system, the greater differentiation of the digestive tract and body wall, and the presence of a definitive anus. They are further distinguished from all other groups of animals by the occurence dorsal to the digestive tract of a long eversible tubular proboscis enclosed in a hollow proboscis sheath. It therefore appears justifiable to regard these worms as constituting an independent phylum.

Outstanding works on the nemertines are the monographs of Burger (1895, 1897–1907), the account by Böhmig in the *Handbuch der Zoologie*, and the numerous papers of Coe, especially those of 1924, 1926, 1940a, and 1943.

II. CHARACTERS OF THE PHYLUM

1. Definition.—The Rhynchocoela or Nemertina are acoelomate Bilateria with an anus, a circulatory system, and an eversible proboscis enclosed in a tubular cavity, the rhynchocoel, situated dorsal to the digestive tract.

2. General Characters.—The nemertines are worms of elongated form, frequently of extreme elongation, with cylindrical or more or less flattened bodies (Figs. 174, 175). There is no very definitely delimited head and the body is not segmented externally, although internal parts often display pseudometamerism. The body surface is clothed with a glandular ciliated epidermis and the interior consists of muscle layers and mesenchyme. The mouth is situated ventrally near the anterior end, or else the digestive tract opens by the proboscis pore so that a separate mouth is lacking. The proboscis pore occurs near the anterior tip and leads into a cavity, the *rhynchodaeum*, to whose inner end is attached the anterior end of the usually elongated, tubular proboscis. This lies free in a cavity, the *rhynchocoel*, situated middorsally above the digestive tract. The posterior end of the proboscis is attached to the wall of the rhynchocoel by a retractor muscle. The digestive tract is often differentiated into several regions, and the intestine frequently bears paired lateral diverticula. An anus is invariably present at the posterior end. The circulatory system consists of a pair of lateral vessels, and many forms are provided in addition with an unpaired dorsal vessel. There are one to many pairs of protonephridia provided with terminal flame bulbs, but in most forms the protonephridia extend for only a small part of the body length. The nervous system consists of a well-developed brain and a pair of main lateral nerves, as well as some minor nerves. The chief sensory organs comprise ciliated slits and furrows on the head,

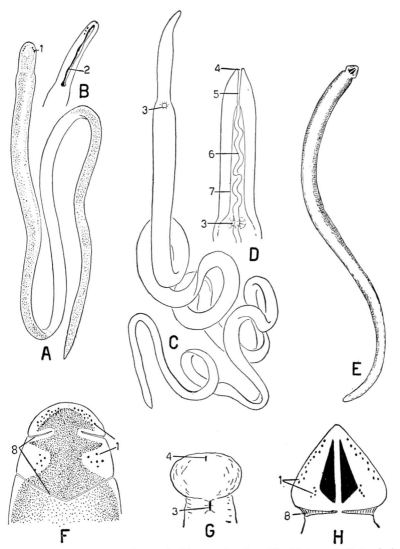

FIG. 174.—Types of nemertines. *A. Lineus ruber*, from life, Maine. *B.* Lateral view of head of same, showing cephalic slit. *C. Procephalothrix spiralis*, from life, Maine. *D.* Head of same, enlarged. *E. Amphiporus bimaculatus*, from life, Puget Sound. *F, G, H.* Cephalic lobes of *Amphiporus angulatus*, *Tubulanus*, and *Amphiporus bimaculatus*, respectively, from life. 1, eyes; 2, cephalic slit; 3, mouth; 4, proboscis pore; 5, rhynchodaeum; 6, proboscis; 7, proboscis sheath; 8, cephalic groove.

two to many eyes limited to the head, and the curious *cerebral organs,* flask-shaped structures attached to the brain. The majority of the nemertines are dioecious. The gonads consist of simple sacs, each with a direct opening to the exterior. Copulatory organs are mostly absent. Development is of the spiral determinate type and in some nemertines includes a free-swimming larva, the *pilidium.* The nemertines are mostly free-living marine animals, of benthonic littoral, or in some cases, bathypelagic, habits, but a few are commensal and some occur in fresh-water and land habitats. There are about 550 known species.

The Rhynchocoela constitute the second and last of the acoelomate Bilateria, that is, of those groups having a solid construction with all space between the epidermis and digestive epithelium filled with mesenchyme and muscle fibers. With them the discussion of this grade of structure will be terminated.

III. CLASSIFICATION OF THE PHYLUM

The nemertines are generally divided into two main groups, each of which is again subdivided into two groups. Because of the great similarity of structure throughout the phylum, it does not seem justifiable to consider the two main groups as meriting the rank of classes. They are therefore here considered subclasses.

SUBCLASS I. ANOPLA. Mouth posterior to the brain; central nervous system situated beneath the epidermis or among the muscle layers of the body wall; proboscis unarmed.

Order 1. Palaeonemertini. Body-wall musculature of two or three layers; if the latter, the innermost layer is circular; dermis gelatinous.

Order 2. Heteronemertini. Body-wall musculature three-layered; innermost layer longitudinal; dermis fibrous.

SUBCLASS II. ENOPLA. Mouth anterior to the brain; central nervous system internal to the body-wall musculature; proboscis may be armed.

Order 3. Hoplonemertini. Proboscis armed with one or more stylets; intestine straight with paired lateral diverticula.

Suborder 1. Monostylifera. Stylet single.

Suborder 2. Polystylifera. With numerous stylets.

Order 4. Bdellomorpha or Bdellonemertini. Proboscis unarmed; intestine sinuous without diverticula; parasitic with posterior adhesive disk.

IV. MORPHOLOGY AND PHYSIOLOGY

1. External Characters.—The body is vermiform, usually slender and elongated, cylindrical, or more or less flattened dorsoventrally, soft, slimy, very elastic and extensile, and unsegmented. Some forms are exceedingly long and slender, resembling a string or cord, but most are less elongated and more band-like, elliptical in section, or flattened below and convex above. The anterior end is pointed, blunt, or rounded and the posterior end generally tapers to a more or less pointed extremity or is sometimes provided with a little tail (Fig. 175A). The pelagic nemertines (Fig. 175D, E) and the parasitic *Malacobdella* (Fig. 198C) are of shorter, broader, more flattened shape. The length varies from a few millimeters to several meters and one species, *Lineus longissimus*, from the North Sea, is reported to attain a length of 30 m.; but the majority are below 20 cm. in length and few reach a length of $\frac{1}{2}$ m. or more.

A definite head is lacking; but in some, especially the unarmed nemertines, the anterior end forms a lancet-, spatula-, heart-shaped, or semi-circular *cephalic lobe* (Fig. 174F–H) that should not be considered the head since it frequently does not include the brain. The anterior end frequently bears *cephalic grooves*, shallow transverse grooves (Fig. 174F, H); or less often, mostly among the Heteronemertini, these grooves run lengthwise along the sides of the cephalic lobe and are then often termed *cephalic slits* (Figs. 174B, 175B). Eyes occur upon the anterior end, chiefly in the armed nemertines, and vary from two, more often four, to a few hundred, arranged bilaterally. The anterior end bears a pair of laterally projecting tentacles or cirri in the pelagic genera *Balaenonemertes* (both sexes, Fig. 196C, D) and *Nectonemertes* (males only, Fig. 175D). The small proboscis pore is situated just below the anterior tip or sometimes on the ventral surface of the cephalic lobe. The rounded or slit-like mouth lies on the ventral surface of the anterior end, immediately behind the brain in the unarmed nemertines, except in the family Cephalothricidae where it has a more posterior location (Fig. 174C), while in the armed nemertines the mouth is anterior to the brain shortly behind the proboscis pore or else the proboscis pore forms a common opening for both digestive tract and rhynchodaeum and a separate mouth is lacking.

The posterior end bears a little slender tail 5 to 10 mm. long, termed *caudal cirrus*, in some Heteronemertini as *Cerebratulus* (Fig. 175A), *Micrura* (Fig. 193C), *Zygeupolia*, and others. Among the swimming bathypelagic nemertines, the posterior end is flattened and broadened into a simple or bilobed *caudal fin*, and fin-like extensions may also occur along the lateral margins of these forms (Fig. 175D, E). The anal opening lies at or dorsal to the posterior tip and is at the base of the caudal cirrus when this is present. The genus *Malacobdella*, short flattened nemertines that inhabit the mantle cavity of clams and snails, possesses at the posterior end a round adhesive disk for clinging (Fig. 198C).

While some nemertines are white or yellowish, many are strikingly colored, mostly on the dorsal surface, in various shades of orange, red, brown, or green, plain or patterned with stripes or crossbars or both, in a

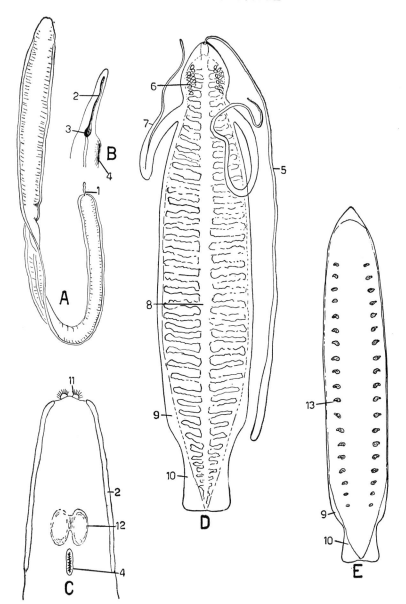

Fig. 175.—Types of nemertines (continued). *A. Cerebratulus* with tail filament. *B.* Side view of cephalic lobe of same, showing cephalic slit. *C.* Cephalic lobe of *Cerebratulus*, ventral view. *D.* Pelagic nemertine, *Nectonemertes mirabilis*, male. *E.* Same, female (not to scale). (*All from preserved specimens.*) 1, caudal cirrus; 2, cephalic slit; 3, opening of cerebral organ; 4, mouth; 5, extruded proboscis; 6, testes; 7, cirrus or tentacle; 8, intestine with lateral branches; 9, lateral fin; 10, tail fin; 11, sensory papillae; 12, brain; 13, ovaries.

contrasting color. Often the pattern of the cephalic lobe or anterior end differs from that of the general body. A few pelagic forms are more or less transparent. Colored figures of nemertines will be found in Bürger's 1895 monograph and in many of the larger articles of Coe.

2. General Histological Structure.—The body is clothed with a columnar ciliated glandular epidermis. This consists of tall ciliated epithelial cells with broad distal ends tapering to slender filamentous bases, one to several, usually two, kinds of gland cells, interstitial cells, and sensory cells (Fig. 176A, B). The gland cells are irregularly strewn between the narrower portions of the ciliated cells and like the latter may have enlarged distal ends and tapering basal stalks. The distal ends containing the secretion are of two general sorts: elongated or rod-like filled with a homogeneous serous secretion (Fig. 176C) and oval, elliptical, or goblet-shaped containing a granular or foamy mucous secretion (Fig. 176C). In addition to these unicellular glands, many nemertines possess the so-called packet glands, clusters of cells opening to the surface by a common duct and hence really representing a compound gland (Fig. 176A, B). The packet glands are abundant in many palaeonemertines (*Tubulanus, Carinina, Carinoma*, etc.) where they lie within the epidermis (Fig. 176A); but in heteronemertines they have sunk into subepidermal tissues (Fig. 176B). The gland cells vary greatly in type and distribution in different nemertines and may be definitely arranged in tracts, or some types may be aggregated in special body regions. The interstitial cells are small, branched, anastomosing cells or form a syncytium in the base of the epidermis between the slender basal parts of the other cells. Hard rod- or sickle-shaped bodies, suggesting rhabdites, occur in the epidermis of a few nemertines (*Zygonemertes, Emplectonema, Amphiporus*) and seem to be glandular products. The colors of nemertines are usually attributable to pigment granules occurring in the ciliated, gland, or interstitial cells of the epidermis.

Beneath the epidermis is found a connective tissue layer that may be termed *dermis* or *cutis* and which is of two sorts: a thin to thick stratum of homogeneous hyaline connective tissue composed of a gelatinous material (Fig. 176A) containing nuclei and a few delicate fibers, characteristic of all the orders except the heteronemertines; and a thick layer of fibrous connective tissue, limited to this order.[1] The fibrous type (Fig. 176B) often contains the bodies of simple and packet glands and strata of

---

[1] In works on nemertines the hyaline type is usually termed basement membrane or ground layer and only the fibrous type is called dermis or cutis; but as both seem to be forms of connective tissue and as subepidermal connective tissue is called dermis or cutis throughout the animal kingdom, these terms seem equally applicable to both types.

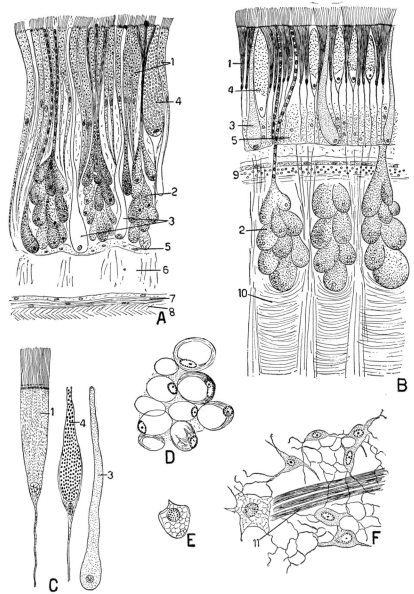

Fig. 176.—Histological structure. *A*. Epidermis of *Tubulanus* (*after Bürger*, 1895) with packet glands in the epidermis. *B*. Epidermis of *Baseodiscus* (*after Bürger*, 1895) with packet glands in the thick fibrous dermis. *C*. Schematic representation of epidermal cell and two most common kinds of gland cells. *D–F*. Types of connective tissue cells of *Lineus* (*after Nussbaum and Oxner*, 1912). *D*. Vesicular cells. *E*. Rounded vacuolated cell. *F*. Branched vacuolated cell and several ordinary mesencyhme cells forming a syncytium. 1, epidermal cell; 2, packet gland; 3, serous gland cell; 4, mucous goblet gland cell; 5, interstitial syncytium; 6, dermis (hyaline type); 7, circular muscle layer; 8, diagonal muscle layer; 9, muscle stratum of dermis; 10, fibrous part of dermis; 11, muscle fibers.

muscle fibers, and in some heteronemertines is extensively penetrated by longitudinal muscle fibers continuous with the body-wall musculature.

Internal to the dermis, the nemertines possess a thick and powerful muscle stratum that appears to be homologous with the subepidermal muscle sheath of the flatworms but that will now be called the *body-wall musculature*. The arrangement of its layers differs in the various orders. In the palaeo- and hoplonemertines there are usually two layers, an outer circular and an inner longitudinal layer (Fig. 177*A*), between which frequently occur two thin layers of diagonal fibers; but in many palaeonemertines there is an additional circular layer to the inside of the longitudinal layer, throughout the body length or in certain regions, particularly anteriorly, and this may connect with the outer circular layer by means of "muscle crosses," fibers crossing through the longitudinal layer. In the heteronemertines, the body-wall musculature is three-layered, comprising an outer longitudinal, middle circular, and inner longitudinal layer (Fig. 177*B*); diagonal fibers may be present between the first two. The muscle layers of the body wall continue practically unaltered into the anterior end in most nemertines; but in some the longitudinal muscles are greatly strengthened as retractors of the tip and the circular fibers weakened while in the heteronemertines the head end contains a dense felt work of fibers with longitudinal ones predominating. The body-wall musculature is everywhere permeated by radial fibers that extend to or into the epidermis. Dorsoventral muscle bundles occur in the mesenchyme and may form strong bands between the intestinal diverticula when these are present. They are especially developed in flat, strongly swimming forms, and in the flattened or fin-like posterior end of the swimming pelagic nemertines. In those pelagic hoplonemertines that are adapted for floating rather than swimming, the body-wall musculature is reduced, especially the circular layer, and the longitudinal layer is limited to dorsal and ventral plates. The muscle fibers of nemertines are of the smooth type.

The general body components, although not differing in kind from those present in the flatworms, have in the nemertines assumed the arrangement characteristic of the higher animals; that is, these elements have organized into a body wall consisting of epidermis, dermis, and muscle stratum.

Several sorts of connective tissue are present, comprising the dermis, occurring between the muscle layers, surrounding the blood vessels, nerves, and nephridia, and filling the space between digestive tract and body musculature. All this tissue corresponds to the parenchyma or mesenchyme of flatworms. That part of the mesenchyme that lies internal to the body-wall musculature is fairly abundant in some forms, very scanty in others where the musculature is practically in contact with

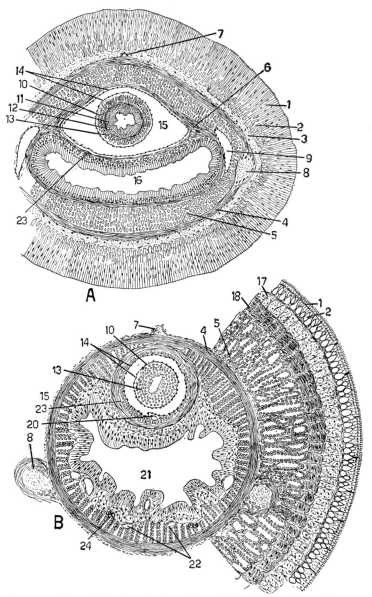

FIG. 177.—Histological structure (continued). *A*. Section through a palaeonemertine (*Tubulanus*). *B*. Section through a heteronemertine (*Lineus*). (*From slides, courtesy Dr. F. G. H. Wheeler.*) 1, epidermis; 2, gland cells; 3, dermis; 4, circular muscle layer; 5, longitudinal muscle layer; 6, inner circular layer; 7, middorsal nerve cord; 8, lateral nerve cord; 9, lateral blood vessel; 10, proboscis; 11, lining epithelium of proboscis; 12, circular muscle layer of proboscis; 13, longitudinal muscle layer of proboscis; 14, endothelium lining of rhynchocoel; 15, rhynchocoel; 16, digestive tube; 17, nonfibrous part of dermis; 18, fibrous part of dermis; 19, inner longitudinal layer; 20, middorsal blood vessel; 21, foregut; 22, lacunar plexus in wall of foregut; 23, proboscis sheath; 24, nephridium.

the digestive tract, and characteristically surrounds the blood vessels, nerves, and proboscis sheath (Fig. 178*A*). It consists of a gelatinous, nearly structureless intercellular material in which occur rounded vesicular cells (Montgomery, 1897, Fig. 176*D*). The mesenchyme of the dermis and that between the muscle layers is of a more fibrous nature and contains branched cells (Nussbaum and Oxner, 1910, 1912; Prenant, 1922) that may form a syncytium (Fig. 176*F*). Prenant (1922) interprets the mesenchyme of nemertines similarly to that of flatworms; i.e., according to his researches, there is a ground substance of fixed cells forming a syncytium in which wander free cells. The latter as in flatworms are operative in gonad formation and regeneration. The mesenchyme also contains cells identical with the lymphocytes of the circulatory system.

In most nemertines the anterior end is provided with clusters of cyanophilous glands that may extend some distance back into the body and that usually open in common by a pore situated on the anterior tip above the proboscis pore (Fig. 179). The homology of these cephalic or frontal glands with those of flatworms is obvious. The glands may also open into a pit or flask-shaped depression provided with sensory cells so that the whole forms a *frontal organ* similar to that of flatworms. In some hoplonemertines, clusters of mucus-secreting cyanophilous glands, termed *submuscular* glands, occur in the submuscular mesenchyme and open directly on the body surface, usually the ventral surface. These are evidently identical with the mucus-forming ventral glands of flatworms.

3. The Proboscis Apparatus.—This structure, peculiar to the Rhynchocoela, consists of *rhynchodaeum, proboscis,* and *proboscis sheath.* The proboscis pore leads into a tubular cavity, the rhynchodaeum, very short in many pelagic nemertines, lacking in the Bdellomorpha. This extends, widening slightly, to about the level of the brain at which point the proboscis begins. The rhynchodaeum is lined by a columnar to cuboidal ciliated epithelium, very similar to the epidermis, provided or not with gland cells. A musculature is generally absent but may be weakly present, and a sphincter of circular fibers usually occurs at the boundary of rhynchodaeum and proboscis.

The proboscis is an elongated muscular tube, blind at its inner end, that is usually two or more times the body length and therefore more or less coiled within its sheath but that may be shorter than the body (very short in *Gononemertes* and *Carcinonemertes*). The proboscis is of two types: the *unarmed,* characteristic of the palaeo- and heteronemertines and the *armed,* typical of the hoplonemertines. The unarmed proboscis is a simple tube narrowing to the blind posterior end and has the same histological construction as the body wall (Figs. 177–179). It is lined by a very tall, mostly unciliated epithelium, frequently pigmented,

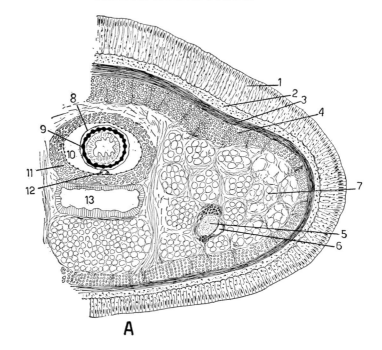

A

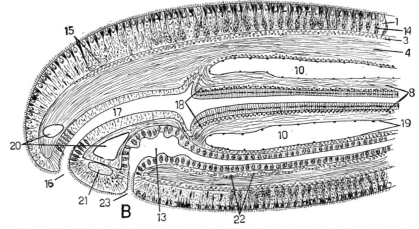

B

Fig. 178.—Histological structure (concluded). Proboscis. *A*. Section through a hoplonemertine (*from slide, courtesy Dr. J. F. G. Wheeler*). *B*. Longitudinal section through the anterior end of a palaeonemertine (*Procarinina*), type with separate mouth and proboscis pore (*after Nawitzki*, 1931). 1, epidermis; 2, dermis; 3, circular muscle layer; 4, longitudinal muscle layer; 5, lateral nerve cord; 6, lateral blood vessel; 7, vesicular type of mesenchyme; 8, proboscis; 9, nerve ring in proboscis; 10, rhynchocoel; 11, proboscis sheath; 12, middorsal blood vessel; 13, foregut; 14, gland cells of epidermis; 15, dorsal brain ganglion; 16, proboscis pore; 17, rhynchodaeum; 18, attachment of proboscis to rhynchodaeum; 19, lining endothelium of rhynchocoel; 20, cephalic blood lacuna; 21, ventral brain ganglion; 22, foregut lacunar plexus; 23, mouth.

and containing an abundance of various types of gland cells. Anteriorly the epithelium is often elevated into numerous flat-topped or pointed papillae or divided into rhomboid fields. The cells of such papillae or fields are packed with rod-shaped secretions that seem to be identical with the rhabdites of Turbellaria; such rhabdites also occur in the general proboscis epithelium when this lacks special elevations. In some nemertines (species of *Micrura*, *Cerebratulus*, *Lineus*) the anterior proboscis epithelium also contains what appear to be typical nematocysts, usually limited to two longitudinal welts; their origin has not been ascertained. Outside the epithelium, the proboscis consists of muscle layers typically arranged

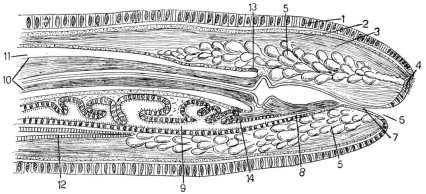

FIG. 179.—Proboscis (continued). Section through the anterior end of the hoplo-nemertine *Nemertopsis* (*after Bürger*, 1895), type in which esophagus enters the rhynchodaeum; also showing large frontal glands. 1, epidermal glands; 2, circular muscle layer; 3, longitudinal muscle layer; 4, outlet of frontal glands; 5, frontal glands; 6, proboscis pore; 7, rhynchodaeum; 8, esophagus; 9, stomach; 10, proboscis; 11, rhynchocoel; 12, caecum; 13, dorsal brain commissure; 14, ventral brain commissure.

as in the body wall, i.e., composed of an inner circular and an outer longitudinal stratum in palaeonemertines; and of an inner longitudinal, middle circular, and outer longitudinal stratum in heteronemertines; but these exhibit many variations and modifications in different species and different regions of the proboscis, often tending to be reduced anteriorly. In many heteronemertines, fibers of the circular layer cross through the longitudinal layer to form a thin outer circular layer. The surface of the proboscis that faces the rhynchocoel is clothed with a thin flat endothelium.

The armed proboscis is differentiated into three regions: an anterior thick-walled tube, a short middle bulbous portion bearing the stylets, and a posterior blind tube, shorter and more slender than the anterior tube (Fig. 180*B*). The epithelium of the anterior tube is thrown into flat-topped, conical, scale-like, or filamentous papillae composed of tall gland cells. The musculature consists of inner circular, middle longi-

tudinal, and outer circular layers.   The bulb is nearly closed off from the
anterior tube by a thick muscular diaphragm pierced by a very slender
canal.   The diaphragm bears on its anterior face the stylet apparatus
that in the Monostylifera consists of a central main or seizing stylet, a
straight or curved thorn set in a pocket on a conical granular mass,
termed the base; and of usually two, sometimes more, lateral pockets
containing two or more reserve or accessory stylets in various stages of
development.   The diaphragm contains many long-stalked gland cells
whose secretion provides the stylet base.   The accessory pouches consist
of a number of large vacuolated cells each of which secretes one stylet in
its interior.   The stylet apparatus of the Monostylifera arises as follows.
An invagination from the anterior wall of the diaphragm forms a pouch
in which the gland secretion accumulates and becomes the stylet base.
An accessory stylet from one of the lateral pouches then moves centrally
and becomes firmly attached to this base.   The main stylet is thus
readily replaced when lost.   The number, size, and shape of accessory
stylets furnish a diagnostic species characteristic.   Reserve stylets and
pockets are lacking in *Carcinonemertes*.   In the Polystylifera, a group
that includes mainly *Drepanophorus* and the pelagic nemertines, there
are numerous minute central stylets set in a sickle-shaped base (Fig.
181*C*) and also numerous accessory stylet pockets.   As the stylets are
glandular secretions they are of organic nature.

The bulb has a thick muscular wall composed mostly of longitudinal
and diagonal fibers that form a strong sphincter at each end and is lined
by a tall epithelium.   The posterior tube of the armed proboscis has a
simple columnar epithelium and a diminished musculature.

The proboscis of the Bdellomorpha is a simple elongated tube as in
the unarmed nemertines but histologically suggests the armed proboscis
from which it was presumably derived.

In 1931 there was discovered on the coasts of Australia a remarkable
heteronemertine to which the name *Gorgonorhynchus* was assigned (Dakin
and Fordham, 1931).   Later specimens were recorded from India and
Bermuda, and detailed accounts of the anatomy have been published
(Dakin and Fordham, 1936; Wheeler, 1936, 1940b).   In *Gorgonorhynchus*,
the proboscis shortly divides dichotomously into a number of proboscides
(up to 32) so that the everted organ looks like a bunch of writhing worms
(Fig. 181*B*).   There is also a fold acting as a valve at each bifurcation.
The remainder of the animal's structure is typically heteronemertine.

The proboscis lies free in a tubular cavity, the *rhynchocoel*, to whose
wall its posterior end is fastened by a retractor muscle (absent in *Cerebratulus lacteus, Zygeupolia, Carcinonemertes,* and *Gorgonorhynchus*),
derived from the longitudinal fibers of the proboscis wall.   The rhynchocoel is blind at both ends, being closed anteriorly by the inner end of

the rhynchodaeum to which the anterior end of the proboscis is fastened (Figs. 178*B*, 179). The rhynchocoel is lined by the same flat endothelium that covers the outer surface of the proboscis and contains a fluid in which float amoeboid disk- or spindle-shaped cells probably originating from the endothelium. The wall of the rhynchocoel, termed *proboscis sheath*, consists outside the endothelium of a dermis and a muscle stratum, usually of inner longitudinal and outer circular fibers. The proboscis sheath in some genera is as long as the body, extending to the anus, while in others it varies in length to as short as the anterior body third. A definite proboscis sheath is lacking in the parasitic *Carcinonemertes*. Although usually a simple tube, the rhynchocoel in *Drepanophorus* and related forms has paired lateral pockets, sometimes branched, corresponding to the intestinal diverticula; there are also sometimes one to several mid-dorsal or mid-ventral pockets.

Structurally the proboscis apparatus duplicates the body wall. The lining epithelium of the proboscis closely resembles the surface epidermis from which in fact it is derived embryologically by an invagination. The muscle layers of the proboscis plus those of the proboscis sheath repeat the body-wall musculature and in many cases comprise exactly the same layers identically arranged, in the everted state of the proboscis. It has therefore become customary with specialists on nemertines to name the layers of the proboscis musculature as they appear in the everted proboscis so that the terms "inner" and "outer" correspond with these terms as applied to the body-wall musculature. The foregoing description applies to the resting state of the proboscis. The musculature of the proboscis apparatus may also undergo some modification from that of the body wall. The rhynchocoel is a split in the musculature separating it into two portions, one of which forms the proboscis musculature while the other is found in the proboscis sheath. The rhynchocoel is therefore a true coelom, a schizocoel, since it conforms to our definition of a coelom. The proboscis apparatus is apparently derived from such a structure as the proboscis of the kalyptorhynchid rhabdocoels (page 143). In that group, it will be remembered, the anterior end is invaginated as a musculo-glandular pouch which can be everted in the capture of prey. If such a pouch deepened to extend the body length and its muscular wall split into two portions, the proboscis apparatus of nemertines would result.

The proboscis is employed in the capture of prey, also in defense, for which purposes it is shot out with explosive force through muscular contraction exerting pressure on the rhynchocoel fluid. As the anterior end of the proboscis is fastened to the inner end of the rhynchodaeum, the proboscis necessarily everts, that is, turns inside out when protruded. This brings the glandular, often papillose inner lining to the outside, and the sticky secretion of this lining holds the prey which is further

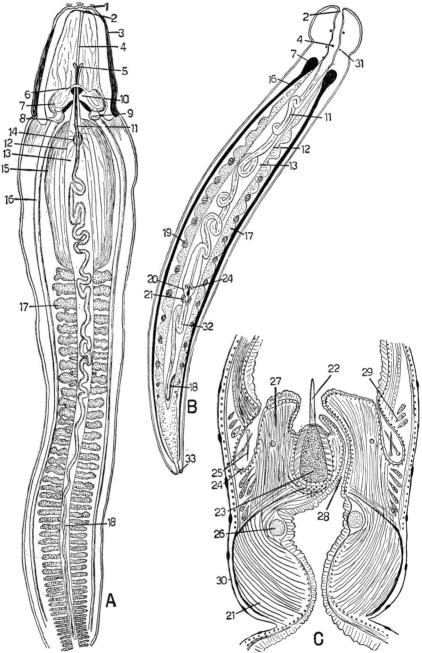

Fig. 180.—Proboscis, digestive system. *A. Cerebratulus*, seen from above, showing general anatomy (*after Bürger*, 1895). *B.* Fresh-water nemertine, *Prostoma rubrum*, showing general anatomy. from life. *C.* Stylet apparatus of *Prostoma* (*after Böhmig*, 1898).

enwrapped by the coils of the proboscis. The armed proboscis everts as far as the stylet apparatus, which thus occupies the tip of the everted proboscis and serves to pierce and hold the prey. Withdrawal of the proboscis is effected by the retractor muscle or in the absence of this by other musculature of the apparatus.

4. Nervous System.—The nervous system consists of the brain or cerebral ganglia, the main ganglionated nerve cords, a main plexus of which the nerve cords are thickened portions, and often also of subsidiary plexi. The brain and main cords are situated in the epidermis in some palaeonemertines (*Carinina, Procarinina,* Fig. 191*B*), in the dermis in most palaeonemertines (Fig. 177*A*), in the body-wall musculature (Fig. 177*B*) in some palaeonemertines and in the heteronemertines, and in the mesenchyme internal to the body-wall musculature in the hoplonemertines and Bdellomorpha (Fig. 178*A*). Among the nemertines there thus occurs a gradual sinking of the nervous system from its original epidermal to an inner mesenchymal position, as was also noted among the Turbellaria.

The brain is usually four-lobed, consisting on each side of a dorsal and a ventral ganglion more or less fused (Fig. 181*D*); in the Bdellomorpha there is a single ganglion on each side (Fig. 190*C*). The two dorsal ganglia are united by a *dorsal commissure* passing above the rhynchodaeum, and the ventral ganglia are similarly connected by a *ventral commissure* beneath the rhynchodaeum; consequently the brain forms a ring through which the proboscis apparatus passes (Fig. 182*B*). The ventral ganglia continue into the two large lateral nerve cords that proceed posteriorly in a lateral or ventrolateral position, lying in epidermis, dermis, musculature, or mesenchyme as already noted, and unite near the anus by an *anal commissure* situated either dorsal or ventral to the intestine.

In addition to the main lateral cords, a number of minor nerves, really ganglionated cords, are present. From the anterior faces of the cerebral ganglia cephalic nerves (Fig. 181*D*) extend forward to the anterior tip and to the eyes and other sensory structures of the anterior end. In the pelagic and other hoplonemertines a pair of dorsolateral nerves proceeds from the posterior face of the dorsal ganglia backward alongside the proboscis sheath. In most nemertines there is present a *middorsal* or *dorsomedian* nerve (Fig. 182*B*) that usually arises from the dorsal com-

---

1, sensory papillae; 2, proboscis pore; 3, cephalic slits; 4, rhynchodaeum; 5, place of attachment of proboscis to rhynchodaeum; 6, dorsal brain commissure; 7, brain; 8, canal of cerebral organ; 9, cerebral organ; 10, ventral brain commissure; 11, proboscis; 12, proboscis sheath; 13, rhynchocoel; 14, mouth; 15, foregut; 16, lateral nerve cord; 17, intestinal diverticula; 18, retractor muscle of proboscis; 19, gonads; 20, stylet apparatus of proboscis; 21, bulb; 22, central stylet; 23, stylet base; 24, lateral pockets; 25, accessory stylets; 26, nerves; 27, diaphragm; 28, canal through diaphragm; 29, gland cells; 30, endothelium; 31, eyes; 32, posterior tube; 33, anus.

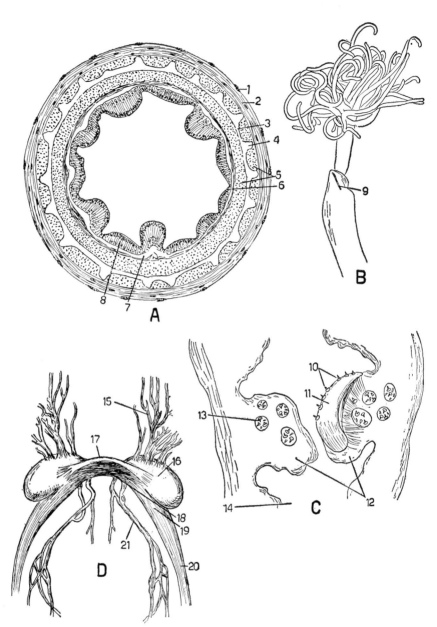

Fig. 181.—Proboscis, nervous system.   A. Section through the proboscis of a pelagic hoplonemertine (*Nectonemertes*), showing numerous nerves united into a ring (*after Coe*, 1926).   B. *Gorgonorhynchus* with extruded proboscis (*after Dakin and Fordham*, 1936). C. Stylet apparatus of one of the Polystylifera (*Pelagonemertes*) with numerous central stylets on a sickle base (*after Coe*, 1926).   D. Brain of *Tubulanus* (*after Bürger*, 1895).   1, endothelium; 2, circular muscle layer; 3, nerve ring; 4, nerve; 5, longitudinal muscle layer; 6, inner circular layer; 7, dermis; 8, epithelium; 9, cephalic slit; 10, central stylets; 11, base; 12, diaphragm; 13, lateral pockets with accessory stylets; 14, posterior tube; 15, cephalic nerves; 16, dorsal ganglion; 17, dorsal commissure; 18, ventral commissure; 19, ventral ganglion; 20, lateral nerve cord; 21, foregut nerves.

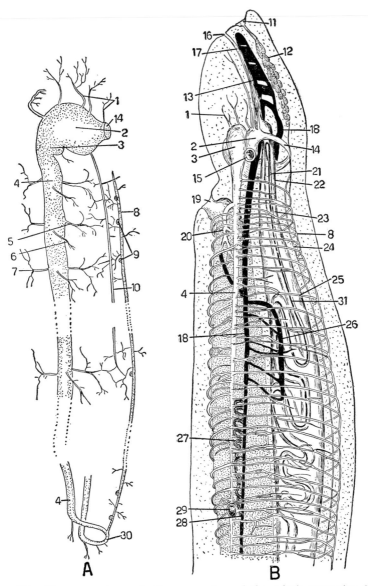

FIG. 182.—Nervous system. *A.* Nervous system of the pelagic nemertine *Neuro-nemertes* (*after Coe*, 1933) with ganglionic swellings on the middorsal nerve. *B.* Side view of the anterior part of *Tubulanus* (*after Bürger*, 1895), showing nervous, circulatory, and digestive systems; circulatory system black. 1, cephalic nerves; 2, dorsal ganglion; 3, ventral ganglion; 4, lateral nerve cord; 5, dorsal peripheral branch; 6, lateral peripheral branch; 7, ventral peripheral branch; 8, middorsal nerve; 9, ganglionic swellings of latter; 10, dorsolateral nerve; 11, pore of frontal gland; 12, frontal glands; 13, cephalic lacunae; 14, dorsal commissure; 15, cerebral organ; 16, proboscis pore; 17, rhynchodaeum; 18, lateral blood vessel; 19, mouth; 20, foregut nerves; 21, proboscis, 22, proboscis sheath; 23, rhynchocoel; 24, lower dorsal nerve; 25, transverse commissure; 26, rhynchocoel vessels; 27, nephridium; 28, nephridiopore; 29, lateral sensory organ; 30, anal commissure; 31, proboscis nerve.

477

missure and runs the body length; but in the pelagic nemertines it is not directly connected with the brain (Fig. 182*A*). This middorsal nerve lies in the same position with respect to the body-wall layers as do the lateral nerves of the same animal except in hoplonemertines where it lies just inside the dermis.   It may give off a *lower dorsal* nerve (Fig. 182*B*) running just beneath itself and innervating the proboscis sheath.   A pair of *foregut* or *esophageal* nerves (Fig. 181*D*) springs from the ventral ganglia or ventral brain commissure, passes to the foregut, and runs posteriorly in the foregut wall in which transverse connections occur between the two nerves of the pair.   A *mid-ventral* nerve is present in the body-wall musculature in some palaeonemertines.   In the unarmed nemertines the proboscis wall is supplied by a pair of proboscis nerves that arise from the ventral commissure and course in the proboscis beneath the lining epithelium or between the muscle layers.   Here they form part of a cylindrical plexus in the proboscis wall.   The armed proboscis is innervated by a number (7 to 50 in different species) of nerves that either spring directly from the anterior face of the cerebral ganglia or arise by the branching of a pair of nerves of such origin. These proboscidial nerves run in a circle in the proboscis wall (Fig. 181*A*), anteriorly in the longitudinal muscle layer, which is thus split into two cylinders, posteriorly (behind the stylet apparatus) beneath the lining epithelium.   They are united by a network of fibers into a plexus in the proboscis wall, and from this plexus radial fibers may extend to form additional plexi, one beneath the epithelium and one inside the outer circular muscle layer.   In the diaphragm and bulb the proboscidial nerves are united by one or more ring commissures and give off nerves into the stylet apparatus.

Among the palaeo- and heteronemertines the lateral cords are connected with each other and with the middorsal nerve by numerous more or less irregularly disposed commissures (Fig. 182*B*).   These commissures form part of a general plexus that lies in the same situation in the body wall as do the main nerve cords.   In the hoplonemertines, the nervous system is best known for the pelagic forms (Coe, 1926); in these each lateral cord gives off at regular intervals between successive intestinal diverticula three main and some smaller branches (Fig. 182*A*). These branches, the *dorsal*, *lateral*, and *ventral peripheral* nerves, supply the body wall in their respective locations and anastomose with each other in the general intermuscular plexus that lies between the outer circular and longitudinal muscle layers and that also involves the middorsal nerve.

Unique among nemertines and, indeed, in invertebrates generally, is the presence in the pelagic *Neuronemertes* of ganglionic swellings on the middorsal nerve repeated at regular intervals corresponding to the

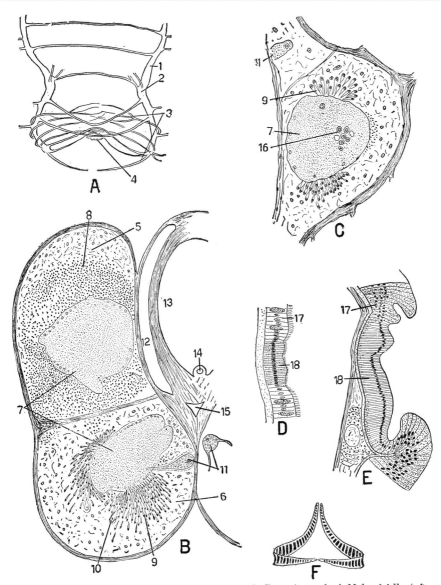

FIG. 183.—Nervous system, sensory organs. *A.* Posterior end of *Malacobdella* (*after Riepen*, 1933), showing nerve supply of adhesive disk. *B.* Section through the brain of *Cerebratulus* (*after Bürger*, 1895). *C.* Section through the lateral nerve cord of *Cerebratulus* (*after Bürger*, 1895). *D.* Section through a cephalic groove of *Amphiporus* (*after Bürger*, 1895). *E.* Section of the lateral sensory organ of *Tubulanus* (*after Coe*, 1943). *F.* Shape of the cephalic grooves of *Amphiporus bimaculatus*, composed of pits, from life. 1, lateral nerve cords; 2, ganglionic swelling at entrance into adhesive disk; 3, branches into disk; 4, anus; 5, dorsal ganglion; 6, ventral ganglion; 7, fibrous core; 8, 9, 10, three types of ganglion cells; 11, neurochord cells; 12, lateral blood vessel; 13, rhynchocoel; 14, rhynchocoel vessel; 15, esophageal vessel; 16, neurochords; 17, ordinary epidermis; 18, epidermis of sense organ.

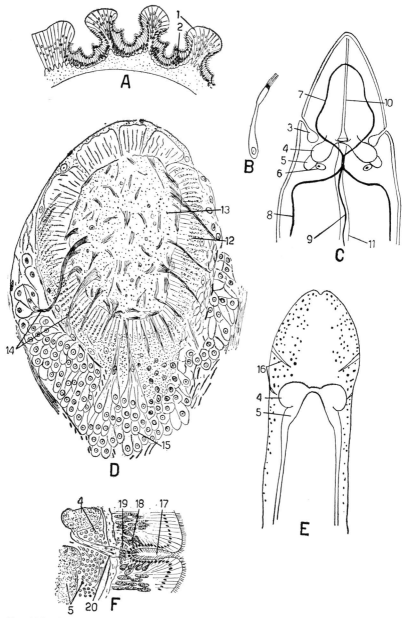

Fig. 184.—Sense organs (continued). *A.* Section through a cephalic groove of *Drepano-phorus*, showing ridges and sensory pits (*after Bürger*, 1895). *B.* One of the sensory cells of a pit. *C.* Anterior end of *Ototyphlonemertes* showing the statocysts (*after Bürger*, 1895). *D.* Section of an eye of *Geonemertes* (*after Schröder*, 1918). *E.* Anterior end of *Zygonemertes* with eyes extending along the lateral nerve cords (*after Coe*, 1943). *F.* Section of the cerebral organ of *Tubulanus* (*after Bürger*, 1895). 1, ridges of ordinary epidermis; 2, pits of sensory epidermis; 3, cerebral organ; 4, dorsal brain ganglion; 5, ventral brain ganglion; 6,

peripheral branches of the lateral cords (Coe, 1933, Fig. 182*A*). In *Malacobdella*, which lacks a middorsal nerve, the lateral cords each present a ganglionic enlargement as they enter the sucker in which they curve around the margin, giving off branches into the interior (Fig. 183*A*).

The brain and lateral cords consist of a peripheral layer of ganglion cells and an inner fibrous mass composed of nerve fibers (Fig. 183*B*) plus a supporting felt work of fine connective tissue fibrils continuous with the sheath of neurilemma that encloses the brain and separates the ganglionic layer from the fibrous mass. In some nemertines the fibrous core is separated into two halves by a central layer of ganglion cells. The ganglion cells are nearly all unipolar and are of several sorts, among which the *neurochord* cells, described only for some hetero- and hoplonemertines, are notable for their large size (Fig. 183*B*). In some genera there is only a single pair of these neurochord cells in the brain while others have several pairs. The single large fibers or neurochords (Fig. 183*C*) of these cells proceed into the lateral cords which may also contain additional, often numerous, neurochord cells. In the lateral cords the neurochords are noticeable by their large size; and, when a number of them is present, they are aggregated to a definite bundle or tract. The lesser nerves, with the probable exception of the cephalic nerves, and the nerve plexi also contain ganglion cells.

The nervous system is built upon the same plan as that of many flatworms but displays a greater concentration of the cerebral ganglia and a greater emphasis on two of the longitudinal cords than obtains in flatworms. There are, however, clear evidences of a derivation from a radial arrangement, such as the presence of a peripheral ganglionated plexus and of other longitudinal cords.

5. Sense Organs.—Sensory nerve cells, presumably tactile, occur especially in the epidermis of anterior and posterior ends as slender cells terminating distally in a projecting bristle, often noticeable in living nemertines. Sensory pits occur strewn over the body in many pelagic nemertines and on the anterior end of the palaeonemertine *Carinoma;* they consist of a depressed cluster of sensory nerve cells interspersed with supporting cells. In some palaeonemertines, as *Tubulanus*, there is found on each side near the excretory pore a pit or *lateral organ* composed of attenuated epithelial cells underlain by nervous tissue and protrusible by means of special muscles (Figs. 182*B*, 183*E*).

Special sense organs are limited to the anterior end. The cephalic grooves, seen chiefly in hoplonemertines, result from a decrease in the height of the epidermis and may consist of a continuous furrow or a row

statocyst; 7, cephalic lacuna; 8, lateral blood vessel; 9, middorsal blood vessel; 10, rhynchodaeum; 11, proboscis sheath; 12, pigment layer of eye; 13, central, possible diffractive, substance; 14, retinal cells; 15, nucleated portions of retinal cells; 16, cephalic grooves; 17, canal of cerebral organ; 18, gland cells; 19, ganglion cells; 20, nerve of cerebral organ.

of pits (Fig. 184*A*).   The cephalic slits, characteristic of heteronemertines, are deep grooves lined by a modified epithelium.   The epithelium
of both grooves and slits is devoid of gland cells and pigment and consists
of ciliated cells shorter, more slender, and of denser cytoplasm than the
regular epidermal cells.   In the slits the epithelium is underlain by a
layer of ganglion cells, and presumably both grooves and slits are chemo-
tactile organs.   The frontal organ of the hoplonemertines is a flask-shaped
protrusible pit opening on the anterior tip and lined by an epithelium
devoid of gland cells and bearing long, bristle-like cilia.   Commonly the
cluster of frontal glands opens in the frontal organ by ducts passing
between the latter's epithelial cells.   Some heteronemertines (*Micrura,
Lineus, Cerebratulus*) bear on the anterior tip three small eminences histologically similar to the frontal organ and hence supposed to be a variety
of this organ (Fig. 180*A*).   The frontal organs are richly innervated from
the brain and presumably serve chemotactile functions.

Eyes occur in most nonpelagic hoplonemertines and a few palaeo- and
heteronemertines.   They are always limited to the anterior end, mostly
to the region anterior to the brain.   Some species possess only two eyes; a
number have four or six as *Prostoma* (= *Tetrastemma*), *Nemertopsis,
Geonemertes* (Fig. 180*B*); while other genera have several up to 250 eyes
arranged in median or paired clusters or rows (Fig. 174*F, H*); and the
number may vary in different individuals of the same species as well as
with age.   In *Zygonemertes* (Fig. 184*E*) eyes occur in a row on each side
for a short distance posterior to the brain.   The eyes are nearly always
beneath the epidermis, lying in the dermis, musculature, or inner mesenchyme or even directly attached to the brain.   They have the same
general structure as the flatworm eye, that is, they are pigment-cup
ocelli of the inverted type.   Each consists of a pigment cup composed of a
one-layered epithelium filled with black, brown, or red pigment granules.
The interior of the cup contains the retinal cells similar to those of flatworms, elongated cells terminating in a rod border in contact with the
pigment cup.   At the opposite end each retinal cell has a swelling containing the nucleus and then continues as a nerve fiber that exits through
the mouth of the cup and joins the fibers from the other retinal cells of
that eye to form an optic nerve entering the brain.   The eyes of the terrestrial genus *Geonemertes* differ somewhat from those of other nemertines
(Schröder, 1918); they consist of a closed oval body the wall of which is
formed by the pigmented epithelium.   Outside this wall are massed the
nucleated portions of the retinal cells.   Their distal parts pass through
the pigment layer into the interior which is filled with a material possibly
having a diffractive function (Fig. 184*D*).

Statocysts occur only in the hoplonemertine genus *Ototyphlonemertes*
(Fig. 184*C*) where they comprise a pair (rarely two pairs) of vesicles

situated in the dorsal ganglion layer of the ventral brain ganglia. The wall of the vesicle consists of an unciliated epithelium, and the interior contains a spherical or dumbbell-shaped statolith or a mass of little spheres.

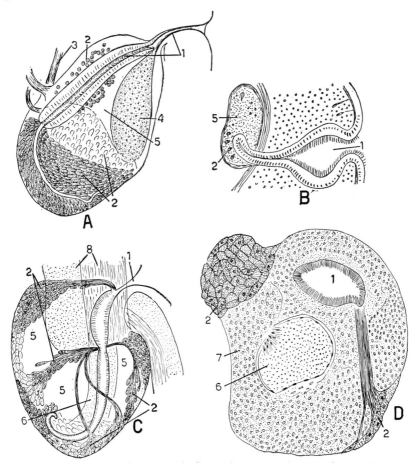

FIG. 185.—The cerebral organ. *A.* Cerebral organ of *Drepanophorus.* *B.* Section through the cerebral organ of *Zygeupolia* (*after Thompson,* 1901). *C.* Cerebral organ of *Cerebratulus.* *D.* Section across the cerebral organ of *Cerebratulus.* (*A, B, D after Dewoletzky,* 1886). 1, canal; 2, clusters of gland cells; 3, nerves to brain; 4, sac; 5, area occupied by ganglion cells; 6, nervous trunk inside cerebral organ; 7, ganglion cells; 8, brain.

Peculiar to and characteristic of the nemertines are the *cerebral organs*, absent only in *Carcinonemertes, Malacobdella*, some palaeonemertines, and the pelagic hoplonemertines. They are a pair of invaginated epidermal canals whose inner end is surrounded by a mass of gland and nerve cells closely associated with the dorsal brain ganglia. They open to the exterior by way of the cephalic grooves and slits when these are present; otherwise they open directly or by a pit on the body surface in the vicinity of the brain.   In their simplest form as found among the palaeonemertines such as some species of *Tubulanus*, they are short tubular invaginations extending into the base of the epidermis or into the dermis (Fig. 184*F*).   The invaginated epithelium bears especially long cilia, and the blind inner end is embraced by gland cells and nerve cells; from the latter a nerve proceeds to the adjacent dorsal brain ganglion. In other nemertines, the canal, termed *cerebral canal*, is more elongated, penetrates the body-wall musculature into the submuscular mesenchyme, and is frequently more or less curved.   Among the hoplonemertines and some palaeonemertines, the inner sensory part of the cerebral canal is embedded in a glandular-nervous mass connected to the dorsal brain ganglion by one or more nerves (Fig. 185*B*).   In the highest development of the cerebral organ as seen among the heteronemertines such as *Lineus* and *Cerebratulus*, the glandular-nervous mass is fused with the dorsal ganglion so that it seems to form an additional ganglion (Fig. 185*C*) and usually projects into the adjacent lateral blood vessel so that it is bathed with blood.   The gland cells in the more complicated types are often arranged in tracts or groups.   In *Drepanophorus* and related forms, the cerebral canal forks; one fork terminates in a sac and the other continues as a long curved canal (Fig. 185*A*).   The cerebral organs seem to be of chemoreceptive nature as a water current is maintained in the canal and is intensified in the presence of food (Reisinger, 1926).   However, the mixture of gland and nerve cells and the close relation to the blood in many cases suggests an endocrine function (Scharrer, 1941).

   6. Digestive System.—The mouth lies ventrally near the anterior tip, either before or immediately behind the brain; except in the family Cephalothricidae, in which it has a more posterior location (Fig. 174*C*). In the simplest cases, as seen among some of the palaeonemertines, such as *Tubulanus*, the digestive tract is an unspecialized tube extending from mouth to anus (Fig. 182*B*).   In most nemertines, however, it is divisible into *foregut* and *midgut* or *intestine* on histological grounds and because of the outpouching of the intestine into several to many serially repeated pairs of lateral pockets or diverticula.   The foregut can frequently be divided on gross or histological grounds into buccal cavity, esophagus, and stomach.   Among the palaeo- and heteronemertines these divisions

Fig. 186.—Digestive system. *A*. Longitudinal section through the anterior part of the pelagic nemertine *Nectonemertes* (*after Coe*, 1926). *B*, *C*. Anterior and posterior parts of the digestive system of the palaeonemertine *Carinoma* (*after Coe*, 1905). *D*. Digestive system of *Amphiporus* with pyloric tube and branched caecum (*after Coe*, 1905). *E*. Intestinal epithelium of *Lineus* (*from slide, courtesy Dr. J. F. G. Wheeler*). 1, proboscis pore; 2, proboscis sheath; 3, rhynchodaeum; 4, mouth; 5, stomach; 6, ventral ganglion; 7, dorsal ganglion; 8, caecum; 9, branches of caecum; 10, intestine; 11, intestinal branches; 12, eosinophilous gland cells; 13, esophagus; 14, lateral nerve cord; 15, gonads; 16, anus; 17, pylorus; 18, place of entrance of pylorus into intestine; 19, esophagus.

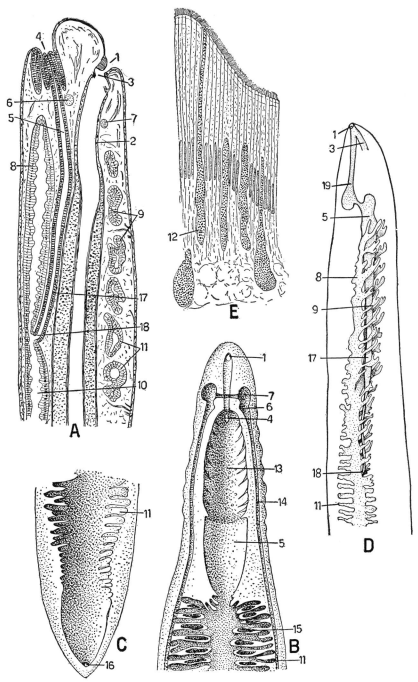

FIG. 186.—For descriptive legend see opposite page.

of the foregut are usually not evident externally but in the hoplonemertines the small buccal cavity is followed by a slender or broad esophagus succeeded by the enlarged bulbous stomach (Fig. 186*B*, *D*). In many hoplonemertines the mouth is lost during development and the esophagus then opens directly into the rhynchodaeum (Fig. 179); among the pelagic hoplonemertines the foregut is greatly shortened so that the stomach follows the buccal cavity almost directly or may open directly into the rhynchodaeum (Fig. 186*A*). From the stomach in the hoplonemertines, a long or short *pyloric tube* enters the dorsal wall of the intestine whose anterior end thus projects forward under the foregut as a blind *caecum* also provided with paired lateral diverticula (Fig. 186*D*). In the Bdellomorpha, the foregut forms an enlarged papillose chamber to whose roof the anterior end of the proboscis is attached and from which the simple coiled intestine extends to the anus (Figs. 190*C*, 198*C*). As already noted, the intestine in most nemertines is provided with lateral diverticula that may branch distally (Fig. 186*D*) and are often so long that they curve dorsally around the proboscis sheath; they usually decrease in size posteriorly. They are sometimes absent from the anterior part of the intestine. At the posterior end a very short, occasionally longer, portion free of diverticula leads to the anus (Fig. 186*C*).

The epithelium of lips and buccal cavity resembles the epidermis, consisting of attenuated epithelial cells with filamentous bases interspersed with gland cells, mostly of the mucous type. In some forms, as *Cerebratulus*, the beginning of the buccal cavity is encircled by a girdle of long-necked salivary gland cells. The esophagus has a lower ciliated epithelium devoid of gland cells while the stomach epithelium is rich in gland cells of the granular type, presumably secretory. The intestinal epithelium consists usually of attenuated ciliated cells containing a variety of inclusions and of elongated eosinophilous gland cells (Fig. 186*E*).

The digestive tract is usually not provided with its own musculature. In many cases the body-wall musculature extends to the digestive tube (Fig. 177). Where the innermost body muscle layer is circular, as in a number of palaeonemertines, this is closely applied to the digestive tract and embraces this and the proboscis apparatus in one muscular sheath (Fig. 177*A*). Otherwise, the inner longitudinal layer comes in contact with the digestive tube, or else the latter is surrounded by mesenchyme. Generally, however, the posterior part of the foregut, or stomach when this is differentiated, is provided with muscle fibers, chiefly longitudinal, that derive from the body-wall musculature. The intestine may have a very thin layer of circular fibers.

7. Circulatory System.—The nemertines are the lowest animals to be provided with a circulatory or blood-vascular system. This system is of

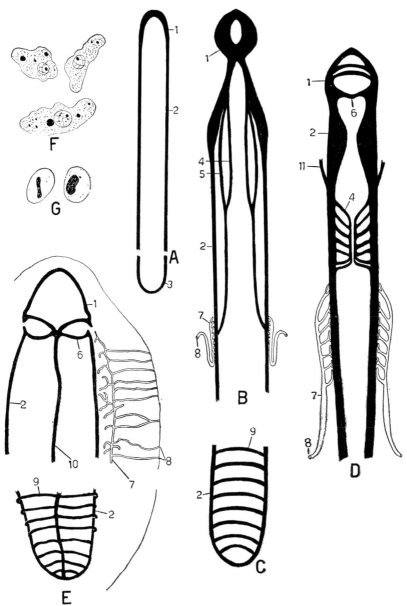

FIG. 187.—Circulatory system. *A.* Circulatory system of *Cephalothrix.* *B, C.* Circu‑ latory system of *Carinoma.* *D.* Circulatory system of *Tubulanus.* *E.* Circulatory sys‑ tem of *Amphiporus.* (*A, E, after Oudemans,* 1885; *others after Bürger,* 1895.) *F.* Lympho‑ cytes of *Malacobdella* (*after Riepen,* 1933). *G.* Red blood cells of *Drepanophorus* (*after Prenant,* 1922). 1, cephalic lacuna; 2, lateral blood vessel; 3, anal lacuna; 4, rhynchocoel vessel; 5, lateral rhynchocoel vessel; 6, ventral connective; 7, nephridium; 8, nephridiopore; 9, connectives; 10, middorsal vessel; 11, esophageal branch.

the *closed* type (see page 42) and consists of two kinds of channels: *blood vessels* with definite walls, and *lacunae*, mesenchymal spaces lined only by a delicate membrane. In its simplest condition as seen in the palaeonemertine family Cephalothricidae, the system comprises a pair of lateral vessels that run in the mesenchyme alongside the digestive tract and are confluent above the rhynchodaeum by a *cephalic lacuna* and posteriorly below the anus by an *anal lacuna* (Fig. 187*A*). There are no principal branches. In other palaeonemertines, various additions to this system occur, chiefly: extension and subdivision of the cephalic lacuna (Fig. 187*B, D*); an esophageal lacuna in the foregut region; a pair of rhynchocoel vessels that spring from the lateral vessels by several roots, run in the proboscis sheath, and join the lateral vessels again (Fig. 187*B, D*); a similar pair of lateral rhynchocoel vessels that run alongside (but not in) the proboscis sheath (Fig. 187*B*); and transverse posterior connections between the lateral vessels (Fig. 187*C*).

In some palaeonemertines and in the heteronemertines, the lateral vessels are connected below the rhynchodaeum by a *ventral connective* (Fig. 187*E*) and from this there springs a *middorsal* vessel that runs at first in the rhynchocoel floor but more posteriorly descends to a position between the proboscis sheath and the roof of the digestive tract (Figs. 187*E*, 188*A*). It connects with the lateral vessels in the intestinal region by transverse vessels between the intestinal diverticula and at the posterior end unites with the lateral vessels by way of the anal lacuna (Fig. 188*C*). In the region of the foregut, the lateral vessels give off a complicated network of lacunae embracing the wall of the foregut. Rhynchocoel and lateral rhynchocoel vessels are usually absent in heteronemertines.

In the hoplonemertines the system is similar, consisting of the middorsal and lateral vessels united throughout the intestinal region by regularly repeated transverse connections (Fig. 187*E*). Anteriorly the system is simpler without cephalic or foregut lacunar networks. In *Malacobdella*, the same three vessels are present and the lateral vessels branch extensively into the gonads, digestive system, and adhesive disk (Fig. 188*D*).

The wall of the larger contractile vessels consists of four layers (Fig. 188*E*): the lining endothelium, flat or of bulging cells, a thick connective tissue layer of homogeneous gelatinous material, a circular muscle layer, and an outer nonnucleated covering layer. The smaller noncontractile vessels have simple walls of inner endothelium, outer epithelium, and a membrane between (Fig. 188*F*). In many hoplonemertines, the gelatinous layer contains cap-shaped cells that on contraction of the vessel protrude into the lumen and apparently act as valves, although this interpretation is disputed.

The blood is usually colorless, although it may be yellow, green,

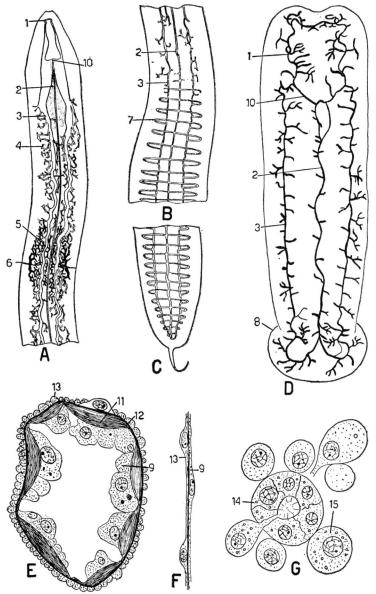

Fig. 188.—Circulatory system (continued). *A, B, C*. Circulatory system of *Ceret-bratulus* (*after Coe*, 1895). *D*. Circulatory system of *Malacobdella* (*combined from Bürger*, 1895, *and Riepen*, 1933.) *E*. Section of a contractile blood vessel. *F*. Section of a noncontractile blood vessel. *G*. Section of the nephridial tubule of *Malacobdella*, showing athrocytes. (*E–G, after Riepen*, 1933.) 1, cephalic lacuna; 2, middorsal vessel; 3, lateral vessel; 4, esophageal plexus; 5, nephridium; 6, neohridiopore; 7, connectives between middorsal and lateral vessels; 8, adhesive disk; 9, lining endothelium; 10, ventral connective; 11, gelatinous layer; 12, circular muscle layer; 13, outer layer; 14 nephridial tubule; 15, athrocytes.

orange, or red. It consists of a colorless fluid in which float blood corpuscles, small oval or rounded flattened nucleated disks, immobile or
capable of slight change of shape (Fig. 187*G*); there may also be present
amoeboid lymphocytes similar to the free cells of the mesenchyme (Fig.
187*F*). In *Lineus*, Ohuye (1942) found four sorts of lymphocytes:
hyaline amoebocytes with clear cytoplasm, eosinophilic amoebocytes with
fine or coarse eosinophilous granules, basophilic amoebocytes with
granules staining with basic dyes, and spindle cells, fusiform cells that
put out filamentous pseudopods. When the blood is colored the color
resides in the corpuscles. These are red in a few nemertines; and, according to Lankester (1872) and Hubrecht (1880), the red substance is haemoglobin as determined by spectroscopic examination. The red pigment
also occurs around the brain and main nerves in some species. The
occurrence of haemoglobins in invertebrates is usually associated with
life in oxygen-poor habitats.

    8. Excretory System.—Nephridia are present except in the bathy-
pelagic nemertines. Primitively they consist of a pair of protonephridial
tubules that are generally limited to the foregut region and open there by
a nephridiopore on each side (Fig. 182*B*). The tubule extends anteriorly
from the pore, usually in close contact with the lateral blood vessel. In
most palaeonemertines, the tubule without branching gives off a number
of terminal flame bulbs that push in the wall of the vessel (Fig. 187*D*).
The vessel wall may disappear so that the flame bulbs are directly bathed
by the blood, but they do not open into it. In some palaeonemertines,
the capillaries may be so thickly placed as to form a ridge in the blood
vessel termed the nephridial gland (Fig. 189*A*, *B*). This nephridial
gland seems to lack flame bulbs, and its capillaries may open directly into
the blood. In the hetero- and hoplonemertines, the nephridia are often
richly branched into many capillaries and flame bulbs closely applied to
the lateral vessels or to the foregut lacunae (Fig. 189*D*); and the nephridia
may extend into the intestinal region or to the posterior end (Fig. 189*E*).
In some genera, as *Prostoma*, *Geonemertes*, and *Malacobdella*, the flame
bulbs are not closely related to the blood vessels but occur throughout
the tissues (Figs. 189*E*, 190*C*).

    With the greater branching of the nephridia, there is a tendency
toward the formation of a number of ducts and nephridiopores as in
Amphiporus (Fig. 187*E*) and some species of *Prostoma* (Fig. 189*E*), and
this tendency eventuates in the breaking up of the original single nephridium into a number of nephridia each with an efferent duct and pore as in
most species of *Prostoma* and in *Geonemertes*. In the latter genus there
may be as many as 35,000 separate nephridia on each side. Each consists of a cluster of 6 or 10 flame bulbs opening into a thick-walled convoluted tubule from which a thin-walled duct passes to the pore (Fig.

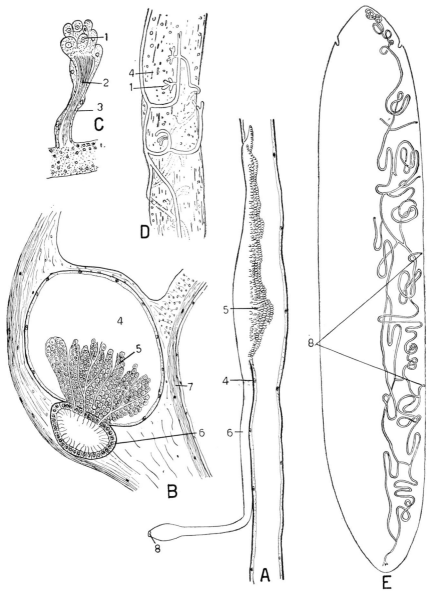

FIG. 189.—Excretory system. *A*. Nephridium of *Procarinina* with nephridial gland projecting into the lateral blood vessel. *B*. Section through the blood vessel and nephridial gland. (*A, B after Nawitzki*, 1931.) *C*. Multicellular flame bulb of *Drepanophorus* (*after Bürger*, 1895). *D*. Nephridial tubules branching over the surface of the lateral blood vessel in *Amphiporus* (*after Bürger*, 1895). *E*. Nephridium of *Prostoma* (*after Böhmig*, 1898) with numerous nephridiopores. 1, flame bulb; 2, ciliary flame; 3, capillary; 4, lateral blood vessel; 5, nephridial gland; 6, main nephridial tubule; 7, proboscis sheath; 8, nephridiopore.

191*A*).   In *Geonemertes palaensis*, a land nemertine common in the South
Pacific islands, in addition to these thousands of protonephridia throughout the body, there are dense masses of them in the head with their
flame bulbs in contact with the cephalic lacunae (Coe, 1940a).   In
several species of the heteronemertine genus *Baseodiscus*, the single pair
of nephridia has numerous ducts, some of which open to the exterior
whereas others open into the foregut.

The most aberrant condition of the nephridial system is found in the
palaeonemertine family Cephalothricidae (Coe, 1930d).   There are numerous nephridia on each side (Fig. 190*A*), up to 300 or more in the very long
Procephalothrix major of the California Coast.   Each consists of a single
bulb, capillary, thick-walled convoluted tubule, thin-walled duct, and
pore (Fig. 190*B*).   The terminal flame bulb is unique among nemertines,
being a thin-walled chamber containing a thick multinucleate ciliated
cushion pierced centrally by the canal leading to the capillary (Fig.
190*B*).   This cushion has some resemblance to the nephrostome of
metanephridia, and in fact these nephridia are called metanephridia by
Coe.   This designation cannot be allowed as the terminal bulbs are completely closed off from the lateral blood vessel whose wall they push in,
and therefore they constitute merely a variety of protonephridial flame
bulbs.   In at least some cephalothricids, the described condition obtains
in the females only; the males are provided with a pair of ordinary protonephridia, each branching into a cluster of typical flame bulbs.

The terminal flame bulbs of nemertines may be single cells but are
often multicellular or at least multinucleate (Figs. 189*C*, 191*A*).   They
are sometimes very elongated and the wall of the capillary may be
strengthened by circular or spiral ridges (Fig. 191*A*).   The tubule wall is
composed of a cuboidal, usually ciliated epithelium.   In *Malacobdella* the
tubules are surrounded by large mesenchyme cells that appear to discharge excretory matters into the lumen and hence act as athrocytes
(Fig. 188*G*).

9. Reproductive System.—The majority of the Rhynchocoela are
dioecious, but hermaphroditic forms occur among the hoplonemertines,
particularly in the fresh-water and terrestrial genera.   The gonads are
rounded or retort-shaped sacs that are usually limited to the intestinal
region where they occur in a row on each side, alternating singly or sometimes in groups with the diverticula of the intestine (Fig. 180*B*).   Where
the intestine lacks diverticula, the gonads may still occur in a regularly
spaced row as in the lower palaeonemertines.   In the semiparasitic
genera *Malacobdella*, *Carcinonemertes*, and *Gononemertes*, and the commensal *Nemertopsis actinophila* the gonads are very numerous and strewn
throughout the mesenchyme without regularity (Fig. 191*C*).   The pelagic
hoplonemertines are peculiar in that the testes are limited to the head or

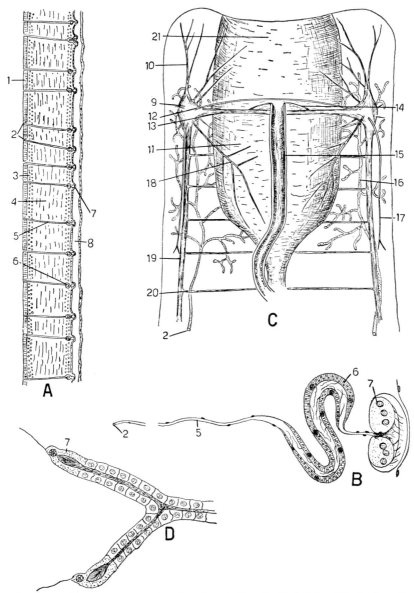

Fig. 190.—Excretory system (continued). *A.* Longitudinal strip of the body wall of *Cephalothrix*, showing a number of nephridia (*after Stiasny-Wyndkoff*, 1910). *B.* Single nephridium of *Cephalothrix* (*after Coe*, 1930d). *C.* Anterior part of *Malacobdella*, showing nervous system, nephridia, and foregut. *D.* Two capillaries and flame bulbs of *Malacobdella*. (*C, D, after Riepen*, 1933.) 1, epidermis; 2, nephridiopores; 3, circular muscle layer of body wall; 4, longitudinal muscle layer of body wall; 5, straight tubule; 6, convoluted tubule; 7, flame bulb; 8, lateral blood vessel; 9, ganglion; 10, cephalic nerves; 11, esophagus; 12, dorsal commissure; 13, ventral commissure; 14, proboscis nerves; 15, proboscis; 16, nephridium; 17, dorsolateral nerves; 18, foregut nerves; 19, lateral nerve cord; 20, transverse connectives; 21, buccal cavity.

foregut region where they occur in a paired row or cluster (Fig. 192E) whereas the ovaries have the usual location (Fig. 175E). Hermaphroditic species may have separate male and female gonads or both kinds of sex cells (Fig. 192D) in the same gonad sac; but these forms are usually markedly protandric and apparently tending toward dioeciousness. In the genus *Dichonemertes* from the San Diego region, the anterior gonads are male, the posterior ones female (Coe, 1938). External sex differences occur in *Nectonemertes mirabilis*, in which the males have a pair of cirri lacking in the females (Fig. 175D, E). At sexual maturity the sexes often display different coloration attributable to the ripe sex cells seen through the body wall.

The gonads originate from mesenchyme cells that aggregate in clumps, each of which becomes a thin-walled sac filled with sex cells; muscle fibers may be present on the outer surface. In the ovaries some cells usually engage in yolk secretion and are later taken into the ovocytes. At the time of sexual maturity, a simple short duct grows out from the gonad sac to the adjacent exterior, where a pore forms. These gonopores occur in a row in the dorsolateral or lateral, less often somewhat ventral, regions of the animal. A simple sort of copulatory organ occurs only in the pelagic genus *Phallonemertes* (Fig. 197A, B) where each male pore is situated on the end of a finger-like projection. In the males of the genus *Carcinonemertes* sperm ductules from the numerous testes enter a median longitudinal sperm duct (Fig. 192C) that discharges into the rear end of the intestine so that the sperm are emitted through the anus. It will be observed that the reproductive system of nemertines is of extreme simplicity as compared with that of the Platyhelminthes.

In most palaeo- and heteronemertines, each ovary produces several, up to fifty, eggs simultaneously (Fig. 191B) whereas in the hoplonemertines, one large egg is matured at intervals by each ovary. The eggs are squeezed out through the genital pores by body contractions but may escape by rupture in some cases. In breeding, males and females may spawn without contact, apparently through chemical stimulation; or the male may crawl over the female discharging sperm; or in many species two to several worms enclose themselves in a common mucous sheath within which the sex cells are discharged. The sperm may pass into the ovaries where fertilization occurs or the eggs may be fertilized on discharge to the exterior. Self-fertilization may occur in hermaphroditic species. Some nemertines, namely, certain species of *Prostoma*, *Geonemertes*, *Prosorhochmus*, and *Lineus*, are viviparous; the eggs develop inside the ovaries into young worms. Otherwise the eggs are laid in gelatinous strings or masses, of which the jelly is secreted by epidermal glands; in this jelly the eggs are separate or grouped inside pyriform capsules produced by the ovary wall (Figs. 194F, 199A). The nemer-

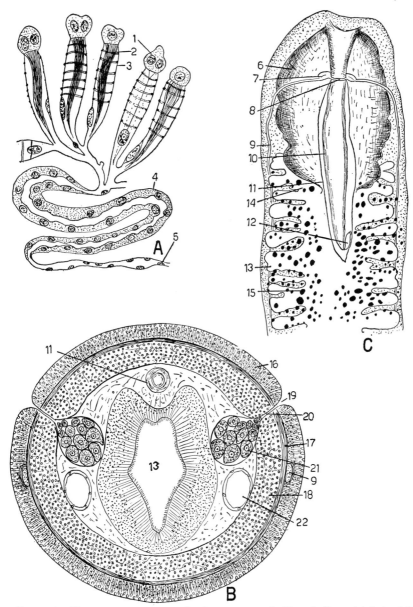

FIG. 191.—Excretory system, reproductive system. *A.* Flamebulbs and tubule of *Geonemertes* (*after Coe*, 1930c). *B.* Schematic section through *Procarinina* (*based on Nawitzki*, 1931), showing regularly placed gonads, each producing several eggs. *C.* Anterior part of *Gonomertes* (*after Brinkmann*, 1927) with numerous irregularly strewn gonads. 1, binucleate flame bulb; 2, ciliary flame; 3, capillary; 4, convoluted tubule; 5, straight tubule; 6, foregut; 7, brain; 8, dorsal commissure; 9, lateral nerve cord; 10, proboscis; 11, proboscis sheath; 12, retractor muscle; 13, intestine; 14, intestinal caecum; 15, gonads; 16, epidermis; 17, circular muscle layer; 18, longitudinal muscle layer; 19, gonopore; 20, gonoduct; 21, ovary; 22, lateral blood vessel.

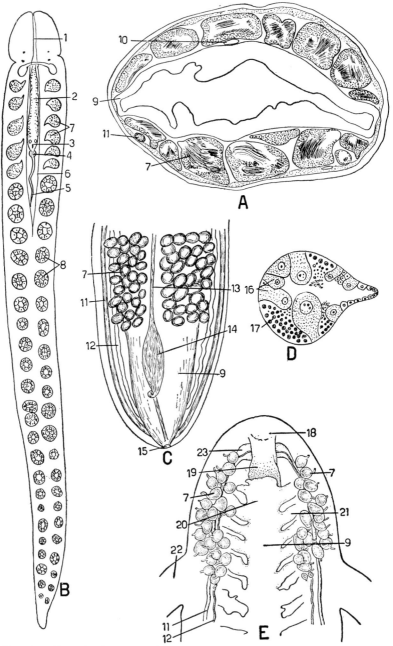

Fig. 192.—Reproductive system (continued). *A.* Section through *Gononemertes* (*after Brinkmann*, 1927), showing numerous gonads (testes). *B. Dichonemertes* (*after Coe*, 1940b) with anterior testes, posterior ovaries. *C.* Rear end of *Carcinonemertes* (*after Humes*, 1942), showing sperm duct. *D.* Ovotestis of *Prostoma rubrum* (*after Coe.* 1943). *E.* Anterior end

tines usually breed annually at some definite season of the year which, however, varies for different species. The majority of the New England species breed during summer.

10. Order Palaeonemertini or Palaeonemertea.—This order is characterized by the arrangement of the body-wall musculature, which is either two-layered, of outer circular and inner longitudinal layers, or three-layered, of outer circular, middle longitudinal, and inner circular strata (Figs. 177*A*, 191*B*). The central nervous system is more peripherally located than in the other orders. Cerebral organs and ocelli are frequently lacking. The circulatory system is usually devoid of a middorsal vessel and of transverse connections between the lateral vessels (Fig. 187*A*, *B*, *D*). The dermis is a thin gelatinous layer. The members of this order are mostly of littoral habits.

There are three main families: Tubulanidae, Carinomidae, and Cephalothricidae. In the first the main genus *Tubulanus* (= *Carinella*) with many littoral species possesses a number of primitive characters. The central nervous system lies just outside the body-wall musculature (Fig. 177*A*), the cerebral organs may be of a simple type (Fig. 184*F*), ocelli are wanting, and the intestine lacks lateral diverticula (Fig. 182*B*). The anterior end usually bears a rounded, flattened cephalic lobe, broader than the neck (Fig. 193*A*). Some other genera are *Procarinina* and *Carinina* with the nervous system in the base of the epidermis (Fig. 191*B*) and with cerebral organs in the form of canals. *Carinoma*, the only genus of the Carinomidae, lacks ocelli, cerebral organs, and cephalic grooves; the nerve cords lie in the longitudinal muscle layer. The Cephalothricidae are known from all other nemertines by the far posterior position of the mouth (Fig. 174*C*). The chief genera are *Procephalothrix* (Fig. 174*C*) with and *Cephalothrix* without an inner circular musculature in the foregut region. They are mostly long slender worms without eyes, cerebral organs, or ciliated grooves, common along shores.

11. Order Heteronemertini or Heteronemertea.—In this order there is a thick, partly fibrous dermis, and a three-layered musculature, of outer longitudinal, middle circular, and inner longitudinal strata (Fig. 177*B*). The lateral nerve cords lie between the outer longitudinal and circular layers (Fig. 177*B*). Cerebral organs and cephalic grooves and slits are generally present. The intestine is provided with regularly spaced lateral diverticula but lacks a caecum (Fig. 180*A*). The middorsal blood vessel is always present and usually has regular transverse connections with the lateral vessels (Fig. 188*A*, *B*, *C*). The principal

of *Nectonemertes* showing testes (*after Coe and Ball*, 1920). 1, rhynchodaeum; 2, proboscis; 3, stylet apparatus; 4, bulb; 5, retractor muscle; 6, proboscis sheath; 7, testes; 8, ovaries; 9, intestine; 10, middorsal vessel; 11, lateral nerve cord; 12, lateral blood vessel; 13, sperm duct; 14, spermiducal vesicle; 15, anus; 16, ovocytes; 17, spermatocytes; 18, mouth; 19, stomach; 20, caecum; 21, caecal branches; 22, tentacle; 23, brain.

family Lineidae contains several of the most common and best known nemertine genera as *Lineus* (Punnett, 1901), *Euborlasia*, *Zygeupolia* (Thompson, 1901, Fig. 207) *Micrura*, and *Cerebratulus* (Coe, 1895). The last three genera have a caudal cirrus, the others not. The genus *Lineus*, with deep cephalic slits, small ocelli, sometimes lacking, and a soft, slender, highly contractile, often filiform, body, comprises numerous species, found entangled in bottom material along shores. *Lineus ruber* (Fig. 174*A*), dark red, green, or brown, is a common species along shores in northern latitudes throughout the world and has been much employed in embryological and experimental studies. The genus has good powers of regeneration, and *L. socialis* and *L. vegetus* reproduce by fragmentation (Coe, 1930a, b, 1931). *Cerebratulus* (Fig. 175*A–C*) is characterized by the large, firm, very flat body adapted for swimming; eyes are generally wanting, but deep cephalic slits are present (Fig. 175*B*). Worms of this genus generally live in burrows in mud or sand bottoms but are apt to take to swimming. *Cerebratulus lacteus* is the largest and one of the more common nemertines of the Atlantic Coast of the United States and has been much utilized in biological studies (anatomy described by Coe, 1895). *Micrura* (Fig. 193*C*) is similar to *Cerebratulus* but has a softer, less flattened body and shorter proboscis sheath, is provided with ocelli, and does not swim. In the family Baseodiscidae, the chief genus *Baseodiscus* (= *Eupolia*) lacks cephalic slits but has oblique grooves and a large mass of frontal glands. *Baseodiscus deliniatus* (Fig. 193*B*), with reddish streaks, is a common, widely distributed form.

12. Order Hoplonemertini or Hoplonemertea.—This order comprises all nemertines in which the proboscis is provided with a stylet apparatus (Fig. 180*B*, *C*). The intestine has lateral diverticula (Fig. 186*D*) and a caecum, and the circulatory system includes a middorsal vessel with transverse connections with the lateral vessels (Fig. 187*E*). The order is divided into two suborders, the Monostylifera with one large central stylet (Fig. 180*C*) and the Polystylifera in which the central part of the stylet apparatus consists of numerous small stylets mounted on a sickle-shaped base (Fig. 181*C*). The Monostylifera included fresh-water, terrestrial, and commensal forms as well as the usual marine littoral species. The principal families are the Emplectonematidae, Amphiporidae, and Tetrastemmatidae. The Emplectonematidae include the genera *Emplectonema*, *Nemertopsis*, *Paranemertes*, *Carcinonemertes*, and the hermaphroditic *Dichonemertes* (Fig. 192*B*). *Emplectonema* species are long slender worms with numerous ocelli (Fig. 194*B*, *C*), rather short proboscis sheath, and esophagus joining the rhynchodaeum. *Nemertopsis*, also of slender form, has only four eyes; *N. actinophila* is an arctic species with commensal habits, being regularly found coiled in slime beneath the pedal disk of anemones (Bürger, 1903, Fig. 195*F*). *Paranemertes*, less slender

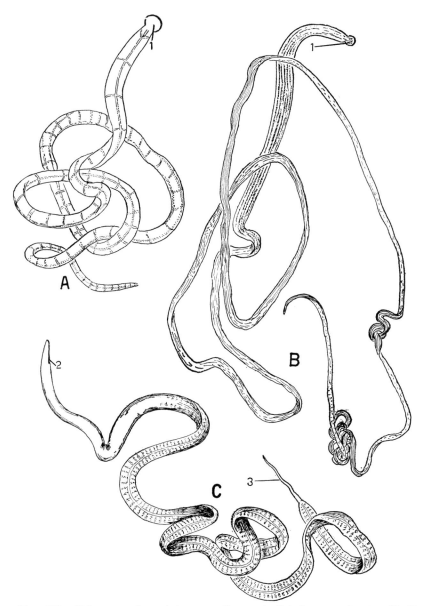

Fig. 193.—Palaeonemertines, heteronemertines. *A. Tubulanus capistratus*, Pacific Coast (*after Coe*, 1904); the pattern shown is a common one in the genus. *B. Baseodiscus delineatus* (*after Bürger*, 1895). *C. Micrura alaskensis*, Pacific Coast (*after Coe*, 1904), with caudal cirrus. 1, cephalic lobe; 2, cephalic slits; 3, caudal cirrus.

and with longer proboscis sheath than *Emplectonema*, has several Pacific Coast species of which *P. peregrina* (Fig. 194*D*) is common. Species of *Carcinonemertes* are ectocommensal on the gills and egg masses of various species of crabs (Coe, 1902; Humes, 1941, 1942). They are small slender worms (Fig. 194*A*), varying from less than 1 mm. to 70 mm. in length, with a pair of ocelli but no cerebral organs, massive cephalic and packet glands, and a very short and apparently functionless proboscis apparatus, scarcely longer than the esophagus and lacking proboscis sheath and accessory stylets (Fig. 195*A*). This genus is remarkable in having a sperm duct into which all the testes discharge (Fig. 192*C*). The young worms live among the gills coiled up in mucous sheaths that they secrete. When the female crabs spawn and their egg masses ("sponge") have become attached to the abdominal appendages, the *Carcinonemertes* move onto the egg masses on which they feed and among which they breed. Their eggs, already considerably developed, are laid inside the mucous sheath with which the worms surround themselves and which therefore also serve as capsules enclosing the embryos. The pilidium-like larvae do not swim free but develop into young worms among the egg masses. The juvenile worms either migrate to the gills of the same host or attempt to find other crabs. It is not clear on what they feed while encapsulated on the host's gills, but they grow during this period; apparently those that come to inhabit male crabs are unable to attain sexual maturity. The foregoing account applies to the best known and most common species, *Carcinonemertes carcinophila*.

In the Amphiporidae there are numerous ocelli, the intestinal diverticula are branched, and the intestinal caecum usually has long anterior branches. The principal genera are *Zygonemertes* in which the ocelli extend posteriorly for a short distance behind the brain (Fig. 184*E*) and *Amphiporus* without such posterior ocelli, represented by numerous species on coasts of the United States (Fig. 174*E*, *F*, *H*).

The Tetrastemmatidae are slender worms of moderate length without branches to the intestinal pouches and with four or six eyes. The chief genera are *Tetrastemma*, marine, and *Prostoma* (= *Stichostemma*), freshwater. The former are small slender worms (Fig. 195*C*) with many species along ocean shores; several species live commensally in the branchial cavity of tunicates. The genus *Prostoma* comprises all the fresh-water nemertines of which a number of species exist throughout the world, especially in northern latitudes, in lakes, ponds, and streams, creeping on vegetation and other objects (Montgomery, 1895, 1897; Child, 1901; Stiasny-Wijnhoff, 1938). Some species of *Prostoma* are dioecious, others are protandric hermaphrodites, and others are strict hermaphrodites. In the United States there is one species, *P. rubrum*, distributed throughout the country but usually found only in small

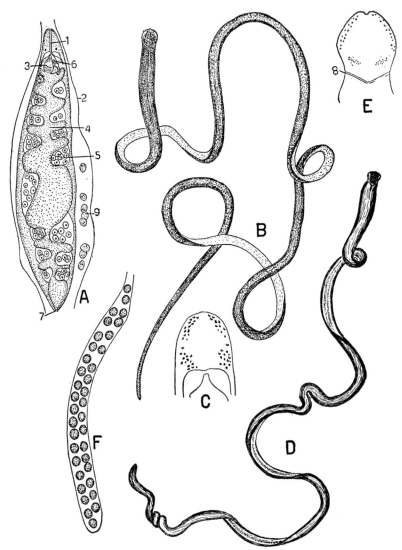

FIG. 194.—Hoplonemertines. *A. Carcinonemertes* inside a mucous sheath (*after Humes*, 1942). *B. Emplectonema gracilis*, Pacific Coast (*after Coe*, 1905). *C.* Cephalic lobe of *B*, showing eyes. *D. Paranemertes peregrina*, Pacific Coast. *E.* Head of *D*, showing eyes. (*D, E, after Coe*, 1904.) *F.* Egg string of *Prostoma rubrum* (*after Coe*, 1943). 1, rhynchodaeum; 2, mucous sheath; 3, foregut; 4, intestine; 5, ovaries; 6, proboscis; 7, anus; 8, cephalic grooves; 9, embryos.

numbers.   This is a small slender worm to 20 mm. in length with usually
six ocelli (Fig. 180*B*), and of a flesh to reddish coloration.   It is generally
most abundant in the autumn; with the advent of freezing weather, it
retires to the bottom mud.   This species feeds on small organisms and
can be kept well in the laboratory on a diet of bits of liver or earthworms
or small aquatic worms.   It is hermaphroditic with a linear series of
ovotestes on each side alternating with the intestinal diverticula.   Usually each gonad discharges only a single ripe egg.   The eggs are laid
inside a mucous sheath (Fig. 194*F*) formed by the worm while spawning,
and the worm then withdraws, leaving the sheath as a protection for the
eggs, which number around 30 to 60.   A larval stage is lacking, and the
worms leave the mucous sheath as juveniles.

Some other monostyliferous hoplonemertines are *Ototyphlonemertes*
(family Ototyphlonemertidae) with a pair of statocysts and no eyes (Fig.
184*C*); *Gononemertes* (familial placing uncertain); and the terrestrial
genus *Geonemertes* (family Prosorhochmidae).   *Gononemertes*, represented by one species, *G. parasita* (Bergendal, 1900; Brinkmann, 1927)
inhabits the branchial cavity of tunicates.   It is a sluggish worm 40 to 50
mm. long without eyes, with weak cerebral organs, a greatly reduced
proboscis that has lost the stylet apparatus, numerous gonads and a large
development of frontal glands (Fig. 191*C*).   It is commensal, feeding on
crustaceans.   The genus *Geonemertes* comprises a number of terrestrial
nemertines found along shores, in soil, under logs, etc., in tropical and
subtropical zones, specifically Bermuda, Australia, New Zealand, and
many South Pacific islands (Schröder, 1918; Coe, 1904, 1929, 1939,
1940a).   The best studied species are *G. agricola* (Fig. 195*B*, *D*) from
Bermuda and *G. palaensis* from the South Pacific.   These nemertines are
small slender worms to 50 mm. in length, of a pale coloration, with four,
six, or numerous ocelli, small cerebral organs, numerous frontal glands
forming a frontal organ, two or four accessory stylet pockets, esophagus
entering the rhynchodaeum, and numerous nephridia and nephridiopores.
Some species are dioecious but others, including the two mentioned, are
protandric hermaphrodites.   In each breeding season, the testes mature
first, and later the ovaries ripen.   Each ovary matures a single large egg
which is fertilized before being emitted to the exterior; in *G. agricola*, the
eggs develop into juvenile worms within the ovarian sacs.   Another
member of the family Prosorhochmidae is *Oerstedia dorsalis*, a minute
nemertine common on both coasts of the United States, with four ocelli
and firm cylindrical body to 20 mm., variously colored and often spotted
or banded (Fig. 195*E*).   In the genus *Oerstedia* an esophagus is wanting
and the mouth opens directly into the stomach.

The polystyliferous hoplonemertines comprise two ecological types,
the reptant type of typical littoral habits, and the pelagic forms.   In the

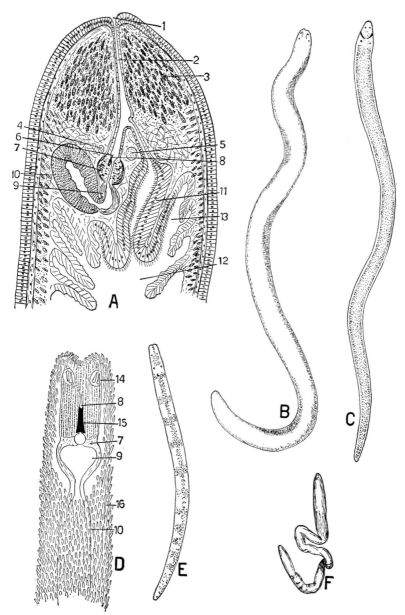

FIG. 195.—Hoplonemertines (continued). *A.* Anterior end of *Carcinonemertes (after Coe,* 1902), showing frontal glands and reduced proboscis. *B. Geonemertes agricola,* from life, Bermuda. *C. Tetrastemma candidum (after Bürger,* 1895). *D.* Extruded proboscis of *Geonemertes agricola,* from life, showing stylet apparatus. *E. Oerstedia dorsalis (after Bürger,* 1895). *F. Nemertopsis actinophila (after Bürger,* 1903). 1, proboscis pore; 2, rhynchocoel; 3, frontal glands; 4, dorsal brain ganglion; 5, ventral brain ganglion; 6, anterior tube of proboscis; 7, diaphragm; 8, stylet; 9, bulb; 10, posterior tube of proboscis; 11, esophagus; 12, intestine; 13, caecum; 14, accessory stylets; 15, base; 16, papillae.

former the principal genus is *Drepanophorus* (Fig. 196*A*), characterized by the broad, flat, muscular body adapted for swimming. There is a narrow pointed cephalic lobe, the rhynchocoel bears lateral branches, and canal of the cerebral organs forks into two canals, one of which widens to a sac (Fig. 185*A*). In recent years several genera, mostly with a single cerebral canal, have been split off from the original genus (Stiasny-Wijnhoff, 1926, 1934, 1936).

The pelagic Polystylifera comprise an interesting group of nemertines that have been the subject of many studies (Brinkmann, 1917; Coe, 1920, 1926, 1927, 1935, 1936, 1945b). Coe in 1945 reported a total of 57 species assigned to 10 families and nearly 20 genera. These nemertines live in the open ocean, chiefly the more southern parts of the North Atlantic, at depths of 200 to 3000 m., mostly below 1000 m. At such depths the water has a nearly constant temperature (around 4°C.) and a constant high salinity. The bathypelagic nemertines are broad, flat forms, a few to 200 mm. in length, and usually colored yellow, orange, pink, or red. They occur in two ecological types: floating with weak musculature and much gelatinous mesenchyme, and swimming with caudal and sometimes also lateral fins (Fig. 175*D*, *E*). The group is singularly devoid of sense organs, lacking eyes (although what appear to be rudimentary ocelli occur in some families), frontal organs, cerebral organs, and cephalic slits and grooves. The occurrence of regularly repeated ganglia on the mid-dorsal nerve in *Neuronemertes* was mentioned above (Fig. 182*A*). The musculature is relatively thin as compared with littoral types. The proboscis apparatus has a variable number of accessory stylet pockets and is provided with a large number (up to 30) of proboscidial nerves radially arranged (Fig. 181*A*). The mouth is usually separate from the proboscis pore and leads directly into the stomach as the esophagus is wanting or greatly reduced. The intestine has numerous closely placed lateral diverticula that are usually themselves provided with many short branches (Fig. 186*A*). Nephridia are absent. The sexes are usually separate, although there seems some tendency to hermaphroditism in certain species. The reproductive system is peculiar in that the testes, few in number, are limited to the anterior end (Figs. 192*E*, 196*B*), whereas the ovaries show the usual regular repetition along the body length (Fig. 198*A*, *B*). Among the swimming types with a more or less developed tail fin may be mentioned the genera *Pelagonemertes* (Fig. 197*C*, *D*), *Dinonemertes* (Fig. 197*E*), *Phallonemertes* with a penis papilla for each testis (Fig. 197*A*, *B*), *Nectonemertes* with cirri in the male sex (Fig. 175*D*, *E*), and *Balaenonemertes* with short cirri in both sexes (Fig.196*C*, *D*). Genera without fins are *Planktonenmertes* (Fig. 198*A*), *Chuniella*, *Bürgeriella*, and *Plotonemertes* with a pair of epithelioglandular areas, better developed in males, on the ventral surface near the posterior end (Fig. 198*B*).

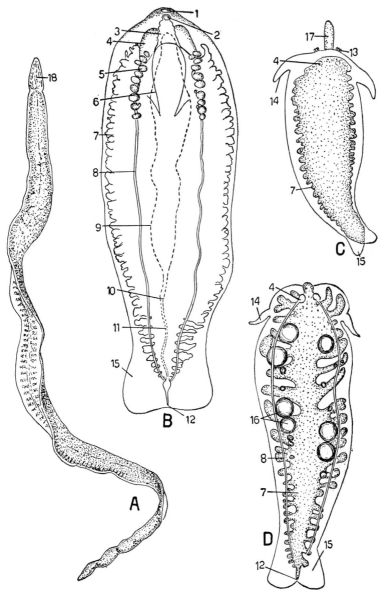

Fig. 196.—Hoplonemertines (continued). *A. Drepanophorus crassus (after Bürger,* 1895). *B. Neuronemertes,* male *(after Coe,* 1926). *C. Balaenonemertes,* male. *D. Balaenonemertes,* female. *(C, D, after Brinkmann,* 1917). 1, proboscis pore; 2, mouth; 3, stomach; 4, brain; 5, testes; 6, caecum; 7, intestine; 8, lateral nerve cord; 9, proboscis sheath; 10, end of proboscis sheath; 11, dorsal blood vessel; 12, anus; 13, ducts of testes; 14, cirrus; 15, tail fin; 16, ovaries; 17, proboscis; 18, cephalic lobe.

13. Order Bdellomorpha or Bdellonemertini.—This order comprises the single genus *Malacobdella* with three species living as ectocommensals in the mantle cavity of marine clams and one in the pulmonary sac of a fresh-water snail (Gering, 1911; Guberlet, 1925; Riepen, 1933; Coe, 1945a). The most common species, *M. grossa,* occurs along both coasts of the United States in a variety of marine clams, and is also common on European coasts. *Malacobdella* is a small, broad, thick nemertine, 5 to 50 mm. in length, devoid of eyes, cerebral, and other special sense organs, and provided at the posterior end with an adhesive disk employed in clinging to the host (Fig. 198*C, D*). Larval stages, however, do have frontal glands and cerebral organs (Fig. 202*A, B*). The esophagus and proboscis open into a common chamber (buccal cavity) at the anterior end (Fig. 190*C*). The weak proboscis is unarmed, and the digestive tract is a simple sinuous tube without differentiations or lateral pouches (Fig. 198*C*). The brain ganglia are undivided (Fig. 190*C*), and the lateral nerve cords present ganglionic enlargements as they enter the adhesive disk (Fig. 183*A*). There is a pair of nephridia in the anterior third branching into numerous flame bulbs (Fig. 190*C*). The circulatory system consists of middorsal and lateral vessels, all provided with numerous branches (Fig. 188*D*). The very numerous gonads pack the region between intestine and body wall. *Malacobdella* is a commensal, not a parasite, since it feeds on plankton brought by ciliary currents into the mantle chamber of the host.

14. Embryology.—The embryonic development and larval metamorphosis of nemertines has been the subject of a number of studies: among palaeonemertines, Dawydoff (1928a) for *Tubulanus* and Smith (1935) for *Cephalothrix;* among heteronemertines, Hubrecht (1886), Arnold (1898), Nussbaum and Oxner (1913), and Schmidt (1934) for *Lineus,* Wilson (1900) for *Cerebratulus,* and Coe (1899) for *Micrura* and *Cerebratulus;* among hoplonemertines, Lebedinsky (1896, 1898) for *Drepanophorus* and *Tetrastemma,* Coe (1904) for *Geonemertes,* Salensky (1896, 1909, 1912, 1914) for *Prosorochmus,* Delsman (1915) for *Emplectonema,* and Reinhardt (1941) for *Prostoma;* and Hammarsten (1918) for *Malacobdella.*

The cleavage follows the spiral determinate plan. Three (*Tubulanus*) or four (*Lineus, Cerebratulus, Prostoma, Malacobdella*) quartets of micromeres are formed. In most cases the micromeres are as large as or even larger than the macromeres (Fig. 199*C*). There results a typical ciliated coeloblastula (Fig. 199*D*). The entoderm generally arises by embolic, sometimes epibolic, invagination of the macromeres (Fig. 199*E*) plus the fourth quartet of micromeres (when present), but in *Prostoma* originates by polar ingression and the resulting embryo is a stereoblastula, in which, however, a cavity later appears (Fig. 200*A, B*). In several genera, cell

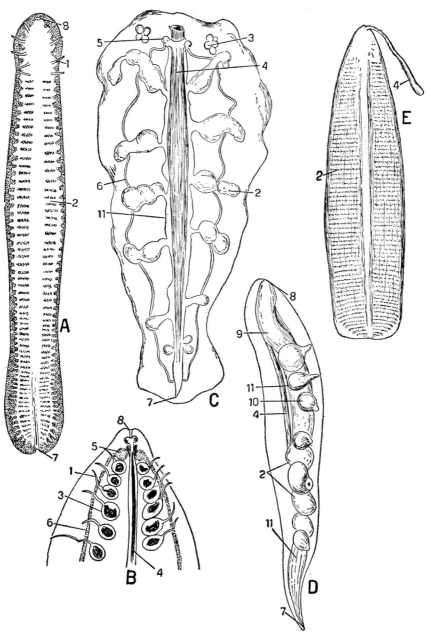

Fig. 197.—Bathypelagic hoplonemertines (continued). *A. Phalionemertes*, male. *B.* Anterior end of *Phallonemertes*, showing penes. *C. Pelagonemertes*, male. *D. Pelagonemertes*, side view, female. *E. Dinonemertes.* (*A, E, after Brinkmann, 1917; others after Coe, 1926, 1936.*) 1, penes; 2, intestinal branches; 3, testes; 4, proboscis; 5, brain ganglia; 6, lateral nerve cords; 7, anus; 8, mouth; 9, stomach; 10, ovaries; 11, intestine.

walls disappear early and it becomes impossible to follow the fate of individual blastomeres. Accounts of the origin of the mesoderm differ, and apparently this layer springs from different sources in different genera. In some forms it is known or at least probable that there are two sorts of mesoderm, an ectomesoderm from the micromeres, probably the second quartet, and an entomesoderm from teloblast cells (Fig. 200*C*, *D*), originating from 3*D* in *Tubulanus*, probably 4*d* in other cases, of uncertain origin in most forms. In *Malacobdella*, the mesoderm is apparently wholly ectodermal (Fig. 201*E*) as no formation of mesoderm from entoderm could be observed and this seems to be also the case in *Cephalothrix*, but in other genera is at least in part of entodermal origin. It may be almost entirely entodermal produced by irregular ingression, or come from one to four teloblast cells that appear near the blastopore, or both ectodermal and entodermal ingression may continue for some time. It has not been possible in any case to follow the mesoderm from various sources, since all the mesoderm cells become mesenchymatous and distribute themselves throughout the blastocoel, which is mostly obliterated. Teloblast cells when present give origin to masses of cells without any definite formation of mesoderm bands. The micromeres that do not contribute to ectomesoderm or entoderm formation give rise to the surface epidermis, the cerebral organs, the nervous system, and the epithelial lining of the foregut, proboscis, and, in some genera, anus; the entoderm furnishes the lining epithelium of the definitive intestine; and the other body tissues—muscles, connective tissue, and gonads—come from the mesenchyme that fills the blastocoel.

The development after gastrulation follows three different types: the direct, seen in *Cephalothrix*, *Malacobdella*, and the hoplonemertines in general; and the indirect with a pilidium or with a Desor's larva, characteristic of the heteronemertines.

In the direct development, the oval or spherical solid gastrula changes from radial to bilateral symmetry by the anterior displacement of the apical pole which in most forms (not in *Cephalothrix*) is marked by a sensory plate bearing long cilia (Fig. 199*F*, *G*). This plate is said by some to become the frontal organ, by others to be a transient embryonic structure. The blastopore closes and the entoderm is thus cut off as a mass of cells lying in the interior. According to most observers, the foregut arises by an ectodermal invagination (stomodaeum) that connects with the entoderm (Fig. 203*D*). In those forms that lack a mouth in the adult state, the embryonic mouth subsequently disappears and the stomodaeum connects with the rhynchodaeum. In *Malacobdella*, the rhynchodaeum disappears, the proboscis invagination connects to the roof of the stomodaeum, the primary mouth then vanishes and the stomodaeum grows forward to establish a new and definitive opening

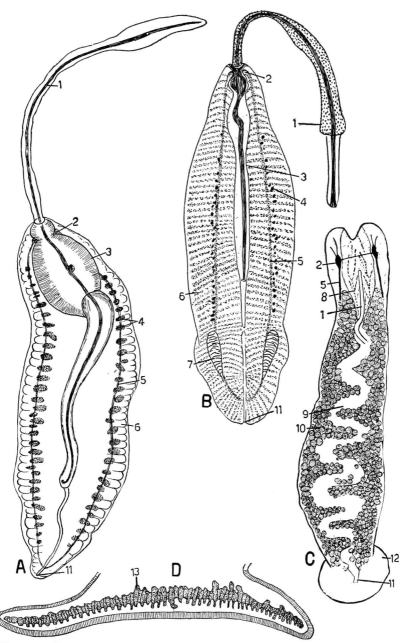

FIG. 198.—Bathypelagic hoplonemertines, *Malacobdella*. *A. Planktonemertes*, female (*after Coe*, 1926). *B. Plotonemertes*, female (*after Coe*, 1936). *C. Malacobdella* (*after Guberlet*, 1925). *D.* Section through the adhesive disk of *Malacobdella*, showing glands (*after Bürger*, 1895). 1, proboscis; 2, brain; 3, proboscis sheath; 4, ovaries; 5, lateral nerve cords; 6, intestinal branches; 7, adhesive areas; 8, esophagus; 9, intestine; 10, gonads; 11, anus; 12, adhesive disk; 13, glands.

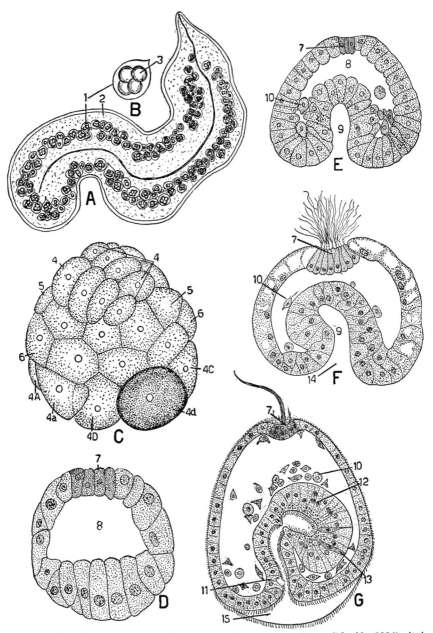

Fig. 199.—Embryology. *A.* Egg string of *Lineus ruber* (*after Schmidt*, 1934); it is doubled on itself and contains capsules embedded in jelly. *B.* A capsule enlarged, containing four eggs. *C.* Embryo of *Lineus* showing spiral cleavage and 4d cell (*after Nussbaum and Oxner*, 1913). *D–G.* Development of *Cerebratulus.* *D.* Blastula, cells of apical sensory plate differentiated. *E.* Early gastrula, entomesoderm arising in the angles of the invagination. *F.* Later gastrula, apical sense organ differentiated. *G.* Early pilidium,

at the anterior tip (Fig. 202C–E). The anus usually arises by way of a proctodaeal invagination (Fig. 201B) but may form by direct growth of the intestine to make contact with the surface ectoderm (*Cephalothrix*). A pair of ectodermal masses from the surface ectoderm become the nervous system (Fig. 201A). The cerebral organs arise as a pair of ectodermal invaginations, and the frontal glands and ocelli are also of ectodermal origin. The lining epithelium of the proboscis arises as a tubular ectodermal invagination below the frontal glands (Fig. 200F). The mesenchyme cells arrange themselves around the proboscis invagination, beneath the surface ectoderm, and around the digestive tract and differentiate into muscles and connective tissue. The mesenchymal layers that embrace the proboscis invagination split in two, one part becoming the musculature of the proboscis, the other that of the proboscis sheath. The blood vessels arise by the hollowing out of mesenchymal cords. The mode of formation of the protonephridia has not been definitely ascertained, but it is usually believed that they are of ectodermal origin. The embryo leaves the egg membranes as a small ciliated worm superficially resembling a rhabdocoel (Fig. 201C).

In many heteronemertines, such as *Cerebratulus* and *Micrura*, the gastrula develops into a free-swimming ciliated larva, the *pilidium* (Fig. 204B, C), discovered and so named by J. Müller in 1847. The gastrula becomes gelatinous and transparent and more or less helmet-shaped through the downgrowth of more or less extensive oral lobes, one to each side of the mouth. The ectoderm flattens to a thin ciliated epithelium except at the aboral pole where it forms an invaginated sensory apical plate of tall ectoderm whose long cilia fuse to one or two tufts; and the edge of the mouth and margins of the oral lobes are also formed of a band of modified ectoderm bearing longer cilia. The wide larval mouth leads into the larval gut differentiated into two portions, an anterior roomy foregut or esophagus and a posterior smaller blind rounded midgut or intestine (Fig. 204B). The latter is obviously entodermal; the former is usually thought to arise by a stomodaeal invagination continuous with archenteron invagination so that the blastopore comes to lie at the boundary between foregut and midgut and the foregut is then ectodermal. The observations upon this question are, however, inconclusive but in fact the foregut later becomes histologically identical with the surface epidermis. The blastocoel is filled with a gelatinous fluid in which are strewn the amoeboid branched mesenchyme cells. Many of these fasten by the tips of their long branches and differentiate into muscle cells that

foregut and midgut differentiated. (*D, F, after Wilson*, 1899; *E, G, after Coe*, 1899.) 1, capsule; 2, jelly; 3, egg; 4, cells of first quartet; 5, cells of second quartet; 6, cells of third quartet; 7, apical sense organ; 8, blastocoel; 9, archenteron; 10, entomesoderm; 11, stomodaeum (foregut); 12, midgut (intestine); 13, definition intestinal cell; 14, blastopore; 15, beginning lobe of pilidium.

aggregate into more or less definite muscle bands. These form a complicated system including fibers from the apical plate to the oral margin and various parts of the gut, fibers beneath the ectoderm and along the gut, and fibers spreading fanwise in the oral lobes. The pilidium appears to be devoid of a nervous system apart from the apical sensory plate. The larva swims about for some time and feeds on minute organisms.

The Desor larva, so named from its discoverer, E. Desor, who in 1848 saw this larva develop from nemertine eggs (*Lineus*) obtained from the New England Coast, is an oval ciliated postgrastula, that remains inside the egg membranes and lacks apical plate and tuft, oral lobes, and ciliated oral band (Fig. 204*A*). Its development, however, quite resembles that of the pilidium.

The pilidium and the Desor larva undergo metamorphosis into a young nemertine by means of a set of ectodermal invaginations, called ectodermal disks or plates, discovered by Metschnikoff in 1869. There are seven or eight of these disks, three pairs, and one or two unpaired ones: a pair of anterior *cephalic* disks, a pair of lateral *cerebral* disks that become the cerebral canals, a pair of posteroventral *trunk* disks, an unpaired posterior *dorsal* disk, and in some forms an anterior unpaired *proboscis* disk (Fig. 203*D*, *E*). The paired disks invaginate and cut off from the larval ectoderm as little flattened sacs with an outer very thin wall, the *amnion*, and an inner wall of columnar epithelium (Fig. 203*E*). The unpaired disks arise by delamination without amnion formation. In the interior of the larva the disks grow, spread, and flatten out and finally fuse together (Fig. 204*D–G*), enclosing the larval gut so that the united amnia form a thin embryonic membrane and the united epithelial walls form a continuous epithelium, the future epidermis, enclosing the gut and the mesenchyme (Fig. 204*A*).

The cephalic disks become the epidermis of the anterior end and give off into the interior a pair of ectodermal masses that differentiate into the cerebral ganglia; from these the nerve cords arise by outgrowth. The proboscis epithelium is an elongated ectodermal tube that comes either from an unpaired disk (Desor type) or from the median region of the fused cephalic disks (pilidium). The trunk and dorsal disks give rise to the epidermis of most of the body. The cerebral disks invaginate as the cerebral canals of the cerebral organs. The larval gut is retained; in the Desor type the foregut is definitely seen to arise as an ectodermal invagination, but in the pilidium as already noted its ectodermal nature is uncertain. Both foregut and intestine undergo considerable alteration into the definitive digestive tract (Fig. 204*A*), for in both some cells of the wall become cylindrical and cytoplasmic and spread throughout the gut wall replacing and absorbing the yolk-filled embryonic stomodaeal and entodermal cells. The anus arises by means of a small ectodermal

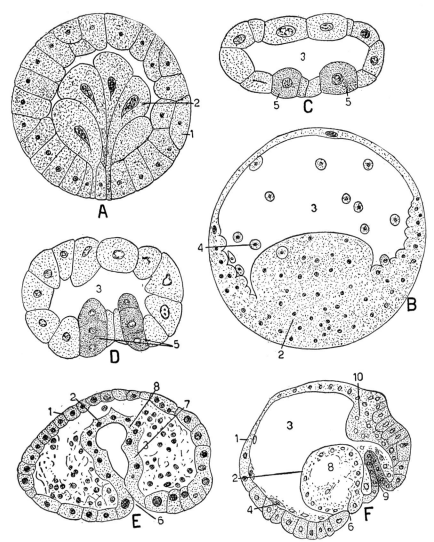

Fig. 200.—Embryology, direct development. *A. Prostoma*, gastrulation by polar ingression. *B. Prostoma*, later stage, blastocoel reformed, entomesoderm arising in angles of gastrulation. (*A, B, after Reinhardt*, 1941.) *C–F.* Development of *Prosorochmus, after Salensky*, 1909, 1914.) *C.* Blastula, with 2 teloblast cells differentiated. *D.* Early gastrulation, teloblasts proliferating the entomesoderm. *E.* Late gastrula, blastopore closing. *F.* Proboscis and nervous system forming. 1, ectoderm; 2, entoderm; 3, blastocoel; 4, entomesoderm; 5, teloblasts; 6, blastopore; 7, foregut; 8, midgut; 9, proboscis invagination; 10, nervous system proliferating.

invagination (proctodaeum) that breaks through into the intestine. The intestinal diverticula form not by outgrowth of the intestinal wall but by the encroachment of mesenchyme. As in direct development, the mesenchyme attaches itself in part to the under surface of the epidermis and to the proboscis invagination and in part to the digestive tract; both parts then differentiate into muscles, connective tissue, etc. No definite conclusion has been reached concerning the mode of formation of the protonephridia, as some workers derive them from the foregut wall and others believe they come from epidermal ingrowths.

When the development is completed the larva sheds the larval ectoderm (including the apical plate of the pilidium that apparently does not contribute to adult structure) and the amnion and emerges as a young worm. It will be perceived that the chief difference between the direct and the larval types of development consists in the replacement in the latter of the larval ectoderm by invaginated ectoderm. The purpose and meaning of this process are obscure. The Desor type appears to be a derivation of the pilidium type as an adaptation to shallow-water conditions that are more variable than those of the open sea.

In *Lineus ruber* along north European coasts, Schmidt (1934) has noticed two kinds of egg strings. One type, laid by green individuals, develops after the usual Desor mode. In the other kind of egg string, laid by red individuals, the eggs are smaller and more numerous and many die in early stages. The survivors engulf the dead eggs and embryos and for this purpose are provided with a relatively large mouth and foregut. These results indicate that color variations of this species may be distinct varieties.

Whether a true coelom appears during the development of nemertines is a question much discussed by workers on this group, and some have described spaces in the larval mesoderm which they consider to represent a coelom of the schizocoelous type. It appears to the author that these spaces are not sufficiently definite or constant to warrant their designation as coelomic or to indicate derivation from coelomate ancestors.

Experiments on the *Cerebratulus* egg confirm the fact of determinate development (E. B. Wilson, 1903; Zeleny, 1904; Yatsu, 1904, 1910; Hörstadius, 1937). Isolated blastomeres of the two- and four-cell stages cleave like fractions of the egg and form an open blastula but may give rise to more or less normal dwarf pilidia (Fig. 205*A, B*). After the eight-cell stage, the aboral half of cleavage or blastula stages forms a larva with apical plate but no or a reduced archenteron and often no oral lobes; while the oral part always lacks the apical organ and has an abnormally large archenteron (Fig. 205*C, D*). Portions of eggs cut during maturation phases cleave and develop like entire eggs; therefore the process of local-

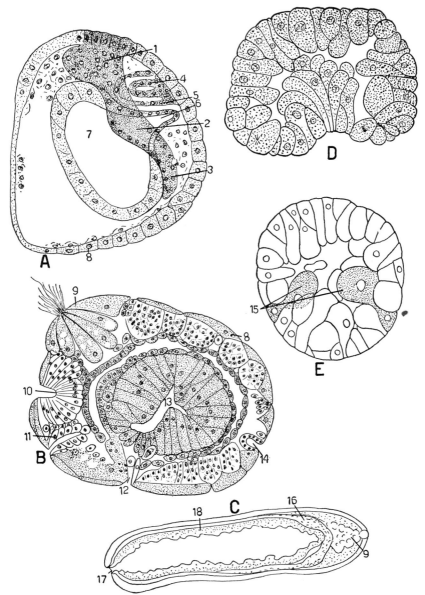

Fig. 201.—Direct development (continued). *A.* Late stage of *Prosorochmus* (after *Salensky*, 1909). *B.* Late stage of *Drepanophorus* (after *Lebedinsky*, 1897). *C.* Newly hatched larva of *Prosorochmus* (after *Salensky*, 1914). *D, E.* Gastrula of *Malacobdella* (after *Hammarsten*, 1918). *D.* Median section, showing embolic gastrulation. *E.* Lateral section, showing 2 of the 4 cells of the second quartet that produce the ectomesoderm. 1, dorsal ganglion; 2, ventral ganglion; 3, lateral nerve cord; 4, proboscis; 5, proboscis sheath; 6, foregut; 7, midgut; 8, definitive epidermis; 9, frontal organ; 10, proboscis invagination; 11, stomodaeal invagination; 12, site of closed blastopore; 13, midgut; 14, proctodaeal invagination; 15, ectomesoderm mother cells; 16, brain; 17, anus; 18, intestine.

ization of the future embryo in definite regions of the egg must occur shortly before cleavage.

15. Asexual Reproduction and Regeneration.—The nemertines when handled or irritated or kept in unfavorable conditions are very apt to break off posterior pieces and also often to evert the proboscis with such force as to rupture its connections. The breaks usually occur in the intestinal region, and the anterior portions that include the foregut will regenerate a new posterior end and a new proboscis; but only in some species of the heteronemertine genus *Lineus* are pieces from levels behind the brain capable of regenerating a new head end. Those species with high powers of regeneration may also reproduce regularly in nature by a process of fragmentation followed by regeneration. Such asexual multiplication has been observed in *Lineus socialis* of the Atlantic Coast and *L. vegetus* of the Pacific Coast (Coe, 1930b, 1931). The posterior half or two-thirds of these species divides up spontaneously into several to twenty or more fragments that may enclose themselves in mucous cysts and that regenerate into perfect small worms (Fig. 206). Longer fragments frequently break up into smaller fragments before regeneration is completed. As the fragmentation results from strong muscular contraction that is inhibited by cold, the process in nature occurs chiefly in summer. Fragmentation will generally occur after 2 to 4 days in worms over 30 mm. long if kept in the dark at around 20°C.

In those species of *Lineus* that multiply naturally by fragmentation, any body pieces, even very small ones, that contain a portion of the lateral nerve cords regenerate into perfect small worms (Coe, 1929, 1930a). *Lineus pictifrons* regenerates an anterior end as far back as the middle of the foregut (Coe, 1932). In other species of *Lineus* tested and in nemertines in general, pieces cut behind the cerebral organs cannot regenerate a new anterior end, but any piece except the extreme anterior end regenerates posteriorly (Fig. 207; Carlgren, 1907; Dawydoff, 1910, 1942; Nussbaum and Oxner, 1910, 1911, 1912; Monastero, 1928, 1939; Coe, 1932, 1934). The anterior tip isolated by cuts before, through, or behind the cerebral ganglia never regenerates posteriorly in any case; posterior portions containing the cerebral ganglia or even only the cerebral organs replace the missing anterior end.

In regeneration the wound is closed over by the migration of the deeper epidermal cells (presumably the interstitial cells) from the adjacent epidermis. Beneath this covering epithelium there accumulates a mass of mesenchyme cells, the regeneration blastema, composed of inwandered mesenchyme cells and phagocytic cells that have ingested pigment granules and tissue debris and that serve for nutrition. In the blastema three cell masses form, two lateral ones close to the covering epithelium but apparently of mesenchymal origin, that become the cerebral ganglia,

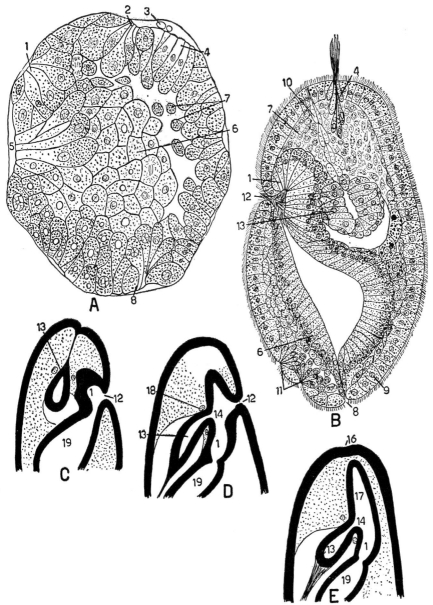

Fig. 202.—Direct development (concluded). *Malacobdella.* *A.* Embryo at 3 days. *B.* Larva at 7 days. *C–E.* Development of the definitive mouth and buccal cavity. (*All after Hammarsten,* 1918.) 1, stomodaeal invagination; 2, proboscis invagination; 3, polar bodies; 4, frontal organ; 5, site of closure of the blastopore; 6, entoderm of midgut; 7, ecto-mesoderm; 8, proctodaeal invagination; 9, definitive epidermis; 10, degenerating stalk of proboscis invagination; 11, gland cells of sucker; 12, larval mouth; 13, proboscis; 14, opening of proboscis into larval stomodaeum; 15, forward growth of stomodaeum to form new mouth; 16, site of new mouth; 17, buccal cavity; 18, brain ganglia; 19, midgut.

and a median one, the beginning of the proboscis and proboscis sheath. The ganglia connect with the old lateral nerve cords. The median mass grows backward as a thin fluid-filled sac of which the wall becomes the proboscis sheath, the cavity, the rhynchocoel. The proboscis and part of the rhynchodaeum derive from a mesenchymal bud that grows backward into the sac from its anterior end; the rhynchodaeum then connects with the surface by an epidermal invagination. The cerebral organs arise by a pair of epidermal invaginations. If the piece contains no part of the digestive tract, foregut and intestine differentiate from mesenchyme cells and connect to the surface by an epidermal invagination. Portions of digestive tract left in the pieces are worked over by phagocytic cells and connect with an epidermal invagination from which arise mouth and foregut if the piece contains none. There is much transformation of old tissues *in situ* through their ingestion by phagocytic cells that then disintegrate, releasing their contents as food for reformation processes by mesenchyme cells. Posterior regeneration is practically the same as normal growth, a lengthening of the various systems through the differentiation of mesenchyme cells.

Regenerating pieces retain the polarity that they had when part of the whole but do not give such clear evidence of a relation to axial level as do planarians.

16. Ecology and Physiology.—The nemertines are mostly marine, bottom dwellers along coasts, mainly in temperate regions, living under stones, among plant tangles, in mud, sand, and gravel, etc. Some inhabit tubular cavities that they line with mucus, and others secrete definite parchment-like tubes. Common along North American coasts are species of *Tubulanus, Carinoma, Cephalothrix, Procephalothrix, Lineus, Cerebratulus, Micrura, Zygeupolia, Emplectonema, Amphiporus, Oerstedia, Zygonemertes, Tetrastemma.* The littoral species occur in the greatest variety in the Mediterranean and along the northern coasts of Europe. Whereas many species have a limited distribution, some are widely distributed in the northern hemisphere, as *Lineus ruber, Oerstedia dorsalis, Cerebratulus marginatus,* and *Tetrastemma candidum.* There are a number of identical or closely related species on both sides of the North Atlantic. Nemertines are less common along tropical and subtropical shores; characteristic of these regions are species of *Baseodiscus, Diplopleura* (= *Langia*), *Drepanophorus* and related nonpelagic hoplonemertines, and *Gorgonorhynchus.* A good nemertine fauna occurs in the arctic and antarctic, with a predominance of species of *Amphiporus, Lineus, Cerebratulus,* and *Tetrastemma* (Bürger, 1903; Wheeler, 1934, 1940a). Several species are circumpolar. A few species of bottom-dwelling nemertines may descend to considerable depths (to 1500 m. or more), but the typical deep-sea nemertines are the pelagic hoplonemertines (page

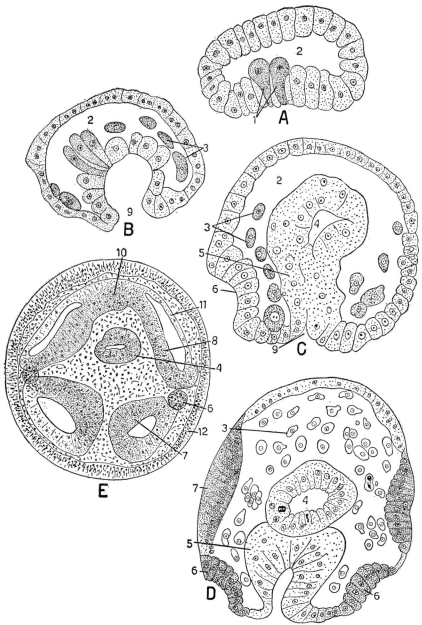

FIG. 203.—Indirect development, Desor larva, *Lineus*. *A*. Blastula with 2 teloblast cells. *B*. Embolic gastrulation with entomesoderm formation from teloblast cells. *C*. Late gastrulation, blastopore closed. *D*. Beginning formation of embryonic disks. (*A–D*, *after Nussbaum and Oxner*, 1913.) *E*. Disks invaginated with amnion formation (*after Schmidt*, 1934). 1, teloblasts; 2, blastocoel; 3, entomesoderm; 4, midgut; 5, foregut; 6, disk for cerebral organ; 7, trunk disk; 8, cephalic disk; 9, blastopore, 10, proboscis proliferation; 11, amnion; 12, larval epidermis.

504). Other ecological types are the fresh-water forms of the genus *Prostoma* (page 500) and the terrestrial nemertines of the genus *Geonemertes* (page 502). An eyeless variant of *Prostoma* has been found in caves in Europe and appears to be a genuine cave animal (Beauchamp, 1932). *Geonemertes* is provided against drying by an especially large equipment of mucous and frontal glands. It lives well in sea water but cannot endure immersion in fresh water. One species, *G. arboricola* from the Seychelles, inhabits the leaf bases of the screw pine, *Pandanus*, and may occur as high as 40 to 50 feet above ground in the tree (Punnett, 1907).

There appear to be no true parasites among nemertines, but several species regularly live as commensals with other animals. Such are species of *Tetrastemma* that inhabit the pharyngeal cavity of tunicates, *Gononemertes* in the atrium of tunicates with head protruding into the pharyngeal cavity, *Nemertopsis actinophila* that regularly lives beneath the pedal disk of anemones (Bürger, 1903), *Malacobdella* in the mantle cavity of bivalves (page 506), and *Carcinonemertes* on the gills and egg masses of crabs (page 500). It is to be noted that most of these commensals occupy situations in which they are in the path of the ciliary currents maintained by their hosts to obtain food and oxygen. Hence they secure food and oxygen without exerting themselves as well as shelter and protection. Whereas they cannot be regarded as parasites because they eat mostly small animals brought in by the ciliary currents, they appear to confer no benefits on the host in return for food, oxygen, and shelter, and may even be a detriment by interfering with the ciliary currents. They may be tending toward parasitism, for many of them show changes characteristic of parasites, as the loss of eyes and other sense organs, reduction of the proboscis apparatus, and increased reproductive capacity, especially noticeable in *Gononemertes* which has large gonads packing the space between digestive tract and body wall (Fig. 192*A*).

Some nemertines swim by undulations of their flattened bodies, but the majority are capable only of locomotion against a substratum. They glide with a smooth motion after the manner of Turbellaria. In several species investigated, the motion was found to result entirely from ciliary waves acting against a slime track secreted by the worms (Eggers, 1924; Friedrich, 1933). If the cilia are paralyzed by lithium salts, gliding ceases, whereas if the musculature is paralyzed by magnesium salts, normal locomotion continues. Coe (1943), however, finds that muscular waves play a role in the crawling of the larger species. The cilia are under nervous control, inhibited by the peripheral plexus, stimulated by the brain; hence the ciliary beat ceases on decapitation but can be elicited by stimulation. Upon stimulation of normally gliding animals, the cilia stop for a short time and the body musculature is brought into action.

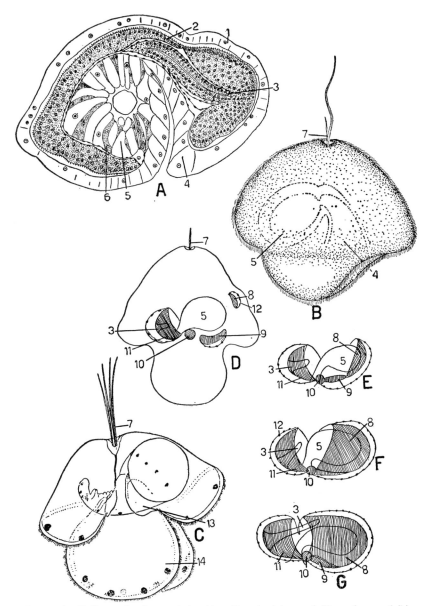

Fig. 204.—Indirect development (continued). *A.* Advanced Desor larva of *Lineus* (*after Arnold*, 1899), after fusion of the disks. *B.* Early pilidium of *Cerebratulus* (*after Coe*, 1899). *C.* Advanced pilidium of *Cerebratulus* containing the larva (*after Verrill*, 1892). *D–G.* Mode of development of larva inside the pilidium from embryonic disks (*after Salensky*, 1912). 1, larval epidermis; 2, definitive epidermis; 3, proboscis invagination; 4, stomodaeum; 5, midgut; 6, definitive intestinal cells; 7, apical sensory organ; 8, dorsal disk; 9, trunk disk; 10, disk for cerebral organ; 11, cephalic disk; 12, amnion; 13, larva; 14, oral lobes.

If the anterior end is touched, this draws back, the posterior end often flattens, and muscular waves pass from behind forward beginning more and more posteriorly until the posterior end is reached, whereupon the animal moves backward. If the rear end is stimulated, this is drawn up into a spiral, and muscular waves run from before backward, beginning nearer and nearer the anterior end, until finally the animal moves forward. Middle body regions are very insensitive to touch. Strong stimulation usually throws the body or part of it into coils. Decapitated worms react to stimulation like normal worms. Experiments on worms with the lateral cords transected at various levels or with isolated posterior pieces indicate that anterior regions contain a nervous mechanism for both peristalsis and antiperistalsis but posterior regions for peristalsis only, so that such pieces move forward no matter where stimulated. In most nemertines the lateral cords are extensively connected by a peripheral plexus since transection of one of them does not interfere with normal conduction; but in the genus *Oerstedia* transection experiments indicate that the lateral cords are not in connection except through the brain. In this genus transection of one lateral cord evokes circus movement toward the operated side. Transection of both cords at the same or different levels by cuts from the body surface inward interferes with conduction but strong enough stimuli enable contraction waves to pass the cuts.

The foregoing experiments indicate that the brain functions to initiate spontaneous and directed movements, to coordinate reactions, and to inhibit the automatic peripheral part of the nervous system. Decapitation or section of the lateral cords immediately behind the brain results in cessation of ciliary action and spontaneous movements; but typical movements can be evoked by proper stimulation of the cut surface. Such decapitated worms usually carry on peristaltic waves over the anterior body third until death, an indication that, as already stated, this portion of the body contains an automatic nervous mechanism normally inhibited by the brain. Separation of the two halves of the brain by a longitudinal cut also results in stoppage of the ciliary beat and cessation of muscular movements; but both can be evoked by stimulation of the cut brain surfaces.

The movements of *Malacobdella grossa* have been investigated by Eggers (1935). This nemertine is extremely sluggish. It moves normally in a leech-like fashion, alternately attaching anterior surface and adhesive disk. When removed from the host it makes a few such movements, then attaches by the disk, and waves the anterior end about in a seeking manner. The dorsal cilia beat forward, the ventral backward, and unlike other nemertines the direction of beat cannot be nervously altered. The adhesive disk maintains its attachment after section of the lateral nerve cords or after complete severance from the trunk. The attachment appears to be controlled by the ganglionic swellings in the disk itself. The release of the disk appears to follow only after the ventral surface of the anterior end has secured a firm hold. If the isolated disk is detached it cannot again attach. *Malacobdella* gives little reaction to external factors except touch; contact applied to the anterior end elicits contraction, to the posterior end, extension.

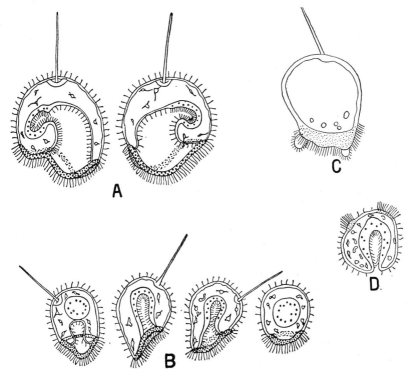

Fig. 205.—Development of isolated blastomeres of *Cerebratulus*. *A*. Half size pilidia from first two blastomeres. *B*. Quarter size pilidia from first four blastomeres. *C*. Type of larva formed from one of the first quartet of micromeres of the 8-cell stage. *D*. Type of larva formed from a macromere of the 8-cell stage. (*All after Hörstadius, 1937.*)

Nemertines will right themselves when placed on their backs; this reaction is also carried out by headless pieces.

The everted proboscis is frequently employed in locomotion, being attached to some object and then contracted to pull the animal along. It is also the chief instrument of burrowing. In *Cerebratulus* (C. B. Wilson, 1900) the proboscis is thrust into the substrate and holds firm while body contractions drive it deeper.

Little definite is known of the function of the numerous sensory organs. Presumably the various anterior structures as the frontal organ, cephalic grooves and slits, cerebral organs, and lateral organs are chemo-tactile receptors.   The nemertines are very sensitive to the chemical properties of the medium and respond to harmful conditions by convul-sive movements, ejection of the proboscis, opening and closing of the cephalic slits and grooves, and eventually body rupture.   Burrowing forms will leave their burrows when the sea water becomes foul or other-wise unsuitable.   Food is detected at a distance, apparently by the cerebral organs; closer perception appears to be mediated by the frontal organ which everts when close to food.   In *Prostoma* accelerated beating of the cilia of the cerebral organs was noted in the presence of food (Reis-inger, 1926); this nemertine is able to detect a minute bit of food at a distance of 17 cm. in still water and to move nearly directly toward it. Reaction to food or chemical substances is evidenced by headless pieces but becomes more definite as the cerebral organs regenerate (Kipke, 1932).   *Cerebratulus* may leave its burrows in daylight when food is available nearby but finds the food chiefly by random wandering (Coe, 1943).

The tactile sense is well developed in nemertines, especially on the anterior and posterior ends.   The presence of the head is not necessary for tactile response.   The proboscis is also highly sensitive to contact. Nearly all nemertines are negative to light and hence have nocturnal habits; during the day they seek dark places, emerging at night to feed. *Oerstedia dorsalis*, however, is positive to light and proceeds directly toward a light; it seldom takes a median path between two equal lights (Buddenbrock, 1923).   The pilidium larvae and juvenile worms are generally positive to light because, according to some, they require a higher oxygen supply than adults and hence seek the surface.   Response to light is presumably vested chiefly in the ocelli but is also exhibited by all regions of the body.   The nemertines are highly thigmotactic, whence their predilection for living under and among objects and in burrows or slime tubes.   A positive reaction to water currents has been observed in *Prostoma* (Reisinger, 1926).

The epidermis of nemertines continually gives off mucus, and the amount is increased on irritation, injury, and exposure to unfavorable conditions.   The mucous secretion forms the slime track left in locomo-tion, the tubes and mucous lining of cavities occupied by the worms, the slime tubes in which spawning may occur, the jelly holding the eggs, the cyst walls surrounding regenerating pieces and starving animals, etc. The fresh-water *Prostoma* may survive drying up of its habitat by enclos-ing itself in a mucous cyst.   It is probable that the slime secreted by nemertines is obnoxious to other animals and possibly even poisonous. Bacq (1936) extracted from the bodies of *Amphiporus* and other nemer-tines an alkaloid "amphiporine," very similar to nicotine in its action on nerve-muscle preparations, and another substance "nemertine," fatal to crabs.

The nemertines are carnivorous, feeding, mainly at night, on live or dead animals, usually annelids, but also mollusks, crusteans, and fish. The proboscis is believed to be employed in the capture of prey, but there are very few direct observations on the feeding of nemertines; the chief ones are those of C. B. Wilson (1900) on *Cerebratulus lacteus* and Reisinger (1926) on *Prostoma*. Both forms feed almost exclusively on annelids, and in both the proboscis is shot out with considerable speed and wound spirally (Fig. 208) around the prey, which is then ingested whole, tail

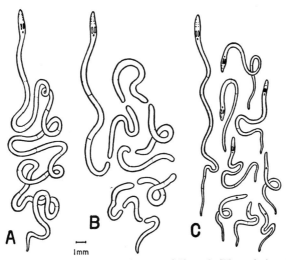

Fig. 206.—Asexual reproduction in *Lineus socialis*. *A.* Worm before fragmentation. *B.* Worm fragmented into 9 pieces. *C.* All pieces regenerate into small worms. (*All after Coe*, 1930b.)

first. The stylet is employed to puncture the prey and may be repeatedly thrust into the latter, after which a toxic fluid secreted by the posterior tube of the stylet apparatus is emitted upon the victim. The rhabdites, nematocysts, and viscid secretions of the papillae of the proboscis also presumably aid in holding the prey. Large prey may be sucked out rather than swallowed whole. There are no exact investigations of the digestive process in nemertines, but numerous observations on live nemertines indicate that the digestive process is mainly extracellular and very rapid, so that the swallowed part of an annelid may be disintegrated before the entire worm has been taken inside. Some claim that digestion takes place mainly in the foregut (stomach), others that the intestine is the main seat of digestive processes. Proteins disintegrate in the digestive lumen, fats are phagocytized by the intestinal epithelium, and carbohydrates are probably not utilized. After feeding, the intestinal epi-

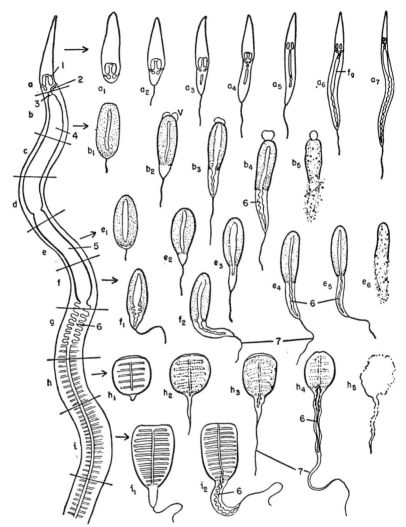

Fig. 207.—Typical course of regeneration in nemertines. Regeneration of *Zygeupolia* (*after Coe*, 1943). At left, worm showing levels of section *a* to *i*. At right, regeneration of each level; only the *a* piece containing the brain regenerates a complete worm; the other pieces cannot regenerate the anterior end and regenerate only those structures posterior to the level from which they were taken. 1, brain; 2, cerebral organ; 3, mouth; 4, esophagus; 5, stomach; 6, intestine; 7, caudal cirrus.

thelium is found packed with protein granules and fat droplets that apparently remain there as a food reserve. Vialli (1927) reported abundant glycogen in the epidermis, mesenchyme, and ovaries of *Prostoma*.

The nemertines can withstand prolonged starvation lasting months or even a year (Child, 1901; Nussbaum and Oxner, 1912; Coe, 1943) and eventuating in great size reduction and dedifferentiation toward an embryonic condition.   Many of the mesenchyme cells become wandering phagocytes that devour pigment and body cells and invade the gut causing degeneration of gut cells.   These phagocytes loaded with food may then disintegrate, furnishing food for the starving worm, and the surviving gut cells may also ingest the disintegrating gut cells and other cells. In this way, the pigment, then much of the digestive tract, and later the muscles and gonads disappear.   The epidermis dedifferentiates to a simple condition and the eyes degenerate, but the nervous system persists for a long time.   Dawydoff (1924) starved regenerated anterior tips of *Lineus* and found that they would reduce down to a size similar to that of *Paramecium* and undergo dedifferentiation to an embryonic condition closely resembling the pilidium larva of the species.   In still more extreme starvation of these regenerates, lasting more than 2 years, they had reduced to an ovoid body consisting of inner and outer epithelia with loose cells between, and finally became morula-like masses of large round cells.

The nemertines lack any special respiratory mechanism, and respiration takes place chiefly through the general body surface by diffusion. Some nemertines, however, pump water in and out of the foregut for respiratory purposes (C. B. Wilson, 1900), and in such species the foregut wall is permeated with blood lacunae.

The circulation of the blood is directly observable in smaller forms that have red blood (Coe, 1943).   The blood usually flows forward in the middorsal vessel, backward in the lateral vessels.   It may also at times flow in the reverse direction or may flow forward or backward simultaneously in all three vessels.

Nothing is known of the nature of the excretory products of nemertines and little of the function of the protonephridia.   The close relation of the latter to the lateral blood vessels in many nemertines is indicative of a true excretory function.   In *Tetrastemma* stained with vital dyes, the dye granules were seen to collect in the walls of the protonephridia

Fig. 208.—*Prostoma* capturing an annelid worm (*after Reisinger*, 1926).

along their entire course but not in the terminal bulbs (Westblad, 1922). The pigment cells and calcareous bodies may have athrocytic functions.

One species of nemertine, a Japanese form, *Emplectonema kandai*, is luminescent along the entire body except the anterior tip (Kanda, 1939). To touch it gives a local flash, but the entire body can be made to glow by stretching it.   Other factors evoking luminescence are acidity, alkalinity, salts of calcium (but not of sodium, potassium, magnesium, or ammonium in physiological concentrations), abrupt alterations of temperature, and electrical stimulation.   The light seems to emanate from epidermal gland cells and does not result from a luciferin-luciferase reaction.

V. PHYLOGENETIC CONSIDERATIONS

Although in the past, nemertines have been derived from various phyla, especially Annelida, at the present time there is little doubt of their derivation from the Platyhelminthes. Their essential body construction—epidermis, muscle sheath, mesenchyme filling the spaces between organs—is similar to that of flatworms. The proboscis apparatus can be regarded as a further development of the proboscis of the kalyptorhynchid rhabdocoels. Other similarities are the occurrence of frontal glands, the general plan of the nervous system, the structure of the ocelli, the occurrence of ciliated grooves, pits, etc., as main sense organs of the head, and the spiral type of cleavage. The cerebral organs can be regarded as derived from the auricular sense organs of flatworms. Many nemertines display a pseudometamerism similar to that of marine triclads. The serological tests of Schepotieff (1913) in which nemertine antiserum reacted with polyclad extract but not with annelid extract support the above conclusion of a platyhelminth origin of the nemertines.

The nemertines represent the culmination of the acoelomate type of construction. In their possession of an anus and a circulatory system as well as in a higher organization of the nervous system and the body wall they have progressed beyond the flatworms but there has been, so far as we know, no further evolution of this type of construction. The solid body form presumably imposes limitations on certain functions, especially the digestive and excretory functions, and hence is in general disadvantageous. At any rate, all the remaining animal groups have a more or less hollow type of body construction.

Bibliography

Arnold, G. 1899. Entwicklungsgeschichte des Lineus. Trav. Soc. Natural. St. Pétersbourg 28. **Bacq, Z.** 1936. Les poisons des Némertiens. Acad. Roy. Belg., Bull. Cl. Sci., ser. 5, 22. **Beauchamp, P. de.** 1932. Sur une némerte obscuricole. Bull. Soc. Zool. France 57. **Bergendal, D.** 1900. Nordische Nemertinen (Gononemertes). Zool. Anz. 23. **Böhmig, L.** 1897. Excretory organs and blood-vascular system of Tetrastemma. Ann. Mag. Natur. Hist., ser. 6, 20. 1898. Anatomie und Histologie der Nemertinen. Ztschr. Wiss. Zool. 64. 1929. Nemertini. In **W. Kükenthal** and **T. Krumbach** (eds.), *Handbuch der Zoologie*, Band II, Pt. 1. **Brinkmann, A.** 1917. Die pelagischen Nemertinen. Bergens Mus. Skrifter 3, No. 1. 1918. Die pelagischen Nemertinen den deutschen Südpolar-Expedition. Dtsch Südpolar Exped. 16, Zool. 8. 1927. Gononemertes parasita. Nyt Mag. Naturwid. 65. **Buddenbrock, W. v.** 1923. Mechanismus der phototropen Bewegungen. Wissenschaft. Meeresuntersuch. Abt. Helgoland 15. **Bürger, O.** 1895. Die Nemertinen des Golfes von Neapel. Fauna und Flora des Golfes von Neapel 22. 1897–1907. Nemertini. In **H. G. Bronn** (ed.), *Klassen und Ordnungen des Tierreichs* 4, Suppl. 1903. Die Nemertinen. Fauna Arctica 3. 1909. Die Nemertinen. Wis·

senschaft. Ergebn. Dtsch. Tiefsee Exped. Valdivia 16. **Carlgren, O.** 1907. Zur Regeneration von Prostoma. Zool. Studien Prof. Tullberg gewidmet. **Child, C. M.** 1901. Habits and natural history of Stichostemma. Amer. Natural. 35. **Coe, W. R.** 1895. Anatomy of Cerebratulus lacteus. Trans. Connecticut Acad. Arts Sci. 9. 1899. Notes on the time of breeding of some common New England nemerteans. Science 9. Development of the pilidium of certain nemerteans. Trans. Connecticut Acad. Arts Sci. 10. Maturation and fertilization of the egg of Cerebratulus. Zool. Jahrb. Abt. Anat. 12. 1902. The genus Carcinonemertes. Zool. Anz. 25. The nemertean parasites of crabs. Amer. Natural. 36. 1904. Anatomy and development of the terrestrial nemertine Geonemertes agricola. Proc. Boston Soc. Natur. Hist. 31. 1905. Nemerteans of the west and northwest coasts of America. Bull. Mus. Comp. Zool. Harvard Univ. 47. 1906. A peculiar type of nephridia in nemerteans. Biol. Bull. 11. 1920. Sexual dimorphism in nemerteans. Biol. Bull. 39. 1926. The pelagic nemerteans. Mem. Mus. Comp. Zool. Harvard Univ. 49. 1927. The nervous system of the pelagic nemerteans. Biol. Bull. 53. 1929. Excretory organs of terrestrial nemerteans. Biol. Bull. 56. 1929, 1930a. Regeneration in nemerteans. Jour. Exp. Zool. 54, 57. 1930b. Asexual reproduction in nemerteans. Physiol. Zool. 3. 1930c. Unusual types of nephridia in nemerteans. Biol. Bull. 58. 1930d. The peculiar nephridia of Cephalothrix. Zool. Anz. 89. 1931. New species of Lineus with asexual reproduction. Zool. Anz. 94. 1932. Regeneration in nemerteans. III. Jour. Exp. Zool. 61. 1933. Metameric ganglia in a nemertean. Zool. Anz. 102. 1934a. Analysis of the regeneration processes in nemerteans. Biol. Bull. 66. 1934b. Regeneration in nemerteans IV. Jour. Exp. Zool. 67. 1935. Bathypelagic nemerteans collected near Bermuda. Zool. Anz. 111. 1936. Bathypelagic nemerteans. Zoologica, New York, 21. 1938. Hoplonemertean having differential bipolar sexuality. Zool. Anz. 124. 1939. Sexual phases in terrestrial nemerteans. Biol. Bull. 76. 1940a. Morphology and sexuality of Geonemertes palaensis. Occas. Papers Bishop Museum Hawaii 15, No. 19. 1940b. Revision of the nemertean fauna of the Pacific coasts of North, Central, and northern South America. Allen Hancock Pacific Exped. 2, No. 13. 1943. Biology of the nemerteans of the Atlantic coast of North America. Trans. Connecticut Acad. Arts. Sci. 35. 1944. Nemerteans from the northwest coast of Greenland and other Arctic seas. Jour. Washington Acad. Sci. 34. 1945a. Malacobdella minuta, a new commensal nemertean. Jour. Washington Acad. Sci. 35. 1945b. Bathypelagic nemerteans of the Bermuda area. Zoologica, New York, 30. **Coe, W. R.,** and **S. C. Ball.** 1920. Nectonemertes. Jour. Morphol. 34. **Dakin, W. J.,** and **M. G. Fordham.** 1931. A new and peculiar nemertine from the Australian coast. Nature, London, 128. 1936. Anatomy and systematic position of Gorgonorhynchus. Proc. Zool. Soc. London. **Dawydoff, C.** 1910. Restitution von Kopfstücken bei den Nemertinen. Zool. Anz. 36. 1924. Sur le retour d'une némerte en inanition à un état embryonaire. C. R. Acad. Sci. Paris 179. 1928a. Sur l'embryologie des Protonémertes. C. R. Acad. Sci. Paris 186. 1928b. Sur la réversibilité des processus du développement. C. R. Acad. Sci. Paris 186. 1942. Régénération créatrice chez les némertes. Bull. Biol. France Belgique 76. **Delsman, H.** 1915. Eifurchung und Gastrulation bei Emplectonema. Tidjschr. Nederland. Dierk. Vereen., ser. 2, 14, Lief. 2. **Desor, E.** 1848. The embryology of Nemertes. Boston Jour. Natur. Hist. 6. **Dewoletsky, R.** 1886–1888. Das Seitenorgan der Nemertinen. Arbeit. Zool. Inst. Wien 7. **Eggers, F.** 1924. Zur Bewegungsphysiologie der Nemertinen. Ztschr. Vergl. Physiol. 1. 1935. Zur Bewegungsphysiologie von Malacobdella. Ztschr. Wiss. Zool. 147. **Ehrenberg, C. G.** 1828. *Symbolae Physicae.* **Friedrich, H.** 1933. Vergleichende Studien zur Bewegungs- und Nervenphysiologie bei Nemertinen. Zool. Jahrb. Abt. Allg. Zool. 52.

1935. Studien zur Morphologie, Systematik, und Ökologie der Nemertinen der Kieler Bucht. Arch. Naturgesch., n. F. 4. 1936. Nemertini. In **G. Grimpe** and **E. Wagler** (eds.), *Die Tierwelt der Nord- und Ostsee*, Teil IV d (Lief. 30). **Gering, G.** 1911. Zur Kenntnis von Malacobdella grossa. Ztschr. Wiss. Zool. 97. **Guberlet, J. E.** 1925. Malacobdella grossa from the Pacific coast of N. A. Publ. Puget Sound Biol. Station 5. **Hammarsten, O.** 1918. Beitrag zur Embryonalentwicklung der Malacobdella grossa. Arbeit. Zootom. Inst. Stockholms Högskola 1. **Hörstadius, S.** 1937. Experiments on determination in the early development of Cerebratulus. Biol. Bull. 73. **Hubrecht, A.** 1880. Zur Anatomie und Physiologie des Nervensystems der Nemertinen. Verhandl. Kong. Akad. Wetensch. Amsterdam, Deel 20. 1886. Contributions to the embryology of the Nemertea. Quart. Jour. Micro. Sci. 26. **Humes, A. G.** 1941. Male reproductive system in Carcinonemertes. Jour. Morphol. 69. 1942. Morphology, taxonomy, and bionomics of Carcinonemertes. Illinois Biol. Monogr. 18. **Kanda, S.** 1939. Luminescence of Emplectonema kandai. Biol. Bull. 77. **Kato, K.** 1939. Luminous nemertean, Emplectonema kandai. Jap. Jour. Zool. 8. **Kipke, S.** 1932. Studien über Regenerationserscheinungen bei Prostoma. Zool. Jahrb. Abt. Anat. 51. **Lankester, E. R.** 1872. Contribution to the knowledge of haemoglobin. Proc. Roy. Soc. London 21. **Lebedinsky, J.** 1896. Zur Entwicklungsgeschichte der Nemertinen. Biol. Centralbl. 16. 1897. Entwicklungsgeschichte der Nemertinen. Arch. Mikro. Anat. 49. **Metschnikoff, E.** 1869. Studien über die Entwicklung der Echinodermen und Nemertinen. Mém. Acad. Imper. Sci. St. Pétersbourg, ser. 7, 14. 1882. Vergleichend-embryologische Studien. Ztschr. Wiss. Zool. 37. **Monastero, S.** 1928. Esperienze sulla rigenerazione dei Nemertini. Boll. Ist. Zool. Univ. Palermo 2. 1939. La regenerazione dell'intestino nei Nemertini. Boll. Zoologia 10. **Montgomery, T. H.** 1895. Stichostemma. Ztschr. Wiss. Zool. 59. 1897. On the connective tissue and body cavities of the nemerteans. On the structure of the nephridia of Stichostemma. Zool. Jahrb. Abt. Anat. 10. **Nawitzki, W.** 1931. Procarinina. Zool. Jahrb. Abt. Anat. 54. **Nussbaum, J.**, amd **M. Oxner.** 1910, 1911, 1912. Regeneration der Nemertinen. Arch. Entw'mech. Org. 30, 32, 35. 1912. Studien über die Wirkung des Hungerns auf Nemertinen. Arch. Entw'-mech. Org. 34. 1913. Embryonalentwicklung des Lineus ruber. Ztschr. Wiss. Zool. 107. **Ohuye, T.** 1942. On the blood corpuscles of Lineus. Sci. Repts. Tohoku Imper. Univ., ser. 4, Biol., **17.** **Oudemans, A. C.** 1885. Circulatory and nephridial apparatus of Nemertea. Quart. Jour. Micro. Sci. 25, suppl. **Prenant, M.** 1922. Recherches sur le paremchyme des Plathelminthes. Arch. Morphol. Gén. Exp. 5. **Punnett, R. C.** 1901. Lineus. Proc. Trans. Liverpool Biol. Soc. 15. 1907. On an arboricolous nemertean. Trans. Linnaean Soc. London, Zool., ser. 2, 12. **Reinhardt, H.** 1941. Entwicklungsgeschichte der Prostoma. Vierteljahrschr. Naturforsch. Gesell. Zürich 86. **Reisinger, E.** 1926. Nemertini. In **P. Schulze** (ed.), *Biologie der Tiere Deutschlands*, Lief. 17. **Riepen, O.** 1933. Anatome und Histologie von Malacobdella grossa. Ztschr. Wiss. Zool. 143. **Salensky, W.** 1896. Bau und Metamorphose des Pilidium. Ztschr. Wiss. Zool. 43. 1909. Embryonale Entwicklung des Prosorochmus. Bull. Acad. Impér. Sci. St. Pétersbourg, ser. 6, 3, Pt. 1. 1912. Entwicklungsgeschichte der Nemertine im Inneren des Pilidiums. Mém. Acad. Impér. Sci. St. Pétersbourg, ser. 8, 30, No. 10. 1914. Entwicklungsgeschichte der Prosorochmus. Mém. Acad. Impér. Sci. St. Pétersbourg, ser. 8, 33, No. 2. **Scharrer, Berta.** 1941. Cerebral organ of the nemerteans. Jour. Comp. Neurol. 74. **Schepotieff, A.** 1913. Ueber die Bedeutung der Wassermann'schen Reaction für die biologische Forschung. Zool. Anz. 41. **Schmidt, G. A.** 1934. Ein zweiter Entwicklungstypus von Lineus gesserensis-ruber.

Zool. Jahrb. Abt. Anat. 58. **Schröder, O.** 1918. Geonemertes palaensis. Abhandl. Senckenberg. Naturforsch. Gesell. 35. **Smith, J. E.** 1935. Early development of Cephalothrix. Quart. Jour. Micro. Sci. 77. **Stiasny-Wijnhoff, G.** 1910. Die Gattung Cephalothrix. Zool. Jahrb. Abt. Anat. 30. 1914. The proboscidian system in nemertines. Quart. Jour. Micro. Sci. 60. 1926. The Nemertea Polystilifera of Naples. Pubbl. Staz. Zool. Napoli 7. 1930. Die Gattung Oerstedia. Zool. Mededeel. 13. 1934. Some remarks on North Atlantic non-pelagic Polystilifera. Quart. Jour. Micro. Sci. 77. 1936. The Polystilifera of the Siboga Expedition. Siboga Exp. 22, Livr. 128. 1938. Das Genus Prostoma. Arch. Neerland. Zool. 3, Suppl. **Thompson, Caroline.** 1901. Zygeupolia. Proc. Acad. Natur. Sci. Philadelphia 53. **Verrill, A. E.** 1892. Marine nemerteans of New England. Trans. Connecticut Acad. Arts Sci. 8. **Vialli, M.** 1927. La morphologia e la funzione del glicogeno in alcuni vermi. Atti Soc. Ital. Sci. Natur. 66. **Wheeler, J. F. G.** 1934. Nemerteans from the South Atlantic and southern oceans. Discovery Repts. 9. 1936. Record of Gorgonorhynchus at Bermuda. Nature, London, 137. 1940a. Nemerteans of Kergulen and the southern ocean. Brit. Austral. New Zealand Antarctic Research Exp. Repts. ser. B, 4, Pt. 8. 1940b. Notes on Gorgonorhynchus bermudensis. Ann. Mag. Natur. Hist., ser. 11, 6. **Wilson, C. B.** 1900. Habits and early development of Cerebratulus. Quart. Jour. Micro. Sci. 43. **Wilson, E. B.** 1903. Experiments on cleavage and localization in the nemertine egg. Arch. Entw'mech. Org. 16. **Yatsu, N.** 1904. Experiments on the development of egg fragments in Cerebratulus. Biol. Bull. 6. 1910. Experiments on germinal localization in the egg of Cerebratulus. Jour. College Sci. Tokyo Imper. Univ. 27. **Zeleny, C.** 1904. Experiments on the localization of developmental factors in the nemertine egg. Jour. Exp. Zool. 1.

INDEX

Pages bearing illustrations are given in boldface when not included in text references

Bibliography, Trypanorhyncha, 450–451
  Turbellaria, 423–435
Bicladus, 140
Bilateral phyla, 1–4
  origin of, 5–10
Bilateral symmetry, 1
Bilharzia (*see Schistosoma*)
Bilharziella, 299
Bipaliidae, 87, 94, 161
Bipalium, 66, **67, 70**, 161, 163, 180
  regeneration of, 187
  water economy of, 193
Bladder worm, 340
Blastocoel, 21
Blood, general, 42, 43
  of Rhynchocoela, 490
Body cavities, 21–28
Boninia, 117
Boniniidae, 171
Bothria, **314**, 315, 321
Bothridia, **314**, 315, **316**, 321
Bothridium, **314**, 315, 370, 372, 377
Bothrimonus, 370, **374**, 375
Bothriocephaloidea (*see* Pseudophyllidea)
Bothriocephalus, 370, 372, 375, 381
Bothriocotyle, 375
Bothriomolus, 148, 151
Bothrioplana, **106**, 151, 419
  ciliated pits, 91
  digestive system, 104, **106**, 148
  nervous system, 85, 87, **88**
  parthenogenesis, 111
Bothromesostoma, **96**, 143
  chemoreception, 91
  reproductive cycle, 135
  rheoreception, 93, **96**
Bowl-shaped body, **96**, 97
Brachycoelium, 278
Brachylaima, 293
Brachylaimidae, 293–295
  miracidium, 256
  sporocyst, 256
Brachylecithum, 279
Brachyurus, 381
Brain, 35
  Cestoda, **319, 322**, 323, 366, **369**, 372
  Rhynchocoela, 475, **477, 479**, 522
  role of, in behavior, 199, 202, 219
  Trematoda, 226
  Turbellaria, 83–**88, 90, 92, 93**
Braunina, 289
Bresslauilla, 123, 140

Brumptia, 267
Buccal capsule, 39
Buccal tube, 39, 99
Bucephalidae, 223, **227**, 266–268
  cercaria, **268**
  metacercaria, **268**
  miracidium, 256, **268**
  sporocyst, 256, **257**
Bucephalopsis, 266
Bucephalus, 266
Bürgeriella, 504
Bunodera, 270, **272**
Bursa copulatrix, 50, 120
Bursa seminalis, 120
Buxifrons, 267

C

Calceostoma, 240
Calliobothrium, 354, 356, **357**
Capsala, 242
Capasaloid Monogenea, 240–241
Capsule, 123
  Cestoda, 333
  Digenea, 238
  Monogenea, **234**, 235
  Rhabdocoela, 134
  Tricladida, **126**, 153
Carcinonemertes, 469, 472, 473, 483, 492, 494, **496**, 498, 500, **501, 503**, 520
Cardiocephalus, 291
Caridinicola, **145**, 149
Carinella, 497
Carinina, 465, 475, 497
Carinoma, 465, 481, **485, 487**, 497
Carinomidae, 497
Carpobothrium, 354, **357**
Caryophyllaeidae, **312**, 370, 372, 375, 377, 381–382
Caryophyllaeides, 377
Caryophyllaeus, 373, 377, **380**–382, **385**, 409
Castrada, 142
Castrella, **133**, 134, 142
Catatropis, 287
Catenotaenia, 391
Catenula, 93, **96**, 133, 137
Catenulida, 59, 104, 109, 137–139, 190
Catenulidae, 137–139, 179
Cell lineage, 10
Cement glands, 122
Cement sac, 122
Cephalic slits, nemertines, 463, **464**, 482